The Overstory Book:

Cultivating Connections with Trees
2nd Edition

Craig R. Elevitch
Editor

**Permanent
Agriculture
Resources**

www.agroforestry.net

The Overstory Book:
Cultivating Connections with Trees, 2nd Edition

Published by:

Permanent Agriculture Resources (PAR)
P.O. Box 428
Holualoa, HI 96725 USA
Tel: 1-808-324-4427; Fax: 1-808-324-4129
Email: par@agroforestry.net
Web: http://www.agroforestry.net

© Copyright 2004 Permanent Agriculture Resources

ISBN 0-9702544-3-1

Library of Congress Control Number: 2004108118

Printed in the United States of America

Recommended citation:

Elevitch, C.R. (ed). 2004. The Overstory Book: Cultivating Connections with Trees, 2nd Edition. Permanent Agriculture Resources, Holualoa, Hawai'i, USA. URL: http://www.agroforestry.net

First edition July 2004

Cover photos: Dappled shade of *Adenanthera pavonina* **(front) and canopy of** *Aleurites moluccana* **(back).**

Contents

Note to the Reader

Whether in a small backyard or a larger farm or forest, trees are vital to the web of life. Protecting and planting trees can restore wildlife habitat, heal degraded land, conserve soil, protect watersheds, diversify farm or garden products, beautify landscapes, and enhance the economic and ecological viability of land use systems. Careful planning and sound information is needed to reach these goals.

The Overstory Book, 2nd Edition distills essential information about working with trees into 127 concise, easy-to-read, single-subject chapters.

Here are some tips to help you use this book:

- You are welcome to read this book in a linear fashion (starting at the beginning and reading to the end). However, the book is not organized sequentially. Instead, short, self-contained chapters are linked to each other in a network of information. Therefore, it works just as well to start on any topic that interests you most.
- Chapters which are reprinted or excerpted from other published sources list the original source for further study.
- The last section of the book has an extensive resource section that includes helpful organizations, web sites, and publications.

Since many chapters are focused on agroforestry, readers unfamiliar with this practice might want to start by reading the first chapter, Agroforestry (page 2).

Enjoy!

Acknowledgments

This book contains the first six years of *The Overstory*, an international electronic journal with subscribers in over 175 countries. It came about after many subscribers asked for hardcopies of past editions for reference in the field or to bring with them to areas without access to computers. I am thankful to the many thousands of subscribers who have shared material, feedback, and unending encouragement.

I am also extremely grateful to the 85 contributing authors and organizations (see Contributing Authors and Organizations (page vii)), who have generously given permission to publish their writings. I am honored to work with such wonderful people devoted to restoring healthy and abundant landscapes.

In addition, numerous publishers have given their permission for us to excerpt or adapt their material; publishers are acknowledged in the Original Source section of each chapter.

A special thanks to Kim M. Wilkinson who co-edited *The Overstory* journal from its inception in March 1998 through June 2003. Kim also co-edited the first edition of *The Overstory Book*, and continues to give advice and creative consulting in publishing *The Overstory*. I greatly admire her lifelong dedication to sharing nature with people in a way that strengthens our connections with and understanding of the natural world.

Thanks to Harold Keyser, Paul Singleton, Padma Somasegaran, Joe Rourke, and Bruce Martin of the University of Hawai'i NifTAL Project for their support and training in biological nitrogen fixation and rhizobia inoculants. Mitiku Habte at the University of Hawai'i, Department of Agronomy and Soil Science gave very valuable feedback in writing Mycorrhizae (page 66), and Biological Nitrogen Fixation (page 81). Gary Kuhn of USDA National Agroforestry Center assisted with Carbon Sequestration (page 174).

These experts generously gave their time to contribute to The Agroforester's Library (page 496): Aaron Becker, Roland Bunch, Ken Crismier, Aly B.K. Dagang, Karlyn Eckman, Chris Evans, Roger Leakey, P. K. Nair, Jim Penn, Martin Price, Jim Roshetko, Eduardo Somarriba, Daniel Sonke, Orlo Colin Steele, Robert W. Wescom, and Bruce Wight. Many thanks to each of them for their assistance!

Thanks also to Christi A. Sobel and Mary-Anne Cotter for their inspired illustrations which have been adapted for this book.

Thanks to *The Overstory*'s committee of supportive advisors which includes Lelei LeLaulu, Counterpart International; Lars Graudal, Danida Forest Seed Centre; Dick Grimshaw, The Vetiver Network; P. K. Nair, Center for Subtropical Agroforestry; Alan Pottinger, International Forestry Review; Jim Roshetko, ICRAF/Winrock; Greg Ruark, National Agroforestry Center; Eduardo Somarriba, CATIE; Samran Sombatpanit, World Association of Soil and Water Conservation; Ida Theilade, Danida Forest Seed Centre

A special thanks to my communication skills coach Kerrith H. "Kerry" King, whose insightful feedback and support were called upon continuously during the publication of this book.

There are many others too numerous to mention here who have sent email messages and letters to comment on and improve *Overstory* articles. All your feedback, comments and encouragement is appreciated!

Aloha kakou,
Craig R. Elevitch
Holualoa, July 2004

Contributing Authors and Organizations

Miguel Altieri is a professor in the Environmental Science, Policy and Management Department at University of California at Berkeley, and is technical advisor to the Latin American Consortium on Agroecology and Development in Santiago. He is one of the world's leading authors and speakers on biodiversity and organic agriculture. In addition to actively supporting numerous international development projects related to sustainable agriculture, Dr. Altieri serves on the Board of Food First and is an advisor to various United Nations agencies, including his role as General Coordinator for the United Nations Development Programme's Sustainable Agriculture Networking and Extension Programme. He is author of over 180 articles and scientific papers and eleven books, including *Agroecology: The Scientific Basis of Alternative Agriculture*, a widely used textbook. His web site is: http://www.cnr.berkeley.edu/~agroeco3/.

ATTRA (Appropriate Technology Transfer for Rural Areas) is the nationwide sustainable agriculture information project of the National Center for Appropriate Technology (NCAT) and is funded through the USDA Rural Business-Cooperative Service. Publications and technical assistance from the ATTRA project are available free to farmers, ranchers, Extension agents, and other U.S. agriculture professionals. Contact information: Appropriate Technology Transfer for Rural Areas (ATTRA), PO Box 3657, Fayetteville, AR 72702 USA; Tel: 1-800-346-9140; Fax: 1-501-442-9842; Web: http://www.attra.ncat.org.

Australian Forest Growers (AFG) represents and promotes the interests of private commercial forestry and farm tree growers throughout the Australia. The organization is run by a voluntary national council of growers, supported by a small professional staff based in Canberra. AFG members include farmers and foresters, urban dwellers with rural land, small block holders,

plantation investors and investment companies, researchers, consultants, tree and equipment suppliers, industrial forestry companies, and tree enthusiasts. AFG publications include "Australian Forest Grower" quarterly journal which covers technical, economic and market news and information as well as special publications, such as: "Getting Started in Farm Forestry" (excerpted here), a "Starter Kit for a Treegrowers Cooperative", and a National Treegrowers Co-operatives Newsletter. AFG is project manager for a new information resource known as Farm Forest Line. Contact: Australian Forest Growers, National Office, PO Box E18, Kingston ACT 2604, Australia; Tel: +61 (0)2 6285 3833; Fax: +61 (0)2 6285 3855; Email: National.Office@afg.asn.au; Web: http://www.afg.asn.au/; Farm Forest Line: http://www.farmforestline.com.au

Peter Bane publishes The Permaculture Activist, a journal of grassroots solutions serving the permaculture movement in North America. Also a certified Permaculture Consultant and instructor, he has organized or taught over 40 permaculture design courses in the United States and internationally. In 1994, he helped to found Earthaven Ecovillage, a planned permaculture community in the Blue Ridge Mountains of North Carolina, and has been occupied with its development for the past 10 years. Contact Peter at: P.O. Box 1209, Black Mountain, NC 28711, USA; Tel: 828-669-6336; Fax: 828-669-5068; Email: pcactivist@mindspring.com; Web: http://www.permacultureactivist.net.

Brian Becker is a research coordinator with the School of Forest Resources and Conservation's Phytoremediation and Short Rotation Woody Crops Program at the University of Florida, Gainesville, Florida. His work with non-timber forest product management spans six years with Nepal's Community Forest Program, the United States' Appalachian Mountains and Southeastern costal plain. Currently finishing his Master's degree specializing in Agroforestry, Brian studied the effects of intercropping medicinal and aromatic plants (MAPs) with multipurpose trees in the U.S. Virgin Islands. His research interests include the biometrics, management, production and marketing of nontimber forest products. He can be reached at: Brian Becker, Building 191 Mowry Rd, PO Box 110831, University of Florida, Gainesville, Florida, 32611-0831, USA; Tel: 01-352-846-3054; Email: brbecker@ufl.edu.

Pierre Binggeli is a researcher and international consultant in plant ecology with special emphasis on the sustainable use and management of natural resources. He has investigated forest ecology, invasive plants and agroforestry systems in Africa, Europe and the Pacific. Email: pierre_binggeli@yahoo.co.uk; Web: http://members.lycos.co.uk/WoodyPlantEcology

Susan Braatz is a Forestry Sector Analyst and coordinator for State of the World's Forests (SOFO) in the Forestry Department of FAO, Rome. Web: http://www.fao.org/forestry/Forestry.asp.

Louise Buck is a Senior Extension Associate with the Department of Natural Resources at Cornell University, and a Senior Associate Scientist with the Center for International Forestry Research. Her interests are centered on actor-based knowledge and information systems to support integrated natural resource management. At Cornell she coordinates and teaches graduate and undergraduate courses in agroforestry, and manages an integrated research and outreach program on forest farming systems of agroforestry practice in the Northeastern US. Louise worked for a decade in Eastern Africa with CARE International and ICRAF on agroforestry and rural development, in program management, research and technical advisory roles. She is senior editor of *Agroforestry in Sustainable Agriculture* (1999, CRC Press). As a social scientist engaged in forest management issues, Louise has facilitated action research to understand relationships among stakeholders in protected area management and to improve protected area management systems. She is senior editor of *Biological Diversity: Balancing Interests through Adaptive Collaborative Management* (2001, CRC Press). Address: Fernow Hall, Department of Natural Resources, Cornell University, Ithaca, NY 14853; Tel: 607-255-5994, Email: leb3@cornell.edu.

Roland Bunch pioneered farmer-to-farmer extension and participatory technology development in the late 1960's, and wrote about these and other facets of farmer-empowering agricultural extension in his book *Two Ears of Corn: A Guide to People-Centered Agricultural Improvement*. The book has now been published in ten languages. Since then he has worked in some 35 nations as a consultant to the Ford Foundation, OXFAM, ILEIA, HELVETAS, GTZ, several national governments and many other development organizations, while coordinating the work of COSECHA, a Honduran nongovernmental organization. Roland was nominated in 1999 for the World Food Prize. COSECHA's

mailing address is: Apartado 3586, Tegucigalpa, Honduras. Contact Roland Bunch at: rolandbunchw@yahoo.com

Steven Burke worked for seven years providing forestry extension services to landholders in Victoria, Australia after graduating with an honors degree in Forest Science from the University of Melbourne. Following his strong interest in windbreaks and other agroforestry systems, he undertook landmark graduate research into crop responses to windbreaks in South-Eastern Australia which resulted in a Masters Degree in Agricultural Science. He has also managed statewide programs in community forestry and community-based revegetation whilst working for the Non-Government Organisation Greening Australia, and managed pest plant and animal management programs for the Victorian Department of Natural Resources and Environment. He is currently managing invasive species and vegetation management programs for King County in Washington State, USA. Steven can be contacted at Burke_s@hotmail.com.

Robert Chambers is a Research Associate of the Institute of Development Studies at the University of Sussex, UK. He has worked mainly in Sub-Saharan Africa and South Asia. He has worked on the methodologies of Rapid Rural Appraisal and Participatory Rural Appraisal. His books include *Rural Development: Putting the Last First* (1983), *Challenging the Professions: Frontiers for Rural Development* (1994), and *Whose Reality Counts? Putting the First Last* (1997).

Stefan D. Cherry was a sustainable agriculture and agroforestry consultant with the Mennonite Central Committee under the auspices of the Christian Council of Mozambique. He worked with agroforestry systems in Cameroon for five years and completed his masters at Cornell University in 1999. He co-authored a web page with Erick Fernandes which can be found at: http://ppathw3.cals.cornell.edu/mba_project/livefence.html.

Mary-Anne Cotter is a graduate of the Queensland College of Art with a major in etching. She is an illustrator for a wide range of clients, including the Food Foresters page of the *Permaculture International Journal*. She also illustrated the book, *A Children's Food Forest*. She is exploring writing and illustrating books for children, and is the Winner of the 1996 Coolola Shire Library Picture Book Competition.

Kurt Cremer is a forest scientist. He graduated in 1957 from the Australian Forestry School in Canberra and gained a Master of Science degree from the University of Tasmania. He started his research in the Tasmanian forest service and finished in 1987 as Principal Research Scientist with CSIRO in Canberra. He published over 50 papers in silviculture, forest ecology, fire ecology, storm damage and, in recent years, on the natural spread of willows in Australia's streams. He can be contacted by email at kcremer@snowy.net.au.

Ian Dawson is a tree germplasm specialist. His main concern is optimising the genetic resource management of tree species in agroforestry systems by assessing the genetic composition of natural and cultivated tree populations. For several years he worked as part of a team at the World Agroforestry Centre (ICRAF), also undertaking seed production research and constructing databases on agroforestry trees. Recently, he has become increasingly interested in historical aspects of tree germplasm use in Latin America and Africa. He is now based in the UK. Email: iankdawson@aol.com.

Hubert de Foresta conducts research on agroforests (complex, multistrata agroforestry systems), which are of high economic and environmental value for forest areas in the humid tropics. Now based in Montpellier, he concentrates on the biodiversity aspects of these systems and testing of potential solutions for improving productivity and profitability. 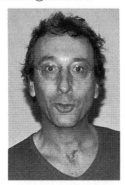 Dr. de Foresta has an MSc in tropical botany and a Ph.D. in tropical forest ecology from the University of Montpelier. He worked in Congo (1986–1989) on the relationships between slash-and-burn cultivation and natural successional vegetation, then in Indonesia, first with the SEAMEO-BIOTROP center (1989–1994), where he was in charge of a multidisciplinary research project on agroforestry practices and biodiversity conservation, and second with the ICRAF S-E Asia Regional Office (1994–1999) where he was in charge of the Krui Community-Based Forest Management programme sponsored by the Ford Foundation. He can be reached at: Hubert de Foresta, Chargé de Recherches à l'IRD (anciennement ORSTOM), ENGREF (Ecole Nationale du Génie Rural et des Eaux et Forêts), B.P. 44494, 34093 MONTPELLIER Cedex 5, FRANCE; Tel: (33) 4 67 04 71 21; Fax: (33) 4 67 04 71 01.

Steve Diver is a permaculture design course graduate and an agricultural specialist in horticulture and agronomy at ATTRA, the National Sustainable Agriculture Information Service, located in Fayetteville, AR. The focus of the ATTRA program is on farming systems that sustain the economic livelihoods of farm families while enhancing the environment. ATTRA offers publications and technical assistance to commercial farmers, including small farmers and market gardeners, in the United States. Please send updates or additions by email to: steved@ncat.org. Physical mailing address: Steve Diver, ATTRA, PO Box 3657, Fayetteville, AR 72702, USA.

Soejatmi Dransfield is a plant taxonomist specializing in bamboos, who gained her first degree in Plant Taxonomy from Academy of Agriculture, Ciawi, Bogor, Indonesia. Born in Nganjuk, Indonesia, she began her botanical career as a staff of Herbarium Bogoriense, Bogor, Indonesia, and gained her Ph.D. from Reading University, United Kingdom (UK), in 1975 with her thesis the "Revision of Cymbopogon (Gramineae)." After she moved to UK in 1978, she continued her research on bamboo taxonomy including the generic delimitation of the Old World tropical bamboos, and has described seven new genera (four from South-East Asia, three from Madagascar) and many new species. She is currently Honorary Research Fellow at the Royal Botanic Gardens, Kew, UK, writing the account of the bamboos from Malesia, Thailand and Madagascar.

Craig R. Elevitch is an agroforestry specialist with both public and private sector experience in tropical agroforest and forest management. Craig is a founding editor of the international journal *The Overstory* and editor of this volume.  He co-authored *Agroforestry Guides for Pacific Islands* (2000) and *Growing Koa: A Hawaiian Legacy Tree* (2003) and edited the first edition of *The Overstory Book: Cultivating Connections with Trees* (2001). Contact Craig at: Permanent Agriculture Resources, P.O. Box 428, Holualoa, Hawai'i 96725 USA; Email: cre@agroforestry.net; Web: http://www.agroforestry.net.

Erick C.M. Fernandes is Assistant Professor of tropical cropping systems and agroforestry at Cornell University. Prior to joining the Cornell faculty in 1995, he was a Visiting Assistant Professor at North Carolina State University (NCSU) and Leader of NCSU's Tropical Soils Research Program in the Brazilian Amazon. He has contributed as a consulting editor to the journal Agroforestry Systems and is a referee for Acta Amazonica, Soil Science Society of America Journal and World Development. He has worked with smallholder farmers, national and international agricultural and natural resource organizations and donor agencies in 16 countries in Africa, Asia, and Latin America. Contact: Cornell University, Department of Crop and Soil Science, 624 Bradfield Hall, Ithaca, NY 14853, USA; Tel: 607-255-1712; Email: ecf3@cornell.edu.

Richard Finlay-Jones is Manager of GHG Management Pty Ltd in Australia. GHG Management specialises in farm forestry, greenhouse mitigation and renewable energy. Richard can be contacted at: GHG Management Pty Ltd, PO Box 574, East Maitland NSW 2323, Australia; Tel: +61 414-555-864 (Australia); Email: finlayjones@ghg.com.au.

John K. Francis grew up on a small dairy farm in Wendell, Idaho. Perhaps because this was desert country with few trees, he always wanted to plant and manage trees and a career in forestry followed naturally. He received a BS in Forest Management from the College of Forestry at the University of Idaho where he also received a PhD in 1974, specializing in forest soils.  For most of his career he has worked as a research forester in tropical silviculture at the USDA International Institute of Tropical Forestry, Rio Piedras, Puerto Rico (now stationed at the Shrub Sciences Laboratory in Provo, Utah). His interests include growth, yield, management, and site adaptability of upland and bottomland hardwoods and conifers; soil nutrient depletion by intensive harvest; silvics of timber and non-timber trees; and thamnics of tropical shrubs. His publications include *Silvics of Native and Exotic Trees of Puerto Rico and the Caribbean Islands* (USDA Forest Service, 2000). He is currently editing a national shrub manual for the United States. He can be contacted at: RMRS Shrub Lab, 735 North 500 East, Provo, UT 84606; Tel: 801-356-5137; Fax: 801-375-6968; Email: jfrancisjr@fs.fed.us; Web: http://www.fs.fed.us/rm/provo/John%20%20Francis.htm

Robert T. Gavenda has been a soil scientist with USDA Natural Resources Conservation Service for the past twelve years. He spent eight years mapping soils on the Island of Hawai'i and is now Resource Soil Scientist in the Pacific Basin Area. His research at the University of Hawai'i concentrated on soil genesis and landscape evolution, Hawaiian paleoenvironments,  and pesticide movement in tropical soils. On Hawai'i Island he collaborated with University of Santa Barbara researchers on a number of soil formation studies. He can be contacted at: bob.gavenda@pb.usda.gov.

Luigi Guarino was Senior Scientist at the Regional Office for the Americas of the International Plant Genetic Resources Institute (IPGRI) when this paper was written. He is now Plant Genetic Resources Adviser at the Secretariat of the Pacific Community (SPC), based in Fiji. He has previously worked in IPGRI regional offices in Africa and the Middle East, and as an FAO consultant on genetic resources documentation in the Pacific. He has co-edited Collecting Plant Genetic Diversity published by CAB International. He can be reached at: SPC, Private Mail Bag, Suva, Fiji; Tel: 679-3370733; Fax: 679-3370021; Email: luigi@spc.int; Web: http://spc.int; http://papgren.blogspot.com.

Ross Gutteridge has recently retired from the School of Land and Food Sciences, the University of Queensland, Australia. He has worked on agroforestry projects throughout Southeast Asia and the Pacific. He is currently growing avocados organically on a farm north of Brisbane utilising agroforestry principals.  His books include *Forage Tree Legumes in Tropical Agriculture* (CAB International) and *Leucaena—Adaptation, Quality and Farming Systems* (ACIAR). He can be reached via email: rgutteridge@optushome.com.au.

Mitiku Habte is Professor of Soil Science at the Department of Tropical Plant and Soil Sciences, University of Hawai'i at Manoa. His interests include the interactions of beneficial soil microorganisms (rhizobia, cyanobacteria, P solubilizing microorganisms, arbuscular mycorrhizal fungi) with economically and ecologically important plant species.  The emphasis of his work is on arbuscular mycorrhizal fungi (AMF), with the goal of contributing to the understanding of the ecological interrelationships involved in order to manage populations of the fungi for enhanced plant productivity, and maintenance of soil and environmental quality. Address: Dr. Mitiku D. Habte, Professor of Soil Science, University of Hawai'i at Manoa, Department of Tropical Plant and Soil Sciences, 3190 Maile Way, St. John 102, Honolulu, HI 96822, USA; Tel: 1-808-956-6498; Fax: 1-808-956-6539; Email: mitiku@hawaii.edu; Web: http://www2.ctahr.hawaii.edu/tpss/faculty_staff/habte.htm

John B. Hall is a Senior Lecturer in Forestry, with widespread experience in tropical woody plant ecology, especially in West, East and Southern Africa. Contact: School of Agricultural and Forest Sciences, University of Wales, Bangor, Gwynedd, LL57 2UW, UK; Tel: +44

1248 383703 or 382446; Fax: +44 1248 354997; Web: http://www.safs.bangor.ac.uk/IWPT

Nazmul Haq is a Senior Lecturer at the School of Civil Engineering and the Environment, University of Southampton, UK. Nazmul is also the Founder Director of the International Centre for Underutilised Crops at Southampton University. His interests include agroforestry and sustainable utilization of fruit trees in global perspectives. The emphasis of his work is on the assessment of diversity in the household systems and development of conservation strategy through sustainable utilization. He has been project leader for many donor agency funded projects including the UN organizations. Address: Dr. Nazmul Haq, Senior Lecturer, School of Civil Engineering and the Environment, University of Southampton, Southampton SO171BJ, UK. Tel: +44(0)23-80594229; Fax: +44(0)23-80677519; Email: haq@soton.ac.uk.

John R. Healey is Senior Lecturer in Forest Ecology, and has worked on invasive plant ecology and management in Jamaica, as well as other aspects of forest ecology, conservation and management in Jamaica, West and East Africa, Central and South America, South East Asia and the UK. Contact: School of Agricultural and Forest Sciences, University of Wales, Bangor, Gwynedd, LL57 2UW, UK; Tel: +44 1248 383703; Fax: +44 1248 382459;

Web sites: http://www.bangor.ac.uk/safs-new/research/home.php (research); http://www.safs.bangor.ac.uk/IWPT (invasive woody plants in the tropics)

Deborah Hill is Professor of Forestry at the University of Kentucky, Lexington, working through the Cooperative Extension Service. Her areas of expertise include small woodlot management, agroforestry (specifically forest farming), international forestry, urban forestry and youth programs in forestry. Currently, in addition to developing programs and materials, and presenting talks  and workshops on forest farming (specifically shiitake mushroom production) and permaculture, she contributes to books and journals in the field of agroforestry. She also consults on forestry and small scale farming issues in Ecuador through the organization, Partners of the Americas. She is currently developing a permacultural forest farm on 25 acres near Lexington, Kentucky, USA. Contact her at: Department of Forestry, University of Kentucky, Lexington, KY 40546-0073, USA; Tel:

859-257-7610; Fax: 859-323-1031; Email: dbhill@uky.edu.

David Holmgren is a permaculture designer and consultant. He is perhaps best known as co-originator of the permaculture concept and for co-authorship of *Permaculture One* (1978) with Bill Mollison, a milestone in the application of environmental design to productive land use. Since 1978 he has authored numerous articles and several books, conducted workshops and courses, and  consulted for urban and rural projects in Australia and New Zealand. His most recent book *Permaculture: Principles and Pathways Beyond Sustainability* provides a broad conceptual framework for permaculture design education. David is also respected for his commitment to presenting permaculture ideas through practical projects. He teaches by personal example that a sustainable lifestyle is a realistic, attractive and powerful alternative to dependent consumerism. Contact David at: Holmgren Design Services, Melliodora (Hepburn Permaculture Gardens), 16 Fourteenth St, Hepburn, 3461, Australia; Tel: +61 (0)353483636; Email: info@holmgren.com.au; Web: http://www.holmgren.com.au.

Marilyn W. Hoskins is an anthropologist with a communications background who has dedicated her professional life to working in the area of local governance and community development with equity, especially in relation to the interface between the local men and women and the tree and forest resources upon which many of them depend. Within the field  of community forestry she has worked on a number of issues including food security, local/communal institutions for resource management, conflict management, tenure and access and gender. She lived and worked five years each in Southeast Asia and West Africa and was Title XII Chair for International Development at Virginia Tech. From 1978–1996 she worked with the Food and Agriculture Organization of the UN (FAO) becoming coordinator of the global community forestry programs, Forestry for Local Community Development and Forests, Trees and People.

These programs produced over 50 documents clarifying the complex issues related to community forestry in the form of concept papers, policy documents, field manuals and educational materials. She is now working with community forestry issues both domestically and internationally and is publishing on participatory approaches, institutional analysis, communication and monitoring and evaluation of process. As one of 27 women invited, she wrote a chapter in a book, *Developing Power: How Women Transformed International Development* edited by Arvonne Fraser and Irene Tinker (in press). Currently she is a Scholar in Residence at the Workshop in Political Theory and Policy Analysis at Indiana University, where she is completing a book entitled, *Changing the Culture of Forestry; Working from Within*. It analyzes the successes, failures and challenges of managing and decentralization the community forestry program within FAO; a participatory demand-driven program managed within a highly bureaucratic structure.

Angela Hughes has been working for the International Centre for Underutilised Crops (ICUC) for the last 5 years as a coordinator of a global project "Fruits for the Future." Her work involves the promotion of indigenous fruit tree species through dissemination of information, overseas training and extension work and the production of scientific and other publications on fruit tree species. Angela holds a Master's degree in Botanical Diversity and Conservation Management. Contact: ICUC, Lanchester Building, School of Civil Engineering and the Environment, University of Southampton, Southampton SO171BJ, UK. Email: A.Hughes@soton.ac.uk.

Peter Huxley is former Director of Research Development at the International Centre for Research in Agroforestry (ICRAF), now the World Agricultural Centre. His professional life has been spent in teaching and research in tropical agriculture/agroforestry, mainly in africa. He is editor/author of numerous books, scientific articles and research papers. His last book was *Tropical Agroforestry* published in 2000 by Blackwell Science (http://www.blackwellpublishing.com). Since leaving ICRAF in 1992, Peter Huxley has been involved in writing about agroforestry and running short courses in the UK and overseas. He is now retired.

Idaho Resource Conservation and Development Association provides a mechanism for local and government partnership to identify and solve social, environmental, economic and human problems in Idaho. Activities address local problems by developing appropriate projects as solutions and by obtaining assistance from the private sector, corporations, foundations and all levels of government while strongly supporting and utilizing science and technology.

Elaine R. Ingham B.A., M.S., Ph.D., is an adjunct Professor in the Graduate School at Southern Cross University in Lismore, New South Wales. She is also President and Director of Research at Soil Foodweb Inc., a small business that grew out of her University research program. Soil Foodweb now has labs all over the world, because of the importance of understanding soil biology in improving plant production without the use of toxic chemicals. Her research focuses on what organisms are present in the soil and on the foliage of plants, which organisms benefit which types of plants, which organisms harm plants, how can these organisms be managed to grow plants with the least expensive inputs into the system while maintaining soil fertility. The research and practical understanding and application of soil organisms continues at Soil Foodweb Inc. and with researchers at Universities around the world. Elaine can be reached through: Soil Foodweb, Inc., 1128 NE 2nd St., Suite 120, Corvallis, OR 97330, USA; Email: info@soilfoodweb.com; Web: http://www.soilfoodweb.com.

Djoko Iriantono has been a researcher for Seed Technology of Tree Species in Seed Technology Center, Forestry Research and Development Agency in Bogor, Indonesia since 1987. He has also worked on tree improvement of Acacia, Mahogany, and Gmelina. He joined IFSP (Indonesia Forest Seed Project) in 2000. The project focuses on development of human, technical, and institutional resources for the tree seed sector in Indonesia. He is currently working as a Project Manager. His address is: Indonesia Forest Seed Project, Taman Hutan Raya Ir. H. Juanda, PO Box 6919, Bandung 40135, Indonesia; Tel/Fax: +62 22 2515895; Email: ifsp@indo.net.id.

Paul Jahnige has B.A. in psychology and a Masters Degree in Forestry and Environmental Studies both from Yale University. He began his career working on international conservation and community development projects in Africa and South America. In 1993 he turned his attention to urban environmental issues in the United States, moved to Baltimore, MD where he worked as an urban community forester for the City of

Baltimore and a local non-profit organization organizing greening initiatives, youth programs and natural resource training in some of East Baltimore's most depressed communities. He then developed Community Resources, a regional urban environmental non-profit organization, to expand and transfer urban environmental programs to other Mid-Atlantic cities. He served and Community Resources Executive Director, overseeing all of the organization's initiatives from urban environmental education to monitoring and evaluation. In 2000, he returned to his childhood home in Western Massachusetts where he consults of community development and environmental issues and serves as the State of Massachusetts' Community Action Forester for Western and Central Massachusetts. Web: http://www.communityresources.org.

Norman Jones was a self-employed Forestry Consultant, after retiring as a Senior Forestry Specialist with the World Bank. After spending 16 years in West Africa, firstly with the Nigerian Government and later as an ODA Technical Officer in Ghana and Nigeria, he joined FAO for assignments in Brazil, Bangladesh and Malaysia, working mainly on species introduction and improvement research. He then moved into the commercial world on a Hilleshog/Swedish Match joint venture, concentrating on poplar improvement for the WIMCO farm forestry program, but carrying out research on other species in India, Thailand, and the Philippines. He stressed the need for forest plantation investors, whether commercial or farmer level, to ensure the quality of the planting stock. Norman passed away in August 2001.

Sylvia Kantor is Agroecology Faculty at Washington State University Extension King County. As an Extension Educator in a rapidly urbanizing region she focuses her work on watershed and foodshed stewardship programming. She has been employed with WSU Extension for over five years. Prior to this, Sylvia managed the Center for Streamside Studies at the University of Washington for three years and edited a textbook on river ecology, *River Ecology and Management* by Naiman and Bilby (1998). She has a Master of Science in natural resource management from the University of Washington and a Bachelor of Arts in Anthropology from the University of California, Berkeley.

Guido Kuchelmeister is an independent consultant specializing in agroforestry and urban forestry issues. With more than 20 years experience, he has worked internationally with many organizations including FAO (Food and Agriculture Organization); GTZ (German Agency for Technical Cooperation) and ADB (Asian Development Bank), KfW (Kreditanstalt fuer Wiedeaufbau and World Bank. He is Coordinator of the TREE CITY Initiative in Illertissen, Germany. Web: http://www.kuchelmeister-consult.de

Ahmad Kusworo is working as a policy analyst. His work examines government spatial planning with a focus on land use, forestry development, and the impact of these on local communities. He was the director of WATALA, an Indonesian conservation non-government organization and a key ICRAF partner in the study and official recognition of the Krui Damar agroforest in Sumatra. He holds a BSc degree in agriculture from the University of Lampung. He completed a policy internship with ICRAF in Bogor and is currently pursuing a Ph.D. in anthropology at the Australian National University (ANU) in Canberra, Australia with field work in Lampung again in collaboration with ICRAF.

Sarah Laird is an independent consultant with a focus on the commercial and cultural context of biodiversity and forest conservation. She has conducted research and provided advice on access and benefit-sharing issues for a range of non-governmental organizations (NGOs), governments, research institutes and community groups, most recently in Cameroon. Recent publications in this field include coauthorship of *The Commercial Use of Biodiversity: Access to Genetic Resources and Benefit-Sharing* (1999), *Benefit-Sharing Case Studies from Cameroon* (1998), *Biodiversity Prospecting in South Africa: Towards the Development of Equitable Partnerships* (1996) and *Biodiversity Prospecting* (1993). She received an MSc in Forestry from Oxford University.

Steve Langill has been a Research Associate with the International Development Research Centre in Ottawa, Canada for the past four years. He holds a Master's degree in Anthropology from Carleton University in Ottawa and has just completed a teaching degree at the University of Ottawa. His publications include *Indigenous Knowledge: A Resource Kit for Sustainable Development Researchers in Dryland Africa* (1999), the *Community-Based Natural Resource Management Social Science Resource Kits on Participatory Research, Indigenous Knowledge, Institutional Analysis and Common Property* (1998), and *Indigenous Knowledge of Desertification: A Progress Report from the Desert Margins Program in Kenya*, co-authored by A.J.N. Ndathi (1998). Mr. Langill can be contacted at slangill@idrc.ca.

Roger Leakey is Professor of Agroecology, and Director of the Agroforestry and Novel Crops Unit, School of Tropical Biology, James Cook University in the wet tropics of Queensland, Australia. Between 1993–97 he was Director of Research at ICRAF (now the World

Agroforestry Centre). He has undertaken studies on vegetative propagation, genetic improvement of tropical trees, tree domestication, soil microbiology, agroforestry in dry and moist tropics and moist forest regeneration, with research projects in Kenya, Cameroon, Ghana, Cote d,Ivoire, Nigeria, South Africa, Namibia, Costa Rica, Indonesia, Malaysia, Solomon Islands. Since 1982, he has undertaken consultancies for ODA, World Bank, European Development Fund, FAO and ACIAR, in Malaysia, Thailand, Vietnam, Laos, Japan, Philippines, India, Bolivia, Costa Rica, ten countries of West Africa and Australia. He can be reached at: PO Box 6811, Cairns, Queensland 4870, Australia; Email: roger.leakey@jcu.edu.au.

Andy Lee is a well known speaker and small farm advocate, and the author of *Backyard Market Gardening*. He and his business partner Patricia Foreman authored *Chicken Tractor: The Permaculture Guide to Happy Hens and Healthy Soils*. Their books are available at Good Earth Publications Company, which publishes books on self-reliant living and sustainable small-scale agriculture. You can reach Andy at: Andy Lee, Good Earth Publications, LLC, 20 Green Way Place, Buena Vista, VA 24416, USA; Tel: 540-261-8874; Fax: 540-261-8775; Email: Info@GoodEarthPublications.com; Web: http://www.goodearthpublications.com/

Art Ludwig is an ecological systems designer. He has broken new ground in design of transport bicycles, gravity feed water systems, greywater and blackwater reuse systems, composting toilets, and understanding wild water systems. He developed the first household cleaners designed to biodegrade into plant food. His specialty is the interconnections between systems. For example,  rainwater harvesting supplies super efficient fixtures, which drain through a greywater system to water and feed fruit trees, which in turn shade the house in summer and let sun pass in the winter, as well as feed the inhabitants. He currently lives and works in a 1920's summer cabin surrounded by a food jungle in a canyon above Santa Barbara, California with his wife two children, and a nice swimming hole. Web: http://www.oasisdesign.net.

Franklin W. Martin is an internationally renowned authority on tropical food plants and food self-sufficiency. He is retired from the USDA Tropical Research Station in Puerto Rico. He is author of many books, including *Perennial Edible Fruits of the Tropics*, *Edible Leaves of the Tropics*, *Techniques and Plants for the Trop-*

ical Subsistence Farm, Survival and Subsistence in the Tropics, and the newly published *Multipurpose Palms You Can Grow: Twenty of the World's Best*. He now lives in Florida and shares his expertise with many, including the nearby Educational Concerns for Hunger Organization (ECHO), 17430 Durrance Road, North Fort Myers, FL, USA. Tel: 941-543-3246; Web: http://www.echonet.org.

J. Louise Mastrantonio is a free-lance writer and antiques dealer living on the central Oregon coast. Louise has a degree in journalism from the University of Oregon and was formerly writer, editor, and public information officer for the USDA Forest Service. She is currently working on a book about the nation's old seed companies and their founders, including W. Atlee Burpee, James Vick, Alexander Livingston, John Lewis Childs, William Henry Maule, David Landreth, Dexter Mason Ferry, Henry Ames Field and other giants of the late 19th and early 20th century American garden seed industry. She may be reached at: P.O. Box 723, Manzanita, OR 97130, USA; Email: wildgoose@nehalemtel.net.

Ken Matthews is the Executive Officer for Private Forestry Southern Queensland (Inc) and is based in Gympie, Queensland, Australia. Ken has had a career in the timber industry in Queensland spanning 24 years. Ken commenced his career working in sawmills at the age of 14. Ken worked throughout Queensland as a qualified timber treatment plant operator, tailor out, order man, bench-  man, timber sales and MDF/Particleboard research officer. At the age of 24 Ken completed an Associate Diploma in Forestry. He worked for State Forestry in the areas of native forest harvesting and marketing, forestry extension, resource assessment and plantation establishment and management for 5 years. Ken worked as a Senior Park Ranger for Local Government for 2 years in Toowoomba and then as a forestry extension officer with Greening Australia Queensland for 4 years. In 2003 Ken was employed by Private Forestry Southern Queensland. Over the last 5 years Ken has delivered 60 field days, presented conference papers, written many publications and developed a number of decision support tools. Ken's contact details are: 11/173 Mary Street Gympie, Queensland, 4570, Australia. Tel: +61 (0)7 54836114; Email: pfsq@bigpond.com.

Jeffrey A. McNeely is the World Conservation Union's (IUCN's) Chief Scientist and has been at IUCN since 1980. McNeely has designed numerous programmes, advised governments and conservation organizations on conservation policy and practice, and produced a variety of technical and popular publications. Books have included: *National Parks, Conservation, and Development* (the proceedings of the III World Congress on National Parks); *People and Protected Areas in the Hindu-Kush Himalaya*; *Culture and Conservation*; *Economics and Biological Diversity*; *Conserving the World's Biological Diversity*; *Biodiversity Conservation in the Asia-Pacific Region*; and *Conservation and the Future: Trends and Options Toward the Year 2025*. He has published over 300 technical and popular articles on a wide range of conservation issues, seeking to link conservation of natural resources to the maintenance of cultural diversity and to economically-sustainable ways of life. He serves on the editorial advisory board of seven biodiversity-related journals. Contact: Jeffrey A. McNeely, Chief Scientist, IUCN, 1196 Gland, Switzerland.

Genevieve Michon conducts research on the interrelations between agricultural societies and forests. Dr. Michon has a master's degree in agricultural science from the Ecole supérieure d'agronomie tropicale de Montpellier, and an MSc in tropical botany and a Ph.D. in tropical forest ecology from the University of Montpellier. She worked for ORSTOM in Congo (1986–1987) on the evaluation of the importance of trees and forests in farmers economy in southern Mayombe, then with the SEAMO-BIOTROP centre in Indonesia where she was in charge of a multidisciplinary research project on sustainability of forest resource management through agroforests. Seconded from ORSTOM, she joined ICRAF in 1994, where she worked on the domestication of forest resources, including non-timber forest products and timber, in agroforestry systems. From 1996 till 2001, she led a EU-funded project on the analysis of the transition between extractive systems in natural forests and agroforestry systems in farmlands for the management of forest resources. She is based in Montpellier since 2000 where she leads a research team on the interrelations between forest dynamics and the evolution of forest-dependant societies.

Bill Mollison, founder and director of the Permaculture Institute, Bill is the most experienced Permaculture teacher and designer today. He has taught and developed projects from the Arctic through Subtropics and Equatorial regions of the planet. The Peoples of the Pacific, South East Asia, South Africa and seven Amazonian language groups have been inspired by and acted on his teachings, embracing Permaculture as a dynamic tool. He has also given Courses in the drylands and developed projects with Native Americans, Indigenous Australians, tribal women of the Deccan, Kalahari, San groups and Pima people of the Sonora. In the USA, Europe and Scandinavia, Bill has lectured and helped to develop ecological designs for urban and rural properties, including many city-farms and CSA's (Community Supported Agriculture). Bill Mollison's many roles include: scientist, naturalist and University professor. Later he became a vigorous campaigner against environmental exploitation which lead him to develop Permaculture as a positive solution. Since then, Bill has devoted his energies towards designing sustainable systems, writing books and articles on Permaculture, and most importantly, teaching. Bill's publications include *Introduction to Permaculture*, *PERMACULTURE: A Designer's Manual*, and *The Permaculture Book of Ferment and Human Nutrition*.

Carmen Sotelo Montes is a forester working with the International Centre for Research in Agroforestry. He conducts research and training on participatory domestication of agroforestry trees in the Peruvian Amazon Basin. Research focuses on the management and conservation-through-use of tree genetic resources for community development. He has conducted studies of farmers' preferences for tree species, farmers' use and management of tree germplasm, the efficiency of phenotypic selection in the field, intraspecific variation in wood-quality and other traits, and methods for the production of improved tree seed in farming communities. He can be reached at: ICRAF, INIA Estación Experimental, Carretera Federico Basadre Km 4.2, Pucallpa, Peru. Email: c.sotelo@cgiar.org

Mulawarman formerly worked as Tree farming Research Officer with World Agroforestry Centre (ICRAF) SEA to enhance smallholder tree farming systems in Indonesia, particularly in Nusa Tenggara. He is currently based in Pangkalan Kerinci, Riau, Indonesia as the Senior Silviculture Researcher with Riau Andalan Pulp and Paper, a member of APRIL Group. He can be contacted at: R&D Forestry, Riau Andalan Pulp and Paper, Pangkalan Kerinci, Riau 28300, P.O Box 1089, Indonesia; Tel: 62 761 95550 Ext. 5204, 5222; Fax: 62 761 95360; Email: Mulawarman@aprilasia.com.

P. K. Ramachandran Nair is Distinguished Professor of Agroforestry at the University of Florida, Gainesville, Florida, USA. He has been a founder-scientist at the International Centre for Research and Agroforestry (ICRAF), Nairobi, Kenya for about 10 years. Dr. Nair is a leading world authority and a pioneering researcher and educator in agroforestry, Editor-in-Chief of *Agroforestry Systems*, and author of *An Introduction to Agroforestry*. Recently (2001), a new Center for Subtropical Agroforestry (CSTAF) was established under his leadership at the University of Florida, with partial funding from the US Department of Agriculture. His web site is: http://www.sfrc.ufl.edu/pknair and email: pknair@ufl.edu.

The Natural Resources Conservation Service

(NRCS) is the US Department of Agriculture's lead conservation agency. No other Federal US agency speaks for the health and fate of America's private land. NRCS relies on many partners to help set conservation goals, work with people on the land, and provide assistance. Its partners include conservation districts, state and federal agencies, NRCS Earth Team volunteers, agricultural and environmental groups, and professional societies. For more information visit: http://www.nrcs.usda.gov/about/

Greg O'Neill is a professional forester who works as a tree breeder in the Research Branch of the British Columbia Ministry of Forests in Canada. His research interests include tree seed transfer, adaptation of forest trees, and climate change. Address: Kalamalka Forestry Centre, 3401 Reservoir Road, Vernon BC V1B 2C7, Canada; Tel: 250-260-4776; Email: greg.oneill@gems6.gov.bc.ca; Web: http://www.for.gov.bc.ca/hre/

N.W. Osorio is a graduate student at the Department of Tropical Plant and Soil Sciences, University of Hawai'i at Manoa. The focus of his dissertation research is the interaction of arbuscular mycorrhizal fungi with phosphate solubilizing microorganisms.

Manuel C. Palada is a professor of horticultural science at the Agricultural Experiment Station, University of the Virgin Islands on St. Croix, U.S. Virgin Islands. He has wide international experience in tropical agriculture starting with senior research assistant at the International Rice Research Institute (IRRI) in the Philippines, senior agronomist at the International Institute of Tropical Agriculture (IITA), Nigeria and recently a visiting scientist and crop production/ecosystem specialist at the Asian Vegetable Research and Development Center (AVRDC) in Taiwan. He has previous assignments with the Rodale Institute, Pennsylvania, World Bank in Kenya and Somalia, Asian Development Bank (ADB) in the Philippines and USAID in Tanzania, Liberia and Uganda. His major research area is focused on sustainable agriculture, agroforestry systems, medicinal and aromatic plants, microirrigation, vegetable production, culinary herbs and farming systems.

Deep Narayan Pandey is Associate Professor of Ecosystem Management and Technical Forestry at the Indian Institute of Forest Management, Bhopal, India. He is coordinator for the International Network on Ethnoforestry, the Asia Forest Network in South Asia and the Master of Philosophy Programme on Natural Resource Management. Deep Narayan Pandey is devoted to cause of the sustainability of forests and livelihood security of indigenous communities and works extensively with communities for protection of forests, afforestation, entitlements to biomass, and environmental protection in ecologically threatened areas. Dr. Pandey can be reached at: IIFM, PO Box No. 357, Nehru Nagar, Bhopal-462 003, India; Tel: 91 755 775716; Fax: 91 755 772878; Email: dnpandey@vsnl.com; Web: http://education.vsnl.com/deep

Michael Pease is Coordinator of the European and Mediterranean Vetiver Network, a nonprofit organisation registered in Portugal. He graduated from the Royal Agricultural College, UK, specialising in Advanced Farm Management. In Kenya he was a farmer, then joined The Ministry of Lands and Settlement before spending 21 years with the World Bank. Later, Mike was Senior Agriculturalist in the European, Mediterranean and North African Region. Mike can be reached at: Quinta das Espargoas, Odiaxere, 8600-252 Lagos, Algarve, Portugal; Tel/fax: 351-282 798 466; Email: mikepeasexx@mail.telepac.pt.

Imants Pone is an Environmental Scientist at a Minnesota Consulting firm. He holds a M.S. degree in Environmental Studies from the University of Minnesota, and has been involved in forestry projects in the United States and Latvia. He can be contacted at pone66@hotmail.com.

Darrell Posey was Titled Researcher (Pesquisador Titular) for the Brazilian National Council for Science and Technology at the Goeldi Museum, Belem, Brazil. He was also Director of the Programme for Traditional Resource Rights of the Oxford Centre for the Environment, Ethics and Society at Mansfield College, and an Associate Fellow of Linacre College, University of Oxford. Posey was the recipient of the first "Chico Mendes Award for Outstanding Bravery in Defense of the Environment" and one of the recipients of the United Nations "Global 500" Award for Environmental Achievement. His main fieldwork was on the ethnobiology of the Kayapo Indians of the Brazilian Amazon. He published over 184 scientific articles and 8 books, which include *Beyond Intellectual Property: Towards Traditional Resource Rights for Indigenous Peoples* and *Local Communities* (IDRC, Ottawa,1996; with Graham Dutfield); and *Indigenous Peoples and Sustainability* (IUCN and Earthscan; 1996). Darrell Posey passed away in May 2001.

Meka R. Rao is an agronomist and worked mostly in CGIAR institutes, first at the International Center for Crops Research in Semi-Arid Tropics (ICRISAT) in India, then at the International Institute for Tropical Agriculture (IITA) in Cameroon and lastly as agroforester at the International Centre for Research in Agroforestry (ICRAF, recently designated as World Agroforestry Centre) based at Nairobi in Kenya. At ICRAF he was leading the Ecosystem Rehabilitation program. He also worked as cropping systems specialist in Brazil for two years. Rao's research covered cropping systems, tree-crop-environment interactions, soil fertility replenishment using trees, and pest management in agroforestry. He is author of over 120 research papers and articles published in leading journals. He has returned back to India after his retirement from ICRAF in 2000 and is available at mekarao@sol.net.in.

Rowan Reid is a Senior Lecturer in Agroforestry and Farm Forestry at the University of Melbourne and the developer of the Australian Master TreeGrower Program (MTG). More than 40 MTG programs have been conducted across Australia involving more than 1,000 farmers. In 2000 the program was awarded the Eureka Prize for excellence in environmental education. Rowan is also a tree grower himself and has recently made furniture out of ten-year-old eucalypt trees he planted and managed on his Otway Ranges farm. He can be reached at: Rowan Reid, Senior Lecturer, Agroforestry & Farm Forestry, Email: rfr@unimelb.edu.au. School of Resource Management, The Institute of Land & Food Resources, The University of Melbourne, Victoria 3010, Australia; Tel: +61 (0)3 8344 5011; Fax: +61 (0)3 9349 4172; The Australian Master TreeGrower web: http://www.mtg.unimelb.edu.au.

Jim Roshetko has worked with agroforestry systems and species for over 20 years in Southeast Asia, South Asia, the Pacific and the Caribbean. He is currently based in Bogor, Indonesia as the Trees and Markets Specialist with Winrock International and the World Agroforestry Centre (ICRAF). His work focuses on methods to enhance smallholder tree farming systems. He can be contacted at: ICRAF/Winrock, PO Box 161, Bogor 16001, Indonesia; Phone 62 251 625-415; Fax 62 251 625-416; email: J.Roshetko@cgiar.org.

Frank Santamour was a Research Geneticist in the Floral and Nursery Plants Research Unit at the United States National Arboretum for 33 years, until his death in July 2000. Frank graduated from the University of Massachusetts with a B.S. in Forestry in 1953; from Yale University with an M.F. (Forestry) in 1954; from Harvard University with an A.M. (Biology) in 1957. He gained his Ph.D. from the University of Minnesota in 1960 with a major in Forestry and minor in Plant Genetics. In over 40 years as a professional scientist, Frank authored or co-authored about 275 publications, with over 200 since he joined the U.S. National Arboretum in 1967. Among many other achievements, Frank used biochemical methods to examine graft incompatibility, insect and disease resistance, and to verify interspecific hybrids in several genera. His work on wound compartmentalization, and on the correct usage of nomenclature to describe landscape trees, was also well known. Frank often used his wit and humor to make points in delivery of his scientific papers talents so well integrated that he was frequently in demand as a speaker. Dr. Santamour was generally regarded as the world's leading authority on the genetics, breeding, and development of superior landscape trees.

Singgih Mahari Sasongko has worked in Ministry of Forestry more than 24 years in Bali, East Timor and Java. His job was focused on Seed Source Development collaboration with Indonesia Forest Seed Project. Now he is the Head of Sub Directorate Seed Source Development in Ministry of Forestry, Jakarta. He can be contact at: Directorate of Forest Tree Seed, Manggala Wanabhakti Building 13th Floor, Jl. Gatot Subroto Senayan, Jakarta, Indonesia, Tel: 62 21 5730179, Fax: 62 21 5730217.
Email: singgih_sasongko@yahoo.com.au

Lars Schmidt is Chief Technical Adviser of the Indonesia Forest Seed Project, a Danish-Indonesian support project to the Indonesian forest seed sector. Lars is a biologist specialising in tropical forest ecosystems and tropical forest seed. He has been adviser to international and bi-lateral forestry projects in Malawi, the Philippines and Indochina. In Indochina he was Technical Adviser for Vietnam, regional training adviser and regional coordinator on conservation of Forest Genetic Resources. He is presently on leave from Danida Forest Seed Centre, Denmark. His publications include mainly technical guidelines and articles. Address: Indonesia Forest Seed Project, Taman Hutan Raya Ir. H. Juanda No. 120, Dago Pagar, Bandung 40198, Jawa Barat, PO Box. 6919 Bandung 40135, Indonesia. Tel/fax: 62-22-2515895. Email: ifsp@indo.net.id

Patricia Shanley has 18 years of experience in temperate and tropical research and education, specifically on non-timber forest products. During the past eight years she has worked with forest-based communities in the eastern Amazon, concentrating on the impacts of logging on locally valued non-timber fruit and medicinals and the comparative economic value of timber and non-timber species for rural communities. In an effort to return research results to forest-based communities, Patricia Shanley has coauthored two non-timber forest product (NTFP) manuals that focus on the use and marketing of significant non-timber forest products in eastern Amazonia: *Forest Fruit Trees in the Life of Amazonians* and *Recipes without Words: Medicinal Plants of Amazonia*, both published in Portuguese. Shanley is currently a research scientist at the Center for International Forestry (CIFOR) in Bogor, Indonesia.

Max Shelton obtained his Ph.D. degree from the University of Queensland and is now an Associate Professor responsible for teaching and research in pasture science and agroforestry. His current research interest is forage tree legumes in tropical agriculture; he was previously involved in research and development programs on pastures for tropical plantation  crops. From 1995, he has been research leader of a project "New Leucaenas for Southeast Asian, Pacific and Australian Agriculture" supported by the Australian Centre for International Agricultural Research (ACIAR). This program has involved collaboration with scientists and extension workers in 7 countries and has comprised work on the germplasm evaluation, environmental adaptation, forage quality and animal productivity of a world germplasm collection representing the entire Leucaena genus. Dr. Shelton has worked extensively on forage and livestock systems in the Southeast Asian and Pacific regions over 25 years. He has published widely including editorship of a CABI book on tree legumes and four ACIAR Proceedings on Leucaena and Forages for Plantation Crops. Dr. Shelton currently works cooperatively with the many Queensland graziers who are planting leucaena as forage for cattle production. They have supported new research programs on breeding of a psyllid resistant forage leucaena cultivar, and on a new investigation of the problem of mimosine toxicity in Queensland cattle herds.

Alex L. Shigo is retired chief scientist with the US Forest Service. He is now an internationally recognized researcher credited with the development of expanded interpretations of decay based on compartmentalization and microbial succession. His research includes over 15,000 longitudinal tree dissections with a chain saw. He has published over 15 textbooks used in many universities worldwide. Contact: Shigo And Trees, Associates, P.O. Box 769, Durham, NH 03824, USA; Tel: 603-868-7459; Fax: 603-868-1045.

The Small Farm Program of the U.S. Department of Agriculture's Cooperative State Research, Education, and Extension Service (CSREES) is designed to improve small farm operations throughout the United States and its territories via partnership and collaboration with the land-grant university system and other public and private sectors, including farmers, community-based organizations, foundations, and others. For additional information about the Small Farm Program, contact Denis Ebodaghe at CSREES, USDA, Mail Stop 2220, Washington, DC 20250-2220; Tel: 202-401-4385; Fax: 202-401-5179; Email: debodaghe@reeusda.gov.

Christi A. Sobel is a freelance scientific illustrator, artist, and graphic designer with a graduate degree in Scientific Illustration from the University of California, Santa Cruz. She has been published by the Royal Botanic Gardens, Kew, Educational Concerns for Hunger Organization (ECHO), Permanent Agriculture Resources, and Cornell University's Lab of Ornithology. Christi's contact information is: PO Box 195, Brooktondale, NY 14817 USA; Tel: 607-539-7805; Email: sobel@clarityconnect.com. Her web site is: http://christisobel.clarityconnect.com.

Paul Stamets has authored five books, including *Growing Gourmet & Medicinal Mushrooms*, which describes methods for incorporating mushrooms and mycotechnologies within a permaculture model. He has discovered and named four new species of mushrooms. Active in sourcing new strains of medicinal mushrooms, his business Fungi Per-  fecti (http://www.fungi.com) serves cultivators and scientists worldwide. He has also established a nonprofit (http://www.mycodiversity.org) whose mission is to the protect the fungal genome of the old growth forests. Paul has been awarded a breakthrough patent on using fungi to replace chemical pesticides in a way that does not harm the environment of the genome. His newest book *Mycelium Running: How Mushrooms Can Help Save the World* will be published early 2005. Paul teaches workshops at his farms located at the base of the Olympic Peninsula of Washington State, USA.

Peter Stephen is a Research Fellow with the School of Resource Management at the University of Melbourne, Australia. He has been involved with farm forestry extension throughout Australia for the past decade of which the last four years have seen a wonderful association with and coordination of the Australian Master TreeGrower Program. Peter has also worked overseas in a number of countries, but principally in India on farm forestry extension, community forestry and rural development and is presently involved in establishing a community forest management project in Australia. Peter can be contacted through the School of Resource Management, The Institute of Land and Food Resources, The University of Melbourne Victoria 3010, Australia; Email: pstephen@unimelb.edu.au

The Sustainable Agriculture and Rural Livelihoods (SARL) Programme of the International Institute for Environment and Development (IIED) seeks to promote sustainable, equitable, decentralised agri-food systems based on local diversity and participatory democracy, thereby contributing to improved livelihoods and entitlements, poverty reduction, and long-term ecological and economic sustainability. By working to develop more effective and equitable forms of agriculture and natural resource management, the SARL Programme helps different interest groups to understand trade-offs relating to their livelihood strategies, identify common ground, and negotiate pathways to positive actions that support rural regeneration. Established in 1986, the aim of the SARL Programme was to provide key policy makers, project designers, and rural development practitioners with concepts, tools, and methods to put into practice the challenges facing sustainable agricultural development. Since then, the SARL approach has evolved, and has emerged out of a growing recognition that sustainable agriculture and rural development cannot be treated in isolation from broader ecological, economic, social, and political processes. It is these broader processes, particularly counterproductive and inappropriate policies, and weak and ineffective institutions, which are limiting the spread of sustainable agriculture and the regeneration of rural economies. Contact: SARL Programme, International Institute for Environment and Development, 3 Endsleigh Street, London WC1H 0DD, United Kingdom; Tel: +44 (0) 20 7388-2117; Fax: +44 (0)20 7388-2826; Email: sustag@iied.org; Web: http://www.iied.org/sarl/index.html.

Wayne Teel is an assistant professor in the environmental science sector with the Department of Integrated Science and Technology at James Madison University in Harrisonburg, Virginia. His work at the university centers on undergraduate teaching and research including water quality, riparian land use, sustainability, and the interface between Shenandoah Valley agricultural systems and woodlands. Before JMU he did work on Special Forest Products with Cornell University (where he did his graduate studies) in cooperation with Dr. Louise Buck and water quality work in the Shenandoah Region. His interest in agroforestry was developed in Africa, where he spent 9 years working with the Mennonite Central Committee in Sudan, Kenya and Mozambique, developing extension materials and doing research on agroforestry practices relevant for small farms. During the time in Kenya he also wrote a small book on trees in that country useful for agroforestry, focusing primarily on indigenous species. A web version on that book is currently under development and should be available in the next year. Dr. Teel, who is originally from Seattle, WA, can be reached via email at teelws@jmu.edu.

Randolf "Randy" R. Thaman is Professor of Pacific Island Biogeography at the University of the South Pacific, Suva, Fiji. His main areas of research interest include environmentally sustainable development, agroforestry, Pacific Island food systems, ethnobiology and traditional environmental knowledge, Pacific Island floras, community-based biodiversity conservation, and ecotourism. Professor Thaman has also published widely on a wide range of topics of importance to the Pacific Islands. Among his major publications, which he has authored or co-authored over the years, are *Applied Atoll Research and Development* (1989), *Agroforestry in the Pacific Islands: Systems for Sustainability* (1993), *A review of Uses and Status of Trees and Forests in Land Use Systems in Samoa, Tonga, Kiribati and Tuvalu* (1996). Professor Thaman also has a long history of community outreach. He was a founding member and served as the Chairman of the Fiji National Food and Nutrition Committee (NFNC) and was the Founder of the South Pacific Action Committee for Human Ecology and the Environment (SPACHEE).

Peter Thomas is a lecturer in environmental science at Keele University, UK, where his teaching encompasses a wide range of tree-related topics including wood structure and identification, tree design and biomechanics, tree ecology and identification, and woodland management. His research interests focus on the reconstruction of past environments from tree rings, the role of trees in nature conservation and the interaction of fire with trees. He can be contacted at: Huxley Building, School of Life Sciences, Keele University, Staffordshire ST5 5BG, UK; Email: p.a.thomas@biol.keele.ac.uk.

The USDA National Agroforestry Center (NAC) is a partnership of the USDA Forest Service, Research & Development (R&D) (Rocky Mountain Research Station), and State & Private Forestry (S&PF) and the USDA Natural Resources Conservation Service. The Center's purpose is to accelerate the development and application of agroforestry technologies to attain more economically, environmentally, and socially sustainable land-use systems. To accomplish its mission, the Center interacts with a national network of cooperators to conduct research, develop technologies and tools, establish demonstrations, and provide useful information to natural resource professionals. Contact:

National Agroforestry Center, North 38th St. & East Campus Loop, UNL-East Campus, Lincoln, Nebraska 68583-0822; Tel: 402-437-5178; Web: http://www.unl.edu/nac/

Julianne (Jackie) Venning specialises in environmental and natural resource management. She holds a Ph.D. in biological environmental science and an MBA. Her earlier work involved the conservation and management of rural landscapes, particularly the retention, rehabilitation and re-establishment of remnant native vegetation in southern Australia. More recently she has been involved in the development and application of environmental auditing tools for monitoring and reporting on planning and performance frameworks for sustainable development. Recent publications include *Towards Sustainability: Emerging Systems for Informing Sustainable Development* (Venning, J. and Higgins, J., Eds, 2001, UNSW Press). Her contact details are: Dr. Jackie Venning, Office of Sustainability, GPO Box 1047, Adelaide, South Australia. 5001 Australia; Tel: +61 8 8204 9278, Fax: +61 8 8204 9144; Email: venning.jackie@saugov.sa.gov.au.

Helen van Houten has a long experience as a Science Writer and Science Editor with, among others, International Development Research Centre (IDRC) and International Center for Research in Agroforestry (ICRAF). She is now a freelance writer living in Kenya.

Meine van Noordwijk researches environmental interactions between agroforestry systems and other land uses, as well as ecological interactions within agroforestry. He works on modelling tree–soil–crop interactions in above and below ground resource capture in a wide range of agroforestry technologies. His research includes biodiversity and environmental aspects of agroforestry and scaling of results from plot to landscape level. He is based at ICRAF's regional headquarters in Bogor, Indonesia. Before joining ICRAF he was a senior research officer in the Root Ecology Section at the DLO Institute for Soil Fertility Research in Haren, the Netherlands, concentrating on the relationships between soil fertility, nutrient use efficiency and root development of crops and trees in various temperate and tropical agroecosystems. He also worked for 2 years as a lecturer in botany and ecology at the University of Juba (Sudan). Born and educated in the Netherlands, he has bachelor's and master's degrees in biology from the University of Utrecht and a Ph.D. from the Agricultural University of Wageningen.

Bruno Verbist is conducting research on the impact of land use change in agroforestry landscape mosaics on watershed functions in Sumberjaya, Lampung, Sumatra in collaboration with ICRAF in Bogor. Since 1 February 2004 he has been working towards a Ph.D. degree at the Katholieke Universiteit Leuven, Belgium, and still spends considerable time in Indonesia. Before that he was seconded for almost 9 years to ICRAF by VVOB, the Flemish Office for Development Cooperation and technical Assistance. Based for over 6 years at ICRAF in Bogor he was responsible for organising research and training activities in Southeast Asia. Before joining the Bogor team, he worked as training officer at the ICRAF headquarters in Nairobi. Before joining ICRAF he worked as a research associate at the University of Ghent, processing and interpreting optical and radar satellite images covering tropical forests. During that time he carried out a forest inventory in the Carara natural reserve in Costa Rica, collecting data for a watershed management research project. With the EU sponsored ERASMUS program he was able to pursue advanced studies in agricultural development at the Agricultural University of Wageningen, Netherlands, during which time he carried out an agroforestry apprenticeship in Senegal. Bruno obtained an ingenieur degree in forestry from the University of Ghent, Belgium, and during that time participated in an inventory of tropical forest vegetation in Meng Yang and Meng Lun in Xishuangbanna, Southwest China, a project supported by the Worldwide Fund for Nature.

Email: B.Verbist@cgiar.org; Web: http://www.icraf.cgiar.org/sea.

John Weber is a forest geneticist working with the International Centre for Research in Agroforestry. He conducts research and training on participatory domestication of agroforestry trees in the Peruvian Amazon Basin. Research focuses on the management and conservation-through-use of tree genetic resources for community development. He has conducted studies of farmers' preferences for tree species, farmers' use and management of tree germplasm, the efficiency of phenotypic selection in the field, intraspecific variation in wood-quality and other traits, and methods for the production of improved tree seed in farming communities. He can be reached at: ICRAF, INIA Estación Experimental, Carretera Federico Basadre Km 4.2, Pucallpa, Peru. Email: j.weber@cgiar.org

James Were was between 1995 and 2002 the research officer in-charge of tree seed research and supply within the Genetic Resources Unit of the World Agroforestry Centre (ICRAF). He was responsible for procuring, testing, handling and dispatching tree seed for ICRAF scientists and their collaborators. His research included determining mechanisms of dormancy in tree seed and investigating the physiology of seed storage behaviour. Before joining ICRAF, he worked for 9 years as a research officer in the forest ecology section of the Kenya Forestry Research Institute (KEFRI). Most recently he was undertaking his Ph.D. research on *Sesbania sesban* seed production and genetic management in Kenya and

Zambia, as a student with Wageningen, The Netherlands. James passed away in February 2004.

Frank H. Wadsworth has been a silviculturist based in Puerto Rico since 1942. He has served as Director of International Institute of Tropical Forestry (USDA Forest Service), Supervisor of the Caribbean National Forest, and international forestry consultant in 15 countries until retirement at the end of 1999. He is currently a Forest Service volunteer editing ISTF News, the quarterly publication of the International Society of Tropical Foresters.

Elizabeth A. Widjaja is a research professor on bamboo taxonomist at the Herbarium Bogoriense, Botany Division, Centre Research for Biology, Indonesian Institute of Sciences at Bogor, Indonesia. Her interest is in the taxonomy of the Indonesian bamboo especially and Malesian bamboo generally. She is also doing some studies on molecular systematics to understand the phylogenesis analysis of the Malesian bamboo as well as studies on the genetic diversity of *Dendrocalamus asper* in Indonesia. Her work has included the population density of the natural bamboo vegetation as well as the community bamboo gardens. Dr. Widjaja has always promoted bamboo for the cultivation to prevent the erosion; because of that she received the World Biodiversity Day from the State Ministry of Environment in 1999 and also got an Indonesian President Award in 2000. She is an author of over 75 articles and scientific papers and three books on bamboo. The field guide on bamboo is a widely used handbook for identification purposes. Beside taxonomy, she is also doing some ethnobotanical studies, which won her the Harsberger Medal given by the Society of the Ethnobotanist, India in 2001. Her email address is ewidjaja@indo.net.id.

Kim M. Wilkinson is a naturalist, reforestation professional and a freelance writer. She has B.A. degrees in Anthropology and Ecology from Emory University as well as certifications as a Permaculture Designer and Master Gardener. An author of four books including *Nursery Manual for Native Plants: A Guide for Tribal Nurseries* (2004, in press), *Growing Koa: A Hawaiian Legacy Tree* (2003), and *Agroforestry Guides for Pacific Islands* (2000), she is currently engaged in graduate work at Yale's School of Forestry and Environmental Studies. Email: kim@kimwilkinson.com, or visit her web site at: http://www.kimwilkinson.com.

Anthony Young has over 40 years of experience in all aspects of land resources, including survey, evaluation, planning, conservation and management. His work has been divided between university-based research into natural resources, and practical contributions to rural development in Africa, Asia and tropical America. He was formerly Professor of Environmental Sciences at the University of East Anglia, Norwich, UK, and Principal Scientist at the International Centre for Research in Agroforestry (ICRAF), Nairobi, Kenya. He has worked in over 40 developing countries, and carried out consultancies for FAO, the World Bank, and commercial organizations. He has written 15 books (and over 130 scientific articles) including *Agroforestry For Soil Management* (1997), *Land Resources: Now and for the Future* (1998), and *Soil Survey and Land Evaluation* (1981). He is currently writing a history of Early Soil and Land Resources Survey in British Overseas Territories, and would be pleased to hear from any reader who can offer information. He can be contacted at: anthony.young@land-resources.com or visit his web site at http://www.land-resources.com for further information.

Jon Young has been a naturalist, tracker, and educator for over 25 years. Jon has pioneered blending indigenous mentoring techniques from around the world with the tools of modern field ecology. He is driven by a vision of a learning model that affects people of all ages and backgrounds to re-establish their relationship with themselves, others, and the environment. As Jon continually shares this model with others he has inspired thousands to reconnect with their native environments. In 1983 Jon Young founded the Wilderness Awareness School. He is the principal author of the Kamana Naturalist Training Program, which serves over 5,000 students worldwide, and the Shikari Tracker Training Program. He created several popular training tape series including, *Seeing through Native Eyes*, *The Art of Mentoring* and *Coyote Teaching*, and *Advanced Bird Language*. He is the leader of a model of mentoring that is currently being used in 29 different schools across the country, he is an advisor to undergraduate and graduate students, and continues to be a consultant for various schools, community leaders and businesses. Because of his success as an educator and inspirational consultant, he was a keynote speaker for the Association for Environmental Outdoor Education and for home schooling conferences in Washington and California; he was also invited to be part of a think tank at The Union Theological Seminary, sponsored by the Nature Institute. Jon Young is a celebrated and gifted presenter, and is a sought after peacemaker to resolve conflicts. For more information about Jon's programs see http://www.natureoutlet.com and http://www.shikari.org.

Traditional Polynesian garden. (photo: C. Elevitch)

Learning from Traditional Knowledge

Traditional practices have been developed over many generations, and have survived the test of time. The knowledge of these successful practices, from home gardening to tree protection to jungle cultivation, can be a foundation for future development.

Section Contents

Agroforestry

Craig R. Elevitch and Kim M. Wilkinson

Tree-based agriculture (agroforestry) has been practiced throughout the world for thousands of years. Agroforestry systems increase species diversity within farming systems, providing for human needs while supporting wildlife, soil microorganisms, rural communities, farmers, economic interests, watersheds, clean air concerns, biodiversity, and more. The continued appropriate and well-managed use of trees in agricultural systems can serve as an effective component for sustainable economic development and environmental protection.

What Is Agroforestry?

Agroforestry is a modern name for an ancient approach to land-use combining trees with other crops and/or animals. Some popular definitions of agroforestry are:

Agroforestry is a dynamic, ecologically based natural resources management system that, through the integration of trees in farmland and rangeland, diversifies and sustains production for increased social, economic, and environmental benefits for land users at all levels. (ICRAF 1997)

Agroforestry is any agricultural system (agro-ecosystem) in which planted or protected trees are seen as economically, socially, or ecologically integral to the system. (Clarke and Thaman 1993)

Agroforestry is an intensive land management system that optimizes the benefits from the biological interactions created when trees and/or shrubs are deliberately combined with crops and/or animals. (Association for Temperate Agroforestry 1997)

Agroforestry is a sustainable land-management system which increases the overall yield of the land, combines the production of crops (including tree crops) and forest plants and/or animals simultaneously or sequentially, on the same unit of land, and applies management practices that are compatible with the cultural practices of the local population. (Nair 1989)

By all these definitions, an agroforestry system:
- involves two or more species, at least one of which is a tree;

- yields two or more outputs;
- has a production cycle of longer than one year; and
- has significant interaction (economic and/or environmental) between trees and the other components (Nair 1993).

Some agroforestry systems are very simple, involving just a few species. Other agroforestry systems are more complex, resembling multi-storied, diverse forest ecosystems.

Agroforestry systems can be diverse and productive

The Benefits of Agroforestry

Population growth, increasing economic needs, environmental degradation, and a shortage of arable land make the development of sustainable and efficient agricultural systems crucial. Agroforestry practices can improve productivity and reduce inputs, while mitigating some of the environmental damage caused by the past processes of deforestation and the removal of trees from the landscape.

Agroforestry systems make more efficient use of natural resources

Soil nutrients	Trees promote nutrient cycling and efficient nutrient use; nutrient status is increased through nitrogen-fixation and the uptake of deep soil nutrients.
Sun	Multi-storied cropping systems intercept and use sunlight at all levels.

Agroforestry systems make more efficient use of natural resources

Water	Trees can increase water availability in the soil by reducing runoff and evapotranspiration, while increasing water infiltration and soil water-holding capacity.

Source: AIS 1992, Young 1997

Agroforestry systems provide a more favorable environment for sustained production

Shade	Filtered shade conserves water, reduces evapotranspiration, keeps topsoil cool, and helps maintain beneficial microbial activity.
Wind protection	Trees protect crops from wind damage and soil from wind erosion and drying.
Soil conservation	Tree root and mycorrhizal systems reduce nutrient leaching, bind soil, and prevent erosion. Tree leaf litter enhances soil physical, chemical, and biological conditions which makes soil more resistant to erosion and more able to absorb and hold water.
Nutrient cycling	Through nitrogen fixing trees and nutrient uptake from deep soil layers, trees promote more closed nutrient cycling and more efficient use of nutrients.
Habitat diversity	Trees provide habitats for birds, insects, and other animals that help maintain biodiversity and pest/predator balance in the system.

Source: AIS 1992, Young 1997

Agroforestry systems can be more profitable

Reduced expenses	Through nutrient cycling and soil and water conservation, trees reduce the need to purchase fertilizer and water. Trees may also reduce the need for pesticides by providing habitat for pest predators.
Diversified products	Mixed cropping systems typically have two or more economic products, reducing dependence on market conditions for a single crop.

Agroforestry systems can be more profitable

Continuous flow of products	Agroforestry systems often combine short-term and long-term crops, which can lead to a high level of total productivity and year-round production.
Greater self-reliance	Agroforestry can reduce farmer's dependence on purchased products and resources, as well as reducing vulnerability to changing market conditions.

Agroforestry systems can improve the environment

Reduced pressure on natural forests	On-farm production of wood and other forest products reduces pressure to exploit natural forests.
Species diversity	Trees and mixed systems provide habitat and support biodiversity (wildlife, microlife, etc.)
Resource conservation	Trees can improve conservation of soil, nutrients, and water in the landscape.
Carbon sequestration	Trees store carbon from the air, helping to reduce carbon dioxide pollution and global climate change.
Decreased pollution	Nutrient cycling of trees may reduce the use of chemical fertilizers, thus reducing chemical and soil run-off.

Agroforestry systems are culturally compatible

Locally-based	Agroforestry systems incorporate species and techniques that have been used traditionally in the Tropics for many generations, in some cases for thousands of years.
Adaptable	Due to farmer experience and acceptance over many decades, traditional systems and species provide a strong, locally-based framework for future agroforestry development (Thaman and Whistler, 1996).
Acceptable	By combining production with conservation and land improvement, the agroforestry approach can increase the acceptability and adoption of sustainable practices (Young 1997).

The Importance of Planning Agroforestry Systems

Agroforestry systems require careful advanced planning. Mixed systems are more complex than single-species monocultures. It is often difficult to predict the results of crop combinations and interactions, and the systems evolve and change over time. Those embarking on an agroforestry project need to be aware of the possible adverse effects of combining trees with crops. Compared to the relative abundance of data from monocultures, there is a scarcity of scientifically-based practical information about mixed systems. There is also a shortage of information about the economic trade-off of agroforestry systems. Managing diverse, dynamic systems and marketing diverse products is a challenge. For these reasons, agroforestry systems require more up-front planning, research, and risk assessment than a simple single-species planting.

References

Agroforestry Information Service (AIS). 1992. Why Agroforestry? Agroforestry Information Service Technology Fact Sheet. USDA Forest Service and NFTA, Paia, Hawai'i.

Association for Temperate Agroforestry (AFTA). 1997. The Status, Opportunities & Needs for Agroforestry in the United States: A National Report. AFTA, Lexington, Kentucky.

Clarke, W.C., and R.R. Thaman. 1993. Agroforestry in the Pacific Islands: Systems for Sustainability. United Nations University Press, Tokyo.

Elevitch, C.R. and K.M. Wilkinson. 2000. Information Resources for Pacific Island Agroforestry. Permanent Agriculture Resources, Holualoa, Hawai'i.

International Centre for Research in Agroforestry (ICRAF). 1997. Redefining Agroforestry—And Opening Pandora's Box? Agroforestry Today Vol. 9 No. 1. ICRAF, Nairobi, Kenya.

International Institute of Rural Reconstruction. 1990. Agroforestry Technology Information Kit. IIRR, Room 1270, 475 Riverside Dr., New York, NY 10115.

Nair, P.K.R., ed. 1989. Agroforestry Systems in the Tropics. Kluwer Academic Publishers and ICRAF, Dordrecht, The Netherlands.

Nair, P.K.R. 1993. An Introduction to Agroforestry. Kluwer Academic Publishers and ICRAF, Dordrecht, The Netherlands.

Thaman, R.R., and W.A. Whistler. 1996. A Review of the Uses and Status of Trees and Forests in Land-use Systems in Samoa, Tonga, Kiribati, and Tuvalu. South Pacific Forestry Development Programme, Suva, Fiji.

Young, A. 1997. Agroforestry for Soil Management, Second Edition. CAB International and ICRAF, New York, NY.

Original Source

This chapter was adapted from:

Elevitch, C.R., and K.M. Wilkinson. 2000. Information Resources for Pacific Island Agroforestry. Permanent Agriculture Resources, Holualoa, HI. Web: http://www.agroforestry.net.

Material from this chapter was also originally published in *The Overstory* #7.

Tropical Homegardens

P. K. Ramachandran Nair

Home gardening has a long tradition in many tropical countries. Tropical homegardens consist of an assemblage of plants, which may include trees, shrubs, vines, and herbaceous plants, growing in or adjacent to a homestead or home compound. These gardens are planted and maintained by members of the household and their products are intended primarily for household consumption; the gardens also have considerable ornamental value, and they provide shade to people and animals. The word "homegarden" has been used rather loosely to describe diverse practices, from growing vegetables behind houses to complex multistoried systems. It is used here to refer to intimate association of multipurpose trees and shrubs with annual and perennial crops and, invariably livestock within the compounds of individual houses, with the whole crop-tree-animal unit being managed by family labor (Fernandes and Nair, 1986).

Homegardens exemplify many agroforestry characteristics, i.e., the intimate mix of diversified agricultural crops and multipurpose trees fulfills most of the basic needs of the local population while the multistoried configuration and high species diversity of the homegardens help reduce the environmental deterioration commonly associated with monocultural production systems. Moreover, they have been producing sustained yields for centuries in a most resource-efficient way.

Structure of Homegardens

In spite of the very small average size of the management units, homegardens are characterized by a high species diversity and usually 3–4 vertical canopy strata, which results in intimate plant associations. The layered canopy configurations and combination of compatible species are the most conspicuous characteristics of all homegardens. Contrary to the appearance of random arrangement, the gardens are usually carefully structured systems with every component having a specific place and function. The Javanese *pekarangan* is a clean and carefully tended system surrounding the house, where plants of different heights and architectural types, though not planted in an orderly manner, optimally occupy the available space both horizontally and vertically (Wiersum, 1982; Soemarwoto and Soemarwoto, 1984). The homegardens in the Pacific Islands present a more clearly

d arrangement of species following the orientation and relief characteristics of the watershed. The West African compound farms (Okafor and Fernandes, 1987) are characterized by a four-layer canopy dominated by a large number of tall indigenous fruit trees. An architectural analysis of the canopy reveals a relatively higher percentage of canopy distribution in the upper strata.

Diverse homegarden

In general terms, all homegardens consist of a herbaceous layer near the ground, a tree layer at upper levels, and intermediate layers in between. The lower layer can usually be partitioned into two, with the lowermost (less than 1 m height) dominated by different vegetable and medicinal plants, and the second layer (1–3 m height) being composed of food plants such as cassava, banana, papaya, yam, and so on. The upper tree layer can also be divided in two, consisting of emergent, fully grown timber and fruit trees occupying the uppermost layer of over 25 m height, and medium-sized trees of 10–20 m occupying the next lower layer. The intermediate layer of 3–10 m height is dominated by various fruit trees, some of which would continue to grow taller. This layered structure is never static; the pool of replacement species results in a productive structure which is always dynamic while the overall structure and function of the system are maintained.

Very little has been reported about rooting patterns and configurations in multi-species homegardens. A dynamic equilibrium can be expected with respect to organic matter and plant nutrients on the garden floor due to the continuous addition of leaf litter and its constant removal through decomposition. Consequently, an accumulation of absorbing roots of all species is to be expected at or near the soil surface. At lower depths in the soil, the root distribution of the various species is likely to conform to a vertical configuration roughly proportional to the canopy layers. However, this remains an important aspect for further investigation.

Food Production from Homegardens

The magnitude and rate of production, as well as the ease and rhythm of maintenance, of the homegarden system depend on its species composition. Although the choice of species is determined to a large extent by environmental and socioeconomic factors, as well as the dietary habits and market demands of the locality, there is a remarkable similarity with respect to species composition among different homegardens in various places, especially with respect to the herbaceous components. This is so because food production is the predominant role of most herbaceous species, and the presence of an overstory requires that the species are shade-tolerant. Thus, tuber crops such as taro, cassava, yam, and sweet potato dominate because they can be grown with relatively little care as understory species in partial shade and yet be expected to yield reasonable levels of carbohydrate-rich produce. Harvesting can be staggered over several weeks depending upon household needs.

A conspicuous trait of the tree-crop component in homegardens is the predominance of fruit trees, and other food-producing trees. Apart from providing a steady supply of various types of edible products, these fruit and food trees are also compatible—both biologically and environmentally—with other components of the system (Nair, 1984). While fruit trees such as guava, rambutan, mango, and mangosteen, and other food-producing trees such as *Moringa oleifera* and *Sesbania grandiflora*, dominate the Asian homegardens, indigenous trees that produce leafy vegetables (*Pterocarpus* spp.), fruit for cooking (*Dacroydes edulis*), and condiment (*Pentaclethra macrophylla*), dominate the West African compound

farms. Produce from these trees often provides a substantial proportion of the energy and nutritive requirement of the local diet. For example, Terra (1954) and Stoler (1975) reported that Javanese homegardens provided more than 40% of the whole energy requirement of the local farming communities. Soemarwoto and Conway (1991) reported that compared with the rice fields of Java, the homegarden has a greater diversity of production and usually produces a higher net income; in West Java, fish production in homegarden ponds is common, with an income of 2–2.5 times that of rice fields in the same area.

Food production is thus the primary function and role of most, if not all, of the homegardens. An aspect of food production in homegardens is the almost continuous production that occurs throughout the year. The combination of crops with different production cycles and rhythms results in a relatively uninterrupted supply of food products. Depending upon the climate and other environmental characteristics, there may be peak and slack seasons for harvesting the various products, but generally there is something to harvest daily from most homegardens. Most of this production is for home consumption, but any marketable surplus can provide a safeguard against future crop failures and security for the interval between the harvests (e.g., rice in Java and Sri Lanka, coffee and maize in Tanzania, coconut and rice in southwestern India, and so on). Additionally, these harvesting and maintenance operations require only a relatively small amount of labor from the members of the family.

Research on Homegarden Systems

Almost all the homegarden systems have evolved over time under the influence of resource constraints. These include population pressure and consequent reduction in available land and capital. Moreover, physical limitations such as remoteness of the area force the inhabitants to produce most of their basic needs by themselves, and lack of adequate market outlets compel the farmers to produce some portions of everything they need. Scientific attention has seldom focused on improving these traditional systems. Scientists who are not familiar with them do not realize the importance and potential contribution of these systems to the framework of agricultural development. Others, who are under the influence of the traditional outlook of monocultural agriculture or forestry, consider homegardens to be very specialized systems adapted to subsistence land-use and structurally too complex to be suitable for manipulation and improvement. There is a small group of scientists, however, who have conducted detailed investigations of homegardens and who appreciate the value of the systems and the wealth of information they offer regarding the behavior of plants grown in intimate proximity.

Homegardens are very complex systems with a very sophisticated structure and a large number of components. In contrast, researchers are, by and large, specialists in a discipline or a commodity. Farmers who practice homegarden systems are guided, in the absence of a unified set of expert recommendations, by their own perceptions and convictions about species selection, admixture, and management, so that each farm unit is a specialized entity in itself. These contradictions and conditions are the main impediments to coordinated research on homegardens. Yet these important systems deserve more serious attention. A systems approach should provide the basis for research on homegardens, and should include studies of both biological and socioeconomic aspects. There is also an urgent need for quantitative data and practical experimentation.

References

Fernandes, E.C.M. and P.K.R. Nair. 1986. An evaluation of the structure and function of tropical homegardens. In: Agricultural Systems 21:279–310.

Landauer, K. and M. Brazil (Eds.). 1990. Tropical Home Gardens. United Nations, University Press, Tokyo, Japan.

Nair, P.K.R. 1984. Fruit Trees in Agroforestry. Working Paper. Environment and Policy Institute, East-West Center, Honolulu, Hawai'i, USA.

Okafor, J.C. and E.C.M. Fernandes. 1987. The compound farms of southeastern Nigeria: A predominant agroforestry homegarden system with crops and small livestock. In: Agroforestry Systems. 5:153–168.

Soemarwoto, 0. and G.R. Conway. 1991. The Javanese homegarden. In: J. Farming Systems Research-Extension 2(3): 95–117.

Soemarwoto, 0. and I. Soemarwoto. 1984. The Javanese rural ecosystem. In: Rambo, T. and Sajise, E. (Eds.), An Introduction to Human Ecology Research on Agricultural Systems in Southeast Asia, pp. 254–287. University of the Philippines, Los Baños, The Philippines.

Stoler, A. 1975. Garden Use and Household Consumption Pattern in a Javanese Village. Ph.D. Dissertation, Columbia University, Department of Anthropology, New York, USA.

Terra, G.T.A. 1954. Mixed-garden horticulture in Java. In: Malaysian Journal of Tropical Geography 4: 33–43.

Wiersum, K.F. 1982. Tree gardening and taungya in Java: Examples of agroforestry techniques in the humid tropics. In: Agroforestry Systems 1: 53–70.

Original Source

The above excerpt is adapted from *An Introduction to Agroforestry* with kind permission of the author, P.K.R. Nair, and the publisher, Kluwer Academic Publishers. For further details, figures, and tables see the original text:

P.K.R. Nair. 1993. *An Introduction to Agroforestry.* Kluwer Academic Publishers, Dordrecht, The Netherlands. Web: http://www.wkap.nl/book.htm/0-7923-2135-9

This excerpt was originally published as *The Overstory #64.*

Further Reading

P.K.R. Nair's "Do Tropical Homegardens Elude Science, or Is It the Other Way Round?" examines strategies for studying ecological and economic unknowns of time-tested multispecies systems. Republished online with kind permission of the author at: http://www.agroforester.com/articles/nairhg.html.

Landauer, K. and M. Brazil (eds). 1985. Tropical Home Gardens. Selected papers from and interview workshop held at the Institute of Ecology, Padjadjaran University, Bandung, Indonesia, December 2-9. Covers the development and management of home garden programs.

Hart, R. 1991. Forest Gardening, Green Books, Devon. Describes the design of temperate multistory garden plantings which incorporate fruit and nut trees.

Introduction to Indigenous Knowledge

Steve Langill

Indigenous knowledge (IK) is, broadly speaking, the knowledge used by local people to make a living in a particular environment (Warren, 1991). Terms used in the field of sustainable development to designate this concept include indigenous technical knowledge, traditional environmental knowledge, rural knowledge, local knowledge and farmer's or pastoralist's knowledge. Indigenous knowledge can be defined as "A body of knowledge built up by a group of people through generations of living in close contact with nature" (Johnson, 1992). Generally speaking, such knowledge evolves in the local environment, so that it is specifically adapted to the requirements of local people and conditions. It is also creative and experimental, constantly incorporating outside influences and inside innovations to meet new conditions. It is usually a mistake to think of indigenous knowledge as "old-fashioned," "backwards," "static" or "unchanging."

Indigenous versus Local Knowledge

Indigenous people are the original inhabitants of a particular geographic location, who have a culture and belief system distinct from the international system of knowledge (e.g., the Tribal, Native, First, or Aboriginal people of an area). Some feel that such a definition is too narrow, in that it excludes peoples who may have lived in an area for a long period of time but are not the original inhabitants. This has led to widespread use of the term local knowledge, a broader concept which refers to the knowledge possessed by any group living off the land in a particular area for a long period of time. Under this approach, it is not necessary to know if the people in question are the original inhabitants of an area, the important thing is to learn how people—aboriginal or non-aboriginal—in a particular area view and interact with their environment, in order that their knowledge can be mobilized for the design of appropriate interventions. To add confusion, the term "indigenous knowledge" may also be used in this latter sense, to refer to "local knowledge," with "indigenous" referring to the in situ nature of the knowledge, rather than to the "origins" of the group in question. To simplify things, the two terms are used interchangeably in this article.

Types of Indigenous Knowledge

While IK research originally emphasized indigenous technical knowledge of the environment, it is now accepted that the concept of IK goes beyond this narrow interpretation. IK is now considered to be cultural knowledge in its broadest sense, including all of the social, political, economic and spiritual aspects of a local way of life. Sustainable development researchers, however, have found the following categories of IK to be of particular interest: resource management knowledge and the tools, techniques, practices and rules related to pastoralism, agriculture, agroforestry, water management and the gathering of wild food; classification systems for plants, animals, soils, water and weather; empirical knowledge about flora, fauna and inanimate resources and their practical uses; and the world view or way the local group perceives its relationship to the natural world (Emery, 1996).

While research may focus on a particular category or type of IK, any IK under investigation must be viewed in terms of the overall cultural context. IK is embedded in a dynamic system in which spirituality, kinship, local politics and other factors are tied together and influence one another. Researchers should be prepared to examine any other aspects of a culture that may play an important role in shaping the IK in question. For example, religion is an integral part of IK and cannot necessarily be separated from technical forms of knowledge. Spiritual beliefs about nature may influence how resources are managed and how willing people are to adopt new resource management strategies (IIRR, 1996a).

Topics Covered by IK Research

local organization, controls, and enforcement

institutions for resource management; common property management practices; decision-making processes; conflict management practices; traditional laws, rights, taboos and rituals; and community controls on harvesting.

social networks kinship ties and their effect on power relations, economic strategies and allocation of resources.

local classification and quantification a community's definitions and classification systems for plants, animals, soils, water, air, and weather; and indigenous methods of counting and quantifying.

learning systems indigenous methods of imparting knowledge; indigenous approaches to innovation and experimentation; and indigenous specialists.

pastoral systems herd movement; range evaluation and monitoring; animal breeding and production; traditional fodder and forage species and their specific uses; animal diseases and traditional ethnoveterinary medicine.

agriculture farming and crop systems; indigenous indicators to determine favorable times to prepare, plant, and harvest gardens; land preparation practices; ways to propagate plants; seed storage and processing; crop planting, harvesting and storage practices; food processing and marketing; and pest management systems and plant protection methods.

agroforestry the management of forest plots and trees; the knowledge and use of forest plants and animals; and the interrelationships between trees, crops, herds and soil fertility.

water traditional water-management and water conservation systems; traditional techniques for irrigation; and use of specific species for water conservation.

soil soil conservation practices; the use of specific species for soil conservation; and soil fertility enhancement practices.

plants as a source of wild food, building material, household tools, personal uses (dyes, perfumes, soaps), fuel wood and charcoal, medicinal purposes.

wildlife animal behavior, habitats, uses.

world view views of the universe and humanity's place within it, relationship between humans and nature, myths, beliefs, customs.

(Source: adapted from Grenier, 1998; and Matowanyika, 1994)

Indigenous knowledge encompasses virtually all aspects of the natural world. Pictured: Loi Letoga, Samoa. (photo: C. Elevitch)

Importance of Indigenous Knowledge

There are two basic reasons why it is important for researchers to consider IK when carrying out research projects. First and foremost, incorporating IK into research projects can contribute to local empowerment and development, increasing self-sufficiency and strengthening self-determination (Thrupp, 1989). Utilizing IK in research projects and management plans gives it legitimacy and credibility in the eyes of both local people and outside scientists, increasing cultural pride and thus motivation to solve local problems with local ingenuity and resources (ibid.). Local capacity-building is a crucial aspect of sustainable development, and researchers and development specialists should design approaches which support and strengthen appropriate indigenous knowledge and institutions.

Second, indigenous people can provide valuable input about the local environment and how to effectively manage its natural resources. Outside interest in indigenous knowledge systems has been fueled by the recent worldwide ecological crisis and the realization that its causes lie partly in the overexploitation of natural resources based on inappropriate attitudes and technologies. Scientists now recognize that indigenous people have managed the environments in which they have lived for generations, often without significantly damaging local ecologies (Emery, 1996). Many feel that indigenous knowledge can thus provide a powerful basis from which alternative ways of managing resources can be developed. IK technologies and know-how have an advantage over introduced forms in that they rely on locally available skills and materials and are thus often more cost-effective than introducing exotic technologies from outside sources (IIRR, 1996a). As well, local people are familiar with them and so do not need any specialized training (ibid.).

The following are some of the features of IK which have relevance to conservation and sustainable development (Source: Dewalt, 1994):

- locally appropriate: IK represents a way of life that has evolved with the local environment, so it is specifically adapted to the requirements of local conditions.
- restraint in resource exploitation: production is for subsistence needs only; only what is needed for immediate survival is taken from the environment.

- diversified production systems: there is no overexploitation of a single resource; risk is often spread out by utilizing a number of subsistence strategies.
- respect for nature: a "conservation ethic" often exists. The land is considered sacred, humans are dependent on nature for survival, all species are interconnected.
- flexible: IK is able to adapt to new conditions and incorporate outside knowledge.
- social responsibility: there are strong family and community ties, and with them feelings of obligation and responsibility to preserve the land for future generations.

Limitations of Indigenous Knowledge

As with scientific knowledge, however, IK has its limitations, and these must be recognized. IK is sometimes accepted uncritically because of naive notions that whatever indigenous people do is naturally in harmony with the environment. There is historical and contemporary evidence that indigenous peoples have also committed environmental "sins" through over-grazing, over-hunting, or over-cultivation of the land. It is misleading to think of IK as always being "good," "right" or "sustainable."

For example, a critical assumption of indigenous knowledge approaches is that local people have a good understanding of the natural resource base because they have lived in the same, or similar, environment for many generations, and have accumulated and passed on knowledge of the natural conditions, soils, vegetation, food and medicinal plants etc. However, under conditions where the local people are in fact recent migrants from a quite different ecological zone, they may not have much experience yet with their new environment. In these circumstances, some indigenous knowledge of the people may be helpful, or it may cause problems (e.g., use of agricultural systems adapted to other ecological zones). Therefore it is important, especially when dealing with recent migrants, to evaluate the relevance of different kinds of indigenous knowledge to local conditions.

Indigenous knowledge can also be eroded by wider economic and social forces. Pressure on indigenous peoples to integrate with larger societies is often great, and as they become more integrated, the social structures which generate indigenous knowledge and practices can break down. The growth of national and international markets, the imposition of educational and religious systems and the impact of various development processes are leading more and more to the "homogenization" of the world's cultures (Grenier, 1998). Consequently, indigenous beliefs, values, customs, know-how and practices may be altered and the resulting knowledge base incomplete.

Sometimes IK that was once well-adapted and effective for securing a livelihood in a particular environment becomes inappropriate under conditions of environmental degradation (Thrupp, 1989). Although IK systems have a certain amount of flexibility in adapting to ecological change, when change is particularly rapid or drastic, the knowledge associated with them may be rendered unsuitable and possibly damaging in the altered conditions (Grenier, 1998).

Finally, an often overlooked feature of IK which needs to be taken into account is that, like scientific knowledge, sometimes the knowledge which local people rely on is wrong or even harmful (Thrupp, 1989). Practices based on, for example, mistaken beliefs, faulty experimentation, or inaccurate information can be dangerous and may even be a barrier to improving the well-being of indigenous people. However, researchers need to be careful when making such judgements.

The Loss of Indigenous Knowledge

With the rapid environmental, social, economic and political changes occurring in many areas inhabited by indigenous people comes the danger that the IK they possess will be overwhelmed and lost forever. Younger generations are acquiring different values and lifestyles as a result of exposure to global and national influences, and traditional communication networks are breaking down, meaning that Elders are dying without passing their knowledge on to children. In some cases, the actual existence of indigenous people themselves is threatened. Researchers can assist in preserving IK through the following:

- record and use IK: document IK so that both the scientific and local community have access to it and can utilize it in the formulation of sustainable development plans.
- raise awareness in the community about the value of IK: record and share IK success stories in songs, plays, storytelling, videos and other traditional or modern means of communication. Encourage people to take pride in their knowledge.

- help communities record and document their local practices: Get local people involved in recording their IK by training them as researchers and providing means of documentation (computers, video equipment, etc.).
- make IK available: disseminate IK back to the community through newsletters, videos, books and other media.
- observe intellectual property rights: have agreements so that IK is not misused and benefits return to the community from which it originates. (Source: IIRR, 1996a)

Summary

Indigenous knowledge (IK) is the knowledge used by local people to make a living in a particular environment. It evolves in situ and is dynamic and creative, constantly growing and adapting to meet new conditions. The term "indigenous knowledge" sometimes refers to the knowledge possessed by the original inhabitants of an area, while the term "local knowledge" is a broader term which refers to the knowledge of any people who have lived in an area for a long period of time. IK is considered to be cultural knowledge in its broadest sense. It is embedded in a dynamic system in which spirituality, kinship, local politics and other factors are tied together and influence one another, and researchers must take this into account when examining a particular part of the IK system. IK has many positive aspects, and incorporating IK into projects can contribute to local empowerment and can provide valuable input for alternative natural resource management strategies. However, IK also has its limitations, and researchers should not make the mistake of romanticizing it and believing that whatever indigenous people do is right or sustainable. IK researchers should also play a part in stemming the loss of IK, by helping local people record and use their knowledge.

References

Dewalt, B.R. 1994. "Using indigenous knowledge to improve agriculture and natural resource management." Human Organization 53 (2). pp.123–131.

Emery, A.R. 1996. The Participation of Indigenous Peoples and Their Knowledge in Environmental Assessment and Development Planning (draft). Centre for Traditional Knowledge: Ottawa, Canada.

Grenier, L. 1998. Working With Indigenous Knowledge: A Guide For Researchers. IDRC: Ottawa, Canada.

IIRR (International Institute of Rural Reconstruction). 1996a. Recording and Using Indigenous Knowledge: A Manual. IIRR: Silang, Cavite, Philippines.

Johnson, M. 1992. Lore: Capturing Traditional Environmental Knowledge. IDRC: Ottawa, Canada.

Matowanyika, J. 1994. "What are the issues on indigenous knowledge systems in southern Africa?" In Indigenous Knowledge Systems and Natural Resource Management in Southern Africa. Report of the Southern Africa Regional Workshop, Harare, Zimbabwe, 20–22 April 1994. IUCN-ROSA: Zimbabwe.

Thrupp, L.A. 1989. "Legitimizing Local Knowledge: From Displacement to Empowerment for Third World People". Agriculture and Human Values. Summer Issue. Pp.13–24.

Warren, D.M. 1991. Using Indigenous Knowledge for Agricultural Development. World Bank Discussion Paper 127. Washington, D.C.

Original Source

This edition of *The Overstory* is excerpted with the kind permission of the publisher from:

Langill, S. 1999. Indigenous Knowledge: A Resource Kit for Sustainable Development Researchers in Dryland Africa. People, Land and Water Program Initiative, IDRC, Ottawa, Canada. ©1999 IDRC. Web: http://www.idrc.ca/plaw/11e-IK.html.

For further information about this publication, contact: Research Officer, People, Land and Water, International Development Research Centre (IDRC), PO Box 8500, Ottawa, Ontario K1G 3H9, Canada; Tel: 1-613-236-6163; Fax: 1-613-567-7748; Email: plaw@idrc.ca; Web site for People, Land and Water Program Initiative: http://www.idrc.ca/plaw/03e-start.html, and International Development Research Centre (IDRC)'s web site: http://www.idrc.ca

This excerpt was originally published as *The Overstory #82*.

Ethnoforestry

Deep Narayan Pandey

Towards the Equity of Knowledge

People throughout the world have effective traditional resource management systems including protection, production and conservation practices which they have validated over time. Many of these traditions have been incorporated into modern practices of scientific forestry by innovative foresters. We can define ethnoforestry as the creation, conservation, management and use of forest resources, through continued practice of customary ways by local communities. Thus, it is specific and appropriate to each community and environment.

Local knowledge on forests is a revolutionary way to recast our conventional approach to development. Virtual non-availability of written material in the subject is the result of long term neglect of local knowledge on forests by scientific forestry scholarship. Local knowledge, institutions, policy, empowerment, livelihood issues and forestry are interlinked. We need to explore the operational part of sustainability of natural resources in association with these issues.

Global Status of Ethnoforestry

Ethnoforestry has mostly been neglected in global forest research and planning. Some pioneering studies, on various sub-disciplines of the subject, specifically from India (see, Pandey 1996, and, Singh and Pandey 1995), China (Menzies 1988), Brazil (Posey 1985), Ecuador (Irvine 1989) and Vietnam (Poffenberger personal communication) have appeared only recently. Recently, Asia Forest Network, based at University of California, has developed a pilot activity to assist minority Thai communities in the reestablishment of traditional "Yumpa" Forest Keeper system in Vietnam. In fact after Chambers (1979) drew attention to the importance of local knowledge little reference has ever been made to ethnoforestry.

However, the subject is important to local people, and development planners alike. We must realize that it enlarges people's range of choices. Environmental security now lies in integration of local knowledge and modern learning. Clifford Geertz (1993), in his famous book, Local Knowledge, demonstrates how local knowledge remains in dynamic tension with global knowledge. We cannot analyse policy developments and their implications if we do not have a more profound understanding of the meaning of forests for their societies.

This is not to say that all so-called prescientific societies lived in a state of ecological balance. Many pleistocene hunter-gatherer communities are believed to have caused the local extinction of a number of large mammals through over-exploitation (Joshi and Gadgil 1991).

Protection Ethnoforestry

Protection Ethnoforestry is also called conservation ethnoforestry. It includes the maintenance of sacred trees, sacred groves, temple forest and saffron-sprinkled forests or *kesar chhanta* forests and landscapes. Another category is closures or *Beed*, the wooded areas, near farmlands and dwelling houses, owned by private people. These practices have helped to maintain the biodiversity of natural forests and wild habitats.

Biodiversity conservation practices are as diverse as the cultural diversity in the world. Indigenous knowledge of local plants, animals, habitat preference, life-history and resource availability is socially transmitted from one individual to another within and across generations (Gadgil, Berkes and Folke 1993), though not necessarily in writings. In addition, there are examples where communities regulate the use of resource by restricting the access to resources, and enforcing compliance through religious belief, ritual and social convention. It is debatable whether these "restraints" evolved after trial and error or as systematic prescriptions. However, it is certain that these restraints definitely contributed for the cause of biodiversity conservation.

Why Bother with Ethnoforestry?

The dynamics of social reciprocity in a poor and marginalised community is almost beyond the capacity of an outsider to imagine (Seeland 1997). The implementation of joint forest management with success in India has proved that those for whom the forests matter most can properly manage forests and sustainable livelihoods. And they may not be the so-called scientific foresters. They are the local people.

Ethnoforestry is very useful for participatory forest management. We have also proved and learnt to a great extent that local knowledge can be revitalized and operationalized within the context of social development and participatory forestry. Even more important, ethnoforestry saves people from the danger of becoming the subordinate participants in their community land use. It prevents people from the danger of further marginalisation, for it regards them as the producers of development, and not the mere spectators of it.

Relevance of Ethnoforestry

I am convinced that our application of knowledge for fieldwork has to be broadened to incorporate local knowledge in order to analyze the policy development and its implications on the life and livelihood of poor people. Forestry students need more understanding of the social and cultural context in which scientific forestry is developed and applied.

Social and political processes at the level of communities reflecting different interests in forests require more attention in policy analysis. National regulation can only be successful if they are meaningful to and accepted by indigenous people. At the global level, forests have become part of worldwide concern and subject to political efforts in order to develop a more consistent cooperation on their management. Policy research has to address such evolutions and their possible impact at the national and local level (Schmithusen 1997).

Conclusions

Ethnoforestry is the creation, conservation, management and utilization of forest resources by local communities through traditional practices and folk beliefs. Ethnoforestry is not to be confused with participatory forestry or joint forest management. Protections provided to habitats are classified as protection ethnoforestry. Traditional methods of regeneration of livelihood species by people are classified as plantation ethnoforestry. These include direct sowing, bamboo rhizome planting, cutting, nursing of wildlings and closures. Traditional methods of growing trees and crops in farmlands are called ethnoagroforestry.

Ethnoforestry will deliver vital and incomparably significant results for the future of world forestry. The reasons are many:

1   Ethnoforestry can ensure equity of knowledge between village communities and the scientific forestry community. It will stop exploitation at the hands of so-called scientific community. Equity of knowledge alone can, ultimately, make the forestry sustainable.

2   Ethnoforestry can provide location-specific solutions. Local knowledge is easily transmitted, used by large section of the society, does not require costly consultancy and other input, and thus, minimises possibility of corruption.

3   Ethnoforestry can reduce the costs of tropical afforestation. Economizing world's tropical forest plantations through ethnoforestry is a distinct possibility.

4   Ethnoforestry is not to be confused by participatory forestry or joint forest management. Ethnoforestry represents the traditional ecological wisdom of world's indigenous people.

Examples of Different Types of Indigenous Forest Management (Source: Wiersum 1997)

Protected natural forests

Sacred forests/sacred groves Abodes of (ancestral) spirits	Asia, Africa
Ceremonial & rainmaking forests	Africa, India Shrine/temple forests S. Asia
Sacred corridors	India
Water protection forests spring forests	Tanzania
Riverine vegetation	Borneo, Kenya
Clan/village forests clan forests	Borneo village forests, Himalaya region
Tribe/clan/lineage grazing woodlands	Africa
Forest belts	T'Olche, Mexico
Protected tree species	Taboo trees, pantropical

Resource-enriched natural forests

Individually claimed trees	Tree marking, S.E. Asia
Enriched natural forests enriched & expanded forest islands & gallery forests	Guinea enriched rainforest groves, Borneo
Enriched fallows	casuarina fallows, New Guinea
Rattan fallow cultivation fallows, enriched w/ fruit/tree	S.E. Asia, Amazon
Palm fallows	Amazon, W. Africa, East Indonesia

Reconstructed (natural) forests

Forest gardens	Ifugao woodlots, Philippines
Mixed damar gardens	Sumatra
Mixed fruit and rubber gardens	Borneo/Sumatra
Planted temple forests	India, Thailand
Fortification forests, defense forests around human habitations	Sahel Village fortresses, Guinea

Mixed arboriculture

Homegardens	Pantropical
Smallholder plantations	Pre-Hispanic cacao plantations, Mexico
Mixed damar/coffee gardens	Sumatra
Mixed rubber gardens	Indonesia

References

Chambers, Robert (19) (ed.) Rural Development: Whose Knowledge Counts? IDS Bulletin 10(2)

Gadgil, Madhav and Berkes, F. and Folke, Carl (1993) Indigenous Knowledge for biodiversity conservation. Ambio. 22(2–3):266–270.

Geertz, Clifford (1993) Local Knowledge. Fontana Press, London, pp 244.

Gupta, Anil K. (1987) Why poor don't cooperate: Lessons from traditional organisations with implication for modern organisations. In: Clare G. Wanger (ed.) Research, Relationship, Politics and Practice of Social Research. George Allen and Unwin, London, 1987 pp 111–127.

Irvine, D. (1989). Succession management and resources distribution in an Amazonian rain forest. Adv. Econ. Bot. 7,223–237.

Joshi, N.V. and Gadgil, Madhav (1991) On the role of refugia in promoting prudent use of biological resources. (quoted in Gadgil and Guha, 1992).

Menzies, N. K. (1988) Trees, Fields, and People: The Forests of China from The Seventeenth to The Nineteenth Century.

Pandey, Deep N. (1996a) Beyond Vanishing Woods: Participatory Survival Options for Wildlife, Forests and People. CSD and Himanshu, Mussoorie/New Delhi/Udaipur, pp.222.

Pandey, Deep N. (1996b) Village Common Fund. In: Kurup, V. S. P., (ed.) New Voices in Indian Forestry. SPWD New Delhi, pp 288–292

Pandey, Deep N. (1996c) Plantation Forestry: India must Change to Advance Closure Technique. Paper presented at the JFM National Network Meeting, October 1996, New Delhi.

Pandey, Deep N.(1996d) Ethnoforestry, Prasashanika, 23(2): 29–47

Pandey, Deep N. (1997) Ethnoforestry by Indigenous People. Paper presented in XI World Forestry Congress, Antalya, Turkey

Pandey, Deep N. and Samar Singh (1995a) Aravalli Ke Deovan. Rajasthan Patrika, 21 May, 1995.

Pandey, Deep N.and Samar Singh (1995b) Traditions of Sacred Groves in Aravallis. Wastelands News, (Hindi), April–June 1995.pp3–6

Posey, D. A.(1985) Indigenous management of tropical ecosystems: The case of the Kayapo Indians of the Brazilian Amazon. Agroforestry Systems, 3, 139–158

Schmithusen, Franz (1997) Local Knowledge on Forests, In: Seeland, Klaus and Schmithusen, Franz (eds.) Local Knowledge of Forests and Forest Uses among Tribal Communities in India, Department Wald und Holzforschung, Zurich.

Seeland, Klaus and Schmithusen, Franz (1997) (eds.) Local Knowledge of Forests and Forest Uses among Tribal Communities in India, Department Wald und Holzforschung, Zurich.

Wiersum, K.F. (1997) Indigenous exploitation and management of tropical forest resources: an evolutionary continuum in forest-people interactions. Agriculture, Ecosystems and Environment. 63: 1, 1–16

Original Source

This article is excerpted with kind permission of the author from:

Pandey, D.N. 1998 (online edition 1999). ETHNO-FORESTRY Local Knowledge for Sustainable Forestry and Livelihood Security. Himanshu Publications, Udaipur/New Delhi.

URL: http://education.vsnl.com/deep.

This excerpt was originally published as *The Overstory* #76.

Cultural Landscapes

Darrell A. Posey

Traditionally, Amazonian Indians have been thought of as merely exploiters of their environments—not as conservers, manipulators and managers of natural resources (e.g., Meggers 1996). Researchers are finding, however, that presumed "natural" ecological systems may, in fact, be products of human manipulation (Alcorn 1981, 1989; Anderson and Posey 1985; Balée 1989a, 1997; Balée and Gély 1989; Clement 1989; Denevan and Padoch 1988; Frickel 1959; Roosevelt 1994; Sponsel 1995; Sponsel, Headland and Bailey 1996; and others). Likewise, old agricultural fallows reflect genetic selection and human enhanced species diversity (Anderson 1990; Balée 1989b; Denevan and Padoch 1988; Irvine 1989; Redford and Padoch 1992).

The Kayapó Indians of the Middle Xingu Valley, Brazil, provide a good example of how scientific assumptions of "natural" landscapes have hidden the complexity and potential of local management practices to modify ecosystems. The modern Kayapó population is still under 5,000, but pre-contact populations were many times larger and presumably had even greater impacts on the vast region they exploited (Posey 1994). They live in an ecologically diverse region that comprises nearly 4 million hectares of *reserva indigena* in the states of Para and Mato Grosso. Ethnohistorical research with the Kayapó Indians shows that contact with European diseases came via trade routes and preceded face-to-face contact with colonizers. Epidemics led to intragroup fighting, fission and dispersal of sub-groups which carried with them seeds and cuttings to propagate their foods, medicines and other resources (Posey 1987).

Human Modified Environments

A form of "nomadic agriculture" developed, based on the exploitation of non-domesticated resources (NDRs) intentionally concentrated in human modified environments near trail sides, abandoned villages and at camp sites (Posey 1985). Agricultural practices also spread, along with techniques for the management of old fields to enhance the availability of wildlife and useful plants. During times of warfare, the Kayapó could abandon their agricultural plots and survive on non-domesticated species concentrated at trail sides, former village sites, forest openings and ancient fields.

Agricultural plots were engineered to develop into productive agroforestry reserves dominated by NDR species, thereby allowing the Kayapó to oscillate between (or blend together) agriculture and gathering. Such patterns appear to have been widespread in the lowland tropics and defy the traditional dichotomies of wild vs. domesticated species, hunter-gatherers vs. agriculturalists, and agriculture vs. agroforestry. Even today, over 76 percent of the useful plant species collected to date are not "domesticated," nor can they be considered "wild" (Posey 1997; Roosevelt 1994). (I suspect that as a more complete floral inventory is completed, this percentage will approach 98 percent.)

Nowhere is this more evident than in the formation of "islands" of forest, or *apêtê*, in the campocerrado (savannah). The Kayapó initiate and simulate the formation of forest patches through the careful manipulation of micro-environmental factors, knowledge of soil and plant characteristics, and intentional concentration of useful species into limited plots. Although most *apêtê* are small (under 10ha), elders reported plant varieties in a 1ha plot as having been introduced by villagers from an area the size of Western Europe (Anderson and Posey 1989).

The principle elements of Kayapó management have been previously described in some detail (Posey 1983, 1985, 1987, 1995, 1997) and include:

- overlapping and interrelated ecological categories that form continua;
- modification of "natural ecosystems" to create ecotones;
- emphasis on long-term ecotone utilization (chronological ecotones);
- concentration on non-domesticated resources;
- transfer of useful plant varieties between similar ecological zones, and
- integration of agricultural cycles with forest management cycles

Resource Management Continuum

Several options are possible for representing indigenous resource management models. The most inclusive and descriptive representation of the Kayapó system places savannah or grasslands (*kapôt*) at one end of a continuum as the "focal type" (example that most typifies the category) and forests (*bà*) at the other end (opposite focal type). *Kapôt* types with more forest elements would be represented to the right of the diagram, while *bà* types that are more open and with grassy elements would lie on the continuum diagram to the left, or toward the savannah pole.

This would put *apêtê* at the conceptual centre of the continuum, since forest elements are introduced into the savannah to produce these anthropogenic zones. Agricultural plots (*puru*) also lie conceptually near the centre of the continuum, because sun-tolerant vegetation is introduced into managed forest openings. *Apêtê* can be thought of as the conceptual inverse of puru: the former concentrates resources in the forest using sun-tolerant species, while the other does the same in the savannah using forest species.

Even though ecological types like high forest (*bà tyk*) or transitional forest (*bà kamrek*) are securely located at the forest pole, they are not uniform in their composition. All forests have edges (*kà*), margins (*kôt*), and openings caused by fallen—or felled—trees (*bà krê-ti*) which provide zones of transition between different conceptual zones. Thus, a plant that likes the margins of a high forest might also grow well at the margin of a field (*puru-ka* or *purukôt*) or in an *apêtê*. A plant that likes light gaps provided by forest openings might also like forest edges (*bà-kà* or *bà-kôt*) or old fields (*puru-tum* or *ibê-tum*). Plants from open forest types or forest edges can predictably proliferate along edges of trails or thicker zones of *apêtê*. Using this logic, the Kayapó can transfer biogenetic materials between matching micro-zones so that ecological types are interrelated by their similarities rather than isolated by their differences. These interfaces can be considered ecotones, which become the uniting elements of the overall system.

There is another interesting dimension to the model that appears when looking diachronically (temporally or historically) across the system. Agricultural clearings are initially planted with rapidly growing domesticates, but almost immediately thereafter are managed for secondary forest and NDR species. This management depends upon planting and transplanting, removal of some varieties, allowing others to grow, encouraging some with fertilizer and ash, and preparing and working the soils to favour useful species.

Management aims to provide long-term supplies of building materials, ceremonial objects, medicinals and other useful products, as well as food for humans and animals. The old fields (*puru tum*) are at least as useful to the Kayapó as agricultural plots or mature forest. A high percentage (an initial estimate is 85%) of plants in this transition have single or multiple uses. When the secondary forest grows too high to provide undergrowth as food for animals (and hunting also becomes difficult), then the large trees are felled to create more hospitable conditions for management and/or reinitiation of the agricultural cycle. Likewise, *apêtê* are managed to maximize useful species in all stages of the forest succession. When their centres become dark and unproductive, openings (*irā*) are created which allow light to once again penetrate the forest and initiate a new cycle.

Conclusion

The Kayapó resource management system is based on the conservation and use of transitional forests in which agriculture is only a useful (albeit critical) phase in the long-term process. *Apêtê* exhibit parallel transitional sequences in the campocerrado and depend almost exclusively on non-domesticated resources. The degree to which genetic materials are transferred between similar micro-zones of different ecological types points to how the Kayapó exploit ecotones that host the highest diversity of plants. Management over time can be thought of as management of chronological ecotones, since management cycles aim to maintain the maximum amount of diversity and the greatest number of ecotones.

The Kayapó model illustrates how previously assumed "natural" ecosystems in Amazonia have been consciously modified by indigenous residents through time. The degree to which this has taken place has yet to be quantified, but Kayapó "forest islands" data show concentrations of plant varieties from a vast geographic area. This case underlines the necessity for historical studies to understand the long-term effects of management of cultural and anthropogenic landscapes. Above all, it exposes the inadequacies of our scientific, educational and political institutions which separate agriculture from forestry and ignore the importance of non-domesticated resources.

References

Alcorn J. (1989) "Making Use of Traditional Farmers Knowledge". In: Common Futures, Proceedings of an International Forum on Sustainable Development. Toronto: Pollution Probe.

Alcorn, J. B. (1981) "Huastec noncrop resource management: implications for prehistoric rainforest management" Human Ecology 9: 395–417.

Anderson, A. (ed.) (1990) Alternatives to Deforestation: Steps Toward Sustainable Use of the Amazon Rain Forest. Columbia University Press, New York.

Anderson, A. B. and Posey, D. A. (1985) "Manejo de cerrado pelos Indios Kayapó. Boletim do Museu Paraense Emilio Goeldi, Botânica 2: 77–98.

Anderson, A. B. and Posey, D. A. (1987) Management of a tropical scrub savanna by the Gorotire Kayapó of Brazil. Advances in Economic Botany 7, 159–173.

Balée, W. (1989a) "Cultura na vegetação da Amazônia," Boletim do Museu Paraense Emilio Goeldi 6: 95–110 (Coleção Eduardo Galvão).

Balée, W. (1989b) "The culture of Amazonian forests". In: Posey, D. A. and Balée, W. (eds) Resource Management in Amazonia: Indigenous and Folk Strategies. Advances in Economic Botany 7: 1–21.

Balée, W. (ed) (1997) Principles of Historical Ecology. Columbia University Press, New York.

Balée, W. and Gély, A. (1989) Managed forest succession in Amazonia: the Ka'apor case. In: Posey, D. A. and Balée, W. (eds) Resource Management in Amazonia: Indigenous and Folk Strategies. Advances in Economic Botany 7: 129–148.

Clement, C. R. (1989) A center of crop genetic diversity in western Amazonia: a new hypothesis of indigenous fruit crop distribution. Bioscience 39:624–630.

Denevan, W. M. and Padoch, C. (eds) (1988) Swidden-fallow agroforestry in the Peruvian Amazon. Advances in Economic Botany 5.

Frickel, P. (1959) "Agricultura dos índios Mundurukú". Boletim do Museu Paraense Emilio Goeldi, n.s. No. 4.

Irvine, D. (1989) Succession management and resource distribution in an Amazonian rain forest. In: Posey, D. A. and Balee, W. (eds) Resource management in Amazonia: indigenous and folk strategies. Advances in Economic Botany 7:223–237.

Meggers, B. J. (1996) Amazonia: man and culture in a counterfeit paradise. Revised edition. Smithsonian Institution Press, Washington and London.

Posey, D. A. (1985) Indigenous Management of Tropical Forest Ecosystems: The Case of the Kayapó Indians of the Brazilian Amazon. Agroforestry Systems 3: pp. 139–154.

Posey, D. A. (1987) Contact before contact: typology of post-Colombian interaction with Northern Kayapó of the Amazon Basin. Boletim do Museu Paraense Emilio Goeldi, Serie Antropologica 3: 135–154.

Posey, D. A. (1993) The Importance of Semi-Domesticated Species in Post-Contact Amazonia: Effects of Kayapo Indians on the Dispersal of Flora and Fauna. In: Hladik, C.

M., Hladik, A., Linares, O. F., Pagezey, H., Semple, A. and Hadley, M.(eds) Tropical Forests, People and Food: Biocultural Interactions and Applications to Development. Man and Biosphere, Vol 13, UNESCO, Paris, pp. 63–71.

Posey, D. A. (1994) "Traditional Resource Rights: de facto self-determination for indigenous peoples". In: Leo van der Vlist (ed.) Voices of the Earth: indigenous peoples, new partners & the right to self-determination in practice. International Books, Utrecht.

Posey, D. A. (1995) Indigenous Peoples and Traditional Resource Rights: A Basis for Equitable Relationships? Proceedings of a Workshop, Green College Centre for Environmental Policy and Understanding, 28th June 1995, Oxford, UK.

Posey, D. A. (1997) The Kayapó. In: Indigenous Peoples and Sustainability: Cases and Actions IUCN Inter- Commission Task Force on Indigenous Peoples. International Books, Utrecht. 240–254.

Redford, K. H. and Padoch, C. (1992) Conservation of Neotropical Forests; Working from Traditional Resource Use. Columbia University Press, New York.

Roosevelt, A. (ed) (1994) Amazonian Indians: From Prehistory to the Present—Anthropological Perspectives. University of Arizona Press, Tucson.

Sponsel, L. E. (1995) "Relationships Among the World System, Indigenous Peoples, and Ecological Anthropology in the Endangered Amazon". In: Sponsel, L. E. (ed.) Indigenous Peoples and the Future of Amazonia. University of Arizona Press, Tucson. 263– 293.

Sponsel, L. E., Headland, T. N. and Bailey, R. C. (eds) (1996) Tropical Deforestation: The Human Dimension. Columbia University Press, New York.

Original Source

This article was excerpted with the kind permission of the United Nations Environment Programme (UNEP) from:

Posey, D.A. (Ed). 1999. Cultural and Spiritual Values of Biodiversity. Intermediate Technology Publications, London on behalf of United Nations Environment Programme (UNEP).

The original book and this article is © 1999 United Nations Environment Programme, P.O. Box 30552 Nairobi, Kenya.

The original title, *Cultural and Spiritual Values of Biodiversity*, is available from:

ITDG Publications
103/105 Southampton Row,
London WC1B 4HH, UK
Tel: +44 202 7436 9761; Fax: +44 020 7436 2013
Email: orders@itpubs.org.uk
Web: http://www.itdgpublishing.org.uk

This excerpt was originally published as *The Overstory* #109.

Forest Islands (Kayapo Example)

Darrell Posey

Indigenous knowledge of nature and agriculture represents thousands of years of accumulated knowledge and experience. Indigenous peoples can teach us effective models for sustainable resource management. The following study of the Kayapo people in Brazil gives an account of how people developed knowledge of complex ecosystems, and worked with nature to meet their needs. Readers may recognize some of the principles practiced by the Kayapo have been adapted for modern use elsewhere in some permaculture and agroforestry settings.

The Kayapo: Experts in Synergy

Indigenous peoples have often been thought of as merely exploiters of their environments—not as conservationists, manipulators, and managers of natural resources. Researchers now find however, that presumed "natural" ecological systems in Amazonia are, in fact, products of human manipulation. Old agricultural fallows are extensive and reflect human-engineered genetic diversity. In the formation of "islands of forest" (Apêtê) in the "campo-cerrado" in Brazil, for example, the Kayapo were found to have concentrated plant varieties collected from an area the size of Western Europe into a ten hectare plot.

The Kayapo, a case study

The knowledge of the Kayapo people is an integrated system of beliefs and practices. In addition to the information shared generally, there is specialised knowledge held by a few. Each village has its specialists in soils, plants, animals, crops, medicines, and rituals. A complete Kayapo view of nature is difficult to convey because of its underlying cultural complexity. It is possible, however, to identify categories of indigenous knowledge that indicate new research directions, even shortcuts, for Western science, as well as alternatives to the destruction of Amazonia.

Ethnoecology (Cultural perspective on organisms and their environments)

The Kayapo identify specific plants and animals as occurring within particular ecological zones. They have a well-developed knowledge of animal behaviour and also know which plants are associated with particular animals. Plant types in turn are associated with soil types. Each ecological zone represents a system of interactions among plants, animals, soils and, of course, the Kayapo themselves.

The Kayapo recognise ecosystems that lie on a continuum between the poles of forest and savanna. They have names, for example, for as many as nine different types of savanna—savanna with few trees, savanna with many forest patches, savanna with shrub, and so on. But the Kayapo concentrate less on the differences between zones than on the similarities that cut across them. Marginal or open spots within the forest, or example, can have microenvironmental conditions similar to those in the savanna. The Kayapo take advantage of these similarities to exchange and spread useful species between zones, through transplanting seeds, cuttings, tubers and saplings. Thus there is much interchange between what we tend to see as distinctly different ecological systems.

Cultivating ecosystems

Kayapo agriculture focuses upon the zones intermediate between forest and savanna types, because it is in these that maximal biological diversity occurs. Villages are often sited in these transition zones. The Kayapo not only recognise the richness of these zones, but they actually create them. They exploit secondary forest areas and create special concentrations of plants in forest fields, rocks outcroppings, trail sides, and elsewhere.

Forest islands

The creation of forest islands, or Apêtê, demonstrates to what extent the Kayapo can alter and manage ecosystems to increase biological diversity. Apêtê begin as small mounds of vegetation, about one to two meters round, created by ant nests in open areas in the field. Slight depressions are usually picked out because they are more likely to retain moisture. Seeds or seedlings are planted in these piles of organic material. The Apêtê are usually formed in August and September, during the first rains of the wet season, and then nurtured by the Kayapo as they pass along the savanna trails.

As Apêtê grow, they begin to look like up-turned hats, with higher vegetation in the centre and lower herbs growing in the shaded borders. The Kayapo usually cut down the highest trees in the centre to create a donut-hole centre that allows the light into older Apêtê. Thus a full-grown Apêtê has an architecture that creates zones that vary in shade, light and humidity.

These islands become important sources of medicinal and edible plants, as well as places of rest. Palms, which have a variety of uses, prominently figure in Apêtê, as do shade trees. Even vines that produce drinkable water are transplanted here. Apêtê look so "natural", however, that until recently scientists in fact did not recognise them as human artifacts.

According to informants, of a total of 120 species inventoried in ten Apêtê, about 75% could have been planted. Such ecological engineering requires detailed knowledge of soil fertility, microclimatic variations, and species niches, as well as the interrelationships among species that are introduced into these human-made communities.

Plants that are good friends

The Kayapo are aware that some species develop more vigorously when planted together. They frequently speak of plants that are "good friends" or "good neighbours." One of the first of these "neighbour complexes" I was able to discover was the "tyrutiombiqua", or "banana neighbours." Among the two dozen varieties of edible tubers and numerous medicinal plants that thrive near bananas are some of the mekrakeldja ("child want not") plants, which are very important in regulating fertility among the Kayapo. Other managed plant communities are concentrated around e.g. papaya, genipapo (*Genipa americana*) and urucu (*Bixa orellana*) which produce their own unique microzones for planting.

The Kayapo characterize such synergistic plant groups in terms of "plant energy." These groups can include dozens of species and require complex patterns of cultivation. Thus a Kayapo garden is created by carefully combining different "plant energies" just as an artist blends colours to produce a work of art. Fields thrive on diversity within the plots.

This diversity is quite ordered to the eye of a Kayapo, with careful matchings between plant varieties and microenvironmental conditions. What appears to us to be random field plantings turns out to have five more or less concentric zones, each with preferred varieties of cultivars and different cultivation strategies.

The Kayapo exploit the properties of fields in transition between new and old but also shows how microenvironmental planting zones are created to modify effects of secondary forest growth. Equally significant is the indigenous conceptualisation of plant communities, rather than individual species, as the basis for ecological management.

Ethnopedology (Cultural perspective on soils)

A survey of Kayapo soil taxonomy shows sophisticated horizontal and vertical distinctions based on texture, color, drainage qualities, friability, and stratification. Soil qualities are frequently related to indicator plant species that allow people to predict floral and faunal components associated with specific soil types, each of which is managed differently according to individual characteristics. Sweet potatoes, for instance, like the hotter soil and thrive in the çentre of fields where shade from the margins rarely penetrates. The plants must be well aerated, however, or soil compaction will smother the root system.

The Kayapo use various types of ground cover such as vegetation, logs, leaves, straw, and bark to affect moisture, shade, and temperature of local soils. Holes are sometimes filled with organic matter, refuse, and ash to produce highly concentrated pockets of rich soil. Old banana leaves, stalks, rice straw and other organic matter are piled and sometimes burned in selected parts of fields to create additional local variations.

Ethnozoology (Cultural perspective on animals)

Like other indigenous groups, the Kayapo conscientiously study animal anatomy, paying special attention to stomach contents of game animals. They are also astute observers of many aspects of animal behaviour. The Kayapo encourage their children to learn the behaviour patterns and feeding habits of different animal species, which are considered to have their own "personalities." Part of this knowledge is gained through pet rearing. In a survey we found over sixty species of birds, reptiles, snakes, amphibians, mammals and even spiders being raised in the village.

Kayapo use a precise knowledge of insect behaviour to control agricultural pests. For example nests of "smelly ants" (*Azleca* sp.) are deliberately placed in gardens and on fruit trees that are infested with leaf-cutting ants (*Atta* spp.). The pheromones of the "smelly ants" repel the leaf-cutters. These protective ants are also highly praised for their medicinal properties and are frequently crushed and their highly aromatic scents inhaled to open up the sinuses.

The Kayapo cultivate several plants containing extra-floral nectars, often on the leaves or stems, which attract predatory ants to serve as "body guards" for the plant, and plant banana trees to form a living wall around their fields, because predatory wasps nest preferentially under the leaves.

Ethnoagriculture (Cultural perspective on agriculture)

Indigenous agriculture begins with a forest opening, into which useful species are introduced and ends with a mature forest of concentrated resources, including game animals. The cycle is repeated when the "old-field" forests develop canopies too high and dense for efficient production and are cleared again.

Agricultural plots are designed to be productive throughout this reforestation cycle. Contrary to persistent beliefs about indigenous slash-and-burn agriculture, fields are not abandoned after a few years from initial clearing and planting. On the contrary, old fields offer an important concentration of diverse resources long after primary cultivars have disappeared. Kayapo "new fields" for example, peak in production of principal domesticated crops in two or three years but continue to bear produce for many years: sweet potatoes for four to five years, yams and taro for five to six years, papaya and banana for five or more years. The Kayapo consistently revisit old fields seeking these lingering riches.

Fields take on new life as plants in the natural reforestation sequence begin to appear. These plants soon constitute a type of forest for which the Kayapo have a special name that means mature old fields. Such fields provide a wide range of useful products, and are especially valuable for their concentrations of medicinal plants. Old fields also attract wildlife to their abundant, low and leafy plants. Intentional dispersal of old fields and systematic hunting extends human influence over the forest by providing, in effect, large "game farms" near human population centres.

The Kayapo do not make a clear distinction between fields and forest, nor between wild and domesticated species. Gathered plants are transplanted into concentrated spots near trails and campsites to produce "forest fields." The sides of trails themselves are planting zones. It is not uncommon to find trails composed of four meter wide cleared strips of forest.

References

Clay, J.W. 1988. Indigenous peoples and tropical forests: Models of land use and management from Latin America. In: Cultural survival report 27, Cambridge Massachusetts, Cultural Survival Inc. 116 pp.

Hecht, S.B. 1990. Indigenous soil management in the Latin American tropics: neglected knowledge of native peoples. In: Altieri M.A., Hecht S.B. 1990. Agroecology and small farm development. Boston, CRC Press, pp 151-160.

Posey, D.A. 1985. Indigenous management of tropical forest ecosystems: the case of the Kayapo Indians of the Brazilian Amazon. In: Agroforestry Systems 3(2):139-158.

Posey, D.A. and W. Balee (eds). 1989. Resource management in Amazonia: indigenous and folk strategies. In: Advances in Economic Botany 7.

Posey, D.A. 1991. Indigenous peoples and conservation: missing links and forgotten knowledge.

Original Source

This article was extracted from the original published in *ILEIA Newsletter* for Low External Input and Sustainable Agriculture, 4/91. PO Box 64, 3830 AB Leusden, The Netherlands; Tel: + 31 33 4 943 086, Fax: + 31 33 4 940 791; Email: ileia@ileia.nl; Web: http://www.oneworld.org/ileia/.

This excerpt was originally published as *The Overstory* #34.

Complex Agroforests

Hubert de Foresta, Genevieve Michon and Achmad Kusworo

Farmers have integrated trees in their farming systems for centuries. They did not wait for scientists to develop the concept of agroforestry, just like man did not wait for agronomists to invent and develop agriculture. Agroforestry is widely promoted as a solution for developing more sustainable land uses. But most policy makers, scientists and extension agents dealing with agroforestry programs rarely consider that most agroforestry systems have evolved from local farmers' practices. What farmers are actually doing indeed differs from one country to the other in the region. However, agroforestry is still mainly understood in terms of "development projects," and therefore is usually promoted from an outside point of view, with outside tree crops or mixed-cropping techniques. With few exceptions, projects do not explore either the local agroforestry knowledge base nor the local farmer-developed agroforestry practices.

How Do Traditional Systems Differ from Modern Systems?

Traditional Systems

Systems usually perceived as "traditional" (or indigenous) are those systems that have been developed by farmers in response to perceived needs and existing opportunities, without the involvement of formal research and extension services.

Modern Systems

Systems usually perceived as modern are those systems that have been developed by scientists and that are promoted by projects using techno-scientific arguments.

Both traditional and modern systems may co-exist at the same time. The main difference is that traditional systems are the result of long evolution and adaptation to local conditions, while long-term suitability of modern systems to local conditions is unproven.

A division can be made between two broad groups of agroforestry systems: simple agroforestry systems and complex agroforestry systems. Simple agrofor-estry systems are tree-crop associations and are easily recognisable once one has accepted that farmers are indeed agroforestry practitioners. Complex agroforestry systems are much more difficult to recognise: they are successional systems and, while early stages usually exhibit typical agroforestry features, their mature "forest" phase—agroforest—has often been confused with natural forests, even by agroforestry experts. Simple agroforestry systems are briefly presented below, followed by a focus on the lesser-known complex agroforestry systems.

Simple agroforestry systems

Simple agroforestry systems can be characterised as follows:

A mix of perennial and annual crops with:

- One tree species and one to a few annual crops, or short-cycle species; or
- Trees as main field components (e.g., coconut with maize or peanut); or
- Trees as borders such as teak (*Tectona grandis*), mahogany (*Swietenia macrophylla*) and rosewood (*Dalbergia latifolia*) in East and Central Java, and *Maesopsis* and *Paraserianthes* in West Java.
- Trees are also commonly associated with irrigated rice fields either on dikes or along roads, and are used in the agricultural system either for their products, for environmental services or for both.

An example is coffee associated with *Erythrina* or *Gliricidia* trees. Reasons for planting *Erythrina/Gliricidia* are:

- to provide a manageable level of shade for coffee trees (through pruning),
- to provide firewood or fodder
- as a live pole for climbers (e.g., vanilla or pepper)
- to improve soil fertility through litter fall, fixing nitrogen from the air, old tree-root channel etc.

Complex agroforestry systems

Common observers often confuse multispecies complex agroforestry systems bordering obvious agricultural areas, especially on the forest margins, with a mix of "virgin" and "degraded" forest.

This kind of agroforestry combination that looks like forest, we call a complex agroforestry system. In its

Krui damar (*Shorea javanica*) agroforestry landscape. (photo: H. de Foresta © ird)

mature phase complex agroforestry is characterised by:

- A complex vegetation structure,
- A high number of components (trees as well as seedlings, shrubs, lianas, herbs), and
- An ecological functioning similar to that observed in natural forests (nutrient cycling, dissemination and regeneration processes, etc.).

Two broad categories of complex agroforestry systems should be distinguished: tree-dominated homegardens and what we have called agroforest or complex agroforests.

Tree-dominated homegardens are always located near the house and are usually small (0.1 to 0.3 ha). These two characteristics allow homegardens to benefit from quite intensive care (manure, tree pruning, weeding, etc.). Being easily recognisable because of their integration within household compounds, tree-homegardens are relatively well known and documented, and their importance is well acknowledged.

Agroforests are composed of a mosaic of small (1–2 hectares) individually-owned, individually managed units which make up forest massifs of various sizes. They are not located in household compounds, even though they often border villages, and they are rarely intensively managed. Agroforests are sometimes managed forests, evolved from progressive and integrated transformations of the original ecosystem through tree planting and natural vegetation management, such as the Benzoin agroforests in North Sumatra province. But most often agroforests in Indonesia evolved from shifting cultivation systems, and are true plantations established after total removal of the original vegetation through planting of desired tree species, and through natural enrichment. Agroforests are definitely part of the world of smallholder tree-crop plantation agriculture. Like coffee or cacao smallholder plantations, agroforests are established and managed by rural households, mainly because of the medium to long-term sources of income they provide.

Examples from Indonesia

- In the hills and lowlands of Kalimantan and eastern Sumatra where the last tracks of mixed *Dipterocarp* forest are being logged and rapidly converted, smallholder jungle rubber agroforests cover an estimated area of 2.5 million hectares. In these systems rubber trees are associated with numerous wild and cultivated tree species, complementing either irrigated or dry rice cultivation.

- In the southwestern coast of Sumatra, an impressive model of agroforest based on *Shorea javanica* (damar) is exploited for its resin. It was developed by villagers more than a century ago and now covers some 50,000 hectares.
- Across Sumatra in the mid-1980's, a mosaic of other agroforest types was estimated to cover more than 1 million hectares in patches of a few hectares. It associates various fruit species as well as economic spice producing trees (cinnamon, clove and nutmeg) and timber species under a canopy of durian (*Durio zibethinus*) or kemiri (*Aleurites moluccana*) trees.
- In East Kalimantan impressive fruit forests have been developed (*lembo*) which seem to be among the richest systems in number of tree species.

Agroforests are definitely not anecdotal in terms of production, at regional nor national levels. They provide:

- 80% of the rubber latex consumed and exported by Indonesia (the world's second largest producer after Thailand);
- 95% of the various fruits marketed in the country;
- 75–80% of the Dipterocarp damar resins traded in and outside the country; and
- A significant portion of rattans, bamboo and firewood used in the country, and the bulk of medicinal plants and handicraft material.

Moreover, agroforests ensure the self-sufficiency of most rural households in complementary foods, fuelwood as well as light and heavy material.

Why Should We Grant Special Consideration to Agroforests?

In spite of their relative success in the conditions in which they were conceived, indigenous agroforests are usually not transferable as such to other regions or other countries. Nor should they be considered as the pinnacle of agroforestry practice in the regions where they do exist.

Rather, they represent a very valuable source of inspiration and should be considered as models of ut-

Maninjau agroforestry landscape (left), cinnamon harvesting (top right), and children with durian (bottom right). (photos: G. Michon © ird)

most interest for the development of sustainable forms of agriculture and/or of forestry. They combine durable economic profitability and long-term conservation of both soil fertility and global biodiversity. Farmer-developed agroforests exhibit qualities that interest the present and future development of both agriculture and forestry, especially in areas where annual food crop cultivation depends on heavy applications of fertilisers or where only perennial crops are capable of sustained production.

For agricultural development

Agroforests provide a proof-tested original model of sustainable and profitable commercial agriculture suited to conditions prevailing in smallholder farms.

The development of commercial agriculture, especially perennial crops, is often planned and implemented as a total conversion of actual production systems to monocultures with high inputs of energy, capital and labour. Experimentation and domestication research on commercial tree crops are almost always conducted under standard conditions which are far from those commonly encountered on smallholder farms.

Local production systems in rural areas, including agroforests, are generally considered as devoted to subsistence production. Promotion of commercial agriculture on smallholder farms includes a technological "package" that entails a total reorganisation of farming systems. There is generally no attempt to develop an integrated process by taking advantage of the existing structures and practices. Agroforests, when they have been recognised, are generally considered by outsiders as mere kitchen gardens, i.e., no more than an anecdotal complement to open field cultivation for self consumption, and providing villagers with complementary foods and light materials like firewood.

Facts and recent studies on agroforests show the tremendous economic importance they have for local communities. Agroforests do provide complementary food and various material products; but, as in other tree-crop plantation systems, their main immediate/direct role for smallholders is to supply a regular flow of income. Agroforests are often the sole source of cash for households: in Sumatra, agroforests provide 50–80% of villages' total income through both products and activities linked to their collection, processing and marketing. Like most tree-crop plantations, agroforests are also part of a capitalization strategy: these long-lived plantations

are created assets and they become part of a patrimony that will stay in the family and be transferred to children.

From Farmer Perspective

As a model for commercial agriculture, agroforests provide additional benefits to farmers:

As a "bank" that enables the diversification of income sources and rhythms. Income from agroforests usually covers both everyday expenses—with regularly harvested products such as rubber latex, resin, cinnamon bark, and, at least partly, annual expenses—with seasonal products such as fresh fruits, coffee, clove, nutmeg. Other commodities, such as timber, provide occasional, but important, sums of cash that often serve as savings for exceptional expenses.

Agroforests provide both security and flexibility through the diversification of commercial crops under a permanent structure. Diversity, though not allowing rapid accumulation of capital in the form of immediately realisable assets, constitutes an important insurance for farmers against risks of single crop failure or risks inherent to the unpredictable evolution of market prices.

Flexibility is an important quality for smallholders: in cases of falling prices of one commodity, the concerned species can simply be neglected in the garden for a while until its exploitation becomes profitable again. This process does not involve any disruption to the system itself In ecological terms, the agroforestry plot will be maintained intact and will still be productive, the concerned species will survive in the structure and will be ready for further exploitation, and new species can be introduced as well. In economic terms, there will still be something to harvest, or even new productions to try without reorganising the farming system. Another mark of flexibility is the shift in economic status that some species may encounter: species, present sometimes for decades in the agroforest, may suddenly acquire a new commercial value following market evolution. This has been the case in the 1980's in many places of Sumatra for fruits such as durian and langsat (*Lansium domesticum*), and more recently for timber.

Agroforests ensure the subsistence needs of farmers through its diversity of secondary products: agroforest acts as a common "kitchen garden" providing complementary foods (fruits, vegetable, spices), medicines and other products.

Krui timber harvest from damar (*Shorea javanica*) agroforestry system. (photo: H. de Foresta © ird)

From shifting cultivator perspective

Agroforest systems provide a tested model for a successful transition from shifting cultivation to sustainable and profitable permanent agriculture.

We have discussed some of the direct benefits agroforests provide to smallholders' economies: diversification of income sources and rhythms, risk reduction and flexibility, diversity of secondary production, and creation of an inheritance. One other point has to be mentioned: establishment of agroforests and subsequent management operations require little investment, in terms of both labour and cash. Therefore, even though yields of the dominant species are not as high as in intensive monoculture plantations, agroforests provide a very good return to labour. This point is especially important as labour and cash resource, not land availability, represent the main constraint farmers' face in most shifting cultivation areas in the humid tropics.

No sophisticated techniques are needed. On the contrary, they are based directly upon shifting cultivators' traditional knowledge of their forest environment.

Agroforest establishment processes are directly linked to shifting cultivation. The planting in the swidden of trees, which is well known to local people and fully acknowledged to target economic value, will divert the whole destiny of the field, from a swidden/fallow cycle to an agroforest. This results in a permanent mosaic of the landscape, with areas permanently devoted to food crops and forest-like areas which are now efficiently protected, as they represent the major economic component of surrounding village communities.

Forestry Development

In the sphere of forestry, agroforests provide a silvicultural model that integrates farmers, a diversified production of forest products, and the conservation of biodiversity.

Benefits of agroforest systems to the field of forestry can be listed as follows:

Simple techniques for managing complexity

Most agroforests are true plantations established, after total removal of the original vegetation, through planting selected species and through natural or directed enrichment. Agroforest establishment does not involve sophisticated techniques. Neither does agroforest maintenance, which involves techniques closer to gardening than to dominant forestry models for tree-crop plantation.

Alternative model for diversified timber production

Commercial timber production is considered as the exclusive domain of big private or State companies. Existing production from complex agroforestry systems is rarely mentioned and statistics are either not accurate or lacking. Nevertheless both the existing and potential resources offered by agroforest systems, and the timber management practices developed by agroforest farmers are worth investigating.

Agroforests as those encountered in Maninjau district, West Sumatra province, illustrate the potential of these systems as alternative models for sustainable timber production by smallholders. Under a canopy dominated by high durian trees, mixed with various forest species, commercial crops (cinnamon, coffee, and nutmeg) are grown, as well as various fruit trees, palms, bamboo, and medicinal plants. Timber production relies on the cultivation of selected timber species, on the management of naturally occurring forest species, and on the value of various fruit tree species.

Even though more research is needed, we can already underline the remarkable adaptation of agroforests to the integration of sustainable timber practices in their already diversified overall management. Agroforests are all characterised by an abundance of potential timber trees, a large supply of timber species seeds and seedlings, and the fact that the species involved are well known and managed by villagers for long.

Alternative model for the conservation of forest biodiversity outside protected areas

It is commonly acknowledged that the replacement of natural ecosystems with agricultural systems by man involves a drastic reduction in biodiversity. This is also the case with forest plantations, even though it is less commonly recognised. As far as species composition is concerned, an *Eucalyptus* plantation for instance, though it is often called a "forest" and succeeds in restoring a forest material, is definitely closer to a cassava field than to a natural forest.

Complex agroforestry systems, such as those encountered in Indonesia, have not only proven to be economically profitable, compatible with high population densities (up to 100–150 inhabitants/km^2), and

ecologically viable in the long term. They also are the only production system in tropical lands, which allows combining agricultural production with the conservation of a high degree of biological diversity. Agroforests replace previous natural vegetation with a complex community of perennial species, which not only allows the direct conservation of numerous useful forest species, but also acts as shelter for hundreds of forest species not directly useful in our present state of knowledge.

In the present global context of degradation and destruction of tropical forest resources, and given the current trends of "dispossession" of traditional rural societies by both economic development and migratory forces, agroforests assert an original but very efficient social takeover of forest richness by local farmers groups. Where natural forests are doomed to destruction, agroforest development re-establishes and maintains diverse and rich forest ecosystems in which farmers are integrated.

In terms of global biodiversity conservation strategy, the strength of agroforests should be clarified. Biodiversity levels achieved in agroforests are still far from those reached by natural rainforests, but they are very impressive compared to other production systems. Agroforests cannot therefore be conceived as substitutes to protected areas of natural forest, but they have a substantial role to play as a supplement, in multiplying for a significant fraction of forest species the opportunities to live and reproduce outside protected areas.

Do Agroforests Have a Future?

With the urgent needs for improved social forestry programs and the promotion of the buffer zone concept for national parks, they have to integrate forest production with forest conservation, and they can no longer afford to ignore rural communities.

From an agricultural perspective, given the failure of many agricultural programs that promoted continuous annual cropping systems in previously forested areas, agronomists have also begun to think of trees as potential vectors for sustainable development.

On the agroforestry side, simple agroforestry associations have been largely tested and promoted, their limits have also been felt, in the fields of biological performance, economic benefits, farmers acceptance, diversification potentials, etc. With the integration of sustainability as a central concept in development, policy makers cannot anymore ignore the environmental consequences of development orientations and programmes they promote.

Trainers and extensionists can now explore their respective countries in search of agroforest systems developed by local farmer and help develop with their colleagues and students a national agroforest knowledge base. Agroforestry trainers have an important role to play in raising public awareness concerning that agroforestry at large and agroforest systems in particular can offer now and in the future.

Further Reading

FAO, IIRR. 1995. Resource management for upland areas in SE-Asia. An Information Kit. Farm field document 2. Food and Agriculture Organisation of the United Nations, Bangkok, Thailand and International Institute of Rural Reconstruction, Silang, Cavite, Philippines. p 207

de Foresta H, Michon G. 1993. Creation and management of rural agroforests in Indonesia: potential applications in Africa. In: Hladik, C M *et al*, eds. Tropical forests, people and food. Biocultural Interactions and Applications to Development. Unesco MAB Series, No 13, Unesco and Parthenon Publishing Group: p 709–724.

Michon G, de Foresta H. 1995. The Indonesian agro-forest model: forest resource management and biodiversity conservation. In: Halladay P, Gilmour DA, eds. Conserving Biodiversity Outside Protected Areas. The Role of Traditional Agro-ecosystems. IUCN: p 90–106.

Michon G, de Foresta H. 1999. Agroforests: incorporating a forest vision in agroforestry. In Buck LE, Lassoie JP, Fernandes ECM, eds. agroforestry in Sustainable Agricultural Systems. CRC Press, Lewis Publishers: p 381–406.

de Foresta H, Michon G. 1997. The agroforest alternative to Imperata grasslands: when smallholder agriculture and forestry reach sustainability. Agroforestry Systems 36:105–120. Dordrecht: Kluwer Academic Publishers

Original Source

This edition of *The Overstory* was excerpted with permission of the publisher from:

de Foresta, H, G. Michon and A. Kusworo. 2000. Complex Agroforests. International Centre for Research in Agroforestry, Bogor, Indonesia.

Publisher contact: International Centre for Research in Agroforestry Southeast Asian Regional Research Programme P0 Box 161, Bogor, Indonesia Tel: +62 251 625415; fax: +62 251 625416; Email: icraf-indonesia@cgiar.org; Web: http://www.icraf.cgiar.org/sea

Printed copies of the original can be purchased from: http://www.icraf.cgiar.org/sea/ICRAFPubsList/Bookstore/BookStoreNew.htm#LectureNotes

This excerpt was originally published as *The Overstory* #105.

Trees, Forests and Sacred Groves

Sarah A. Laird

Every culture has narratives or beliefs which answer in different ways the fundamental questions about how we came to be, and articulate how and where people originated, collective transformations undergone by the community, and how people should behave towards one another and their environment (Elder and Wong 1994). Forests are the subject of a great deal of myth, legend and lore. Societies most closely entwined with forests tend to regard them with a healthy respect, an awe at their splendour and majesty, sometimes dread and fear of the powerful spirits that lurk within them. Ancestors often find their resting places in forests, many wandering in various states of unease and spitefulness.

In European culture, the word "savage" was derived from silva meaning a wood, and the progress of mankind was considered to be from the forest to the field. Schama (1995) describes how from Ireland to Bohemia, penitents fled from the temptations of the world into forests, where in "solitude they would deliver themselves to mystic transports or prevail over the ordeals that might come their way from the demonic powers lurking in the darkness". The "indeterminate, boundless forest," then, was a place where the faith of the true believer was put to a severe test. The forests in European culture were also considered to be a more positive site of miracles, the source of great spiritual awakenings; and the forest itself was held to be a form of primitive church or temple. The first temples in Europe were forest groves, and although progressively replaced with temples made of wood, and subsequently by churches made of stone, places of worship – particularly those of Gothic architecture – continue to evoke the forest with their design and proportions (Rival in Posey 1999; Schama 1995; Burch in Posey 1999).

Schama (1995) quotes a poem by Bryant called Forest Hymn which expressed the American, or New World, version of the forest as a form of primitive church or temple:

The groves were God's first temples.
Ere man learned
To hew the shaft and lay the architectrave
And spread the roof above them—ere he framed

The lofty vault, to gather and roll back
The sound of anthems; in darkling wood
Amidst the cool and silence, he knelt down,
And offered to the Mightiest solemn thanks
And supplication.

In other regions of the world there also exists a relationship to forests that combines fearful respect and awe at the beauty and mystical source of life held within forests. Buddha would sit alone in the depths of the forest, lost in meditation, and it was in the midst of a beautiful forest that he was shown the four great truths (Porteous 1928). In Ghana, beliefs about forests include the belief that they are the home of dwarfs, and the domain of the mythical Sasabonsam—a legendary figure responsible for all the woes of mankind and to which mishaps and everything evil are attributable (Abbiw 1990). The Dai people of Yunnan Province, China, believe that the forest is the cradle of human life, and that forests are at one with the supernatural realm. They believe that the interrelationship of human beings with their physical environment consists of five major elements: forest, water, land, food and humanity (Pei Shengji, Posey 1999).

In sacred groves are manifested a range of traditions and cultural values of forests. Although they occur throughout the world, sacred groves share many similar features, which are summarized in part by Pei Shengji (Posey 1999) in his reference to the four hundred "dragon hills" (*lung shan*) in the Yunnan Province of China: "...a kind of natural conservation area... a forested hill where the gods reside. All the plants and animals that inhabit the Holy Hills are either companions of the gods or sacred living things in the gods' gardens. In addition.... the spirits of great and revered chieftains go to the Holy Hills to live following their departure from the world of the living".

Sacred groves are specific forest areas imbued with powers beyond those of humans; they are home to mighty spirits that can take or give life; they originate from a range of roots, and include: sites linked to specific events; sites surrounding temples; burial grounds or cemeteries housing the spirits of ancestors; the homes of protective spirits; the homes of deities from which priests derive their healing powers; homes to a powerful animal or plant species; forest areas that surround natural sacred features such as rivers, rocks, caves and "bottomless" water holes; and sites of initiation or ritual (Falconer, Pei, Bharucha, Zoundjihekpon and Dossou-Glehouenou, Pramod Parajuli in Posey 1999; Vartak and Gadgil 1981).

Sacred Groves and Biological Diversity

Access to most sacred forests is restricted by taboos, codes and custom to particular activities and members of a community. Gathering, hunting, wood chopping and cultivation are strictly prohibited in the Holy Hills of China. The Dai people believe that these activities would make the gods angry and bring misfortune and disaster upon the community. A Dai text warns: "The Trees on the Nong mountains (Holy Hills) cannot be cut. In these forests you cannot cut down trees and construct houses. You cannot build houses on the Nong mountains, you must not antagonize the spirits, the gods or Buddha" (Pei Shengji, Posey 1999). In Maharashtra, India, regulations and religious customs are set down by priests (known as *pujaris* or *bhagats*) with a knowledge of the forest deities, their ties to the surrounding landscape, and their influence on the daily lives of the community. Ancient folklore and stories are told which include fairly specific detail on the supernatural penalties that will result should the groves be desecrated, for example by felling trees. However, control over extractive activities in sacred groves varies by village, and in many places a complete ban is not in place, and limited collection of fallen wood, fruit from the forest floor, medicinal plant collection, honey collection, tapping of *Caryota urens* to make an alcoholic beverage, and other activities are permitted, if strictly controlled (Bharucha in Posey 1999).

Sacred groves have survived for many hundreds of years and today act as reservoirs of much local biodiversity. The 40 contiguous groves studied by Bharucha (Posey 1999) account, as a whole, for most of the plant species present in the Maharashtra region. The forest structure is also unique, representing the least disturbed islands of old growth. The Holy Hills in China also make a significant contribution to biodiversity conservation on a number of levels: they contribute to the conservation of threatened forest ecosystems; they protect a large number

of endemic or relic plant species; and the large number of Holy Hills distributed throughout the region form "green islands" or "stepping stones" between larger nature reserves (Pei Shengji in Posey 1999).

Sacred Groves as a Conservation Model

As a result of the high conservation and biodiversity values held in sacred groves, increasing attention is being paid to their potential as a tool and model for biodiversity conservation. For example, in its 1996 Sacred Sites – Cultural Integrity, Biological Diversity (1996) UNESCO found that:

Sacred groves have served as important reservoirs of biodiversity, preserving unique species of plants, insects, and animals. Sacred and taboo associations attached to particular species of trees, forest groves, mountains, rivers, caves, and temple sites should therefore continue to play an important role in the protection of particular ecosystems by local people. Particular plant species are often used by traditional healers and priests who have a strong interest in the preservation of such sites and ecosystems. In some regions of the world, beliefs that spirits inhabit relict areas have served to quickly regenerate abandoned swidden plots into mature forest. In other areas, sacred places play a major part in safeguarding critical sites in the hydrological cycle of watershed areas. Furthermore, in a number of instances sacred sites have also been instrumental in preserving the ecological integrity of entire landscapes. For these reasons, sacred sites can help in assessing the potential natural vegetation of degraded ecosystems or ecosystems modified by humans.

Sacred groves have survived in many regions despite tremendous economic pressure on forest resources. In some parts of India, for example, sacred groves have retained high levels of biodiversity and remain largely intact, while government-controlled forest reserves are often in poor condition. Local level control has been vital to the protection of these areas, but economic pressures are mounting, and changing land-use patterns have contributed to a serious depletion of resources and a phenomenal rise in the price of land. This in turn has provided an irresistible incentive for some local people to sell the groves, irrespective of the sentiment that at one time was sufficient to preserve them (Bharucha, Pramod Parajuli in Posey 1999).

Temples often have associated forests that have been protected for centuries. Chantaburi, Thailand. (photo: C. Elevitch)

Even in cases where local communities are determined to retain sacred groves, they are often as vulnerable to outside political and economic forces as other forest areas. In East Kalimantan, for example, oil palm plantation and logging operations are clearing ancestral (*adat*) forest. The *adat* covers four types of forest: *Sipung Bengkut* (perennial tree gardens which have been developing since 1912), *Sipung Bua* (fruit tree gardens), *Sipung Payo* (swampy areas) and *Sipung Uwe* (rattan gardens). The companies promise in return to encourage "community participation," "the development of sustainable forest management," and "income generating schemes," which are considered "empty and pointless" offers for a priceless ancestral forest that cannot be equated with monetary and material conditions (Enris and Sarmiah in Posey 1999).

Although sacred groves undoubtedly contribute to the conservation of biodiversity, it is questionable whether the complex history and traditions that have created and maintain these areas can be operationalized as a tool or model for further conservation efforts. Conservation is often a side-effect of customs that associate or dedicate forest resources to the deities. In the Western Ghats of India, rather than managing resources for future use, communities are instead attempting to benefit from the protection and good-will afforded by the deity in return for not disturbing the sanctity of the sacred grove (Bharucha in Posey 1999). This would be a difficult dynamic to reproduce in a conservation programme. In Southern Ghana, Falconer (Posey 1999) argues that sacred groves exist as part of a system so complex and variable that a much clearer understanding of the spiritual, mystical and political functions and beliefs of sacred groves is needed before they can be incorporated into conservation programmes.

In South India, sacred groves are populated by dead spirits prevented from transforming and hence remaining ghosts forever. Their life force engenders trees to grow wild, and gives rise to highly fertile but extremely dangerous sacred groves, which are frightening and highly ambivalent (Rival in Posey 1999). Rival warns against environmentalists' views of sacred groves and trees as sanctuaries of biodiversity, home to benign and protecting deities. The suggestion that the belief systems that have protected these groves should be promoted to encourage the conservation of larger forest areas ignores the fact that—while both environmentalists and local peoples view trees as vital and holding regenerative power—trees in traditional India are not benign protectors: they are frightful and the power of their life force is extremely dangerous. While important reservoirs of biodiversity, it is unlikely that with the exception of a few areas, the cultural beliefs and management systems that have led to the conservation of sacred groves could easily be incorporated into the Western cultural conservation ethos.

Tree Lore and Symbolism

Trees are universally powerful symbols, a physical expression of life, growth and vigour to urban, rural and forest dwellers alike. They can symbolize historical continuity and human society. They are often of frightening magnitude, linking earth and heavens, arbiters of life and death, incorporating both male and female aspects, and home to both good and bad spirits, including the souls of ancestors. Trees provide protection from harm, cure disease and increase fertility. Trees preside over marriages, are planted at the birth of a child and at burial sites. In some origin myths, the first men and women were made of wood.

The Tree of Life in Mesopotamia and India brings fertility by linking death with life. The birds visiting its branches are the souls of the dead. The cross on which Jesus died grew into a tree on Mount Golgotha. The fig tree opened for Mary to seek shelter for the infant Jesus from the soldiers of Herod. The date palm was the staff of St. Christopher which helped him to carry the weak and small across a raging river. The birch in Scandinavia, larch in Siberia, redwood in California, fig in India, and iroko in West Africa are widely revered and respected.

The Cosmic Tree, Tree of Life, or Axis Mundi, features in many of the world's religions. In Amazonia, the World Tree is often ceiba/kapok, *Ceiba pentandra*, or a yuchan, *Chorisia insignis*. The trunks of these tall emergent trees are characteristically bulbous, hollow and spongy, and the wood is rather soft. The ceiba has a life-span of up to 200 years and is arguably the tallest of Amazonian forest trees. It reaches maturity and starts to flower some time between its fortieth and sixtieth year, thus beginning its reproductive cycle at the oldest age people live to in the region. It lives a life corresponding roughly to four Huaorani generations. In Huaorani culture, the Amazon basin was born from the fallen giant ceiba tree (Rival in Posey 1999).

Ties to nature manifest themselves most notably in Turkish culture through attitudes to plants in general, and trees in particular. After conversion to Islam, the importance of trees grew in local culture because Mohammed compared a good Muslim to a palm tree and declared that planting a tree would be accepted as a substitute for alms. Trees are planted after children are born, when a son is drafted into military service, after a wedding, and as a memorial to the dead (Tont in Posey 1999). In one of the oldest collections of Turkish tales which make up the Book of Dede Korkut, the unknown poet agonizes over his failure to find a more exalted name for his beloved plant:

Tree, tree, do not be embarrassed because I call you by that [after all]
The doors of Mekka and Medine are made of wood
The staff of Moses is also made of wood
The bridges spanning over big rivers are also made from you
The ships which roam the black seas are also of wood.

The oak tree was worshipped by Romans, Druids, Greeks and Celts as the home of deities. In Europe, fairies were said to make their homes in old oak trees, departing through holes where branches had fallen; it was considered healing to touch the fairy doors with diseased parts (T. Shanley 1997, personal communication). In Scotland in the last century, mistletoe growing on the famous Oak of Errol was bound up with the fortunes of the family Hay, acting as a "sure charm against all glamour and witchery" (Porteous in Posey 1999). Cowley and Evelyn in seventeenth-century England wrote about the oak (as in Schama 1995):

Our British Druids not with vain intent Or without Providence did the Oak frequent, That Albion did that Tree so much advance Nor superstition was, nor ignorance Those priest divining even then bespoke The Mighty Triumph of the Royal Oak

Conclusion

In forest culture we find the common threads of human experience. Whether the "dangerous and highly fertile" sacred groves of India, the oak tree in Britain, the graveyard forests in Côte d'Ivoire, or in the fall of the great *Ceiba pentandra* which created the Amazon Basin: throughout the world we see a shared focus on the origin, force and power of life expressed in trees and in the forest.

References

Abbiw, D. K. (1990) Useful Plants of Ghana: West African Uses of Wild and Cultivated Plants. Intermediate Technology Publications, London.

Elder, J. and Wong, H. D. (1994) Family of Earth and Sky: Indigenous Tales of Nature from Around the World. Beacon Press, Boston.

Porteous, A. (1928) The Lore of the Forest: Myths and Legends. Guernsey Press Co. Ltd., Guernsey.

Posey, D. A. (1995) Indigenous Peoples and Traditional Resource Rights: A Basis for Equitable Relationships? Proceedings of a Workshop, Green College Centre for Environmental Policy and Understanding, 28th June 1995, Oxford, UK.

Schama, S. (1995) Landscape and Memory. Alfred A. Knopf, New York.

UNESCO (1996) Sacred Sites—Cultural Integrity, Biological Diversity. Programme proposal, November 1996, Paris.

Vartak, V. D. and Gadgil, M. (1981) Studies on sacred groves along the Western Ghats from Maharashtra and Goa. Role of Beliefs and Folklore. In: Glimpses of Indian Ethnobotany, pp. 272–278.

Original Source

This edition of *The Overstory* is excerpted with the kind permission of the United Nations Environment Programme (UNEP) from:

Laird, S.A. 1999. "Forests, Culture and Conservation." In: Posey, D.A. (Ed). Cultural and Spiritual Values of Biodiversity. Intermediate Technology Publications, London on behalf of United Nations Environment Programme (UNEP).

The original book and this article is © 1999 United Nations Environment Programme, P.O. Box 30552 Nairobi, Kenya.

The original title, Cultural and Spiritual Values of Biodiversity, is available from: ITDG Publications 103/105 Southampton Row, London WC1B 4HH, UK Tel: +44 202 7436 9761; Fax: +44 020 7436 2013; Email: orders@itpubs.org.uk; Web: http://www.itdgpublishing.org.uk.

This excerpt was originally published as *The Overstory* #93.

Biodiversity and Protected Areas

Office of Technology Assessment

This article covers protection of ecosystems for the purpose of maintaining biological diversity. Protected areas on both small and large scales can conserve biodiversity, as well as protect other essential ecosystem functions such as watershed, carbon storage, and erosion control. Although this edition does not directly cover farm systems, many farms have wild areas such as gulches, forests, and areas that have long been unused and are returning to forests. Protected areas are important on both large and small scales.

Establishment of Protected Areas

The world's first two national parks were established in the 1870s. Growth the number and size of protected areas was slow at first. It accelerated during the 1920s and 1930s, halted during World War II, and regained momentum by the early 1950s. The number doubled during the 1970s. Before 1970, most protected areas were located in industrial countries. In more recent years, the Developing World has led in both numbers added and rates of establishment.

Acquisition and Designation

Most protected areas are established by official acts designating that uses of particular sites will be restricted to those compatible with natural ecological conditions. At the Federal level in the United States, designating a land area or water body for conservation involves making a formal declaration of intent to assign a certain category of protection and then providing an opportunity for extensive public comment on the proposed action. Other governments use similar processes, although the extent of public participation varies.

The degree of protection depends partly on the objectives of the acquisition or designation. There are many different types of designations. Kenya, for example, has national parks, national reserves, nature reserves, and forest reserves. The wildlife sanctuaries in Kiribati in the South Pacific are very different in conservation terms from wildlife sanctuaries in India. Designated national parks of the United Kingdom are quite different from national parks in the United States. And in Spain, national parks, nature parks, and national hunting reserves indicate different types of protection.

To clarify this situation and to promote the full range of protected area options, the International Union for the Conservation of Nature and Natural Resources (IUCN) provides a series of 10 management categories (IUCN 1978, 1982). Protected areas are categorized according to their management objectives, rather than by the name used in their official designations (see table). Thus, the national parks of the United Kingdom are placed under category V (protected landscape or seascape), rather than under category II (national parks). Standardization of the categories also facilitates international comparisons and provides a framework for all protected areas.

Categories and Management Objectives of Protected Areas

(Source: Thorsell 1985)

1   Scientific reserve/strict nature reserve: To protect and maintain natural processes in an undisturbed state for scientific study, environmental monitoring, education, and maintenance of genetic resources.

2   National park: To protect areas of national or international significance for scientific, educational, and recreational use.

3   Natural monument/natural landmark: To protect and preserve nationally significant features because of their special interest or unique characteristics.

4   Managed nature reserve/wildlife sanctuary: To assure the conditions necessary to protect species, groups of species, biotic communities, or physical features of the environment that require specific human manipulation for their perpetuation.

5   Protected landscape or seascape: To maintain nationally significant landscapes characteristic of the harmonious interaction of humans and land,

while allowing recreation and tourism within the normal lifestyles and economic activities of these areas.

6 Resource reserve: To protect the natural resources of the area for future use and prevent or contain development activities that could affect the resource, pending the establishment of objectives based on knowledge and planning.

7 Natural biotic area/anthropological reserve: To allow the way of life of societies living in harmony with the environment to continue.

8 Multiple-use   management   area/managed resource area: To provide for the sustained production of water, timber, wildlife, pasture, and outdoor recreation, with conservation oriented to the support of the economic activities (although specific zones may also be designed within these areas to achieve specific conservation objectives).

9 Biosphere reserve: To conserve an ecologically representative landscape in areas that range from complete protection to intensive production; to promote ecological monitoring, research and education; and to facilitate local, regional, and international cooperation.

10 World heritage site: To protect the natural features for which the area was considered to be of world heritage quality, and to provide information for worldwide public enlightenment.

Criteria for Selection of Areas to Protect

Protected areas can be located and managed to protect biological diversity at three levels:

1 at the ecosystem level: by protecting unique ecosystems, representative areas for each main type of ecosystem in a nation or region, and species-rich ecosystems and centers of endemic species;

2 at the species level: by giving priority to the genetically most distinct species (e.g., families with few species or genera with only one species), and to culturally important species and endemic genera and species; and

3 at the gene level: by giving priority to plant and animal types that have been or are being domesticated, to populations of wild relatives of domesticated species, and to wild resource species (those used for food, fuel, fiber, medicine, construction material, ornament, etc.).

References

Harrison, J. 1985. Status and Trends of Natural Ecosystems Worldwide. OTA commissioned paper.

International Union for the Conservation of Nature and Natural Resources (IUCN). 1978. Categories, Objectives, and Criteria for Protected Areas. Morges, Switzerland.

International Union for the Conservation of Nature and Natural Resources (IUCN). 1982. Categories, Objectives, and Criteria for Protected Areas. In: J.A. McNeely and K.R. Miller (eds). National Parks, Conservation, and Development: The Role of Protected Area in Sustaining Society, Proceedings of the World Congress on National Parks, Bali, Indonesia. Smithsonian Institution Press, Washington, DC.

International Union for the Conservation of Nature and Natural Resources (IUCN). 1985. The United Nations List of National Parks and Protected Areas. Gland, Switzerland.

Thorsell, J.W. 1985. "The Role of Protected Areas in Maintaining Biological Diversity in Tropical Developing Countries," OTA commissioned paper.

U.S. Congress, Office of Technology Assessment (OTA). 1984. Technologies to Sustain Tropical Forest Resources, OTA-F214. U.S. Government Printing Office, Washington, DC.

Original Source

This article is excerpted from:

U.S. Congress, Office of Technology Assessment. 1987. Technologies to Maintain Biological Diversity. U.S. Government Printing Office, Washington, DC.

This excerpt was originally published as *The Overstory* #90.

Traditional Pacific Island Agroforestry Systems

Randolf ("Randy") R. Thaman, Craig R. Elevitch, and Kim M. Wilkinson

Agroforestry was traditionally practiced in many parts of the tropics. Most traditional agroforestry species and techniques have not yet been subject to institutional scientific experiments. However, they have been well-tested by local farmers, often over many generations. These traditional systems and species can provide a strong, locally-based framework for future agroforestry development. Indigenous knowledge systems are now being regarded as an invaluable resource.

This chapter describes three traditional agroforestry systems from the Pacific Islands.

Traditional Pacific Island Agroforestry Systems

Trees have always been important to Pacific Island societies. Pacific Island peoples planted and protected trees as a part of their multi-species and multipurpose agroforestry and land use systems. They have also been willing to accept new trees that can make their life and their island environments better. Traditional Pacific Island agricultural and land use systems were agroforestry systems, built on a foundation of protecting and planting trees. These systems made Pacific Islanders among the most self-sufficient and well-nourished peoples in the world.

Future agroforestry development in the Pacific Islands would do well based on the conservation, strengthening, and expansion of the many time-tested multipurpose agroforestry species and systems that already exist in the Pacific Islands. The emphasis on the protection, as well as the planting, of these species is of utmost importance. Experience has shown that it is far more difficult to replace forests, agroforests, trees, and rare cultivars of trees (e.g., breadfruit, coconut, pandanus and banana cultivars), than it is to protect what already exists. Minimizing the loss of knowledge about these systems and species is also essential.

Pacific Island agroforests were developed and managed to meet not only people's needs for food and other products, but also the needs of the system as a whole for fertilizer, mulch, animal food, shade. The trees in the system also provide protection from erosion, wind, and salt spray.

Examples from Traditional Pacific Island Agroforestry Include:

Tongan Agroforestry Example

In Tonga the multispecies agroforestry system is a very complex mixture of trees, shrubs, and short-term ground crops. It is usually practiced as a short-term shifting agriculture system on pieces of land averaging eight acres or less in size. When the land is prepared for a new garden, some of the fast-growing pioneer tree species, most shrubs, and grasses are cut and allowed to dry. The dried material is then placed in piles for burning. Other valuable trees that are present in the fallow, such as breadfruit, mangoes, avocado, citrus trees, Malay apple (*Syzygium malaccense*), Polynesian plum (*Spondias dulcis*), perfume tree or ylang-ylang (*Cananga odorata*), and, of

Indigenous Pacific Island agroforestry system depicting breadfruit, coconut, banana, *Cananga odorata*, Inocarpus *fagifer*, *Hibiscus tiliaceus* with: taro, sweet potatoes, yams (*Dioscorea* spp.), and kava.

Polynesian homegardens can be extremely complex, with innumerable species included for both short and long term needs. (photo: C. Elevitch)

course, coconut palms, are protected or, in some cases, slightly pruned to allow the sunlight to enter the garden area.

Other culturally important trees, like koka (*Bischofia javanica*), Pacific litchi (*Pometia pinnata*), maululu (*Glochidion ramiflorum*) and toi (*Alphitonia zizyphoides*) are then pruned, often by cutting almost all of the branches off. This practice does not kill the tree, and accomplishes a number of objectives. It allows the entry of sunlight needed by the first crop to be planted, which is usually yams (*Dioscorea alata*). It also allows the leaves to fall providing organic material to the soil, and allows for fresh new branches to grow as the garden matures. The larger branches that have been cut from the trees are used as trellises over each yam mound. Yams climbing off the hot volcanic soils on these trellises have higher yields,

are more disease free, and are more easily weeded. Because Tonga has frequent serious tropical cyclones (known elsewhere in the Pacific as hurricanes or typhoons), the lower trellises are much more appropriate that the higher trellis on poles used in other countries. Finally, when the yams are harvested, after 7–9 months, the branches make perfect firewood for the underground oven.

In the garden, the yams are usually intercropped with rows of giant taro (*Alocasia macrorrhiza*), plantains (*Musa cultivars*), and taro (*Colocasia esculenta*). Along the borders, sweet yams (*Dioscorea esculenta*) are often planted next to the fence posts, and pandanus for weaving, sugarcane or bush hibiscus spinach (*Abelmoschus manihot*), a very important leafy green vegetable, are often planted along the borders or fence lines of the garden. The living fencing will often be candelnut tree (*Aleurites moluccana*), beach hibiscus or fau (*Hibiscus tiliaceus*) or dadap or ngatae (*Erythrina variegata*). In some cases, timber trees, such as casuarina (*Casuarina equisetifolia*) or introduced species, such as Australian kauri (*Agathis robusta*) or West Indian mahogany (*Swietenia macrophylla*), are planted in a few rows along the perimeter or along the roadside border of the allotment, or sometimes as a small woodlot on part of the allotment. Other short-term crops such as green onions (*Allium fistulosum* and *A. ascalonicum*), Chinese cabbage or paak tsoi (*Brassica chinensis*), and corn (*Zea mays*) are often planted systematically, or bird-sown chili peppers (*Capsicum frutescens*) are protected in the garden.

After the yams are harvested, taro or tannia (*Xanthosoma* sp.) is planted as the next crop in the soft soil left over after the yam harvest. The giant taro and taro that were planted with the yams are then harvested. The second crop of taro or tannia and the bananas remain. When this crop is harvested, sweet potatoes or cassava are then planted, and if sweet potatoes are planted, another crop, usually cassava is planted which completes the three to four-year shifting agricultural cycle. Sometimes, the cycle is extended for a further three to five years by planting kava (*Piper methysticum*), the important social beverage plant, or paper mulberry (*Brousonnetia papyrifera*), so important for the making of tapa cloth used in Tongan ceremonies and to sell to tourists and for export. As the garden is allowed to slowly return to fallow for four to up to ten years, the plantains continue to bear fruit, the fruit trees and other multipurpose trees continue to provide food, medicines, and other products.

Marquesan Agroforestry Example
Home-gardens in the Marquesas Islands of French Polynesia are characterized by a great diversity of mainly exotic plants that have been introduced during some 1,500 years since the first arrival of humans to the islands. Many of these plants have been added since European contact. Dominant species include the important staple food trees coconut, breadfruit, mango and kapok (*Ceiba pentandra*) which are both very common, and the ubiquitous beach hibiscus tree (*Hibiscus tiliaceus*) which forms part of the backdrop of every village. Common spreading ornamental shade trees include the rain tree or monkeypod (*Albizia saman*) and the flame tree or poinciana (*Delonix regia*), with *Albizia lebbeck* also present in dwelling areas.

Home gardens also include a wide variety of staple plants and important fruit trees. These include banana cultivars, mango, papaya, lime, avocado, soursop and sweetsop (*Annona muricata* and *A. squamosa*), guava, and tamarind. Sugar cane is also common. The cultivated pandanus (*Pandanus tectorius* var *laevis*), so important in the production of plaited ware, and kapok are also common in home gardens. Ornamentals planted as hedges or along borders, which are commonly used for garlands and fragrant flowers include *Gardenia taitensis*, ylang-ylang (*Cananga odorata*), the common hibiscus (*Hibiscus rosa-sinensis*), an the hedge panax (*Polyscias guilfoylei*).

Immediately surrounding dwelling areas and in wild places on the islands of Nukuhiva ad Uapou, are extensive stands of *Leucaena leucocephala*. These stands of trees provide the main source of lowland fodder for horses, which are highly useful and abundant draught animals in the Marquesas and which are rotationally fed on *Leucaena* in the lowlands and grazed on limited areas of upland pasture.

Kiribati Atoll Agroforestry Example
Coconut palms, usually of a number of different varieties, are planted as a major cash and multipurpose crop. Sometimes they are planted in rows and sometimes allowed to grow in irregular patterns. Other multipurpose trees, such as screw pine (*Pandanus* species), *Guettarda speciosa*, *Tournefortia argentea*, and the shrub *Sida fallax* (*te kaura* in Kiribati or *ilima* in Hawai‘i) are protected, or sometimes planted to provide soil improvement and leaves or mulch (fertilizer) for the swamp taro (*Cyrtosperma chamissonis*) pits that have been excavated down to the water table. The pandanus is also a very important staple food plant on the atolls, as well as being the source of timber for house building, thatch, fibre for mat and basket making, medicines, and many other products. Because of the many uses that the people of Kiribati have for the pandanus tree, they have been referred to as the "Pandanus People." Breadfruit, papaya, native fig (*Ficus tinctoria*), and sometimes bananas and true taro (*Colocasia esculenta*) are also planted in or around the taro pit. The coastal forest on both the ocean and lagoon sides of the garden area, and the mangroves on the lagoon side, are protected to shelter the inland plantation from salt spray, high waves, extremely high tides, and from coastal erosion. The protection of these forests, and the protection of the other trees also ensures that the wood, medicine, and many other products provided

by the trees and forests are still available. This practice also ensures the continued availability the fish, shellfish, crabs, birds, and other animals and small plants that depend on these forests and trees will be protected for future generations.

Conclusion

A traditional agroforestry system represents a long-term investment of time, knowledge, and effort in a living, growing, "bank account." If protected and improved, traditional agroforestry is a time-tested (for thousands of years) foundation for future develop-

ment. It can help to ensure that the needs of future generations of Pacific Islanders will be satisfied.

References

Clark, W.C., and R.R. Thaman (eds). 1994. Agro-Forestry in the Pacific Islands: Systems for Sustainability. Unipub. A very useful treatment of agroforestry practices in the Pacific, including lists and descriptions of many agroforestry species.

Original Source

This chapter was originally published as *The Overstory* #49.

Protecting and Expanding Traditional Agroforests

Randolf ("Randy") R. Thaman, Craig R. Elevitch, and Kim M. Wilkinson

This chapter introduces the concept of agrodeforestation, and the important role that existing and remnant agroforests can play in agroforestry development. There are many regions of the tropics where agroforestry has been practiced traditionally. Traditional systems and species can provide a strong, locally-based framework for future agroforestry development. Emphasis should be placed on the conservation, strengthening, and expansion of the time-tested agroforestry species and systems that already exist. A ten step process for identifying and rehabilitating remnants of traditional agroforests is suggested. Examples from the Pacific Islands are used, but the principles are applicable anywhere.

Agrodeforestation: the removal of trees or the de-emphasis on the planting and/or protection of trees in agricultural ecosystems.

Pacific Island peoples have always planted and protected trees as a part of their multi-species and multipurpose agroforestry and land use systems. They have also been willing to accept new trees that can improve their lives and island environments. Traditional Pacific Island agricultural and land use systems were agroforestry systems, built on a foundation of protecting and planting trees. These traditional agroforestry systems once made Pacific Islanders among the most self-sufficient and well-nourished peoples in the world.

As we enter the 21st Century, the destruction of trees and the failure to plant and protect trees in the process of modern agricultural development has led to a loss of trees in agricultural systems throughout the Pacific Islands. This process is referred to as "agrodeforestation." This process opposes agroforestry or agroforestation, the protection and planting of trees as an integral part of agricultural systems.

As a result of the deterioration of traditional agroforestry-based food systems, urbanized Pacific Island populations now have some of the highest rates of nutritional disorders and nutrition-related non-communicable disease in the world.

The Process of Agrodeforestation in the Pacific Islands

For the past 200 years, and particularly this century, colonial governments actively promoted small- and large-scale monocultural export cropping and livestock grazing. Very little emphasis was placed on the promotion or the maintenance of existing agroforestry systems. On one hand, the introduction of new crops and animals enriched existing indigenous Pacific Island agroforestry systems, particularly smallholder farms. However, promotion of a narrow range of cash crops and the expansion of livestock grazing led to accelerated clearance of forest lands, and the destruction of valuable trees in and around existing agricultural lands (i.e., agrodeforestation).

Resource-rich agroforests can be protected and expanded

Because export crops commonly occupied the best agricultural lands, food gardens were pushed to the outskirts of settlements and onto increasingly marginal lands (sloping or mountainous areas, poorly drained sites and areas with poorer soils). Some crops or cultivars and wild and cultivated trees lost importance relative to the new cash crops and pastures, and began to disappear from Pacific Island agriculture.

World War II brought the Pacific Islands into greater contact with the outside world. Increasing desire for consumer goods and cash incomes and increasing access to markets further intensified pressures to plant cash crops and to promote monocultural plantation agriculture and monocultural plantings of exotic timber trees in plantation forests.

Agricultural departments almost exclusively promoted export cropping, at the expense of the traditional agroforestry systems. In some cases (such as Fiji, Tonga, the Cook Islands, Hawai'i, and Kiribati), traditional agroforestry practices were actively discouraged while export cropping was encouraged. As a result, traditional agroforestry-based food systems have deteriorated, along with the health of urbanized Pacific Island populations.

Formal schooling and agricultural and forestry education ignored traditional agroforestry systems and the importance of multipurpose trees. As the older people passed away, there occurred a widespread loss of traditional agroforestry knowledge among the younger generation, and what could be called an "agrodeforestation of the Pacific Island mind."

21st Century Multi-Species Agroforestry Development

The active promotion of multi-species agroforestry may be the most economically, culturally and ecologically effective means of addressing the serious trends of deforestation, forest degradation and agro-deforestation. Agroforestry development should not be imposed from outside the Pacific Islands on the basis of exotic species destined for export or for improving export crop production. Rather, it should be multi-species agroforestry based firmly on the many time-tested agroforestry species and systems that already exist in the region, strengthened, where appropriate, with some appropriate new introduced trees and technologies. The protection and planting of these trees could serve as an important, locally achievable, and cost-effective first step in promoting sustainable development in the rapidly modernizing island countries and territories of the tropical Pacific Ocean.

The systematic promotion of multi-species agroforestry will bring about the expansion, intensification, strengthening, and adaptation of existing agroforestry systems. New sources of cash income, new technologies and new crops and trees should contribute to the trees and forests that already exist in agricultural areas, rather than replacing, degrading or destroying existing flora.

Appropriate adoption of agroforestry ensures that additions or improvements maximize the existing plant resources and agroforestry practices as a foundation for sustainable development. New developments should also minimize the loss of the existing agroforestry trees, resources and knowledge.

Protection and Rehabilitation of Existing or Remnant Agroforestry Systems

Existing species should be protected and emphasized in planting programs as a basis for future agroforestry development. The utmost priority is placed on the protection, as well as the planting, of these species in and around agricultural areas. Experience has shown that it is far more difficult to replace forests, agroforests, trees, and rare cultivars of trees (e.g., breadfruit, coconut, pandanus and banana cultivars), than it is to protect what already exists.

In some regions of the Pacific Islands, traditionally-based multi-species agroforestry is alive and well, in active practice by local agroforesters. In other areas, however, agroforests may only be found as remnants, surrounded by a sea of modern single-species agriculture (such as sugar cane fields) or urban development. These remnants may be encountered in the home gardens or farms of older or more traditional members of the community, or on unmanaged or abandoned areas such as gulch edges. Sometimes the only evidence of traditional agroforests may be individual species scattered in the landscape.

Agroforesters who are reestablishing agroforestry systems can benefit greatly from the presence these remnant plantings and species, as they can form the foundation of future development. Remnants also provide important information about time-tested, successful agroforestry systems for the area, and may be a valuable source of plant materials. Remnants can be identified, protected, and rehabilitated so they can continue to be productive and useful for the future.

The following steps are suggested as a guideline when working with remnant agroforestry systems.

Purpose To identify, protect, and rehabilitate existing or remnant traditional agroforestry systems or species to enhance their use and productivity.

1   Conduct field surveys of the local environment, existing gardens, agroforests and communities to determine what trees already successfully grow in a given area, what trees are already known and culturally acceptable to the local community, and what planting materials are available.

2   Create an inventory or listing of existing trees, their habitats, associated trees, plants and animal and uses or functions. This is, perhaps the best way of finding out what trees and assemblies of trees will work best. Also include an inventory of seedlings and planting materials that might be available for planting or transplanting.

3   Collect traditional knowledge of local communities about the characteristics and use of different trees and their environmental requirements. This should also include information about important local tree species or varieties that the people would like to see planted and protected, and, species or varieties that are now rare, endangered, locally extinct or in short supply, the reasons for the loss of these trees, and possible actions that can be taken to protect or reestablish these trees.

4   Determine what aspects of the current species could provide for some current needs. For example, is there some product that is currently being purchased that could be provided instead by this tree? An important function this tree could serve on the farm? Could this tree be managed for a future economic products, such as providing seeds, timber, handicrafts, animal feed, firewood, etc.

5   Based on the results of steps 1-4, identify the priorities with respect to what trees should be protected, rehabilitated, planted or reintroduced into a given area.

6   Identify the threats or constraints to the protection and planting/rehabilitation of these species or systems. Are there competition problems from invading weeds, grasses or weedy tree species that are inhibiting the productivity of the tree? Are there animals such as livestock that are damaging the trees? Are the trees in decline due to lack of maintenance such as weeding, mulching, or fertilizing? Are there new pests, diseases, climatic changes?

7   Conduct the maintenance necessary to enhance productivity and remove threats.

8   Identify species that can be added to enhance the existing system and improve its productivity. For example, perhaps some traditional plants can be added to the understory for garlands (leis) or other ornamental materials, medicinal products, etc.

9   Test species, new varieties and the different mixtures of multipurpose species to see what works best

10   Expand on successes on the farm, and share them with neighbors and the community.

Conclusion

Traditional Pacific Island agroforestry systems once made Pacific Islanders among the most self-sufficient and well-nourished peoples in the world. The protection and expansion of traditional agroforestry systems can serve as an important, locally achievable, and cost-effective step in stimulating sustainable development and healthy rural enterprises in the Pacific Islands.

Original Source

This chapter was originally published as *The Overstory* #51.

Further Reading

Clark, W.C. and R.R. Thaman (eds). 1994. Agro-Forestry in the Pacific Islands: Systems for Sustainability. Unipub. A very useful treatment of agroforestry practices in the Pacific, including lists and descriptions of many agroforestry species.

Wild Foods In Agricultural Systems

Ian Scoones, Mary Melnyk, Jules N. Pretty

Throughout the world, agricultural systems are potential sites for a great diversity of managed and collected plant and animal foods. Conventional agricultural research and extension, by focusing only on the main food crops, chiefly cereals, roots and domesticated livestock, have long ignored the range of other plants and animals that also make up agricultural systems.

Studies of this diversity and attendant complexity are demonstrating the importance of understanding the full range of products harvested. For instance, in the apparently maize-dominated agricultural system of Bungoma in Kenya, people consume at least 100 different species of vegetables and fruits drawn from 70 genera and belonging to 35 families (88; 729). Similarly, the agropastoral Tswana people in Botswana use 126 plant species and 100 animal species as sources of food (261). Similar patterns are shown in SE Asia (179; 132; *152;* 188), Himalayan areas (160), Central America (682), Latin America (2; 3; 126), northern Europe (866; 867) and elsewhere in Africa (47–49; 82; 273; 400a; 493; 494; 770).

Studies of settled agriculture worldwide, whether in semi-arid, temperate or humid settings, on the plains or in mountain areas, show that hunting and gathering remains an important component of the livelihoods of agricultural peoples. There is no progressive evolutionary trend of "development" from hunter-gatherer to small-scale settled agriculture and livestock keeping to intensive agricultural systems. Livelihood strategies in all social, economic and ecological settings encompass a wide range of activities. These include the exploitation of a hidden harvest of wild food sources. Diversification of livelihood strategies, combining agricultural sources of food and income with that derived from wild resources, is particularly important for the poorest households, and for women and children (48; 49; 608–630).

Agroecological Change

As agroecosystems change through expansion of cultivated areas or changes in cropping patterns, so the availability of wild foods alters. As woodlands are cleared, new edible weeds and pests linked with agricultural lands appear as other foods associated with the woodland ecology disappear (170; 171 for southern Zimbabwe). The simplification of agroecosystems, such as in the conversion of forest areas to cattle pastures in Brazil and the intensification of small-scale agriculture through Green Revolution technologies worldwide, has the greatest impact on the poor, as key sources of food are lost (76).

Although the greatest diversity of wild foods are found in multi-layered, complex agroforestry systems and home gardens, wild foods are still important in apparently simple, monoculture systems. For instance, canals feeding extensive rice areas are habitats for fish, frogs and plants associated with excess irrigation water (4; 69; *152).* Similarly, other forms of intensive agriculture may harbour particular pests such as rats, mice and locusts, which may be eaten. Intensification of agriculture, with increased use of pesticides and fertilisers, may have a negative effect on the wild food crop by killing off the potential foods "pests" or "weeds." However fertiliser inputs may increase the prevalence of certain species (152).

Wild foods are not only associated with undisturbed systems that replicate the ecological diversity of the uncleared forest, they are also found in degraded sites. Sometimes disturbance increases the diversity of wild products (173). For instance, in Kenya and Tanzania, the greatest prevalence of wild vegetables was found in gullies caused by erosion on farmland (90; 173). Pathways, roadsides, home sites and field edges are also potential sites for wild products; sites which otherwise might be considered valueless. Areas that are logged within forests may become the site for mushroom fruiting (861).

More often, the diversity of wild foods declines during the conversion of complex woodland to simplified cropped land. For instance, in three Tanzanian villages there is a correlation between the diversity of edible plants being eaten and the degree of deforestation (400a). Similarly, twenty years of agricultural change in Kenya have had a major impact on Mbeere wild food collection and use strategies, causing them to use fewer wild food sources, because of reduced access to bush land as a result of land privatisation (28–30; 137).

As agricultural systems change there are new pressures on wild food resources. One response is actively to domesticate the wild foods. Vegetables and fruit trees, formerly harvested in the forest or grazing areas, are increasingly protected or planted (1). In north-west Uganda valuable weeds in the diet of farmers have started to be cultivated within the home compounds (156; 729 for western Kenya). Similarly bush-fallow systems may be transformed by enrichment planting (108), such as the planting of fruit trees in fruit-poor *Acacia* fallow areas (39).

Agroforestry Systems

Farmers have always incorporated trees into farming systems. An increased interest in agroforestry during the past decades has resulted in a more thorough documentation of agroforestry practices from Africa (1; 24; 56; 89; 105; 114; 138; 139), home gardens in SE Asia (40; 62; 102–104; 116; 151a; 151b; 168), kitchen gardens in the West Indies (27) and agroforestry systems in Latin America (2; 3; 9; 53; 58; 99; 117–119). The complexity and diversity of many managed agroforestry systems is immense (23).

The inclusion of trees as a component of the agricultural system increases the structural complexity of the field environment, provides a degree of complementarity in seasonal and interannual production patterns with annual crops and changes the labour commitments to an area of land. Retaining trees on farm land during clearance for agriculture or subsequent planting of trees produces a range of ecological habitats and seasonal niches ideal for wild food production.

During the selective clearing of land for agriculture, farmers usually retain particular tree species. These are often fruit trees, the providers of seasonally important wild foods. In Zimbabwe, clearing of *Julbernadia globiflora* dominated miombo woodland reduced canopy cover from 52% to 8%. But the canopy cover of fruit trees was only reduced from 7% to 1%. Some favoured fruit tree species, notably *Diospyros mespilliformis*, *Strychnos cocculoides* and *Azanza garkeana*, showed no reduction in cover when forested areas and cultivated areas were compared. Despite widespread deforestation for land clearance in one site, patterns of fruit use in two agricultural areas were similar because trees had been selectively

retained in cleared fields during woodland clearance (36).

In other settings, trees within farming systems have been enriched by planting. The complex multi-storey home garden systems found in Indonesia (104), Mexico (7), Tanzania (63), Kenya (110), tropical America *(165)* and elsewhere *(56;* 65; 101; 102) are examples of intensively managed multi-species systems. Within such gardens wild foods can be found occupying a diversity of ecological niches.

Wild fruit trees may be collected from forest areas and planted in agricultural land to enrich on-farm tree species. This has been recorded in many instances (89; 126; 132). The fruit producing potential of wild cultivars can also be upgraded by simple grafting and breeding techniques (115).

Home Gardens

Complex home gardens have been described in West Sumatra (104) and Java (102; 151a) in Indonesia. Here a range of annual and perennial crops are grown together, complementing the main rice crop derived from other fields. In Java, home gardens containing 500 species are found within a single village (102). There are several different types of garden, including the intensively managed home garden, the village/forest gardens and the forest fringe gardens. The importance of wild foods increases in gardens towards the forest fringe; these gardens resemble more closely the ecological conditions of the forest itself. In Western Sumatra a range wild foods including 22 fruits, 8 vegetables and spices and 3 fern species are protected and harvested in different garden types, while in migrant communities' gardens in Mexico some 338 species are found (7). Home gardens are also important as a site for experimentation with new varieties, domestication attempts and evaluation of different cropping rotations and patterns (128; 188; 243).

Weeds as Food

Trees are not the only component of the agricultural system that are potential sources of food. Along with the major crops planted by the farmer, a range of plant material can be found in agricultural fields that represent potential food (25; 70; 90; 111–113; 175; 703b). These wild foods (vegetables, tubers, grasses) may be potential competitors with the major crop, but whether they are weeds depends on the observer. To many agronomists anything but the major crop itself is regarded as a weed, and so the monocrop ideal (or at most, simple intercropping) is preached by agricultural extension workers throughout the world. Yet many plants deemed "weeds" may have a variety of uses to local people. To a woman attempting to find cheap and nutritious ingredients for relish, the wild food resource found in agricultural lands may be critical.

Many studies document the importance of wild vegetables in local diets; many of these are available from farmlands. A particularly extensive set of literature exists for east and southern Africa (e.g., 79; 86; 135; 143 for Zambia; 111–113 for Swaziland; 171; 172 for Zimbabwe; 98, 139 for Kenya; 90 for Tanzania; 50; 148; 149 for southern Sudan; 96 for Zaire). Most studies note that it is women who are primarily engaged in the collection and management of wild vegetables in Africa (139). Similar findings are re-

ported from elsewhere (876 for Assam; 152, 153 for SE Asia; 528 for Mexico).

Plants collected from fields may be either managed or simply left to grow. Four categories of weed have been identified in southern Sudan: self-sown species, wild species whose seeds are collected and scattered in the fields, those collected as they appear and those eaten only when under severe food shortage (148; 149).

Pests as Food

Arable lands also attract certain pest species. Rodents tend to be at a higher density in fields compared to surrounding areas *(51)*. The abundance of rodent species thus often changes with agricultural clearance (e.g., 57 for the New Guinea Highlands). Rodents of various sorts are an important source of

Balinese homegarden showing tremendous diversity of edible plants. (photo: C. Elevitch)

food in agricultural communities (317; 747). In Zimbabwe, roasted mice fetch a high premium as a snack food at beer parties (172). The African giant rat (*Cricetomys gambiani*) is also important in southern Nigeria (382; 286). Changes in bushmeat availability have occurred as a result of land clearance in West Africa with increasing rodent hunting possibilities, e.g., of the grasscutter rodent, *Thyrononmys swinderianus* (292).

Insects also represent an important dietary component in many agricultural societies (21; 54; 140; 547). Such insects may also be crop pests, but their role as supplementary food is well documented. For instance, termites are an important fat and protein supplement across southern Africa (97; 109; 172) and in southern Sudan (148; 149). Caterpillars (e.g., *Gonimbrasia belina*, the mopane worm) are also widely eaten and marketed (26; 106). In Zambia there is a wide range of edible insects in the diet (159). This has a seasonal dimension. The importance of caterpillars may rise to 40% of relish items in the period November to January *(159)*. Locust or cricket swarms can also provide important additions to local diets (45; 100; *155)*.

Hunting and Gathering

There are few groups who can sustain livelihoods solely on the basis of hunting and gathering from wild resources (19). Most "hunting and gathering" communities have some food inputs from arable agriculture or livestock, either from their own plots (48; 49; *65)* or through trade and exchange with farming communities *(55;* 212; 236).

Hunting and gathering is dependent on a diverse source of products that can offset seasonal and interannual variability in wild food production (11; 49; 67; 174). Alternatively a highly reliable and plentiful food source must be available. For instance, the !Kung San rely on mongongo (*Ricinodendron rautenenii*) as their major food source, with two to three days' supply gathered at any one time (20; 93; 94; 154; 415). Together with the hunting of a variety of wild animals and the collection of a range of wild plants, this is a highly labour and energy efficient survival strategy for the harsh environment of the Kalahari (92–94; *415)*. Similarly, in the past, Australian aborigines were able to collect a day's food from the bush in two to four hours (259; 260). In the Fertile Crescent of the Middle East, highly nutritious wild wheat and barley provided food for people before the origins of agriculture some 10,000 years ago

(134; 263; 279b, 264). With such an abundance of wild produce, the alternative investment of land, labour and capital into the domestication of plants and animals with settled agriculture and livestock keeping appears to make little sense.

Patterns of Use: Seasonality, Regulation and Sustainability Issues

Wild foods in agricultural systems often fit a particular seasonal niche. They may provide green vegetables early in the rainy season, or can be dried and stored for the dry season. They may also provide counter-seasonal food with fruit bearing in the dry season when little else is available. Wild foods may be particularly important in years when harvests fail (49; 170; 400a–d; 484; see 374–452).

Wild foods may only be available occasionally. For instance, insect outbreaks may only be sporadic (or cyclical) or mushroom fruiting dependent on particular (rare) conditions. Diets changed rapidly in a Sudanese village following locust swarms (45), and in Kenyan agricultural areas after rat outbreaks (157). However when such events do occur, as in extensive mushroom fruiting, labour may be diverted away from normal agricultural activities to collection and marketing (121 for southern Zaire; 123 for Zambia; 861 for northern Thailand; 146 for north India).

Collection and consumption of wild foods is often differentiated between socio-economic groups and gender (see 608–630). Women are primarily engaged in wild food management and harvesting, particularly of green vegetables (90; 113). Wild foods are also important nutritional supplements for children (139; 623 for Kenyan case material; 617 for forest edge communities in Sierra Leone; 125 for central Indian tribal areas). These may be eaten as snack foods or as main meals. The importance of wild foods is greatest amongst poorer households, where main field crops are often insufficient to provide food for the family for the whole year. In a dry miombo area of Zimbabwe poor households use fruits as the alternative to grain for a quarter of all dry season meals (172).

The use of wild products may be regulated by local rules and institutions (see 569–607). Large fruit trees in farmland are often protected (170 for Zimbabwe; 129 for West Africa) by local communities. Rights over wild products may change as land is cleared for agriculture. In Zimbabwe, fruit trees retained on farm plots effectively become individually owned by farmers during the cropping season, although they may revert to common property in the dry season (but still are protected from cutting by community rules). In other settings all products are privatised by the process of conversion of land to agriculture, reducing the access of those without control over land. Recently, Malawian farmers have sold the rights to the collection of wild resources to Mozambican refugees (171).

Few studies, however, have addressed the degree of dependency on these food sources or their economic value as part of agroecosystems and peoples' livelihoods (see 631–702b). As a consequence, it is difficult to assess the impact of patterns of land-use and land tenure change on different groups of people.

The sustainability of wild food use has also received relatively little attention in the literature. Sustainable harvesting levels for different plant and animal populations remain largely unknown. A number of studies report that wild foods are diminishing with the clearance of forest areas (e.g., 152 for NE Thailand; 90; 400a for Tanzania) or the heavy harvesting of wild animals (108; 284; *353).* The consequences of agricultural intensification on wild food production are also poorly studied (152).

Unlike large game animals (342), small animals, especially rodents, may be heavily harvested without affecting the viability of the population (170; 353).

Insects for sale at Thai market. (photo: C. Elevitch)

They are also less susceptible to changes in agricultural land-use and agronomic practice. Indeed rodent populations increase with arable land expansion (292). The same applies to weedy plant species which quickly regenerate following collection and can survive in ephemeral environments on field edges or degraded lands (170; 172; 628). This is in contrast to many fruit tree species which are less resilient to agroecological change, as they may take many years to regrow to maturity.

The study of wild foods in agricultural systems requires an interdisciplinary approach that can examine the role of wild foods in the context of local people's livelihoods.

References

Due to the extremely large number of references cited in this article (well over 200), the reader is referred to the original source for cited literature. The citation numbers in the text correspond to the numbers in the bibliography of the original source. See below for information about where to purchase the book.

Original Source

This article is excerpted with the generous permission of the publisher and authors from:

Scoones, I., M. Melnyk and J. Pretty. 1992. The Hidden Harvest: Wild Foods and Agricultural Systems, A Literature Review and Annotated Bibliography. IIED, London.

To order this publication online, visit: http://www.iied.org/sarl/pubs/hidharvest.html or contact:

EARTHPRINT Ltd.
P.O. Box 119
Stevenage
Hertfordshire SG1 4TP
England
Tel: +44 1438 748 111; Fax: +44 1438 748 844
Email: customerservices@earthprint.com

This excerpt was originally published as *The Overstory* #128.

Underutilised Indigenous Fruit Trees

Angela Hughes and Nazmul Haq

The term underutilised indigenous fruit trees (UIFT) refers to fruit bearing trees that are not highly researched and which are generally ignored by the commercial sector. Little research has been carried out on these species and information documented about their basic biology, growing habits, management practices, processing and utilisation is scant and scattered. Research is often carried out by isolated groups with their findings restricted to academic journals, and dissemination of information to a wider audience is poor.

Nevertheless, UIFT are an important source of food and nutrition, and contribute to the income of rural and urban people through the marketing of their products. They are grown mainly in home gardens and small farms and resource poor people, particularly tribal people, also gather wild fruits from the forests and other noncultivated areas for their multi-purpose uses. Women often play a major role in the gathering of UIFT (Ruiz Pérez et al 1997) and are frequently involved in decisions about the sale of the fruits and their products. The extra income from the fruits is often spent on education, nutrition and health, and controlled by the women who gain greater respect from their families and communities through these activities.

Fruit trees also play a vital role in crop diversification programmes and agroforestry systems. Their inclusion in production systems reduces the risks inherent to monocultures of staple food crops such as susceptibility to pests and diseases, soil nutrient depletion, price fluctuations, and reliance on a single crop for income. It has been reported in countries such as China, Nepal and the Philippines (Shakaya 2002; Castillo 2002), that farmer income from indigenous fruits is much higher than from traditional agricultural crops.

Why Promote Indigenous Fruit Trees?

Of a diverse range of tropical fruit tree species, many are only known regionally. They are a valuable source of vitamins, minerals and antioxidants and make an important contribution to the diet of poor families. Fruit trees are a valuable family asset. In addition to their fruit, they are important sources of timber, fodder and fuel, and many have medicinal and industrial uses. Organised collection of these fruits and products from forest trees can create employment, particularly for the landless poor. The reason for this is that small-scale food processing responds to local needs, builds on local knowledge and skills, and uses local resources. However, researchers, policy makers and commercial enterprises and the international community have just started to recognise their value because of the relation with non-timber forest products (NTFP).

Fruit trees provide environmental benefits by protecting the soil and generating leaf litter. This decreases the runoff from the soil surface, preventing erosion, maintaining a stable, moist surface and improving the physical properties of the soil. Tree roots can also loosen the topsoil by radial growth and improve the porosity in the subsoil (Sanchez and Leakey 1997). Fruit trees, particularly UIFT, can establish on poor soils and improve the productivity of the soil. They are suited to marginal and wastelands, and can resist harsh conditions such as moisture stress and salinity. In addition, farmers can obtain a decent crop from trees growing in areas where other crops would not survive.

Constraints for Sustainable Production, Processing and Marketing

Effective development and utilisation of UIFT requires the identification of the constraints and the implementation of actions to overcome these constraints. The constraints listed below have been identified through participatory research work and regional workshops implemented by various organisations on UIFT (Haq and Hoque 2000; UT-FANET 2003), but refer mainly to practical issues relating to fruit tree development.

Lack of quality planting material

Good quality planting material provides farmers with better trees, tastier fruits and higher yields. Improved varieties may also be adapted to local climate, topography and farming systems providing specific benefits for farmers in different regions.

Lack of standardised propagation and production technology

Standardised propagation and production technology is important in the development of high quality products. This can be highlighted by using mangosteen as an example, the fruit of which is very desirable with some demand in local, national and international markets (Dassanayake 1996). However, because of production constraints, demand exceeds supply. Mangosteen has a long maturation period, is slow growing and is susceptible to drought due to its shallow root system. A disorder referred to as "Gamboge disease" leads to its poor marketability due to a yellowish exudate on the fruit skin and inside the fruit (Dassanayake 1996). The presence of exudate has been linked to physical stress of the trees such as fertiliser deficiency or drought (Dassanayake 1996). Research trials with fertigation methods are underway in Thailand and the Philippines (UTFANET) (Rondolo 2002) and may have implications in the prevention of Gamboge disease through the improved growing conditions. Studies indicate that fruit yields are increased and the cost of fertiliser on a per ha basis was reduced by almost 16% (Lertrat 2001).

Mangosteen is an apomictic species, usually propagated by seed. Traditional breeding methods are difficult and although progress has been made with vegetative propagation (UTFANET 2003) it has thus far been slow. Multiplication methods and production technologies have not yet been fully developed for many UIFT.

Fruit ripening period

Narrow fruiting periods result in the simultaneous ripening of all fruits, causing an oversupply in the market and lowering of the prices, followed by a relative fruit scarcity with high prices. Tamarind for example, sometimes exhibits cyclic yields with a bumper harvest every 2–3 years (Jambulingam and Fernandes 1986). Mangosteen also exhibits uneven and unreliable bearing (Dassanayake 1996). This causes a particular problem for farmers as they often have to wait for traders before harvesting. Uneven

and unreliable harvests can result in losses throughout the market chain. This also presents a problem for exporters as the supply of fruits is not continuous (Dassanayake 1996).

Lack of information

Access to information is lacking throughout the production to consumption pathway. Areas of particular concern are:

- Production technology and propagation methods – propagation by seed is the most commonly used method throughout rural Asia, however grafted plants provide far better trees.
- Appropriate processing technologies—often small-scale processors are unaware of the technologies that may be appropriate to their needs, despite the fact that the technologies are being widely used elsewhere.
- Marketing information and economics – is essential in the successful commercialisation of fruit tree species.

The demand for information comes from a variety of groups and organisations including NGOs, CBOs, and from participatory research and survey reports carried out in countries in Asia including Bangladesh, India, Nepal, Pakistan, Philippines and Sri Lanka (UTFANET 2003, Azam-Ali unpublished). Farmers, small-scale entrepreneurs, businesses and research institutions have all expressed a need for access to current information on aspects of the production to consumption pathway (Haq and Hughes 2002). Evidence of this is also reflected through participatory research and regional meetings in Africa (Haq and Atkinson 1999) and Latin America (UNICACH 1999). The particular challenge here is to develop information that can be effective in a country with high levels of illiteracy (Azami 2002).

Lack of standardised processing and postharvest technologies

Processing and marketing strategies and consumer requirements are different. In addition, quality control standards and certification schemes for many UIFT are lacking, however such controls may improve the products available in the market (NRI 2000). Better utilisation of these fruits can provide a number of opportunities to raise household income.

Local market structures are poor or lacking

In the past, a large majority of the consumption of forest produce has taken place through non-market channels and subsistence use, which goes some way to explaining the poor marketing channels for UIFT. Marketing pathways remain poorly organised for these fruits in many countries throughout Asia and indeed globally. Lack of infrastructure and transport systems also lead to damaged fruits and high wastage. In Nepal, for example, annual fruit production is 46,492 MT with over 55 different species under production; however 30–40% of the demand of the urban population is still met by imports due to the lack of roads to transport local produce (Shakaya 2002).

Some small entrepreneurs do not have structured ideas about business practices, including how to market their produce, which is low quality (Haq 2000a) and fetches a low price (Vinning and Moody 1997). But the issues involved in capacity building that are sustained over time are not simply a matter of technical know-how. It is also about understanding the processes whereby change in farming and marketing practices occur, how people can feel they "own" these changes and how they can be sustained in the long-term.

Lack of access to credit

The majority of small scale farmers and processors, especially women, face a variety of problems when seeking credit, including lack of information, high interest rates, lack of collateral, bureaucratic, and prejudice against women and small scale farmers and processors (Azami 2002).

Lack of national policy

Although many farmers are interested in UIFT, the inclusion of such species in the national agricultural research programmes in developing countries is limited. According to Williams and Haq (2002), only eight developing countries worldwide have national programmes on underutilised species, including UIFT. Four of these countries are in Asia, with only India having a clear list of priority species.

Conclusion

Strategy development for UIFT is limited due, in part, to lack of government support and also lack of information and documentation on the constraints mentioned above. Attention has been focused on the need to conserve and better use the botanical diversity in traditional agroecosystems and natural forest systems, but support at the national, regional and in-

ternational level has been limited. The socio-economics and well-being of the farmers and communities needs to be taken into account, and agricultural policy linked to forestry and export policy, which currently provides huge incentives for the local people to cut down indigenous species for veneer and timber production stimulated by the demand in the furniture industry (Williams and Haq 2002).

References

Azam-Ali, S. (Unpublished) Assessment of the current status of post harvest handling, processing and marketing of underutilised tropical fruits in Bangladesh, India, Nepal, Sri Lanka and Vietnam. Report, Fruits for the Future Project, ICUC.

Azami, S. 2002. Use of information for promotion of underutilised fruit trees. In Haq, N. and Hughes, A. (Eds) Fruits for the Future in Asia. Proceedings for the Consultation meeting on the Processing and marketing of underutilised tropical fruits in Asia. International Centre of Underutilised Crops, Southampton, UK. Pp 81–84.

Castillo, R. 2002. Current industry situation of underutilised crops in the Philippines. In Hag, N. and Hughes, A. (Eds) Fruits for the Future in Asia. Proceedings for the Consultation meeting on the Processing and marketing of underutilised tropical fruits in Asia. International Centre of Underutilised Crops, Southampton, UK. Pp 191–198.

Dassanayake, E.M. 1996. Information gathering in plant genetic resources, propagation and production, postharvest, socio-economic and marketing of mangosteen. UTFA-NET Report.

Haq, N. 2000a. Report on Evaluation of Fruit Trees in Homesteads of Bangladesh and their possible marketing opportunities. DFID-SHABJE Project. CARE Bangladesh.

Haq, N. and Atkinson, M. 1999. Tropical and subtropical fruits of West Africa. Proceedings of the 1st regional meeting held in Accra on 15th–16th October 1998. International Centre for Underutilised crops, Southampton, UK. 146 pp.

Haq, N. and Hoque, A. 2000. Research needs and assessment for fruit production and improvement. Final Report, SHABGE–DFID Project, CARE Bangladesh.

Haq, N. and Hughes, A. (Eds) 2002. Fruits for the Future in Asia. Proceedings for the Consultation meeting on the Processing and marketing of underutilised tropical fruits in Asia. International Centre of Underutilised Crops, Southampton, UK. 236 pp.

Jambulingam, R. and Fernandes, E.C.M. 1986. Multipurpose trees and shrubs in Tamil Nadu State, India. Agroforestry Systems, 4(1): 17–32.

Lertrat, P. 2001. Fertigation research on mangosteen in Thailand. Global newsletter on Underutilised Crops. International Centre for Underutilised Crops, Southampton, UK. (June). Pp16–18.

Natural Resource Institute. 2000. Labour standards and social codes of conduct: what do they mean for the forest industry? Ethical Trade Policy Watching Brief 3. Natural Resources and Ethical Trade Programme, Ethical Trade and Forest Dependent People Project. Kent.

Rondolo, M. 2002. ICUC-UTFANET and its role in Asia. In Haq, N. and Hughes, A. (Eds) Fruits for the Future in Asia. Proceedings for the Consultation meeting on the Processing and marketing of underutilised tropical fruits in 180 A. Hughes and N. Haq Asia. International Centre of Underutilised Crops, Southampton, UK. Pp 29–40.

Ruiz Perez, M., Broekhoven, A.J., Aluma, J.R.W., Iddi, S., Lowroe, J.D., Mutemwa, S.M. and Odera, J.A. 1997. Research on non-timber forest products in selected countries in southern and East Africa: themes, research issues, priorities and constraints. CIFOR Working Paper No. 15. 21pp.

Sanchez, P.A. and Leakey, R.R.B. 1997. Land use transformation in Africa: three determinants for balancing food security with natural resource utilisation. European Journal of Agronomy, 7: 15–23.

Shakaya, D.B. 2002. Status report of processing and marketing of underutilised fruits in Nepal. In Haq, N. and Hughes, A. (Eds) Fruits for the Future in Asia. Proceedings for the Consultation meeting on the Processing and marketing of underutilised tropical fruits in Asia. International Centre of Underutilised Crops, Southampton, UK. Pp 156–181.

UNICACH. 1999. Proceedings of 2nd International Congress on Annonaceae. Universidad de Ciencias y Artes del Estado de Chiapas, Tuxtla Gutiérrez, México, 26th–28th October 1999. 278 pp.

UTFANET 2003. UTFANET Report. Scientist Meeting, April 2003, Hanoi, Vietnam.

Williams, J.T. and Haq, N. 2002. Global research on underutilised crops. An assessment of current activities and proposals for enhanced cooperation. International Centre for Underutilised Crops, Southampton, UK. 46 pp.

Vinning, G. and Moody, T. 1997. A market compendium of tropical fruit. Rural Industries Research and Development Corporation No. 97/74. Canberra, Australia. 275 pp.

Original Source

This excerpt was reprinted with the kind permission of the authors and publisher from:

Hughes, A. and N. Haq. 2003. Promotion of indigenous fruit trees through improved processing and marketing in Asia. International Forestry Review 5(2): 176–181.

Publisher contact information:
Alan Pottinger
International Forestry Review
2 Webbs Barn Cottage, Witney Road
Kingston Bagpuize
Abingdon, Oxon OX13 5AN
United Kingdom
Email: alan.pottinger@cfa-international.org
Tel: +44 (0) 1865 820935
Fax: +44 (0) 1865 820935
Web: http://www.cfa-international.org/IFR.html

This excerpt was originally published as *The Overstory* #136.

Forest Biodiversity

Jeffrey A. McNeely

In seeking to apply ecosystem approaches to forest biodiversity, especially forests that are being influenced by increasing levels of use by people, it is helpful to focus on some key questions. First, are people part of forest ecosystems? Second, what are the impacts of human harvesting on forest ecosystems? Third, how can forest ecosystems be managed so that they provide both the goods and the services that are required by modern society? This article briefly explores these key issues, and indicates appropriate lines of action to be taken in future.

It is now widely accepted that biodiversity is the measure of biological variety at many scales, from the gene to the ecosystem. Much attention has been given to diversity of species within forests, especially trees that are being harvested. The challenge is to see the forest for the trees: How can the idea of biodiversity at the ecosystem level be translated into practical action for better management of forest ecosystems?

The definition of "ecosystem" is reasonably well agreed. For example, the Convention on Biological Diversity (CBD) defines the term as "a dynamic complex of plant, animal and micro-organism communities and their non-living environment interacting as a functional unit." The living components of an ecosystem interact in very complex food webs (Schoener, 1989). Ecosystem approaches to forest management take into consideration the complexity of these interactions and seek both to maintain the productivity of forest ecosystems and to enhance their capacity to adapt to change.

Focusing on the ecosystem level provides a strong basis for solving critical problems in resource management. For example, conserving forest biodiversity at the ecosystem level helps to support services such as maintaining the balance of atmospheric gases, recycling nutrients, regulating climate, maintaining hydrological cycles and creating soil (Daily, 1997). While scientists are still developing their understanding of the relationships among taxonomic diversity, productivity, stability and adaptability of ecosystems, new research indicates that species diversity enhances the productive capacity of many forest ecosystems and their ability to adapt to changing conditions (Johnson et al 1996).

Another important implication of considering forest biodiversity at the ecosystem level is the potential of mismanagement leading to the essentially permanent transformation of a highly productive forest into a much less productive system (such as a grassland). Recent research has indicated that even gradual changes in climate, the flow of nutrients, extraction of natural resources and habitat fragmentation can lead to sudden drastic switches in the character of a forest ecosystem (Scheffer et al 2001). While many different factors can lead to such shifts, a critical factor is a loss of resilience (the ability to recover from external events) through declining biodiversity at the ecosystem level.

Are People Part of Forest Ecosystems?

The ecological literature is replete with terms such as "primary forest", "undisturbed forest" and even "primeval forest." But a growing body of evidence indicates that virtually all forests on the planet have been substantially influenced by humans, most for at least several thousand years. Studies by foresters, ecologists, historians and anthropologists on forests in tropical, temperate and boreal regions conclude that forests and people have evolved together over thousands of years, with people planting the trees they prefer, using fire to burn forests to improve hunting conditions, and managing forest fallows to maintain their agricultural fields. Forests are part of the human landscape, and the biodiversity found in today's forests has been profoundly influenced by people.

For example, the vast boreal forest-covered wilderness of northern North America is often considered to be natural. But people have occupied this forest from its very beginnings, as the great ice sheets withdrew northwards at the end of the Pleistocene era. New studies have established that native Americans in northern Alberta, Canada, regularly and systematically burned habitats to influence the local distribution and relative abundance of plant and animal resources. This pyrotechnology is similar to that reported for hunter-gatherers elsewhere in the world, which created an overall fire mosaic that characterizes the northern boreal forests (Lewis and Ferguson, 1988). Hunter-gatherers elsewhere in North America and in several parts of Australia also employed habitat fires, specifically in the maintenance of "fireyards" and "fire corridors" in widely separated and different kinds of biological zones.

Further south, Gomez-Pompa and Kaus (1992) found that many of the tree species now dominant in the mature vegetation of tropical America are the same species protected, spared or planted when the land was cleared for crops as part of the ancient practice of shifting agriculture. They contend that the current composition of mature vegetation is the legacy of past civilizations, the heritage of cultivated fields and managed forests abandoned hundreds of years ago.

Numerous other examples can be cited from Amazonia (Roosevelt, 1994), Central Africa (Fairhead and Leach, 1998), Europe (Delacourt, 1987) and tropical Asia (Spencer, 1966), but the conclusion is clear: While forest ecosystems are "natural", humans are an essential part of this "nature." Hence building resilience into forest ecosystems requires building resilience into the human management systems, enabling them to adapt to changing conditions.

What Are the Human Impacts on Forest Ecosystems?

While the human impact on forest ecosystems has been profound throughout history, only in the past few decades has the human influence spread comprehensively and simultaneously in virtually all forests. By far the greatest impact has been in forest clearing, both to create new agricultural lands and to harvest valuable timber. A review of a wide range of studies on the impacts of logging practices on tropical forest ecosystems and biodiversity (Johns, 1997) indicated that logging of mature forest commonly leads to a local increase in species diversity as structural and associated microclimatic changes create patches of habitat and food resources attractive to species that typically live in secondary forest and on forest edges. However, populations of many species that typically live in the forest understorey markedly decline and remain locally low or absent for many years. Johns (1997) concludes that the most appropriate way to manage tropical forests for producing

timber, without losing other values, is to have small undisturbed forest areas preserved within a larger matrix of production forest, a prescription that is being attempted in some parts of Malaysia. On the other hand, commercial loggers have been notably reluctant to adopt sustainable forestry practices because they earn greater short-term profits when they externalize more of the costs, such as conservation of biodiversity.

In tropical forests, the large canopy and emergent trees that are most attractive to loggers are critically important sources of food (fruits and flowers) and shelter for animal populations. They are reproductively dominant and strongly influence forest structure, composition, gap dynamics, hydrology and biodiversity. Forest fragmentation in central Amazonia is having a disproportionately severe effect on large trees, the loss of which will have major impacts on forest ecosystems (Laurence, 1999). Mortality of trees, and especially of large trees, is highest near forest edges. This has significant implications for conserving rain forest ecosystems and the biodiversity they contain. The rapid rate of mortality of large trees may reduce the fecundity of canopy and emergent species, diminish forest volume and structural complexity, promote the proliferation of short-lived pioneer species and alter biogeochemical cycles affecting evapotranspiration, carbon cycling and greenhouse-gas emissions—key ecosystem services.

The problem is not simply the result of harvesting trees that support other species. In the Congo, roads established and maintained by logging concessions intensify bushmeat hunting by providing hunters greater access to relatively unexploited populations of forest wildlife and by lowering the costs of transporting bushmeat to market (Wilke *et al* 2000). The trade in bushmeat is now reducing many species to mere remnants in many parts of the African forest zone. Reconciling the contrary effects of roads on economic development and biodiversity conservation is one of the key challenges to ecosystem managers in all nations. Failing to address this problem could lead to forest ecosystems that are virtually empty of wildlife populations that play essential roles in pollination, seed dispersal and nutrient cycling (Redford, 1992). This is no trivial matter; about 70 percent of the trees in the Atlantic forest of Brazil have seeds that are dispersed by vertebrates, mostly birds and mammals (Cardoso Da Silva and Tabarelli, 2000). Where key vertebrate dispersers have been eliminated, seed flow of tree species through the landscape is very limited, and the large fruit-producing species are being replaced by others that may be less useful. Such processes can lead to profound, and unpredictable, changes at the ecosystem level (Scheffer *et al* 2001).

Deforestation is widely recognized as a major conservation issue, but the related issue of habitat fragmentation receives insufficient attention. In the Brazilian Amazon alone, the area of forest that is fragmented (with forests less than 10 000 ha in area) or prone to edge effects (less than one kilometre from clearings) is over 150 percent greater than the area that is deforested. A similar pattern is found throughout the tropics, so the fate of the world's tropical forest ecosystems is greatly affected by the capacity of their various species to survive in fragmented landscapes. Small fragments have very different ecosystem characteristics than larger areas of forest, supporting more light-loving species, more trees with wind- or water-dispersed seeds or fruits and relatively few understorey species (Laurence, 1999). As mammals and birds that disperse fruits disappear from these habitats, trees with fruits dispersed by them decline. The smaller fragments also have a greater density of tree falls, a more irregular canopy, more weedy species and unusually abundant vines, lianas and bamboos; thus they conserve only a subset of the original flora, and the fauna that is adapted to these species.

As human impacts on forests continue to increase, areas that were once continuous forest with sporadic clearings become agricultural landscapes with sporadic forests. This leads to a significant decline in population for at least some species of forest birds because fragmentation reduces nesting success, and thereby the number of offspring that can be produced. One recent study found that the reproduction rates were so low for some species in the most fragmented landscapes that their populations had to depend on immigration from other populations from habitats that had more extensive forest cover (Askins, 1995). Conservation strategies need to ensure the preservation and restoration of large, unfragmented forest habitats in each region (Robinson *et al* 1995; Askins, 1995) and to support greater efforts to build linkages between ecosystems at the landscape level (Bennett and Wit, 2001).

How Can Forests Be Managed As Ecosystems?

Ecosystem approaches to conserving forest biodiversity should recognize that all environmental policy is best considered as the testing of a hypothesis, where proposed management actions are expected to target precise objectives and lead to predicted results. In this sense, ecosystem management is always an experiment, always an exercise in learning from experience. An essential element to feed learning back into ecosystem management is monitoring, which provides the information basis for modifying management actions in light of experience. Many ecological networks have now been established, indicating how such monitoring and feedback systems can function in a wide range of forest ecosystems (Bennett and Wit, 2001). An important aspect will therefore be to define the management objective as precisely as possible, taking into account the information available.

In seeking to manage forest ecosystems, it is important to keep in mind that resource managers are dealing with systems that are dynamic at many scales, ranging from individual leaves up to very large landscapes (Holling, 1992). The natural range of variability at each of these scales is often very wide, and it is not yet possible to predict how changes in the patterns and processes at any given scale are likely to affect processes at other scales. Deciding the extent and level of appropriate human impacts on such constantly changing systems is challenging in the face of limited knowledge. But new tools and techniques, such as remote-sensing imagery, simulation modelling, geographic information systems, and the increased capacity of data processing can help enrich understanding of the dynamism of forest ecosystems, and thus help enhance human capacity to adapt to changing conditions. Considering forest biodiversity at the ecosystem level helps to reinforce this perspective.

What Can Be Done to Conserve Forest Biodiversity at the Ecosystem Level?

While this question remains a challenging one for resource managers, some general directions already seem apparent.

- Protect large areas of forest rather than small ones where possible.
- Rebuild connectivity among small adjacent protected areas by including intervening habitat and promoting reforestation of the landscape.
- Protect forest edges against structural damage, damage by fire and colonization by exotics, by leaving a natural buffer zone of forest that could be managed to resemble a natural ecotone (a boundary or transition zone between adjacent communities) rather than an abrupt edge.
- Minimize the harshness of the adjacent matrix by diversifying and promoting less intensive types of land use around forests, controlling the use of fire in ecosystems that are not fire climaxes (plant communities whose succession is maintained by periodic fires), minimizing the application of toxic chemicals and controlling the introduction of potentially invasive alien plant species. This approach is well illustrated by the proposed large-scale biodiversity corridors in Meso-America, Amazonia (Gascon, Williamson and da Fonseca, 2000) and elsewhere. The general aim is to apply the principles that enable forests to function as ecosystems to the practice of forest management, for example by ensuring natural regeneration, using low-impact logging that does not disrupt soils and avoiding excessive fragmentation.

Given that people are part of forest ecosystems, involving local communities may be an important way to help resolve conflicting interests between local people and forest departments and may help contribute to conservation objectives. For example, in Nepal, management of village forests by local forest user groups has created a strong feeling of ownership and helped improve forest management practices. Local men and women, including poorer members of the village, are involved in activities like thinning, pruning, fire control surveillance and harvesting. As a result of their efforts, species composition of flora and fauna, crown coverage, habitat and micro-habitat of invertebrates, mosses, fungi and lichens are all improved, with positive impacts on the forest ecosystems. The community forests are providing ecological stability and the forest user groups are becoming more sensitive to conservation objectives. In at least some forests, wildlife populations have increased along with species diversity (aus der Beek, Rai and Shuler, 1997).

While local and indigenous people are as tempted as anyone else to overexploit forest resources for short-term gains, some have instituted their own ecosystem management measures. For example, the Emberà, a group living in the forests on the Colombia-Venezuela border, reserve large areas in upper watersheds and along the spines of mountain chains as areas protected by spirits; the areas that benefit from this protection are remarkably similar to those typically set aside as protected areas by modern governments. These large areas of old-growth forest provide refuges for the reproduction of wildlife resources and protection of watersheds. The Emberà maintain ecological stability through a range of techniques that have parallels in many other parts of the world, both North and South: local technology; protection of important sites; appropriate settlement patterns; flexible social rules; egalitarian social structure; religious commitment; and a strong tradition of self-interested management of forest resources (Harp, 1994).

Faith in local communities as forest ecosystem managers needs to be balanced with recognition that forests achieve numerous national objectives, including meeting needs for timber and fuelwood, retaining options for future economic use, addressing ethical and aesthetic values and providing global benefits such as biodiversity conservation. Thus simply ensuring local management of forest resources may not always lead to socially optimal levels of biodiversity conservation. Instead, the larger society must mobilize additional resources and approaches to support a socially desirable level of conservation effort, appropriate for its ecological, social, historical and political setting. As in every other field, management means setting objectives and making the trade-offs necessary to achieve them.

References

Askins, R.A. 1995. Hostile landscapes and the decline of migratory songbirds. Science, 267: 1956–1957.

aus der Beek, R., Rai, C. & Schuler, K. 1997. Community forestry and biodiversity: experiences from Dolakha and Ramechhap Districts (Nepal). Kathmandu, Nepal, Nepal-Swiss Community Forestry Project (NSCFP).

Bennett, G. & Wit, P. 2001. The development and application of ecological networks. Gland, Switzerland, AIDEnvironment and World Conservation Union (IUCN).

Cardoso Da Silva, J.M. & Tabarelli, M. 2000. Tree species impoverishment and the future flora of the Atlantic forest of north east Brazil. Nature, 404: 72–75.

Daily, G.C., ed. 1997. Nature's services: societal dependence on natural ecosystems. Washington, DC, USA, Island Press.

Delacourt, H.R. 1987. The impact of prehistoric agriculture and land occupation on natural vegetation. Trends in Ecology and Evolution, 2(2): 39–44.

Fairhead, J. & Leach, M. 1998. Reframing deforestation: global analyses and local realities—studies in West Africa. London, UK, Routledge.

Gascon, C., Williamson, G. & da Fonseca, G. 2000. Receding forest edges and vanishing reserves. Science, 288: 1356–1358.

Gomez-Pompa, A. & Kaus, A. 1992. Taming the wilderness myth. BioScience, 42(4): 271–279.

Harp, W. 1994. Ecology and cosmology: rainforest exploitation among the Emberà-Chocò. Nature and Resources, 30(1): 23–27.

Holling, C.S. 1992. Cross-scale morphology, geometry, and dynamics of ecosystems. Ecological Monographs, 62(4): 447–502.

Johns, A.G. 1997. Timber production and biodiversity conservation in tropical rainforests. Cambridge, UK, Cambridge University Press.

Johnson, K.H., Vogt, K.A., Clark, H.J., Schmitz, O.J. & Vogt, D.J. 1996. Biodiversity and the productivity and stability of ecosystems. Trends in Ecology and Evolution, 11(9): 372–377.

Laurence, W.F. 1999. Habitat fragmentation: introduction and synthesis. Biological Conservation, 91: 101–107.

Lewis, H.T. & Ferguson, T.A. 1988. Yards, corridors and mosaics: how to burn a boreal forest. Human Ecology, 16: 57–78.

Redford, K.H. 1992. The empty forest. BioScience, 42(6): 412–422.

Robinson, S.K., Thompson, F.R. III, Donavin, T.M., Whitehead, D.R. & Faaborg, J. 1995. Regional forest fragmentation and the nesting success of migratory birds. Science, 267: 1987–1990.

Roosevelt, A. 1994. Amazonian anthropology: strategy for a new synthesis. In A. Roosevelt, ed. Amazonian Indians: from prehistory to the present, p. 1–29. Tucson, Arizona, USA, University of Arizona Press.

Scheffer, M., Carpenter, S.R., Foley, J.A., Folke, C. & Walker, B. 2001. Catastrophic shifts in ecosystems. Nature, 413: 591–596.

Schoener, T.W. 1989. Food webs from the small to the large. Ecology, 70(6): 1559–1589.

Spencer, J.E. 1966. Shifting cultivation in Southeast Asia. Berkeley, California, USA, University of California Press.

Wilke, D., Shaw, E., Rotberg, F., Morelli, G. & Auzel, P. 2000. Roads, development, and conservation in the Congo Basin. Conservation Biology, 14(6): 1614–1622.

Williams, M. 1989. Americans and their forests: a historical geography. Cambridge, UK, Cambridge University Press.

Original Source

This article is excerpted with the generous permission of the publisher and author from:

McNeely, J.A. 2002. Forest biodiversity at the ecosystem level: where do people fit in? Unasylva 209, Vol. 53- 2002/2. FAO, Rome.

Web: http://www.fao.org/DOCREP/004/Y3582E/y 3582e00.htm

This excerpt was originally published as *The Overstory* #113.

Native eucalyptus forest, New South Wales, Australia. (photo: C. Elevitch)

Small and Unseen Allies

The air, soil, and water on Earth are infused with microscopic life forms. Soil is alive with a vast network of microorganisms vital for healthy plants and viable ecosystems.

Section Contents

Microlife

Kim M. Wilkinson and Craig R. Elevitch

Microorganisms permeate the soil, water, and air of our planet. They existed for billions of years before any plants or animals existed, and continue to be the most abundant form of life on Earth. Microorganisms created the atmosphere, turned bare rock and lava into soil, made possible the eventual evolution of larger life-forms, and continue to dominate the lives and functions of all living plants and animals. They are of key importance to every ecological process happening on the planet.

Microlife plays a role in all aspects of life cycles

The general public normally only hears about microorganisms in terms of viruses or harmful bacteria, to be battled with soap, disinfectants, and other weapons in our modern arsenal. However, in general the functions of most microorganisms are benign or very much to our benefit, and to destroy them would be to destroy ourselves. The human body, for example, is teeming with microlife—about 10% of the average human's body weight is made up of microorganisms! Each square centimeter human skin hosts an average of 100,000 bacteria, maintaining the health of the skin, and countless millions occupy our intestines. Our vital abilities to breathe and digest food are all intricately linked to the microorganisms that reside within us and make our life possible. As the biologist Lynn Margulis said, "Beneath our superficial differences we are all of us walking communities of bacteria." The web of life depends on this vast network of microorganisms.

For agriculturalists, the greatest interest in microlife is in the complex communities of microorganisms that are part of the soil. One gram (the same weight as a small paperclip) of healthy soil can contain between one and ten billion microorganisms. If the microbes underground were spread over the land surface of Earth, they would make a layer 5 feet thick. Next time you see cows or sheep raised in a pasture, remember that the invisible soil microorganisms on that same piece of land can outweigh the livestock per hectare (2.4 acres) by factors of 10–100 times!

For the past century, the trend in university research and in modern farmer's practice has been to focus on the physical and mechanical properties of soil, and only recently has the living component gained recognition for its central role in land productivity and plant health. Communities of bacteria, fungi, algae, protozoa, and other microorganisms aerate the soil, make nutrients available to plants, create water and air channels, maintain soil structure, and recycle nutrients and organic matter that allow vegetation to grow. Every chemical transformation that happens in soil involves microorganisms. Some microorganisms excrete enzymes and other growth substances that stimulate plant feeding. Microorganisms provide a living reserve of nutrients like nitrogen and sulfur that would otherwise be easily leached. A healthy population of soil microorganisms can also maintain ecological balance, preventing the onset of major problems from the viruses or other pathogens that live in the soil.

Introduction to a Few Soil Microorganisms

Thousands of species of microorganisms have been recognized and named, but the number of unknown species is estimated to be in the millions. Almost every time microbiologists search in a soil sample, they discover a previously unknown species. A few that are known to be of benefit to agriculture and forestry are listed below, as examples.

Mycorrhizae a fungi that associates with the roots of many kinds of plants, acting as a conduit for soil nutrients. Many scientists believe it was tree's association with this fungi that enabled them to colonize large tracts of land, giving rise to the forests. Widely used in forestry (see Mycorrhizae, page 66)

Rhizobia bacteria that live in nodules on the roots of nitrogen-fixing plants, gathering the atmospheric nitrogen for plants like legumes (see Biological Nitrogen Fixation, page 81)

Actinobacteria a kind of bacteria whose members break down the difficult-to-digest cellulose of trees on forest floors. Some kinds of actinobacteria, like *Frankia*, can also fix atmospheric nitrogen and can form nitrogen-fixing nodules with non-leguminous plants like alder trees.

Cyanobacteria (blue-green algae) These tiny entities can photosynthesize, and some 100 strains of cyanobacteria are also able to fix nitrogen from the air. This enables them to colonize and thrive on barren areas, such as immediately following a lava flow—or even a nuclear blast! They are important in the early stages of pioneering harsh conditions. Some forms of cyanobacteria have also been used traditionally in rice agriculture, to fix nitrogen for rice crops

Slime molds colonies of microorganisms that help decompose and recycle organic matter in forest soils

Lichens symbiotic beings that are combinations of fungi and algae, lichens can break down solid rock, releasing phosphates and nitrates, which generates food for plant's roots.

Other fungi, bacteria, yeasts, algae, protozoans, and many, many more play crucial roles in maintaining the health and integrity of the soil, and the productivity of the land.

Improving Productivity of Land with Microorganisms

Often in dealing with land that has been cleared of natural vegetation and depleted of microlife, people have tried to improve productivity by adding soluble fertilizers. However, given the increasing recognition of the role of microorganisms, the way the future may focus on fostering and, when necessary, reintroducing healthy populations of microlife in the soil to enhance productivity. The use of mycorrhizal fungi and rhizobia inoculants has become almost standard in forestry and agriculture. Other ways to increase productivity with microlife are being researched and practiced worldwide. These techniques range from simply bringing in small amounts of healthy soil to inoculate new plantings in degraded areas, to the manufacture and application of special biostimulants to feed and encourage microlife, or to

introducing blends of selected beneficial microorganisms to be used in nursery or field production.

Ways to foster microlife

The daily activities of farmers and foresters can help in maintaining and improving healthy populations of soil microorganisms, and therefore improving the productivity of the land. The use of mulch and organic matter is vital for healthy soil life, providing the moist, fertile conditions that allow microlife to thrive. Other activities that are highly beneficial include:

- Using no-till practices
- Using green manure or cover crops
- Maintaining species diversity of vegetation (encourages diversity of soil organisms)
- Reduce or eliminate the use of soluble fertilizers
- Reduce use of fungicides, disinfectants, and other chemicals that kill microlife unnecessarily
- Control erosion

Intimately connected to the subvisible world are the tiny meso- and macrofauna like earthworms, centipedes, beetles, termites, snails, and others. Many sustainable growers are enthusiastic about these small animals when they find them in their soils, not only for the services that these larger animals provide, but also because their presence indicates a healthy and thriving population of microlife on a level that we cannot see, but that is essential to the health of our crops.

References

Margulis, L., D. Sagan, and L. Thomas. 1997. Microcosmos: Four Billion Years of Evolution from Our Microbial Ancestors. University of California Press.

Linderman, R.G., and G.J. Bethlenfalvay. 1992. Mycorrhizae in Sustainable Agriculture (ASA Special Publication Number 54). American Society of Agronomy.

Gershuny, G., and J. Smillie. 1996. The Soul of Soil: A Guide to Ecological Soil Management. Chelsea Green Pub.

Tompkins, P., and C. Bird. 1998. Secrets of the Soil: New Age Solutions for Restoring Our Planet. Earthpulse Press.

K. Mulongoy, K., and R. Merckx (eds). 1993. Soil Organic Matter Dynamics and Sustainability of Tropical Agriculture: Proceedings of an International Symposium. John Wiley & Sons.

Subba, N.S., and Rao. 1995. Soil Microorganisms and Plant Growth. Science Pub.

Original Source

This article was originally published as *The Overstory* #28.

The Soil Foodweb: It's Role in Ecosystem Health

Elaine Ingham

What is the soil foodweb? It's the set of organisms that perform the functions that allow plants to grow normally, without the need for toxic chemical inputs. A set of healthy organisms, a healthy soil foodweb if you will, gives plants the following necessary functions:

Disease suppression A healthy foodweb includes thousands of species of bacteria and fungi, protozoa and nematodes all of whom combat diseases causing organisms. Unfortunately, they are among the first to be killed when using pesticides and high levels of inorganic fertilizers.

Nutrient retention Ever wonder why fertilizers have to be added every year in chemically intensive systems? Because it is the organisms in the healthy foodweb that retain those nutrients, and once those organisms are killed, soil cannot hold on to those nutrients. N, P, S, and calcium, as examples, will leach from the soil without the nutrient-retention abilities of the millions if not billions or more living bacteria and fungi that should be present in your soil.

Nutrient recycling If bacteria and fungi hold onto the soil's nutrients, then how do those nutrients become available back into leachable forms that the plant requires? And this process has to happen to the greatest extent around the root system of the plant. Of course, the organisms that will do this are present in soil, and were present in soil long before higher plants came into existence. The important critters in this function are protozoa, who eat bacteria and release nutrients in plant available forms, beneficial nematodes, who eat bacteria, or fungi or each other, (99% of the nematodes in soil are beneficial to plant growth, not root-feeding or foliar-feeding nematodes as pesticides salesmen would have you believe), and microarthropods and earthworms, the power-cyclers of the soil, that eat bacteria, fungi, protozoa, nematodes, and anything else they can chow down on. Most of this happens in the root-zone, because plants make exudates (cake and cookies for soil bacteria and fungi!) which they release right around the roots, in order to grow the disease-suppressive bacteria and fungi right around their roots. These bacteria and fungi growing on plant-made goodies immobilize nutrients right there,

around the roots. Then the protozoa, beneficial nematodes and microarthropods are attracted to the root zone, and release those nutrients right where the plant can grab them! Plants are "smarter" than we thought!

Decomposition of plant residues and plant-toxic compounds Many microbiologists have the attitude that any organic compound that can be made will be decomposable by an already existing bacterium or fungus. There's no need to make genetically-engineered species—plants and microbes already exist which perform whatever function humans might need. But can you sell it to someone? That's a different story, but we need a healthy soil foodweb present in our soils to get rid of any toxins that might be there. Plant litter ought to decompose and be long gone by spring-time. If it isn't, there's something wrong with your foodweb, and you need to fix it!

Well-structured soil You are stuck with the sand, silt and clay that you were given in your soil, but you can improve the life in your soil immensely. And by improving that life, the right life, you improve water-infiltration into the soil (does water puddle on the surface of your soil? You have an unhealthy foodweb, fix it!), you'll improve water-holding capacity so you don't have to water so much in the summer, and you'll improve root growth into your soil, so you don't need the pesticides, fertilizers, etc. Imagine less work to do all the time on your lawn! Let the critters in the soil do that work for you!

How Many of Each Functional Group?

Per gram of healthy soil, which is about a teaspoon of soil plus organic matter, the following organisms—most of whose names are not known to scientists—are found:

1 million (in arid soils) to 100,000 million bacteria (in forest soils) [1 million=10^6] Bacteria break down easy to-use organic material (sugars, proteins, carbohydrates), retain nutrients, like N, P, and S in the soil and combat disease causing organisms. About 60% of the carbon in those organic materials is respired as carbon dioxide, but 40% of that carbon is retained as bacterial biomass and organic matter. The waste products bacteria produce become soil organic matter. This "waste" material is more recalcitrant than the original plant material, but can be used by a large number of other soil organisms, exemplifying the classic statement that "One man's garbage is another's treasure." Productive garden soil should contain more bacteria than any other kind of organism, although care must be taken to make sure beneficial bacteria, instead of disease-causing bacteria, are most prevalent. How do you do that? By feeding the foods the suppressive bacteria like. That also means, no nitrate fertilizers (which selects for the disease-causing bacteria and fungi) and no compaction (that means poorly structured soils, and reduced oxygen levels which help the root-rot fungi more than anything else).

150 to 500 micrograms of fungal hyphae Fungi break down the more recalcitrant, or difficult-to-decompose, organic matter (like newspaper, cardboard, bark, sawdust, corn stalks) and retain those nutrients in the soil as fungal biomass. Just like bacteria, fungal waste products become soil organic matter, which are used by other organisms. Gardens require some fungal biomass for greatest productivity, but in order for best CROP growth, there should be an equal biomass of bacteria as compared to fungi. Most grasslands or pastures have less fungi than bacterial, while all conifer forests have much more fungal, as compared to bacterial, biomass. As with bacteria, we need to feed the "good-guy" fungi, not the "bad-guys." Feed the soil complex mixtures of humic acids and algae, and avoid nitrate fertilizers and prevent soil compaction.

10,000 to 100,000 protozoa These organisms are one-celled, highly mobile organisms that feed on bacteria and on each other. Because protozoa require 5 to 10-fold less nitrogen than bacteria, N is released when a protozoan eats a bacterium. That released N is then available for plants to take up. Between 40 and 80% of the N in plants can come from the predator-prey interaction of protozoa with bacteria.

15 to 500 beneficial nematodes Beneficial nematodes eat bacteria, fungi, and other nematodes. Nematodes need even less nitrogen than protozoa, between 10 and 100 times less than a bacterium con-

A healthy soil foodweb gives plants what they need to thrive. (photo: C. Elevitch)

tains, or between 5 and 50 times less than fungal hyphae contains. Thus when bacterial- or fungal-feeding nematodes eat bacteria or fungi, nitrogen is released, making that N available for plant growth. However, plant-feeding nematode are pests because they eat plant roots. These "bad" nematodes can be controlled biologically, as they are in natural systems, by fungi that trap nematodes, by having fungi that colonize root systems and prevent nematode attack of roots, or by predation of nematodes by arthropods. In cases of extreme outbreaks, however, the only answer may be the use chemicals to control these plant-feeding nematodes. However, once a chemical is used which kills the beneficial nematodes as well as the plant-feeding ones, the beneficial nematodes need to be replaced through inoculation. What inoculants are there for these beneficial fungi? Compost, and compost tea are the only commercially available sources of the whole community of these beneficial nematodes, or protozoa, for that matter.

A few to several hundred thousand microarthropods These organisms chew the plant leaf material, roots, stems and boles of trees into smaller pieces, making it easier for bacteria and fungi to find the food they like on the newly revealed surfaces. The "comminuting" arthropods can increase decomposition rates by 2–100 times, although if the bacteria or fungi are lacking, increased decomposition will not occur because it takes ALL the organisms working together to make nutrient cycling work. In many cases, however, the arthropods carry around an inoculum of bacteria and fungi, making certain the food they want (bacteria and fungi) are inoculated onto the newly exposed surfaces! Because the C:N ratio of arthropods is 100 times greater than the bacteria and fungi, they release nitrogen which then is available for plant growth. Some arthropods eat pest insects, while others eat roots. Again, it's important to encourage the beneficial ones and discourage the ones that eat plants!

The Web of Life Can Be Lost

The interactions between these organisms form a web of life, just like the web that biologists study above ground. What most people don't realize is that the above ground world wouldn't exist without below ground systems in place and functioning. Soil biology is understudied, compared to life above ground, yet it is important for the health of gardens, pastures, lawns, shrub lands, and forests. If garden soil is healthy, there will be high numbers of bacteria and bacterial-feeding organisms, which means the beneficial, disease-suppressive organisms will be present. If the soil has received heavy treatments of pesticides, chemical fertilizers, soil fungicides or fumigants that kill these organisms, the tiny critters die, or the balance between the pathogens and beneficial organisms is upset, allowing the opportunist, disease-causing organisms to become problems.

Overuse of chemical fertilizers and pesticides have effects on soil organisms that are similar to over-using antibiotics. When we consider human use of antibiotics, these chemicals seemed a panacea at first, because they could control disease. But with continued use, resistant organisms developed, and the organisms that compete with the disease-causing organisms were lost. We found that antibiotics couldn't be used willy-nilly, that they must be used only when necessary, and that some effort must be made to replace the normal human-digestive system bacteria killed by the antibiotics.

Soils are similar, in that plants grown in soil where competing organisms have been knocked back with chemicals are more susceptible to disease-causing organisms. If the numbers of bacteria, fungi, protozoa, nematodes and arthropods are lower than they should be for a particular soil type, the soil's "digestive system" doesn't work properly. Decomposition will be low, nutrients will not be retained in the soil, and will not be cycled properly. Ultimately, nutrients will be lost through the groundwater or through erosion because organisms aren't present to hold the soil together.

The best way manage for a healthy microbial ecosystem is to routinely apply organic material. To keep garden soil healthy, the amount of organic matter added must be equal to what the bacteria and fungi use each year.

Indiscriminate use of chemical fertilizers and pesticides should be avoided. If the soil is healthy for the type of vegetation desired, there should be no reason to use pesticides, or fertilizers. If a decision is made to change from grass to garden, or forest to lawn, a massive change in the soil foodweb structure is required but all that is needed is addition of the right kind of compost with the right kinds of organisms to do that conversion. Once the correct soil foodweb structure is in place, there should be no reason to apply chemicals.

If both bacteria and fungi are lost, then the soil degrades. If bacteria are killed through pesticide or chemical applications, and especially if certain extremely important bacteria like nitrogen-fixing bacteria or nitrifying bacteria are killed, the wrong kinds of bacteria, or too much fungal biomass can result (often seen in tropical soils!) can take over and crop production can be harmed. For example, current research indicates that the reason moss takes over in lawn ecosystems is because the soil is converted from a bacterial dominated system to one dominated by fungi. Or the soil may become saturated with water because of poor soil structure during heavy downpours, and the iron in the soil is reduced into plant unavailable forms. Without the right biology present, reduced iron cannot be taken up by grass, and weeds flourish.

Without the right biology present, nutrients are lost, erosion increases and plant yield is reduced. If inorganic fertilizers are used to replace the lost nitrogen, the immediate effect may be to improve plant growth. However, as time goes on, it is clear that inorganic fertilizers can't replace the other kinds of food that bacteria and fungi need and may damage soil through accumulation of salts. After a while, fertilizer additions are a waste of money, because there aren't enough soil organisms to hold on to the nutrients added. Surface and groundwater will become contaminated with the lost nutrients, causing problems.

Original Source

This article was updated by the author in April 2001 from an article that appeared online at: http://www.rain.org/~sals/ingham.html. Please check the author's web page for more information, pictures and for testing services: http://www.soil-foodweb.com.

This excerpt was originally published as *The Overstory* #81.

Mycorrhizae

Craig R. Elevitch and Kim M. Wilkinson

People have taken plants out of their natural environments to cultivate them in agricultural systems such as plantations, orchards and farms. However, we have not changed the plant's basic needs. Plants co-evolved with soil life over hundreds of millions of years. Many plant and tree species adapted to depend on some kinds of soil microlife. Soil fungi known as mycorrhizal fungi make vital contributions to plant and soil health.

Mycorrhizae literally means, "root fungus," and refers to fungi which live in close association with the root systems of plants, extending out from the plant's own roots. By nurturing and, where necessary, re-introducing mycorrhizal species, we can cultivate an essential ecological connection that will benefit our crops, our environment, and our own bottom line in agriculture or forestry.

Mycorrhizal fungi have evolved in association with plants, acting to greatly increase the ability of plants to take up water and certain nutrients, while often protecting associated plants from pests and diseases. They live in and around the root zone of plants, extending far out from the plant's roots with their own network of thread-like filaments known as hyphae. This greatly extends the effective surface area of the plants roots. The association with mycorrhizal fungi greatly enhances plant health in most species, and has even become essential for the survival of certain types of plants. Avocados, bamboos, bananas, cassava, coconuts, coffee, mahogany, mangoes, palms, papayas, soybeans, and sweet potatoes are just a few examples of plants that benefit from mycorrhizae.

One challenge in restoring degraded lands is that many important soil organisms including mycorrhizal fungi have died off or are dormant. Mycorrhizal fungi are particularly vulnerable because they can multiply only while living on the root system of a host plant, and so they cannot survive long in bare-soil conditions. Nor can they thrive in conditions where soluble fertilizers have been used continually for many years.

Poor mycorrhizal activity is a problem many people would like to remedy in forestry, organic agriculture, and land reclamation. There is currently a great interest in restoring these degraded lands by replanting a diverse range of vegetation. In order to have healthy plants, we must also make sure that essential soil microorganisms are present. This can be accomplished in part by nurturing and re-introducing mycorrhizal fungi.

How Mycorrhizal Fungi Benefit Plants

Better uptake of nutrients

With the help of mycorrhizal fungi, a plant can take up many times more nutrients, particularly phosphorous, than would be possible in the absence of the fungi. When a dependent plant lacks mycorrhizae, growers often have to load the soil with high levels of soluble nutrients. This heavy feeding is expensive, and further damages the health of the soil and water.

Soil improvement

Mycorrhizae enhance the soil by improving the structure of soil. This helps to increase water holding capacity, and traps nutrients that otherwise could be leached by rains.

Faster rehabilitation of degraded sites

Because they enhance the plant's ability to take up nutrients and water, mycorrhizal fungi can help plants compensate for low nutrient availability, poor soil structure, low water holding capacity often prevalent on harsh sites.

Healthier plants, less disease and fewer pests

Most experts in integrated pest management say that plant health is the most important aspect of pest management—healthy plants have much fewer pest problems. Better nutrition and water uptake through mycorrhizae helps plants stay healthy.

Biocontrol of certain pathogenic organisms

By infecting the root system of a plant, mycorrhizae can interfere with pathogenic organisms, effectively protecting the host plant from diseases.

Tolerance for problem soils

Mycorrhizal fungi may also help regulate the uptake of soil toxins, allowing plants to better tolerate salty or problem soil conditions.

Strategies for Improving Mycorrhizae Activity on Your Site

1 Use green manures and mulch. Using plenty of organic matter will foster beneficial soil microorganisms.

2 Refrain from using soluble chemical fertilizers, especially those which have high levels of phosphorous. Use organic fertilizers when possible.

3 If the soils are degraded, consider adding a small amount of soil from a nearby healthy forest area to each planting hole to "inoculate" the soil with healthy microlife.

4 For badly degraded sites, plants can be inoculated with commercially-available mycorrhizae prior to planting.

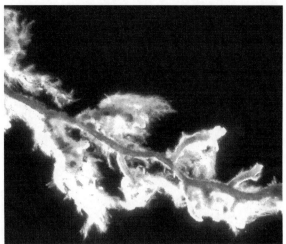

Mycorrhizal hyphae (the white fluffy material) can greatly extend the root system of plants. (photo: USDA Forest Service)

Original Source

This article was originally published as *The Overstory* #8.

Mycorrhizas: Producing and Applying Arbuscular Mycorrhizal Inoculum

M. Habte and N.W. Osorio

To one degree or another, most plants in their natural habitats function under the influence of a special group of soil fungi known as arbuscular mycorrhizal fungi ("AM fungi" or AMF). The existence of these fungi has been recognized for more than a century, although they did not receive the attention they deserve until approximately 40 years ago. Worldwide, interest in AM fungi has now reached a point wherein any discussion of agricultural biotechnology that does not include their role in plant productivity can hardly be considered complete.

Many individuals and organizations concerned with managing native plant species, restoring natural ecosystems, and producing agronomic, horticultural, and forest plants with minimal chemical inputs are interested in applying AMF technology. A major challenge to the large-scale utilization of AMF is the unavailability of large quantity of high quality inoculum to introduce the fungi into plant growing media. The problem of producing inoculum is largely due to that AM fungi are "obligate symbionts," which means they require the presence of actively growing plants during their reproduction. Therefore AMF cannot be cultured on laboratory media in the same manner as other beneficial soil microorganisms such as *Rhizobium* bacteria. Fortunately, specialized techniques for AMF inoculum production have been in development at the University of Hawai'i and elsewhere.

Arbuscular Mycorrhizal Associations

The term "mycorrhiza" was coined by A. B. Frank, a researcher in Germany, more than 100 years ago. It means "fungus-root," and stands for the mutualistic association existing between a group of soil fungi and higher plants. There are many types of mycorrhizal associations (15) of which the endomycorrhizal association of the vesicular arbuscular (VA) type are the most widespread geographically as well as within the plant kingdom. VA mycorrhizal fungi invade cortical cells inter- and intra-cellularly and form clusters of finely divided hyphae known as arbuscules in the cortex. They also form membrane-bound organelles of varying shapes known as vesicles inside and outside the cortical cells.

Arbuscules are believed to be sites of exchange of materials between the host and the plant. Vesicles generally serve as storage structures, and when they are old, they could serve as reproductive structures. Because vesicles are absent in two of the seven genera containing these fungi, the term that is currently preferred by many researchers to represent the association is arbuscular mycorrhizal (AM) fungi rather than vesicular-arbuscular (VA) mycorrhizal fungi. Arbuscular mycorrhizal fungi occur on a wide spectrum of temperate and tropical plant species and are absent in less than 30 plant families (26, 42).

AMF Functions

Roles in plant nutrition

AM fungi absorb N, P, K, Ca, S, Fe, Mn, Cu, and Zn from the soil and then translocate these nutrients to the plants with whose roots they are associated (11, 16, 33, 43). Their most consistent and important nutritional effect is to improve uptake of immobile nutrients such as P, Cu, and Zn (29, 35). AM fungi have their greatest effect when a host plant not associated with them is deficient in P. They are also very useful to plant species that inherently lack morphological or physiological mechanisms for efficient P uptake (26, 30). Consequently, enhancement of growth of plants associated with AMF is explained in most instances by improved P nutrition (5).

Another advantage to associated plants is improved maintenance of a balanced supply of nutrients. This occurs because plants grown in association with AMF can grow with only a fraction of the P required for growth by plants lacking a mycorrhizal association. Moreover, when P is applied at high concentrations, as is commonly done when growing plants in soil where AMF are absent, it can cause nutritional disorders because of its antagonistic interactions with other nutrients, or because it inhibits mycorrhizal formation (27). Studies with the forage tree *Leucaena leucocephala*, which is highly dependent on mycorrhizal association, have shown that the AMF symbiosis can decrease the plant's external P requirement, reducing it to as much as 40 times less than the plant would require for good growth in the absence of AMF (MH, unpublished).

The ability of AMF to reduce plants' external P requirement has an important environmental benefit. High levels of P in soils can result in pollution of bodies of water when eroded soil rich in P is deposited in them. P enrichment of water bodies causes eutrophication (7, 38) due to excessive development of algae, cyanobacteria, and aquatic plants, and this condition impairs the usefulness of these waters. When plants rely on AMF association rather than heavy P fertilization, risks to water quality are reduced. Arbuscular mycorrhizal fungi, therefore, are an important component of nutrient management programs that aim to reduce environmental pollution.

Mechanisms of enhanced P uptake

In soils not adequately supplied with P, plant demand for this nutrient exceeds the rate at which it diffuses into the root zone, resulting in zones of P depletion surrounding roots. It is believed that AMF help overcome this problem by extending their external hyphae from root surfaces to areas of soil beyond the P depletion zone, thereby exploring a greater volume of the soil than is accessible to the unaided root (17, 21). The external hyphae of some AMF may spread 10–12 cm from the root surface. Assuming a radial distribution of hyphae around roots, it has been estimated that the volume of soil explored by the mycorrhizal root exceeds that explored by the unaided root by as much as 100 times (39).

AM fungal hyphae are 2.5–5 times smaller in diameter than plant roots and therefore have a greater surface area per unit volume. This surface area makes the fungi much more efficient than roots in the uptake of P (5). Moreover, the smaller diameter of AMF hyphae allows them to explore micropores in the soil that are not accessible to roots. And, studies carried out in solution culture have shown that AMF hyphae have a higher affinity for P than do roots (20).

AM fungi may have biochemical and physiological capabilities for increasing the supply of available P or other immobile nutrients. These mechanisms may involve acidification of the rhizosphere (2), increases in root phosphatase activity (10) and excretion of chelating agents.

Roles not directly related to nutrition

A growing body of research suggests that AMF could contribute to plant health and productivity independently of their role in enhancing nutrient uptake. For example, the fungi have been found to be involved in the suppression of plant diseases, (19, 33, 44) including nematode infection (6,13). AMF stimulate hormone production in plants, aid in improving soil structure (4, 46, 47), enhance leaf chlorophyll levels, (45) and improve plant tolerance to water stress, salinity, soil acidity, and heavy metal toxicity (3). Some of these functions may be the indirect effects of improved P nutrition (34, 39).

Factors Influencing the AMF Inoculation Effect

The degree to which mycorrhizal fungi enhance the nutrition and health of associated plants depends on many biotic and abiotic soil factors, as well as other environmental factors that influence the host, the fungi, and their association. The most important factors include abundance of AMF infective propagules, soil P status, variation in the degree to which target plant species rely on the mycorrhizal condition at the prevailing soil-solution P concentration, and soil treatment, including the type of previous crop or native vegetation.

Abundance of AMF Propagules

Effectiveness of mycorrhizal fungi may not be rapidly expressed if the number of infective propagules contained in an inoculum is low. Many instances of poor inoculum performance may in fact be a result of a low level of infective propagules. All other things being equal, if high-quality inoculum is introduced into a soil containing a very low density of indigenous AMF fungi, the probability of obtaining a positive response to inoculation is high (12). However, if the soil contains high levels of infective propagules to begin with, it is unlikely that plants will respond to additional inoculation.

Soil P Status

There are critical ranges of soil-solution P concentration at which the host-fungus association is truly mutualistic, i.e., where the benefit each partner derives from the association outweighs the costs (9).

Mycorrhizal inoculation will have its maximum effect on plant growth at soil P concentrations near-optimal for mycorrhizal activity or at soil P concentrations that are barely accessible to the unaided root. Consequently, AMF play crucial roles in certain conditions:

- native ecosystems (e.g., forests) where applications of large quantities of fertilizer P to extensive land areas is not usually done or is not practical
- agricultural systems on soils with strong P-fixing capacity, or where P fertilizer is unavailable or prohibitively expensive
- situations where it is essential to reduce soil fertilizer applications because of environmental concerns such as nutrient pollution of surface waters
- situations in which rock phosphate is readily available and used instead of more soluble P sources.

Variation in the dependence of plants on AM fungi

Mycorrhizal dependency is a measure of the degree to which a plant species relies on the mycorrhizal condition for nutrient uptake and growth as the concentration of P in the soil solution is increased. It is well established that plant species and cultivars within a given species vary in their response to AMF colonization (36, 37, 18, 25). Most of the variation may have to do with the ability of plant species to take up P at very low soil-P concentrations in the absence of mycorrhizal fungi (1, 11, 31).

Soil disturbance

The activities of AM fungi can be severely curtailed by soil disturbance in both native and agricultural ecosystems. In native ecosystems, soil disturbances caused by land cleaving and mining operations can be so severe that mere inoculation of the affected areas with AMF may not be able to restore the symbiotic function of the fungi (14, 40). The impacts of disturbances that have been studied in agricultural ecosystems are generally less drastic (32). On the other hand, the activities of AMF are known to be adversely impacted even by disturbance such as mechanical planting operations in otherwise undisturbed soils (28). Numerous investigations have been undertaken over the past 15 years with the intent of understanding the mechanisms by which soil disturbance hampers AMF development and function. Soil disturbance due to tillage can adversely influence the abundance and diversity of AMF, but

data on the subject is very scant at present. Nevertheless, there is evidence to indicate that the diversity of AMF communities tends to decline upon the conversion of native ecosystems into agricultural ecosystems and with the intensification of agricultural inputs (23). Pot studies involving the use of split compartments separated from each other by sealed nylon meshes have clearly demonstrated that tillage suppresses the effectiveness of AMF by destroying the hyphal network that develops in soil in association with the previous mycorrhizal crop (8, 22, 24).

In no-till and reduced-tillage systems, maintenance of the integrity of this hyphal network contributes to more rapid AMF infectivity and more efficient nutrient uptake than is possible in more severely disturbed soils. In soils severely disturbed by tillage, the native AMF populations are not likely to initiate AMF formation on the target crop rapidly, and the process can be enhanced by inoculating the soil with high-quality AMF inoculum.

Sources of AMF Inoculum

Soil as inoculum

Soil from the root zone of a plant hosting AMF can be used as inoculum. Such soil inoculum is composed of soil, dried root fragments, and AMF spores, sporocarps. and fragments of hyphae. Soil may not be a reliable inoculum unless one has some idea of the abundance, diversity, and activity of the indigenous AMF.

An additional concern with the use of soil as inoculum is the possible transfer of weed seeds and pathogens with the soil. Figuring out how much soil to add as inoculum to a growth medium or a field is another challenge, because the abundance and viability of AMF propagules in the soil is often uncertain. Soils are thus AMF inoculum sources of last resort, and their use should be avoided if other types of inoculum are available.

Crude inoculum

Crude inoculum is obtained after a known AMF and a suitable host are grown together in a medium optimized for AMF development and spore formation. Such inoculum is the most common type available for large-scale crop inoculation. It consists of spores, fragments of infected roots, pieces of AMF hyphae, and the medium in which the inoculum was produced.

Root inoculum

Infected roots of a known AMF host separated from a medium in which crude inoculum was produced can also serve as a source of inoculum.

Inoculum Storage

Both root and crude inocula must be dried to a moisture content of less than 5% before they are stored. We recommend that inoculum be stored in closed plastic containers in a dehumidified room at 22°C. We have been able to store high-quality crude inoculum at 22°C for up to two years with minimal loss in viability. It is possible to extend the shelf life of root inoculum through cold storage (41). However, this can add substantially to the cost of inoculation.

Inoculum Application

Methods of applying AMF inoculum include mixing inoculum with soil, placing inoculum as a layer at various soil depths, applying it as a core below the seed, banding it in much the same way as fertilizers are applied in bands, dipping roots of seedlings in a viscous suspension containing AMF propagules, and placing AMF propagules adjacent to roots at the time of transplanting.

Mixing inoculum thoroughly with the soil is the most straightforward method of applying inoculum in the field as well as in the greenhouse, but it is effective only when large amounts of inoculum are applied. This approach is better with crude inoculum than it is with root inoculum, because root fragments do not readily disperse in soil. Inoculum can be placed at various depths (up to 5 cm) from the surface of the soil as a layer or applied in bands near the seed row (generally 5 cm below and 5 cm to the side of it).

Any type of inoculum can be placed close to seedling roots at the time of transplanting. For example, spores can be applied directly onto roots either at the time of transplanting or to roots of an established plant after making a hole adjacent to the roots. Crude inoculum and root inoculum can also be applied to established plants by placing inoculum in holes bored into the soil where roots are likely to be contacted. Before planting, seedling roots can be inoculated by dipping them in a viscous medium (1% methyl cellulose or 10–20% gum arabic) containing AMF propagules, usually spores.

Seed application of AMF inoculum is rare, but has been tried with citrus in Florida with variable results and with *Leucaena leucocephala* at the University of Hawai'i (MH, unpublished data).

Amount of Inoculum to Apply

The amount of inoculum to apply directly to soil is dependent on the quality of the inoculum. If a crude inoculum contains four to eight infective propagules per gram, application of 50 g/kg soil usually produces rapid initiation of AMF colonization of target plants with a minimal lag period. Root inocula are generally more effective in stimulating plant growth in quantities substantially lower than are normal for crude inocula. Our investigations (MH, unpublished data) showed that if root inoculum contains 4000 cm of infected root per gram, application of 0.5–1 g/kg of medium produced good results.

References

1 Baon, J.B., S.E. Smith, and A.M. Alston. 1993. Mycorrhizal response of barley cultivars differing in P efficiency. Plant and Soil 157:97–105.

2 Bago, B., and C. Azcon-Aguilar. 1997. Changes in the rhizosphere pH induced by arbuscular mycorrhiza formation in onion (Allium cepa). Zeitschrift Fur Pflanzen Und Bodenkunde 160:333–339.

3 Bethlenfalvay, G.J. 1992. Mycorrhiza and crop productivity. In: G.J. Bethlenfalvay and R.G. Linderman (eds), Mycorrhizae in sustainable agriculture. ASA/CSSA/.SSSA, Madison, Wisconsin, USA. pp. 1–27.

4 Bethlenfalvay, G.J., I.C. Cantrell, K.L. Mihara, and R.P. Schreiner. 1998. Relationship between soil aggregation and mycorrhiza as influenced by soil biota and nitrogen. Biology and Fertility of Soils 28:356–363.

5 Bolan, N.S. 1991. A critical review on the role of mycorrhizal fungi in the uptake of phosphorus by plants. Plant and Soil 134:189–293.

6 Cooper, K.M., and G.S. Grandison. 1986. Interaction of vesicular-arbuscular mycorrhizal fungi and root knot nematode on cultivars of tomato and white clover susceptible to Meloidogyne hap/a. Annals of Applied Biology 108:555–565.

7 Culley, J.L.B., E.F. Bolton, and B. Bernyk. 1983. Suspended solids and phosphorus loads from a clay soil; I. Plot studies. Journal of Environmental Quality 12:493–503.

8 Evans, D.G., and M.H. Miller. 1990. The role of the external mycelium network in the effect of soil disturbance upon vesicular-arbuscular mycorrhizal colonization of maize. New Phytologist 114:65–71.

9 Fitter, All. 1991. Cost benefits of mycorrhizas; implications for functioning under natural conditions. Experientia 47:350–355.

10 Fries, L.L.M., R.S. Pacovsky, G.R. Safir and J. Kaminsky. 1998. Phosphorus effect on phosphatase activity endomycorrhizal maize. Physiologia Plantarium 103:152–71.

11 Gerdemann, J.W. 1975. Vesicular-arbuscular mycorrhiza. In: J.G. Torrey and D.T. Clarkson (eds), The development and functions of roots. Academic Press, London, UK. pp. 575–591.

12 Habte, M., and R.L. Fox. 1993. Effectiveness of VAM fungi in nonsterile soils before and after optimization of P in soil solution. Plant and Soil 151:219–226.

13 Habte, M., Y.C. Zhang and D.P. Schmidt. 1999. Effectiveness of Glomus species in protecting white clover against nematode damage. Canadian Journal of Botany 77:135–139.

14 Habte, M., R.L. Fox, T. Aziz, and S.A. El Swaify. 1988. Interaction of vesicular-arbuscular mycorrhizal fungi with erosion in an Oxisol. Applied Environmental Microbiology 54:945–950.

15 Harley, J.L. and S.E. Smith. 1983. Mycorrhizal Symbiosis. Academic Press, New York.

16 Hayman, D.S. 1982. Influence of soils and fertility on the activity and survival of arbuscular mycorrhizal fungi. Phytopathology 72:1119–1125.

17 Hayman, D.S. 1983. The physiology of vesicular-arbuscular endomycorrhizal symbiosis. Canadian Journal of Botany 61:944–963.

18 Hetrick, BAD., D.G. Kitt, and G.T. Wilson. 1988. Mycorrhizal dependence and growth habits of warm-season and cool-season tall grass prairie plants. Canadian Journal of Botany 66:1376–1380.

19 Hooker, JE., M. Jaizme-Vegas, and D. Atkinson. 1994. Biocontrol of plant pathogens using arbuscular mycorrhizal fungi. In: S. Gianinazzi and H. Schuepp (eds), Impacts of arbuscular mycorrhizal on sustainable agriculture and natural ecosystems. Birkhauser Verlag, Basel, Switzerland. pp. 191–199.

20 Howeler, R.H., D.G. Edwards, and C.J. Asher. 1981. Applications of the flowing solution culture techniques to study involving mycorrhizas. Plant and Soil 59:179–183.

21 Jakobsen, I., E.J. Jones, and J. Larse. 1994. Hyphal phosphorus transport, a keystone to mycorrhizal enhancement of plant growth. In: S. Gianinazzi and S. Schuepp (eds), Impacts of arbuscular mycorrhizal on sustainable agriculture and natural ecosystems. Birkhauser Verlag, Basel, Switzerland. pp. 133–146.

22 Jasper, DA., L.K. Abbot, and AD. Robson. 1989. Hyphae of a vesicular-arbuscular mycorrhizal fungus maintain infectivity in dry soil, except when the soil is disturbed. New Phytologist 112:101–107.

23 Johnson, NC., and FL. Pfleger. 1992. Vesicular-arbuscular mycorrhizae and cultural stresses. In G.J. Bethlenfalvay and R.G. Linderman (eds), Mycorrhiza in sustainable agriculture. Soil Science Society of America, Madison, Wisconsin, USA. pp. 71–79.

24 Kabir, Z., I.P. O'Halloran, and C. Hamel. 1999. Combined effects of soil disturbance and fallowing on plant and fungal components of mycorrhizal corn (Zea mays L.). Soil Biology and Biochemistry 31:307–314.

25 Khalil, S., TE. Loynachan, and MA. Tabatabai. 1999. Plant determinants of mycorrhizal dependency in soybean. Agronomy Journal 91:135–141.

26 Koide, R.T., and R.P. Schreiner. 1992. Regulation of the vesicular-arbuscular mycorrhizal symbiosis. Annual Review of Plant Physiology and Plant Molecular Biology 43:557–581.

27 Lambert, D.H., DE. Baker, and H. Cole, Jr. 1979. The role of mycorrhizae in the interactions of phosphorus with zinc, copper and other elements. Soil Science Society of America Journal 43:976–980.

28 McGonigle, T.P., D.G. Evans, and M.H. Miller. 1990. Effect of degree of soil disturbance on mycorrhizal colonization and phosphorus uptake by maize in growth chamber and field experiments. New Phytologist 116:629–636.

29 Manjunath, A., and M. Habte. 1988. The development of vesicular-arbuscular mycorrhizal infection and the uptake of immobile nutrients in Leucaena leucocephala. Plant and Soil 106:97–103.

30 Manjunath, A., and M. Habte. 1991. Root morphological characteristics of host species having distinct mycorrhi2 al dependency. Canadian Journal of Botany 69:671–676.

31 Manjunath, A., and M. Habte. 1992. External and internal P requirements of plant species differing in their mycorrhizal dependency. Arid Soil Research and Rehabilitation 6:27 1–284.

32 Miller. M.H., T.P. McGonigle, and H.D. Addy. 1995. Functional ecology of vesicular-arbuscular mycorrhizal fungi as influenced by phosphate fertilization and tillage in agricultural ecosystems. Critical Reviews in Biotechnology 15:241–255.

33 Newsham, K.K., A.H. Fitter, and AR. Watkinson. 1994. Root pathogenic and arbuscular mycorrhizal fungi determine fecundity of asymptomatic plants in the field. Journal of Ecology 82:805–814.

34 O'Keefe, D.M., and D.M. Sylvia. 1991. Mechanisms of vesicular-arbuscular mycorrhizal plant growth response. In: D.K. Arora; B. Rai, KG. Mukerji, G.R. Knudsen (eds), Handbook of applied mycology; vol. 1., Soil and plants. Marcel-Dekker, Inc., New York. pp. 35–53.

35 Pacovsky, R.S. 1986. Micronutrient uptake and distribution in mycorrhizal or phosphorus-fertilized soybeans. Plant and Soil 95:379–388.

36 Plenchette, C., J.A. Fortin, and V. Furlan. 1983. Growth response off several plant species to mycorrhiza in a soil of moderate P fertility; I. Mycorrhiza dependency under field conditions. Plant and Soil 70:191–209.

37 Pope, PE., W.R. Chaney, J.D. Rhodes, and S.H. Woodhead. 1983. The mycorrhizal dependency of four hardwood tree species. Canadian Journal of Botany 61:412–417.

38 Sharpley, AN., S.J. Smith, O.R. Jones, W.A. Berg, and GA. Coleman. 1992. The transport of bioavailable phosphorus in agricultural run-off. Journal of Environmental Quality 21:30–35.

39 Sieverding, E. 1991. Vesicular-arbuscular mycorrhiza management in tropical agroecosystems. Deutsche Gesellschaft fur Technische Zusammenabeit, Bremer, Germany.

40 Stahl, PD., SE. Williams, and M. Christensen. 1988. Efficacy of native vesicular-arbuscular mycorrhizal fungi after severe soil disturbance. New Phytologist 110:347–354.

41 Sylvia, D.M. and J.A.G. Jarstfer. 1992. Sheared-root inocula of vesicular-arbuscular mycorrhizal fungi. Applied and Environmental Microbiology 58:229–232.

42 Tester, M., S.E. Smith, and F.A. Smith. 1987. The phenomenon of mycorrhizal plants. Canadian Journal of Botany 65:419–431.

43 Tinker, P.B., and A. Gildon. 1983. Mycorrhizal fungi and ion uptake. In: DA. Rob and W.S. Pierpoint (eds), Metals and micronutrients, uptake and utilization by plants. Academic Press, London, UK. pp. 21–32.

44 Trotta, A., G.C. Varese, E. Gnavi, A. Fusconi, S. Sampo, and G. Berta. 1996. Interaction between the soil-borne root pathogen Phytophthora nicotianae var. parasitica and the arbuscular mycorrhizal fungus Glomus mosseae in tomato plants. Plant and Soil 185:199–209.

45 Tsang, A., and MA. Maun. 1999. Mycorrhizal fungi increase salt tolerance of Strophostyles helvola in coastal foredunes. Plant Ecology 144:159–166.

46 Wright, S.F., and A. Upadhyaya. 1996. Extraction of an abundant and unusual protein from soil and comparision of hyphal protein of arbuscular mycorrhizal fungi. Soil Science 161:575–586.

47 Wright, S.F., and A. Upadhyaya. 1998. A survey of soils for aggregate stability and glomalin, a glycoprotein produced by hyphae of arbuscular mycorrhizal fungi. Plant and Soil 198:97–107.

Original Source

This article was adapted with kind permission of the authors from:

Habte, M. and N.W. Osorio. 2001. Arbuscular Mycorrhizas: Producing and Applying Arbuscular Mycorrhizal Inoculum. College of Tropical Agriculture & Human Resources (CTAHR), University of Hawai'i at Manoa.

This publication answers common questions about AM fungi and provides information that will enable interested individuals to produce and then evaluate AMF inocula with minimal external assistance.

For information on purchasing the book, contact: Publications and Information Office CTAHR-UHM 3050 Maile Way Gilmore Hall 119 Honolulu, HI 96822 Tel: 808-956-7036, Fax: 808-956-5966; Email: ctahrpub@hawaii.edu; Web: http://www2.ctahr.hawaii.edu/ctahr2001/P IO/ForSalePubs.html

This excerpt was originally published as *The Overstory* #102.

The Role of Mushrooms in Nature

Paul Stamets

Fungi have vital roles in ecosystem health. There are numerous fungi that produce fleshy fruiting bodies known as mushrooms, many of which are prized for their edible and medicinal uses. This chapter explores the role of mushroom-producing fungi (commonly referred to as mushrooms) in the health of forests and other landscapes.

The article covers three basic ecological groups of mushrooms:

- those that form a symbiosis with host plants called mycorrhizal mushrooms;
- those that act on living plants called parasitic mushrooms; and
- those that recycle dead plant material, the saprophytic mushrooms.

The Mycorrhizal Gourmet Mushrooms

Mycorrhizal mushrooms form a mutually dependent, beneficial relationship with the roots of host plants, ranging from trees to grasses. "Myco" means mushrooms, while "rhizal" means roots. The collection of filament of cells that grow into the mushroom body is called the mycelium. The mycelia of these mycorrhizal mushrooms can form an exterior sheath covering the roots of plants and are called ectomycorrhizal. When they invade the interior root cells of host plants they are called endomycorrhizal. In either case, both organisms benefit from this association. Plant growth is accelerated. The resident mushroom mycelium increases the plant's absorption of nutrients, nitrogenous compounds, and essential elements (phosphorus, copper, and zinc). By growing beyond the immediate root zone, the mycelium channels and concentrates nutrients from afar. Plants with mycorrhizal fungal partners can also resist diseases far better than those without.

Most ecologists now recognize that a forest's health is directly related to the presence, abundance, and variety of mycorrhizal associations. The mycelial component of topsoil within a typical Douglas fir forest in the Pacific Northwest approaches 10% of the total biomass. Even this estimate may be low, not taking into account the mass of the endomycorrhizae

and the many yeast-like fungi that thrive in the topsoil.

The nuances of climate, soil chemistry, and predominant microflora play determinate roles in the cultivation of mycorrhizal mushrooms in natural settings. Species native to a region are likely to adapt much more readily to designed habitats than exotic species. I am much more inclined to spend time attempting the cultivation of native mycorrhizal species than to import exotic candidates from afar.

One method for inoculating mycorrhizae calls for the planting of young seedlings near the root zones of proven Truffle trees. The new seedlings acclimate and become "infected" with the mycorrhizae of a neighboring, parent tree. In this fashion, a second generation of trees carrying the mycorrhizal fungus is generated. After a few years, the new trees are dug up and replanted into new environments. This method has had the longest tradition of success in Europe.

Another approach, modestly successful, is to dip exposed roots of seedlings into water enriched with the spore-mass of a mycorrhizal candidate. First, mushrooms are gathered from the wild and soaked in water. Thousands of spores are washed off the gills, resulting in an enriched broth of inoculum. A spore-mass slurry coming from several mature mushrooms and diluted into a 5-gallon bucket can inoculate a hundred or more seedlings. The concept is wonderfully simple. Unfortunately, success is not guaranteed.

Broadcasting spore-mass onto the root zones of likely candidates is another venue that costs little in time and effort. Habitats should be selected on the basis of their parallels in nature. For instance, Chanterelles can be found in oak forests of the Midwest and in Douglas fir forests of the West. Casting spore-mass of Chanterelles into forests similar to those where Chanterelles proliferate is obviously the best choice. Although the success rate is not high, the rewards are well worth the minimum effort involved. Bear in mind that tree roots confirmed to be mycorrhized with a gourmet mushroom will not necessarily result in harvestable mushrooms. Fungi and their host trees may have long associations without the ap-

Examples of primary saprophytes (clockwise from top left): shiitake, pearl oyster, reishi, and maitake. (photos: P. Stamets © www.fungi.com)

pearance of edible fruit bodies. (For more information, consult Fox, 1983.)

On sterilized media, most mycorrhizal mushrooms grow slowly, compared to the saprophytic mushrooms. Their long evolved dependence on root by-products and complex soils makes media preparation inherently more complicated. Some mycorrhizal species, like *Pisolithus tinctorius*, a puffball favoring pines, grow quite readily on sterilized media. A major industry has evolved providing foresters with seedlings inoculated with this fungus. Mycorrhized seedlings are healthier and grow faster than non-mycorrhized ones. Unfortunately, the gourmet mycorrhizal mushroom species do not fall into the readily cultured species category. The famous Matsutake may take weeks before its mycelium fully colonizes the media on a single petri dish! Unfortunately, this

rate of growth is the rule rather than the exception with the majority of gourmet mycorrhizal species.

Given the huge hurdle of time for honing laboratory techniques, I favor the "low-tech" approach of planting trees adjacent to known producers of Chanterelles, Matsutake, Truffles, and Boletus. After several years, the trees can be uprooted, inspected for mycorrhizae, and replanted in new environments. The value of the contributing forest can then be viewed, not in terms of board feet of lumber, but in terms of its ability for creating satellite, mushroom/tree colonies. When industrial or suburban development threatens entire forests, and is unavoidable, future-oriented foresters may consider the removal of the mycorrhizae as a last-ditch effort to salvage as many mycological communities as possible by simple transplantation techniques, although on a much grander scale.

Parasitic Mushrooms: Blights of the Forest?

Parasitic fungi are the bane of foresters. They do immeasurable damage to the health of resident tree species, but in the process create new habitats for many other organisms. Although the ecological damage caused by parasitic fungi is well understood, we are only just learning of their importance in the forest ecosystem. Comparatively few mushrooms are true parasites.

Parasites live off a host plant, endangering the host's health as it grows. Of all the parasitic mushrooms that are edible, the Honey mushroom, *Armillaria mellea*, is the best known. One of these Honey mushrooms, known as *Armillaria gallica*, made national headlines when scientists reported finding in Michigan a single colony covering 37 acres, weighing at least 220,000 pounds, with an estimated age of 1,500 years! Washington State soon responded with re-

ports of a colony of *Armillaria ostoyae* covering 2,200 acres and at least 2,400 years old. With the exception of the trembling Aspen forests of Colorado, this fungus is the largest known living organism on the planet. And, it is a marauding parasite!

In the past, a parasitic fungus has been looked upon as biologically evil. This view is rapidly changing as science progresses. Montana State University researchers have discovered a new parasitic fungus attacking the yew tree. This new species is called *Taxomyces andreanae* and is medically significant for one notable feature: it produces minute quantities of the potent anti-carcinogen Taxol, a proven treatment for breast cancer (Stone, 1993). This new fungus was studied and now a synthetic form of this potent drug is available for cancer patients. Recently, a leaf fungus isolated in the Congo has been discovered that duplicates the effect of insulin, but is orally active. Even well known medicines from fungi harbor surprises. A mycologist at Cornell University (Hodge *et al* 1996) recently discovered that the fungus responsible for the multibillion dollar drug, cyclosporin, has a sexual stage in *Cordyceps subsessilis*, a parasitic mushroom attacking scarab beetle larvae. Of the es-

Example secondary saprophyte *Agaricus bisporus* (left) and tertiary saprophyte *Paneolus subbalteatus* (right). (photos: P. Stamets © www.fungi.com)

timated 1,500,000 species of fungi, approximately 70,000 have been identified (Hawksworth *et al* 1995), and about 10,000 are mushrooms. We are just beginning to discover the importance of species hidden within this barely explored genome.

Many saprophytic fungi can be weakly parasitic in their behavior, especially if a host tree is dying from other causes. These can be called facultative parasites: saprophytic fungi activated by favorable conditions to behave parasitically. Some parasitic fungi continue to grow long after their host has died. Oyster mushrooms (*Pleurotus ostreatus*) are classic saprophytes, although they are frequently found on dying cottonwood, oak, poplar, birch, maple, and alder trees. These appear to be operating parasitically when they are only exploiting a rapidly evolving ecological niche.

Saprophytic Mushrooms: The Decomposers

Most of the gourmet mushrooms are saprophytic, wood-decomposing fungi. Saprophytic fungi are the premier recyclers on the planet. The filamentous mycelial network is designed to weave between and through the cell walls of plants. The enzymes and acids they secrete degrade large molecular complexes into simpler compounds. All ecosystems depend upon fungi's ability to decompose organic plant matter soon after it is rendered available. The end result of their activity is the return of carbon, hydrogen, nitrogen, and minerals back into the ecosystem in forms usable to plants, insects, and other organisms. As decomposers, they can be separated into three key groups. Some mushroom species cross over from one category to another depending upon prevailing conditions.

Primary Decomposers: These are the fungi first to capture a twig, a blade of grass, a chip of wood, a log or stump. Primary decomposers are typically fast-growing, sending out ropy strands of mycelium that quickly attach to and decompose plant tissue. Most of the decomposers degrade wood. Hence, the majority of these saprophytes are woodland species, such as Oyster mushrooms (*Pleurotus* species), Shiitake (*Lentinula edodes*), and King Stropharia (*Stropharia rugosoannulata*). However, each species has developed specific sets of enzymes to break down lignin-cellulose, the structural components of most plant cells. Once the enzymes of one mushroom species have broken down the lignin-cellulose to its full-

est potential, other saprophytes utilizing their own repertoire of enzymes can reduce this material even further.

Secondary Decomposers These mushrooms rely on the previous activity of other fungi to partially break down a substrate to a state wherein they can thrive. Secondary decomposers typically grow from composted material. The actions of other fungi, actinomycetes, bacteria, and yeasts all operate within compost. As plant residue is degraded by these microorganisms, the mass, structure, and composition of the compost is reduced, and proportionately available nitrogen is increased. Heat, carbon dioxide, ammonia, and other gases are emitted as by-products of the composting process. Once these microorganisms (especially actinomycetes) have completed their life cycles, the compost is susceptible to invasion by a select secondary decomposer. A classic example of a secondary decomposer is the Button Mushroom, *Agaricus brunnescens*, the most commonly cultivated mushroom. Another example is *Stropharia ambigua*, which invades outdoor mushroom beds after wood chips have been first decomposed by a primary saprophyte.

Tertiary Decomposers An amorphous group, the fungi represented by this group are typically soil dwellers. They survive in habitats that are years in the making from the activity of the primary and secondary decomposers. Fungi existing in these reduced substrates are remarkable in that the habitat appears inhospitable for most other mushrooms. A classic example of a tertiary decomposer is *Aleuria aurantia*, the Orange Peel Mushroom. This complex group of fungi often poses unique problems to would-be cultivators. *Panaeolus subbalteatus* is yet another example. Although one can grow it on composted substrates, this mushroom has the reputation of growing prolifically in the discarded compost from Button mushroom farms. Other tertiary decomposers include species of *Conocybe*, *Agrocybe*, *Pluteus*, and some *Agaricus* species.

The floor of a forest is constantly being replenished by new organic matter. Primary, secondary, and tertiary decomposers can all occupy the same location. In the complex environment of the forest floor, a "habitat" can actually be described as the overlaying of several, mixed into one. And, over time, as each habitat is being transformed, successions of mushrooms occur. This model becomes infinitely complex when taking into account the interrelationships of not only the fungi to one another, but also the fungi to other microorganisms (yeasts, bacteria, protozoa), plants, insects, and mammals.

Primary and secondary decomposers afford the most opportunities for cultivation. To select the best species for cultivation, several variables must be carefully matched. Climate, available raw materials, and the mushroom strains all must interplay for cultivation to result in success. Native species are the best choices when you are designing outdoor mushroom landscapes.

The Global Environmental Shift and the Loss of Species Diversity

Studies in Europe show a frightening loss of species diversity in forestlands, most evident with the mycorrhizal species. Many mycologists fear many mushroom varieties, and even species, will soon become extinct. As the mycorrhizal species decline in both numbers and variety, the populations of saprophytic and parasitic fungi initially rise as a direct result of the increased availability of deadwood debris. However, as woodlots are burned and replanted, the complex mosaic of the natural forest is replaced by a highly uniform, mono-species landscape. Because the replanted trees are nearly identical in age, the cycle of debris replenishing the forest floor is interrupted. This new "ecosystem" cannot support the myriad fungi, insects, small mammals, birds, mosses, and flora so characteristic of ancestral forests. In pursuit of commercial forests, the native ecology has been supplanted by a biologically anemic woodlot. This woodlot landscape is barren in terms of species diversity.

With the loss of habitat of the mycorrhizal gourmet mushrooms, market demands for gourmet mushrooms should shift to those that can be cultivated. Thus, the pressure on this not-yet-renewable resource would be alleviated. I believe the judicious use of saprophytic fungi by homeowners as well as foresters may well prevent widespread parasitic disease vectors. Selecting and controlling the types of saprophytic fungi occupying these ecological niches can benefit both forester and forestland.

Mushrooms and Toxic Wastes

In heavily industrialized areas, the soils are typically contaminated with a wide variety of pollutants, particularly petroleum-based compounds, polychlorinated biphenols (PCBs), heavy metals, pesticide-re-

Starting at top: wood chips, wood chips with fungal mycelium, and soil. (photos: P. Stamets © www.fungi.com)

lated compounds, and even radioactive wastes. Mushrooms grown in polluted environments can absorb toxins directly into their tissues, especially heavy metals (Bressa, 1988; Stijve 1974, 1976, 1992). As a result, mushrooms grown in these environments should not be eaten. Recently, a visitor to Ternobyl, a city about 60 miles from Chernobyl, the site of the world's worst nuclear power plant accident, returned to the United States with a jar of pickled mushrooms. The mushrooms were radioactive enough to set off Geiger counter alarms as the baggage was being processed. Customs officials promptly confiscated the mushrooms. Unfortunately, most toxins are not so readily detected.

A number of fungi can, however, be used to detoxify contaminated environments, in a process called "bioremediation." The white rot fungi (particularly *Phanerochaete chrysosporium*) and brown rot fungi (notably *Gloephyllum* species) are the most widely used. Most of these wood-rotters produce lignin peroxidases and cellulases, which have unusually powerful degradative properties. These extracellular enzymes have evolved to break down plant fiber primarily lignin-cellulose, the structural component in woody plants, into simpler forms. By happenstance, these same enzymes also reduce recalcitrant hydrocarbons and other manufactured toxins. Given the number of industrial pollutants that are hydrocarbon-based, fungi are excellent candidates for toxic waste cleanup and are viewed by scientists and government agencies with increasing interest. Current and prospective future uses include the detoxification of PCB (polychloralbiphenols), PCP (penrachlorophenol), oil, and pesticide/herbicide residues. They are even being explored for ameliorating the impact of radioactive wastes by sequestering heavy metals.

Bioremediation of toxic waste sites is especially attractive because the environment is treated in situ. The contaminated soils do not have to be hauled away, eliminating the extraordinary expense of handling, transportation, and storage. Since these fungi have the ability to reduce complex hydrocarbons into elemental compounds, these compounds pose no threat to the environment. Indeed, these former pollutants could even be considered "fertilizer," helping rather than harming the nutritional base of soils.

The higher fungi should not be disqualified for bioremediation just because they produce an edible fruitbody. Indeed, this group may hold answers to many of the toxic waste problems. Mushrooms

Micrograph of mycelial network (photo: P. Stamets © www.fungi.com)

grown from toxic wastes are best not eaten, as residual heavy metal toxins may be concentrated within the mushrooms.

Mushroom Mycelium and Mycofiltration

The mycelium is a fabric of interconnected, interwoven strands of cells. One colony can range in size from a half-dollar to many acres. A cubic inch of soil can host up to a mile of mycelium. This organism can be physically separated, and yet behave as one.

The exquisite lattice-like structure of the mushroom mycelium, often referred to as the mycelial network, is perfectly designed as a filtration membrane. Each colony extends long, complex chains of cells that fork repeatedly in matrix-like fashion, spreading to geographically defined borders. The mushroom mycelium, being a voracious forager for carbon and nitrogen, secretes extracellular enzymes that unlock organic complexes. The newly freed nutrients are then selectively absorbed directly through the cell walls into the mycelial network.

In the rainy season, water carries nutritional particles through this filtration membrane, including bacteria, which often become a food source for the mushroom mycelium. The resulting downstream effluent is cleansed of not only carbon/nitrogen-rich compounds but also bacteria, in some cases nematodes, and legions of other microorganisms. The voracious Oyster mushrooms been found to be parasitic against nematodes (Thorn and Barron, 1984;

Hibbett and Thorn, 1994). Extracellular enzymes act like an anesthetic and stun the nematodes, thus allowing the invasion of the mycelium directly into their immobilized bodies.

The use of mycelium as a mycofilter is currently being studied by this author in the removal of biological contaminants from surface water passing directly into sensitive watersheds. By placing sawdust implanted with mushroom mycelium in drainage basins downstream from farms raising livestock, the mycelium acts as a sieve, which traps fecal bacteria and ameliorates the impact of a farm's nitrogen-rich outflow into aquatic ecosystems.

References

Bressa, G.L., L. Cima, and P. Costa. 1988. Bioaccumulation of Hg in the mushroom Pleurotus ostreatus. Ecotoxicology and Environmental Safety Oct. 16(2):85–89.

Fox, F.M. 1983. Role of Basidiospores as inocula for mycorrhizal fungi of birch. In: Tree Root Systems and Their Mycorrhizas. Nijhoff, The Hague.

Hawksworth, D.L., P.M. Kirk, B.C. Sutton, and D.N. Pegler. 1995. Ainsworth and Bisby's Dictionary of the Fungi (8th ed.). CAB International, Wallingford, UK.

Hibbett, D.S. and R.G. Thorn. 1994. Nematode trapping in Pleurotus tuberregium. Mycologia 86:696–699.

Hodge, K.T., S.B. Krasnoff, and R.A. Humber. 1996. Tolypocladium inflatum is the anamorph of Cordyceps subsessilis. Myologia 88(5):715–719.

Stijve, T. 1992. Certain mushrooms do accumulate heavy metals. Mushroom, the Journal of Wild Mushrooming 38(1):9–14.

Stijve, T., R. Fumbaux, and B. Philippossian. 1986. Agaritine, a p-hydroxymethylphenylhydrazine derivative in cultivated mushrooms (Agaricus bisporus), and in some of its wild-growing relatives. Deutche Lebensmittel-Rundschau 82:243–248.

Stijve, T. and R. Roschnik. 1974. Mercury and methyl mercury content of different species of Fungi. Trav. chim. alimen. Hyg. 65:209–220.

Stone, R. 1993. Surprise! A fungus factory for taxol? In: Science April, 260:9.

Thorn, R.G. and G.L. Barron. 1984. Carnivorous Mushrooms. Science 224:76–78.

Original Source

This article was reprinted with permission from *Growing Gourmet and Medicinal Mushrooms*, Third Edition, by Paul Stamets. Copyright ©2000. Ten Speed Press, Berkeley, CA.

Growing Gourmet and Medicinal Mushrooms offers detailed guidance for growing and using gourmet and medicinal mushrooms. It is available from the publisher at http://www.tenspeed.com.

This excerpt was originally published as *The Overstory* #86.

Biological Nitrogen Fixation

Kim M. Wilkinson and Craig R. Elevitch

Biological nitrogen fixation is an important part of many agroforestry, sustainable agriculture, and land rehabilitation practices. Although the terms "nitrogen fixing plants" and "nitrogen fixing trees (NFTs)" are widely used, the plants themselves do not have the ability to make use of the nitrogen gas in the air—it is only through the symbiotic association with rhizobia bacteria that the process takes place. Simply planting leguminous "nitrogen fixing" plants or trees will not ensure that nitrogen will be accumulated; the process of biological nitrogen fixation depends on the presence of the correct rhizobia bacteria. This chapter describes how biological nitrogen fixation works, why inoculation is advantageous, and how to use rhizobia inoculants.

Biological Nitrogen Fixation

Nitrogen is commonly the most limiting element in agricultural production, and one of the most expensive to purchase as fertilizer (NifTAL 1984). There is an abundant supply of nitrogen in the air (the air is 80% nitrogen gas, amounting to about 8000 pounds of nitrogen in the air over every acre of land, or 6400 kilograms above every hectare). However, the nitrogen in the air is a stable gas, normally unavailable to plants. Many leguminous plants are able to utilize this atmospheric nitrogen through an association with rhizobia, bacteria which are hosted by the root system of certain nitrogen fixing plants.

Rhizobia are able to convert the nitrogen gas in the atmosphere into amino acids, which are the building blocks of proteins. The legume is then able to use this for its nitrogen needs. Rhizobia exchange nitrogen for carbohydrates from the plant. As the plants drop organic matter, or when the plants die, the nitrogen from their tissues is made available to other plants and organisms. This process of accumulating atmospheric nitrogen in plants and recycling it through organic matter is the major source of nitrogen in tropical ecosystems. Various agroforestry practices such as alley cropping, improved fallow, and green manure/cover cropping exploit this natural fertility process by using nitrogen fixing plants.

Examples of Nitrogen Fixing Plants

Examples of tree and shrub genera and that form this relationship include: *Acacia, Leucaena, Gliricidia, Erythrina, Sesbania, Inga, Dalbergia, Cajanus,* and *Albizia*. Ground cover or annual crops include: *Crotalaria* species, *Mucuna pruriens* (velvet bean), *Dolichos lablab* (lablab, hyacinth bean), *Canavalia* species (jack or sword beans), and *Arachis pintoi* (perennial peanut).

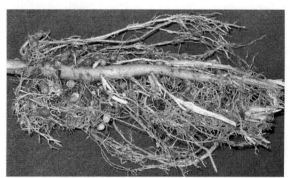

Bacteria housed in root nodules fix nitrogen from air. Root system of *Acacia koa*. (photo: C. Elevitch)

Why Use Rhizobia Inoculants?

There are many species of rhizobia, and each will work only with certain legumes. Likewise, each legume species will only associate with the proper rhizobia. Unless the strain of rhizobia suited to the legume species is present in the soil, no biological nitrogen fixation will take place. In some cases, one *Rhizobium* strain may provide some nitrogen fixation, but will be less effective than another.

Rhizobia inoculants are live bacteria cultures that are applied to seeds or young plants, infecting their root systems with the beneficial bacteria. A tremendous amount of research has been done over the past few decades to match plant and rhizobia species not only for compatibility, but also to maximize nitrogen fixation and enhance growth. Using inoculants ensures that the plants receive the best *Rhizobium* strain for optimum effectiveness.

Whether an uninoculated plant will spontaneously associate with rhizobia in the field depends on several factors:

1   If the correct rhizobia for that plant species is present in the soil;

2   If the rhizobia are available in sufficient quantity to infect roots;

3   If the rhizobia in the soil are healthy and still able to fix nitrogen (researchers have found that over a period of years, rhizobia in the soil can and do lose the ability to fix nitrogen) (Keyser 2000).

However, even if the correct rhizobia is present in the soil, its nitrogen fixing effectiveness (compared to the recommended and tested inoculant strain applied in the greenhouse prior to transplanting) will be unknown—the soil population may consist of mediocre strains. Also, if the bacteria is present in the soil, it may take several weeks, months or even years for the association to develop, and this delay will cost the farmer unnecessary time and money in early maintenance.

Using rhizobia inoculants ensures that the correct rhizobia bacteria associate with the plant, and also that the association forms early in the plant's life to accelerate its early growth and establishment.

How Is Inoculant Applied?

Inoculation (infecting the plant roots with the rhizobia) should take place as early in the plant's life as possible, when the plant will most readily form the association. Rhizobia inoculant can be applied to seeds or to young plants. Usually, Rhizobium bacteria come in a peat-based inoculant, with billions (10^9) of cells per gram. The inoculant is usually coated onto the seed immediately before plating, or dispersed in clean water and soaked into the planting medium. One hundred grams of inoculant is usually sufficient for 20,000–100,000 seeds. The cost is very small per plant inoculated—a few dollars worth of inoculant can replace a hundred or more dollars worth of nitrogen fertilizer over the life of the plant.

How Can the Effectiveness of Inoculation Be Verified?

When rhizobia are present and nitrogen is being fixed, nodules can be seen on the roots of the plants. Each one of the nodules houses millions of rhizobia bacteria. When a nodule is opened, a pink or red color inside is usually a good indicator that it is ac-

tive, that biological nitrogen fixation is taking place. Thus the effectiveness of inoculation can be verified easily with the naked eye. The rhizobia will survive and multiply as the plant grows.

Conclusion

Biological nitrogen fixation in legumes depends on the presence of the correct rhizobia bacteria for the plant species. Inoculating with rhizobia ensures that nitrogen fixing plants form the necessary association to be able to fix nitrogen. Using rhizobia inoculants can be a key part of accelerating rehabilitation of degraded land and ecosystem function, enhancing survival and growth of plants, and reducing costs in establishment and maintenance. A few dollars worth of inoculant can replace hundreds of dollars worth of purchased nitrogen fertilizer over the life of the plant, and return organic matter and nitrogen to the farm ecosystem naturally.

References

Keyser, H. 2000. Personal communication. University of Hawai'i NifTAL Project, 1000 Holomua Road, Paia, HI 96779-9744 USA.

Nitrogen Fixation for Tropical Agricultural Legumes (NifTAL) and Food and Agriculture Organization of the United Nations. 1984. Legume Inoculants and Their Use. FAO, Rome, Italy.

Original Source

This article was originally published as *The Overstory* #65.

Further Reading

Nitrogen Fixation for Tropical Agricultural Legumes (NifTAL) and Food and Agriculture Organization of the United Nations. 1994. Legume Inoculants and Their Use. FAO, Rome, Italy.

Elevitch, C.R., and K.M. Wilkinson. 1998. Nitrogen Fixing Tree Start-Up Guide Includes instructions for the use of rhizobia inoculants. Download the Guide at:
http://www.agroforester.com/articles/articles.html.

Somasegaran, P., and H.J. Hoban. 1994. Handbook for Rhizobia: Methods in Legume-Rhizobium Technology. Covers *Rhizobium* technology at a research level.

The Rhizosphere

Alex L. Shigo

The rhizosphere is the absorbing root-soil interface. It is the zone, about one millimeter in width, surrounding living root hairs and the boundary cells of mycorrhizae as well as hyphae growing out from some mycorrhizae.

The rhizoplane is the boundary where soil elements in water are absorbed into the tree. Under an electron microscope, the rhizoplane appears as a jelly where microorganisms and tree cells mix, making it impossible to tell which side is tree and which is soil.

A constantly changing mix of organisms inhabit the rhizosphere and surrounding soil. Bacteria, actinomycetes, fungi, protozoa, slime molds, algae, nematodes, enchytraeid worms, earthworms, millipedes, centipedes, insects, mites, snails, small animals and soil viruses compete constantly for water, food, and space.

The rhizosphere is a battleground and the wars are continuous. Amoebae are eating bacteria. Some bacteria are poisoning other bacteria. Fungi are killing other fungi. Nematodes are spearing roots. Fungi are trapping nematodes. Earthworms are eating anything they can find. Sometimes the victors benefit the tree and sometimes they do not.

Every tree treatment affects the rhizosphere in some way. The more you know about the rhizosphere, the better the chances are that your treatments will lead to benefits rather than harm.

Tree Declines and the Starving Rhizosphere

Go anywhere in the world and you will learn that some local trees have a "new" decline problem. Declines usually mean the trees are sick because there is a problem in the rhizosphere.

Trees die, as all organisms do, in three basic ways: depletion, dysfunction and disruption. Disruption means wounding, severe mechanical impacts and fracturing. Dysfunction means some parts and processes of the living system have developed problems that retard or prevent their functioning and growth. Depletion means that the basic substances for life begin to decrease to the point where injury and

death are certain. One of the ways depletion injures organisms is by starvation.

Soils and wood share a common problem: They are thought of as dead substances. This has come about because wood-products research gained an early lead over research on wood in living trees. With soils, many texts still define soils as "loose material of weathered rock and other minerals, and also partly decayed organic matter that covers large parts of the land surface on Earth."

Sapwood in living trees has many more living cells than dead cells. In upper layers where most absorbing roots of plants grow, soils have more soil organisms than grains of weathered rock. In great disrespect, most people still refer to soil as dirt! When researchers first discovered the great value of soil microorganisms for human antibiotics and profit, the living nature of the soil began to emerge.

Trees require a healthy rhizosphere

A more correct definition of soil should be that it is a substance made up of sands, silts, clays, decaying organic matter, air, water and an enormous number of living organisms. Survival of all living systems depends greatly on synergy and efficiency to optimize the functioning of all processes and to keep waste as low as possible. When synergy and efficiency begin to wane, declines follow.

Trees are dependent on the light energy from the sun for their energy, water and 14 elements from the soil for their building blocks of life. Some trees decline when incorrect treatments or abiotic injuries lead to starvation of organisms in the rhizosphere. When there are troubles in the rhizosphere, there will be troubles with the tree.

Energy & Root Exudates

Microorganisms compete in the rhizosphere, an area rich in exudates from the tree. The exudates contain carbohydrates, organic acids, vitamins and many other substances essential for life. From 5% to 40% of the total dry matter production of organic carbon from photosynthesis may be released as exudates! When trees begin to decline, the amount of organic carbon released as exudates increases. Mineral deficiencies, low amounts of soil air and severe wounding are major causes for the increase. An increase in exudates can be caused by over-pruning, construction injury, planting too deeply, over-watering, compaction and planting trees in soils that have a pH too high or too low for their optimal growth.

You would think that a tree in decline would decrease, not increase, exudates. A possible explanation might come from the self-thinning rule of ecology, which states that when energy input into a site equals output, there will be no further growth unless some trees die. As many suppressed trees die, a much fewer number continue to grow bigger. Or, on the basis of the mass-energy ratio law, as some trees on a site get bigger, many smaller suppressed trees will die. As the suppressed trees decline, they contribute a higher percentage of their soluble carbohydrates to the rhizosphere.

The increase in exudates from a declining tree with a defense system weakened by low energy reserves would give root pathogens an advantage over other soil organisms. When the tree dies, its dead wood adds a great amount of carbon to the soil, thus benefiting all soil organisms. If this scenario is correct, then the codes for the increase of exudates as trees decline would have been set in the genes of the forest trees. Then, even after trees are taken out of their groups in forests and planted as individuals, the genetic codes for increasing exudates as the tree declines for reasons other than crowding would still be in effect.

A tree does not "know" why it is dying. In a crowded, young, growing forest, the self-thinning rule of ecology does benefit tree survivors and all soil organisms. But, when one or two trees in a yard, city or park start to decline, their early death may benefit only the root pathogens. And even worse, since the tree will be cut and removed from the site, there would be no benefits from added carbon to the soil.

A Closer Look at Roots

Woody tree roots are organs that support the tree mechanically, store energy reserves, transport water and the substances dissolved in it and synthesize substances such as growth regulators, amino acids and vitamins that are essential for growth.

Trees have different types of root systems. For example, mangroves along coastlines have stilt roots. Many trees growing in tropical areas have aerial roots that become prop roots when they grow into the soil. Other trees have strangling roots that eventually kill the host tree that first supported their growth. Trees in sandy soils can have roots that grow downward over 90 feet. Palms have roots that are adventitious and grow from meristematic regions in their base. Many tree species have deep roots when they are young and more shallow roots later. It would be nearly impossible for the strongest person to pull out young saplings of beech, oak or hickory from forest soil.

It is important to remember that woody roots store energy reserves, and root defense is dependent on energy reserves. When reserves are low, defense is low. When defense is low, weak or opportunistic pathogens attack. It is nature's way.

Non-Woody Roots

Non-woody tree roots are organs that absorb water and elements dissolved in it. The two basic types of non-woody roots are:

1   Root hairs on non-woody roots are extensions of single epidermal cells. Common on seedlings, root hairs grow to maturity in a few days. They function for a few weeks and then begin to die. On mature trees, they are usually not abundant. When they do form, they do so when soil conditions are optimum for absorption of water and elements. I have found root hairs growing in non-frozen soils beneath frozen soils in winter.

2   Mycorrhizae are the other type of non-woody roots. Mycorrhizae are organs made up of tree and fungus tissues that facilitate the absorption of phosphorus-containing ions and others essential for growth.

The fungi that infected developing non-woody roots to form mycorrhizae were very "biologically smart."

Rather than competing with other microorganisms in the rhizosphere for exudates from the tree, the mycorrhizal-forming fungi went right to the source inside the tree. And, even more to their advantage, many of the mycorrhizal fungi grew thread-like strands of hyphae-long, vegetative tubes of fungi-out from the mycorrhizae. This inside and outside presence gave the fungi a distinct advantage over other microorganisms in the rhizosphere.

The tree gains efficiency with mycorrhizae in several ways. First, with their extended hyphae, mycorrhizae not only greatly extend the absorbing potential into the soil, but the hyphae may connect with other hyphae on other trees. In this way, the mycorrhizae serve to connect trees of the same or a different species. This leads to the conjecture that the natural connections that developed over long periods in the natural forest may have some survival value. That is why forest types are often named for the groups of species commonly found growing together. For example, we speak of the birch-beech-maple forest, or the pine-oak forest. From a practical standpoint, when trees are planted in cities and parks, there may be great survival advantages by planting groups of trees made up of the species that are normally found together in natural stands.

Second, the mycorrhizae have been shown to provide some resistance against root pathogens. It may be that the pathogens would have difficulties in building their populations in the rhizosphere dominated by the mycorrhizal fungi.

Perhaps the most important feature of the mycorrhizal fungi is that their boundary material is mostly chitin. Chitin is slightly different from cellulose by the replacement of some cellulose atoms by a chain of atoms that contain a nitrogen atom. This slight change in some way makes chitin a material better suited for absorption of elements. Remember that the fungus hyphae gain all their essentials for life by absorption through their boundary substance.

There are other advantages, to the chitin and the tube-like hyphae that ramify the soil in the rhizosphere and beyond. When the hyphae die, they add a nitrogen source for other organisms. Also, when the hyphae are digested, they leave tunnels in the soil that are about eight to 10 microns in diameter. For the bacteria, these small tunnels may mean the difference between life and death. The bacteria quickly colonize the tunnels. The survival advantage here is that the major threats to their survival are protozoa that are usually much larger than 10 microns. So the hungry amoebae are not able to get at the bacteria inside the eight-micron tunnels.

A common treatment for compaction is to fracture the soil and add water. The fracturing allows air to penetrate the soil, but does not provide any eight-micron tunnels for the bacteria. The only way to bring back the tunnels is to bring back the fungi in well-composted wood and leaf mulch, as nature does, or by inoculating the mulch with mycorrhizal fungi.

Who Was First?

I do not know if the fungi were the first to grow into the root to get first chance at exudates or whether it was the bacteria. Regardless, bacteria and their close relatives, the actinomycetes, also infect non-woody roots to form organs that serve for the fixation of atmospheric nitrogen. Fixation means that the nitrogen that makes up almost 80% of the air is converted to a soluble ionic form by the action of the bacteria and actinomycetes within the nodules on the roots. (Some free-living soil bacteria can also fix nitrogen.) An enzyme called nitrogenase is the catalyst for the reaction that will take place only under very exacting conditions. There must be soluble molybdenum and iron and no free oxygen available. These conditions are present within the nodules. Here again, the microorganisms benefit the tree by providing a source of soluble nitrogen, and, in turn, the bacteria and actinomycetes get first chance at exudates. Even more importantly, the nodules protect them from foraging protozoa.

Infections that result in benefits to both parties are called mutualistic. When the benefits are greater than the sum of the parts, the association is called synergistic.

Species of legumes commonly have bacterial nitrogen-fixing nodules and mycorrhizae. The mycorrhizae facilitate absorption of elements, and the nodules provide a nitrogen source. Many species of trees have actinorhizae, which are the nodules formed by the root infections by actinomycetes. Species of *Alnus* have very large nodules. The actinorhizae are common on tropical and subtropical trees, and especially on trees that have adapted to soils low in available elements essential for life.

On some subtropical and tropical trees, such as the macadamia, multi-branched clusters of non-woody roots called proteoid roots form. The proteoid roots alter the rhizosphere by acidification processes that facilitate the absorption of phosphorus-containing ions. When I examined the roots of dying macadamia nut trees in an orchard in Hawai'i, I could not find proteoid roots, yet only a few days earlier I had found them on macadamia nut trees growing in the wild. I learned later that the orchard where trees were dying was heavily fertilized on a regular basis with phosphorus.

Another type of nodule forms on species of cycads. These nodules harbor blue green algae, or cyanobacteria, that have the ability to fix atmospheric nitrogen.

My point is that many different synergistic associations have developed in, on and about non-woody roots that provide elements, not an energy source. These associations are of extreme benefit to all connected members. At the same time, the conditions that provide for the associations are very delicate and exacting. It does not take much to disrupt them.

It Does Not Take Much to Disrupt Them

This statement deserves repeating and repeating. The delicate "threads" that hold these powerful associations together need to be recognized and respected. Trees in cities grow only so long as these threads remain connected.

Trees grow as large oscillating pumps, with the top trapping energy and pumping it downward. The bottom absorbs water and elements and pumps them upward. The pumps have developed over time to work on the basis of many synergistic associations that maximize benefits for all connected members and to minimize waste.

Many of life's essentials for the bottom associates come from the top of the tree. And, the top works only because the bottom works. Energy is required to move things, and elements and water are required to build things.

Tree Treatments and the Rhizosphere

When trees are over-pruned, the top will be injured first. When it is injured, it will not serve the energy requirements of the bottom. Soon root diseases start and are blamed for the decline or death of the tree. Where over-pruning is common, so are root diseases.

Compacted soil blocks air and water to the bottom and crushes all the microcavities where the microorganisms live. In nature, decomposing wood and leaves keep conditions optimal for the rhizosphere inhabitants.

Over watering stalls the respiration processes in the roots. When respiration stops, carbonic acid is not formed. When carbonic acid is not formed, ions necessary for the absorption process do not form. When absorption is down, the tree system is in trouble.

Fertilizers can be very beneficial for healthy survival of trees planted outside their forest homes. How beneficial will depend greatly on an understanding of some basic chemistry. For example, the use of urea could be a contributing factor to decline where trees with genetic codes for growth on low pH soils are planted in high pH soils. If fertilization is a desired treatment, then a fertilizer that has nitrogen in a positive charged ion, such as an ammonium ion, would help to reduce the rhizosphere pH.

Primary Causes of Diseases

It is often very difficult to have people recognize the importance of small organisms in small places doing big things. Blame for the death of a tree is often placed on big things that can be seen or felt. Most pathogens are opportunistic weaklings waiting for a defense system to decrease. Many small disrupting events often lead to the decrease in a defense system. Then after the tree has been weakened, the final agent comes along and gets the full blame for the cause. A perfect example is the cankers on honey locust. Flush pruning is usually the real cause.

The organisms in the rhizosphere and surrounding soils have many different ways to weather rocks and to get nitrogen and other elements essential for their growth. What they cannot get in the soil is a sufficient energy source. Yes, some small animals die and provide carbon, and some microorganisms can get energy by chemosynthesis, but the requirements for carbon are much greater than what could be supplied by those sources alone. Carbon must come from the top of the leaves and photosynthates from the top of the tree. When the energy source from the top begins to decrease, the rhizosphere organisms will begin to starve.

I believe there is a way to decrease the potential starvation problem. In forests, more wood should be left on the ground, and in cities, more composted wood and leaves should be added in correct quantities to the soil about the base of trees. Incorrect treatments of pruning, watering, planting and fertilizing should be corrected, because they often start the imbalance that leads to decline. If these simple adjustments can be made, rhizosphere starvation will decrease and our trees will lead healthier and longer lives.

References

Foster, R.C., A.D. Rovira, and T.W. Cock. 1983. "Ultrastructure of the Root-Soil Interface." The American Phytopathological Society, St. Paul, MN.

Kilham, K. 1994. Soil Ecology. Cambridge University Press. Cambridge, UK.

Wild, A. 1994. Soils and the Environment: An introduction. Cambridge University Press. Cambridge, UK.

Original Source

This excerpt of "Troubles in the Rhizosphere" was reprinted with the kind permission of the author. The full text of this article including many excellent full color images can be viewed at:

http://www.chesco.com/~tree-man/shigo/rhizo.html, or purchased from Shigo and Trees, Associates, P.O. Box 769, Durham, NH 03824, USA. Tel: 603-868-7459; Fax: 603-868-1045.

This excerpt was originally published as *The Overstory* #70.

Microsymbionts

Lars Schmidt

Microsymbionts encompass soil-living organisms that form symbiosis with plant roots. There are three types of organism that are important for cultivated plants: mycorrhizas, rhizobia, and frankiae. Mycorrhiza (meaning "fungus-root") is formed by virtually all forest trees. Many trees grow poorly, especially under infertile soil conditions, without a mycorrhizal symbiont. A large group of important forest and agroforestry trees of the family Leguminosae depends on the bacterial symbionts, rhizobia (largest genus *Rhizobium),* which cause the formation of nitrogen-fixing root nodules. Some trees like *Alnus* and *Casuarina* species form nitrogen-fixing symbiosis with the bacteria *Frankia.* The bacterial associations rhizobia and *Frankia* are exclusively linked to nitrogen fixation while mycorrhiza play multiple roles in nutrient uptake (mainly phosphorus) and in protecting roots from infection and stress. Many leguminous and actinorhizal (associated with *Frankia)* trees depend on an association with both mycorrhiza and rhizobia or *Frankia* and must consequently be inoculated with both.

Microsymbionts are often present in the soil at the planting site if the site has borne trees of the same or a closely related species within a fairly recent past. In these cases seedlings will normally be infected and form symbiosis with the organism soon after outplanting. Where forest soil is used as sowing or potting medium, seedlings may easily be inoculated via the soil, and some types of microsymbiont may be naturally dispersed to the nursery plants from other host plants or from a closely located forest. However, in modern nursery and planting practices, microsymbionts are often absent, and must consequently be applied by active inoculation, e.g.:

1   Where species are grown on a site for the first time, and the species need specific types of symbiont not likely to be naturally present.

2   Where seedlings are raised on sterile medium such as vermiculite or fumigated soil.

3   Where planting is undertaken on denuded and eroded land, poor in nutrients and depleted of natural soil microsymbionts. Generally the survival of symbionts is short when their host species has disappeared.

Failure to establish appropriate symbiosis may cause complete crop failure, or production may be very low, especially on poor soil. On the other hand, productivity may increase significantly by using selected inoculant species or strains instead of naturally occurring ones. For example, in *Pseudotsuga menziesii,* wood production in trees inoculated with a superior strain was more than 100% above the naturally inoculated control after an 8-year study period (Le Tacon *et al* 1992). In *Paraserianthes* (former *Albizia) falcataria,* the best *Rhizobium* strain gave 48% better height growth than the poorest strain (Umali-Garcia *et al* 1988). Smaller, yet significant differences have been found between different strains of *Frankia* on inoculation of *Casuarina* (Rosbrook and Bowen 1987) and *Alnus* species (Prat 1989).

Because microsymbionts are associated with established trees and often species specific, they are often conveniently collected at the same time as the seed. Since application ("inoculation") is normally undertaken in connection with propagation (whether vegetatively or by seeds), microsymbiont management forms a natural extension of seed handling, and often runs parallel with seed handling. Many forest seed centres, seed banks and other seed and propagule suppliers, who collect, store and distribute seeds and propagules also supply inoculants. Effective management of microsymbionts implies the technical skill of and facilities for identification, collection, extraction, propagation, storage, distribution and inoculation. Detailed descriptions and guidelines have been elaborated for many temperate species, for mycorrhizae especially on pines, for rhizobia especially for agricultural crops. Many of these methods can be generalised to other species and conditions. Some research has been carried out and experience achieved for the most important tropical trees.

Unfortunately, a major drawback of microsymbiont management and handling is the requirement for technical facilities. Whereas the actual inoculation is relatively simple, several methods of inoculant production require facilities for aseptic (sterile) operation. This is especially true for rhizobia identification and cultivation, which requires a laboratory equipped for microbiology. If these facilities are not available, one must either rely on inoculants purchased from other places or use simpler methods where less advanced equipment is required.

Terminology and Classification

Microsymbionts are either bacteria or fungi that form a close association with a host plant. The association is denoted a symbiosis, which strictly means "living together", but often implicitly means "to mutual benefit." Microsymbionts infect the feeder root of the host. However, unlike pathogenic infection there are no disease symptoms, and in contrast to a parasitic infection there is a two-way benefit, a nutrient exchange: the plant provides the infecting organism with photosynthesates (e.g., sugar); the microsymbiont in turn provides nitrogen or phosphorus depending on infection type. In the two types of bacterial symbiosis the infection is concentrated in special parts of the root, where the host plant forms root nodules, which are bacterial colonies surrounded by host tissue. The symbioses exist both in herbal and woody plants, and many plant species have both bacterial and fungal symbiosis.

Fungal symbionts are the mycorrhizas, which form the most wide-spread symbiosis between plants and microorganisms. There are two types of bacterial symbionts: rhizobia, named after the most important genus, *Rhizobium,* which forms symbiosis with host species of the family Leguminosae, and Frankiae with the one genus, *Frankia,* which lives in association with a number of tree species from different families. Frankiae are actinomycetic bacteria which infect roots of their host plants; therefore the hosts are collectively called **actinorhizal plants.**

Mycorrhiza

Mycorrhizal symbiosis functionally forms an extension of the plant root system. A fine net of fungal hyphae in close contact with the plant roots extend their threads into a large volume of soil where they explore and extract nutrients from the soil beyond the reach of the plant roots. The nutrients are translocated through the fungal hyphae, hence bringing them to the plant roots, where they can be assimilated and used by the plant. The fungus, in return, is provided with simple sugars and possibly other compounds from the plants' photosynthesis. Some mycorrhizal fungi produce plant hormones, which stimulate root development, e.g., *Pisolithus tinctorius* on poplars (Navratil and Rachon 1981).

Mycorrhiza is known to protect the roots of the host plant against pathogens and certain toxins, and mycorrhizal plants generally have a higher resistance to drought, soil acidity, and high soil temperatures (Redhead 1982). The fungal sheath surrounding the feeder roots of ectomycorrhiza often has a higher resistance to toxins (acids, etc.) than the plant root and can consequently form a physical barrier to the soil. Further, soil will adhere to the mycorrhizal net thereby decreasing "shock" when the seedlings are exposed to field conditions; that is especially important for bare-root seedlings, where mycorrhiza may also reduce the risk of desiccation of the roots during transportation. Mycorrhizal symbionts are grouped into two main types according to the symbiotic structure of the root system: ectomycorrhiza and vesicular-arbuscular mycorrhiza (VAM).

Rhizobia

Rhizobia are a group of soil-living bacteria, which are able to live in symbiosis with and nodulate members of the plant family Leguminosae. Leguminosae is subdivided into three subfamilies, Caesalpinioideae, Mimosoideae and Papilionoideae. More than 30% of species of the Caesalpinioideae and more than 90% of the species in the other subfamilies form nodules (Brewbaker *et al* 1982, Dart 1988). Within the subfamilies some genera are characterised by high frequency of nodulated species and others by low. There are also species within an otherwise highly nodulating genus which fail to nodulate. Most acacias, for example, nodulate but there are exceptions (Dommergues 1982). The species-specific capability of nodulation and N-fixation is, however, subject to uncertainty since many species capable of nodulation do not form nodules in some areas, either because of absence of the proper symbiont or because environmental conditions are unfavourable to the symbiosis. There are also differences between provenances in their susceptibility to nodulation by rhizobia (Dart 1988).

Some rhizobium-legume associations are very specific and the legume will form nodules only when infected with a specific rhizobium. Others will form nodules with a range of rhizobia. That means in practice that for the first group, inoculants must be collected from the same host species, for the second group a broad range of host species can be used as inoculant sources. Therefore, for practical purposes, legumes have been assembled into cross-inoculation groups. A cross inoculation group consists of species that will form nodules when inoculated with rhizobia obtained from nodules from any member of the group. A cross inoculation group may, in the extreme, consist of one species only. Cross inoculation groups are well established among agricultural crops but only superficially established among tree crops.

Obviously, host-specific rhizobia must be applied as inoculant when the host species is grown on a site for the first time. For other species the requirement depends on the possible available rhizobia in the soil, that is, whether other compatible legume hosts have grown on the site within a fairly recent past. Some Australian *Acacia* spp. grown in Africa nodulate freely with the indigenous rhizobia.

Frankia

Frankia are bacteria which infect roots of their host plants; the hosts are collectively called actinorhizal plants. *Frankia* are filamentous, branching, aerobic, gram-positive bacteria. They differentiate into three different cell types viz. (1) vegetative cells which develop into mycelia almost like mycorrhizal fungi, (2) sporangia forming numerous spores, and (3) vesicles which are the site of nitrogen fixation (Lechevalier and Lechevalier 1990).

Frankia may live free in the soil as saprophytes. They are dispersed in the soil via the vegetative hyphae. The long-distance dispersal probably takes place via spores or vegetative cells in moving soil or by wind dispersal of spores; spores are relatively resistant to desiccation (Torrey 1982).

Frankia form symbiosis with plant species from a number of distinct genera and families, many of which have no close taxonomic relation. So far, around 200 actinorhizal plants are known, distributed over 8 families and 25 genera. The most important forest trees with symbiotic relationship with *Frankia* belong to the plant family Casuarinaceae, a family that comprises almost exclusively actinorhizal plants. Apart from *Casuarina,* the family includes two other actinorhizal genera viz. *Allocasuarina* and *Gymnostoma.* Betulaceae contains only one actinorhizal genus, *Alnus.* The genus *Rubus* contains only one known actinorhizal species viz. *Rubus ellipticus* (Gauthier *et al* 1984). *Frankia* also form symbiosis with species of the genera *Aelaeagnus* and *Hippophaë*.

Some actinorhizal plants can be inoculated with a range of *Frankia* strains while others are very specific. For example the genus *Allocasuarina* can be inoculated with strains obtained from that genus only, while *Gymnostoma* are the least specific one and can be inoculated with inoculants even from species outside Casuarinaceae; *Casuarina* spp. are intermediate between those two in terms of specificity (Torrey 1990, Gauthier *et al* 1984).

Collection and Handling

Mycorrhizae, rhizobia and frankiae are soil-living organisms and spend their entire or the greater part of their life cycle under the soil surface. They are adapted to moist, dark and relatively cool conditions with small temperature fluctuations. These conditions should be maintained during handling. Some microsymbionts form dispersal units, e.g., spores which are relatively resistant to above-soil conditions. They can survive desiccation, higher temperatures and light and have relatively long viability. Generally however, the viability of most microsymbionts is short in comparison to seeds, but there is a great variation between species within the three types. Proper handling and storage conditions can greatly improve the viability of microsymbionts.

Where inoculant material, whether soil, nodules or spores, is collected from the field, a site with mature, healthy and vigorous trees should be selected. Mature trees are likely to support the largest amount of symbionts, healthy and vigorous trees may also be an indication of good inoculation, and the risk of collecting material infected with pathogens, which could be a nuisance later on, is smaller.

Collection should be made from or under trees of the same species or species with compatible microsymbionts, for rhizobia and *Frankia* within the same cross inoculation group (Baker 1987). Collection should be made from trees growing on typical growth sites; these are likely to contain symbionts adapted to the prevailing soil type. Exceptionally good or poor sites should be avoided unless the trees to be inoculated are supposed to be grown on similar sites (Benoit and Berry 1990).

The best time of collection differs for different types of inoculant material. Soil usually contains a reasonable amount of inoculant and can be collected at almost any time of the year. Sporocarps of ectomycorrhizal fungi are only available for a short period of the year. The moist season normally supports the greater number of sporocarps, but both duration and season of sporocarp formation vary with species. Inoculant collected from or together with host roots should generally be collected during the most active growth season, which normally is the rainy season.

+R+M   +R-M   -R+M   -R-M

Left to right: *Gliricidia sepium* seedlings inoculated with both mycorrhizae and rhizobia, only rhizobia, only mycorrhizae, and with no inoculation. (photo: K. Mudge)

This is also practical as the soil is easier to dig up and there is less risk of damage to both the host tree and the inoculant.

Rhizobium nodules should preferably be collected from young roots. The nodules of older roots are likely to be senescent and contain few infective bacteria. Seedlings or young trees are the best source of nodules. Cutting and examining the interior of a few nodules with a hand lens gives an indication of the condition: fresh and active N_2-fixing rhizobia nodules are typically pink, red or brown, *Frankia* whitish or yellowish; senescent nodules are typically greyish green (Benoit and Berry 1990).

Inoculant Types and Inoculation Techniques

Inoculant types vary from simple forms in which microsymbiont-infected soil is applied to the nursery soil, to sophisticated production of pure culture inoculants, incorporated into carriers and applied to seeds as pellets or beads. Which species and method is used is a result of balanced consideration of various factors:

1   Some commercial pure culture inoculants contain microsymbiont species which promote productivity under particular environmental conditions, but may be less productive than local species under other conditions.

2   Different methods of inoculant production and inoculation apply to different species and situations. Some tree species may only form symbiosis with specific bacteria or fungal species. Sometimes compatibility between the two organisms varies with the environment.

3   Pure culture production is usually both technically complicated and expensive. In many cases, inoculants purchased from specialised manufacturers and dealers may be more economical than starting independent production or using unselected material.

Apart from soil mixtures which may contain all types of organisms, both type of inoculant and application methods vary with type of symbiont. Mycorrhizal inoculants can be applied as spores or mycelium. Mycelium inoculates usually give faster infection but are more sensitive to desiccation and other environmental factors. They have short viability and are relatively bulky as compared to spores. Some ectomycorrhizal fungi can be grown in pure culture on a nutrient medium to obtain a mycelial culture. The spores are often initially germinated on agar prior to cultivation. Some ectomycorrhizal fungi can be multiplied by applying spores directly to the nutrient medium (Marx 1980).

VAM fungi cannot be grown in pure culture on nutrient media and are therefore multiplied by infecting roots of an intermediate host e.g., sorghum or sweet potato with the spores of VAM. Both rhizobia and *Frankia* can be grown in pure culture but the method is too slow and too expensive for most *Frankia*. Many plants need dual inoculation with mycorrhiza and either rhizobia or *Frankia*. Generally the two types of organism are not antagonistic to each other and can sometimes be mixed. However, in many cases it is difficult to control the application rate if the two inoculants are mixed, and they are therefore usually handled separately throughout.

Inoculation rate, i.e., the amount of inoculant used per seedling, varies with application method, and the concentration of infective bacteria, spores or mycelium in the inoculant. Increasing amount of applied inoculum generally speeds up the colonisation process and symbiont formation. Plants are usually inoculated in the nursery rather than during planting in the field. Nursery inoculation has the following rationale:

- Inoculated seedlings are generally much more competitive and able to withstand the inevitable stress they will be exposed to immediately after outplanting especially if the plants are planted under harsh environmental conditions.
- Early inoculation usually reduces requirement for fertilizer and pesticides in the nursery. In addition to reducing the cost and possible harmful effects of these applicants, mycorrhizal seedlings are known to be generally more resistant to pests, diseases and adverse environments.
- Nursery inoculation opens the potential for selective inoculation with superior microsymbiont strains or types, specifically adapted to the species and the planting site and is hence potentially more effective (Trappe 1977, Marx *et al* 1982).

Field inoculation has its main advantage in that the seedlings are exposed to the future environment when inoculated and may consequently preferably form symbiotic association with the species that are better adapted to that particular field condition. It is known for mycorrhiza that even if seedlings are inoculated in the nursery, fungal associations often change when the plants are transplanted into the field, provided that a microsymbiont is present at the planting site (Marx *et al* 1982). Where seedlings are inoculated with several species or strains, one or few usually become dominant under the prevailing field conditions.

Soil Inoculant

Forest soil or litter collected under appropriate tree species often contains a balanced population of adapted microsymbionts. As freshly collected forest soil is often used as planting medium because of its physical properties, seedlings are naturally exposed to inoculation in this way. It may also be used deliberately as inoculation material, e.g., by applying a small amount of inoculated soil or litter (leaves, needles and root fragments) to the planting medium. This method is often used for mycorrhizal inoculation, whereas for rhizobia and *Frankia* the amount of inoculant provided this way is often too small. Soil collected from nursery beds previously supporting seedlings with good mycorrhiza is appropriate. About 10–15% by volume of soil is mixed into the top approximately 10 cm of the nursery bed or mixed in the same ratio into the potting soil (Molina and Trappe 1984). If soil is scarce, a handful of soil can be placed at root level during pot filling.

Problems of using soil as inoculant material are the bulk to be transported and that soil may contain infective pathogens. Fumigation and other soil sterilisation normally kill microsymbionts.

Infected roots and nodules

Problems with bulk and potential pathogens may be reduced by collecting infected mycorrhizal roots and bacterial nodules only. Roots are chopped and nodules crushed before application. However, for mycorrhiza relatively large quantities are needed if the material is used as inoculant directly. Cruz (1983) estimated that at least one kg of ectomycorrhizal roots should be used per cubic meter of nursery soil to assure proper inoculation. VAM is often applied as chopped roots of intermediate hosts after being multiplied in pot culture. Crushed nodules are rarely used as inoculant for rhizobia because the number of bacteria that can be applied in this way is too small. The nodules are more often used as a source for cultured inoculants. Because the root nodules of *Frankia* are relatively large, and because culture of *Frankia* is slow, crushed nodules are often used directly as inoculant for this type. Both fresh and stored Frankia nodules can be used, but dry nodules should be rehydrated before crushing.

The principle of "nurse seedlings" is that microsymbionts from already inoculated seedlings will spread naturally to neighbouring seedlings in the nursery. Hence a precondition is that there is likelihood of movement in the soil which is the case with both ectomycorrhiza and VAM. The inoculated seedlings are planted in the nursery bed at intervals of one to two meters before the seeds are sown. Mycorrhiza will spread from the infected to the newly germinated seedlings. Alternatively, chopped roots of mycorrhizal seedlings are incorporated into the soil of the nursery bed (Castellano and Molina 1989, Cruz 1983, Marx 1980, Mikola 1970, and Molina and Trappe 1984).

The main advantage of nurse seedlings is that fresh inoculant material is always available and that the inoculant is adapted to the prevailing climate and nursery soil. However, the method also has certain drawbacks:

- The nurse seedlings may compete with the young established seedlings for nutrients and light
- The nurse seedlings may interfere with the preparation and management of the seed bed
- Inoculation may be slow and uneven
- Fumigation or other soil sterilisation procedures cannot be undertaken after the nurse seedlings have been planted. Therefore there is a higher risk of soil pathogens and competition with naturally disseminated mycorrhizal fungi

References

Baker, D.D. 1987. Relationships among pure cultured strains of Frankia based on host specificity. Physiologia Plantarum. 70: 2, 245–248.

Benoit, L.F. and Berry, A.M. 1990. Methods for production and use of actinorhizal plants in forestry, low maintenance landscapes, and revegetation. In: The Biology of Frankia and Actinorhizal Plants (Schwintzer, CR. and Tjepkema, J.D., eds.). 281–298. Academic Press.

Brewbaker, J.L., Belt, R. van Den and MacDicken, K. 1982. Nitrogen-fixing tree resources: Potentials and limitations. In: Biological Nitrogen Fixation Technology for Tropical Agriculture (Graham, P.H. and Harris, S.C., eds.): 413–425.

Castellano, MA. and Molina, R. 1989: Mycorrhiza. In: The container tree nursery manual, Vol. 5. Agric. Handbook 674. (Landis, T.D., Tinus, R.W., McDonald, SE. and Barnett, J.P., eds.). 101–167. US Department of Agriculture, Forest Service. Washington DC.

Cruz, R.E. de la 1983: Technologies for the inoculation of mycorrhiza to pines in ASEAN. In: Workshop on nursery and plantation practices in the ASEAN. (Aba, T.T. and Hoskins, M.R., eds.). 94–111.

Dart, P. 1988. Nitrogen fixation in tropical forestry and the use of Rhizobium. In: Tropical forest ecology and management in the Asia-Pacific region. Proceedings of Regional Workshop held at Lae, Papua New Guinea. (Kapoor-VijayP., Appanah, S. and Saulei, SM., eds.). Commonwealth Science Council. U.K.: 142–154.

Dommergues, Y.R. 1982. Ensuring effective symbiosis in nitrogen-fixing trees. In: Biological Nitrogen Fixation Technology for Tropical Agriculture. (Graham, P.H. and Harris, S.C., eds.). 395–411.

Gauthier, D., Diem, H.G., Dommergues, Y.R. and Ganry, F. 1984. Tropical and subtropical actinorhizal plants. Pesquaria Agropecuaria Brasileira, Brasilia. 19 (Special Issue): 19–136.

Lechevalier, M.P. and Lechevalier, H.A. 1990. Systematics, isolation, and culture of Frankia. In: The Biology of Frankia and Actinorhizal Plants. (Schwintzer, C.R. and Tjepkema, J.D., eds.). 35–60. Academic Press.

Le Tacon, F., Alvarez, I.F., Bouchard, D., Henrion, B., Jackson, R.M., Luff, S., Parlade, J.I., Pera, J., Stenstrom, E., Villeneuve, N. and Walker, C. 1992. Variations in field response of forest trees so nursery ectomycorrhizal inoculation in Europe. In: Mycorrhizas in Ecosystems. (Read, D.J., Lewis, D.H., Fitter, A.H. and Alexander, I.J., eds.). 119–134. CAB International.

Marx, D.H. 1980. Ectomycorrhizal fungus inoculations: a tool for improving forestation practices. In: Tropical Mycorrhiza Research. (Mikola, P., ed.). 13–71. New York: Oxford University Press.

Marx, D.H., Jarl, K., Ruehle, J.L., Kenney, D.S., Cordell, CE., Riffle, J.W., Molina, R.J., Pawuk, W.H., Navratil, S., Tinus, R.W. and Goodwin, O.C. 1982. Commercial vegetative inoculum of Pisolithus tinctorius and inoculation techniques for development of ectomycorrhiza on container-grown tree seedlings. Forest Science 28: 373–400.

Mikola, P. 1970. Mycorrhizal inoculation in afforestation. In: International Review of Forest Research (Romberger, J.A. and Micola, P., eds.). 3:123–196.

Molina, R. and Trappe, J.M. 1984. Mycorrhiza management in bareroot nurseries. In: Forest Nursery Manual, production of bareroot seedlings. (Duryea, M.L. and Landis, T.D., eds.). 211–223. US Dept. Agric.

Navratil, S. and Rachon, G.C. 1981: Enhanced root and shoot development of poplar cuttings induced by Pisolithus inoculum. Can. Jour. For. Res. 11:4, 844–848.

Prat, D. 1989. Effects of some pure and mixed Frankia strains on seedling growth in different Alnus species. Plant and Soil 113, 31–38.

Redhead. 1982. Ectomycorrhiza in the tropics. In: Microbiology of Tropical Soils. (Dommegues, Y.R. and Diem, H.G. (eds.)).

Rosbrook, P.A. and Bowen, G.D. 1987. The abilities of three Frankia isolates to nodulate and fix nitrogen with four species of Casuarina. Physiol. Plantarum 70, 373–377.

Torrey, J.G. 1990. Cross-inoculation groups within Frankia and host endosymbiont association: In: The Biology of Frankia and Actinorhizal Plants. (Schwintzer, C.R. and Tjepkema, J.D., eds.). Academic Press. 83–106.

Torrey J.G. 1982. Casuarina: Actinorhizal nitrogen fixing tree of the tropics. In: Biological Nitrogen Fixation Technology for Tropical Agriculture. (Graham, P.G. and Harris, S.C., eds.). 427–439.

Trappe, J.M. 1977. Selection of fungi for ectomycorrhizal inoculation in nurseries. Annual Review of Phytopathology 15: 203–222.

Umali-Garcia, M., Libuit, J.S. and Baggayan, R.L. 1988. Effects of Rhizobium inoculation on growth and nodulation of Albizia falcataria (L.) Fosh. and Acacia mangium Willd. in the nursery. Plant and Soil 108, 71–78.

Original Source

This article was adapted with the kind permission of the author and publisher from:

Schmidt, L. 2000. Guide to Handling of Tropical and Subtropical Forest Seed. Danida Forest Seed Centre. Humlebaek, Denmark.

This exceptional guide covers forest tree seed handling from scientific, practical and administrative perspectives. Much of this text is available online at: http://www.dfsc.dk/Guidechapters.htm.

For further information about the book and a wide range of other publications contact:

Danida Forest Seed Centre
Krogerupvej 21
DK-3050 Humlebaek, Denmark
Tel: +45-49 19 05 00; Fax: +45-49 16 02 58
Email: dfsc@dfsc.dk; Web: http://www.dfsc.dk

This excerpt was originally published as *The Overstory* #131.

Animal Assistants

Animals can be key players in healthy, productive farms and forests. Animal assistants include insect pollinators enhancing fruit production, wild birds keeping pests in balance, poultry and livestock cycling nutrients and providing food, as well as wildlife creating ecotourism opportunities.

Section Contents

Microlivestock

Kim M. Wilkinson and Craig R. Elevitch

"Farm animals" to most Westerners usually means pigs, cows, goats, and sheep. Indeed, these same animals have been heavily emphasized by development projects. However, in many parts of the world, the major protein sources are not from these animals, but instead from "microlivestock"—small animals managed for food. There are over a thousand kinds of reptiles, rodents, insects, birds, and other small animals that can be categorized as microlivestock. Some of these, like the guinea pig, are highly domesticated and raised in close quarters with people. Others are only semi-domesticated, and live out on the farm or forest, like iguanas. Some microlivestock are currently collected from wild areas, with domestication projects underway, like the giant forest rats of Africa. Microlivestock have been essential to human nutrition for thousands of years. In the future, these small animals may be major players in food security, environmental conservation, and economic diversity.

Microlivestock are often adapted to niches that agroforests provide. (photo: C. Elevitch)

Environmental Advantages of Microlivestock

The environmental destruction resulting from inappropriate use of large animals such cattle is well known. Microlivestock, in contrast, can occupy forest niches that large animals can not. For example, the green iguana, long an important food source for eggs and meat, has been semi-domesticated in Costa Rica. It can be a prolific producer, and thrives in both forest and farm environments. Food insects can also be a tremendously abundant resource from forested areas. In conservation areas as well as agroforests, microlivestock can enhance total yields and supply diversified products in a way that is compatible with trees and the environment.

Microlivestock can also be highly productive in environments that are not suitable for other kinds of animals, such as steep hillsides, highly degraded areas, and even urban environments. In some parts of the tropics, large introduced farm animals may not be suitable at all, while a local species of microlivestock may thrive. For example, in the hot, humid, seasonally flooded lowlands of some parts of South America, cattle are almost impossible to raise, being plagued by disease and malnutrition. However, the local capybara, a semi-aquatic rodent weighing about 100 pounds, thrives (although its large size stretches the definition of microlivestock!). Using locally adapted animals like these reduces the pressure to alter the environment dramatically in order to accommodate conventional livestock production.

Economic Advantages of Microlivestock

The use of microlivestock has many economic advantages over the raising of larger animals, particularly for the small farmer. Large animals by their nature must be bought and sold in large units. For example, saving up to buy a cow may take a very long time, and if an accident or illness befalls the cow, the entire investment is lost. A farmer who chooses microlivestock, in contrast, can invest in small increments. The investment can be spread out over a number of animals, reducing the risk of loss. Smaller animals tend to reach sexual maturity faster, and can reproduce quickly, expanding the investment. Many varieties of microlivestock can be raised in backyards or even inside the home, not requiring the larger spaces necessary to raise bigger animals. Production for home use or market can be distributed more evenly throughout the year, rather than all at once, resulting in a steady income that can be more easily controlled in response to market conditions.

Although many kinds of microlivestock can be used for subsistence, they can also be a good source of income. Most small-scale farmers cannot hope to compete in the market with large, high-input, single-species industrial systems. However, microlivestock producers can cater to specialized niche or exotic markets and get a good price for their product. For example, consumers in Ghana will pay up to three times more for the meat from a forest rodent called a cane rat or grasscutter (*Thryonomys* spp.) than they do for beef. Even in very affluent areas, health concerns about the high fat content of highly domesticated animal protein is adding to consumer interest in alternate protein sources. In European markets, specialty foods like ostrich meat and snails sell for premium prices.

Examples of Microlivestock

Rodents and rodent-like animals Guinea pigs, capybaras, giant rats, cane rats (aka grasscutters), agouti, and rabbits are some examples of rodents used as microlivestock. Many rodents are highly adaptable and prolific, and can do well on a diet of weedy vegetation and kitchen scraps. Their meat is higher in protein and lower in fat than more conventional meat. Secondary rodent products, such as manure and fur, can also be important for farm use or to sell.

Food insects Water beetles, palm grubs, grasshoppers, and agave worms are just a few of the over 2000 species of insects that are used for food. Insects are essential sources of proteins, fats, and important vitamins in many parts of the world. For example, 100 grams of termites can provide over 500 calories of food energy, while bee larvae contains ten times more vitamin D than cod liver oil and twice as much vitamin A as egg yolk. Some insects are harvested from the wild, providing abundant food from degraded or marginal areas as well as forests; others are cultivated intensively. Some edible insects are important secondary products from agroforests; for example, in Irian Jaya, the sago grub (*Rhynchophorus* sp.) is cultivated as part of sago palm production. Insects take up very little space and can also fit naturally into agroforests. They are efficient producers of protein, needing less feed to produce more meat than any other kind of animal.

Reptiles Some reptiles, such as alligators, crocodiles, and monitor lizards, are used for food and other products, although they may never gain wide acceptance as farm animals. Other reptiles are smaller and more user-friendly, like green iguanas and black iguanas. These smaller reptiles may become important, forest-friendly protein sources, for eggs as well as meat.

Birds While the chicken has been emphasized, there are many other kinds of birds that are important food sources. Pigeons, quails, guinea fowl, and many others have been part of food production. Birds can be highly variable in needs and abilities, and are used differently. For example, pigeons are sometimes grown in urban environments, where they are released to scavenge for food out in the city, returning home to eventually feed their keepers. Other birds, such as some kinds of turkeys, are tough and forage in harsh or degraded environments.

Other promising species Armadillos, snails, water deer, South America's microdeer, duikers (rodent-sized antelopes from Africa), and many other kinds of animals may be important for food security in the future.

Many kinds of microlivestock are best used locally, in their native environment. Any farmer attempting to introduce a new species should research carefully to be sure the species is adapted to local conditions, but will not become invasive. Another challenge is to create a market niche for the product, which may involve overcoming consumer reluctance to try a product from an unfamiliar animal.

Microlivestock can fit well as components in agroforestry systems, increasing total yields and adding to food security.

Original Source

This chapter was originally published as *The Overstory* #41.

Further Reading

Board on Science and Technology for International Development (BOSTID). 1991. Microlivestock: Little-known small animals with a promising economic future. National Academy of Sciences. A valuable reference on microlivestock, highlighting 35 underexploited species.

Agroforestry and Biological Diversity

Kim M. Wilkinson and Craig R. Elevitch

Agroforestry plantings should not be considered a replacement for the conservation of native tropical forests, but agroforesters can play a key role in helping to conserve biological diversity (biodiversity) of species. Agroforestry plantings can provide expanded habitat for a wide range of species, from soil microlife to insects to mammals.

Trees support wildlife and visa versa

How much benefit can agroforestry plantings have for biodiversity? In Latin America, for instance, numerous studies have shown that the traditional coffee agroforests (coffee integrated with 2–5 other tree species) are second only to undisturbed tropical forests in their diversity of birds, insect life, bats, and even mammals. For example, The Smithsonian Migratory Bird Center discovered at least 180 species of birds in Mexican coffee agroforests—up to ten times more than the bird diversity found in monoculture coffee plantations studied elsewhere. In the lowlands of Sumatra, resin-producing agroforests planted several generations ago are now some of the last reservoirs of biodiversity in the region, harboring rare epiphytes and herbs as well as 46 species of mammals, 92 species of birds, and much of the native soil fauna (See References). Many effective conservation organizations now include agroforestry as a component of their programs.

The value of agroforestry for biodiversity is especially high when agroforestry replaces or expands into pastures or monoculture plantations or farms. A well designed agroforest, modeled after healthy, diverse natural forests will spontaneously attract and support biodiversity. While most of us have productivity as a primary focus, there are some things we can do to optimize the positive impact of our plantings on biodiversity.

Tips to Improve Biodiversity in Your Planting

As a general rule, the more forest-like in form and diverse in species a planting is, the more kinds of life it will attract and support. Here are some design tips that can help your agroforestry project become a safe harbor for biodiversity in your area:

Create a variety of habitat niches for wildlife

These include overstory, understory, and ground layers. If feasible, avoid clean culture in your management practices. Instead, leave some dead logs, leaf litter, scrub, etc.

Provide shade Shady conditions are prevalent in natural forests, and shade fosters a wide range of species, from larger animals to soil microlife. If you have some practices on your project that require sunny open spaces (annual crops, open pasture, etc.), remember that most wildlife does not like to cross open spaces. Use open spaces in smaller patchworks throughout the project, rather than in a contiguous open area without overstory shade.

Create wildlife corridors These are areas or zones of the planting that are not often disturbed or entered by people, leaving them to be colonized naturally. Ideally, connect these areas together to form safe corridors throughout the project, and connect them to neighboring habitats for wildlife.

Plant many different kinds of species Complex, multi-storied agroforests have much more benefit than just one or two additional species integrated with a monoculture.

Conserve and store water on the land In dry areas, water sources are especially attractive to wildlife. In addition to protecting natural streams or springs on the site, water-holding management practices like mulching, water catchment, ponds, and swales are also valuable.

Learn about habitat requirements If you are targeting a specific native species, learn about your intended guest's needs and plant the known food source, habitat environment, and other necessities to attract it. Encourage or actively cultivate native plant species within the project, as they are more likely to support native life, from soil fauna to birds. Also be aware of the exotic species that native wildlife may have become accustomed to as food or habitat that will also be of value. If you are near a native forest area, your chances of wildlife moving in spontaneously are greater than if you are isolated from natural areas. Contact a local biology school or conservation program for the information you need. They may also be able to help you identify the most important species in need of conservation support.

From an agroforester's perspective, it is important to recognize that the same practices that attract desirable wildlife may also attract species that could be problematic for production. In Hawai'i, for example, wild pigs that cross through or reside in tree plantings may be welcomed by some projects, but may cause too much damage to trees or crops for others. In other areas of the world, species such as monkeys, fruit-eating birds, and other native animals may adversely affect productivity. If neighboring areas are sources for these kinds of wildlife, decide at the outset how you will exclude, manage, or possibly benefit from their presence. If necessary, you may be able to find ways to make up the revenues lost on crops directly from the biodiversity of your project through tours or field visits from people who want to see wildlife.

Ideally, large agroforestry plantings should work in cooperation with local conservation efforts (reserves, parks, and so forth) to optimize the benefit of the work.

Keep it up and who knows, your planting may one day be mistaken for a natural forest! If not by a person, at least by a wild creature who's happy to find a new home.

Original Source

This chapter was originally published as *The Overstory #21.*

Further Reading

de Foresta, H., and G. Michon. Agroforests in Sumatra- where ecology meets economy. In Agroforestry Today 6(4): 12-13. ICRAF, United Nations Avenue, Gigiri, PO Box 30677, Nairobi, Kenya. Email: icraf@cgnet.com; Web: http://www.cgiar.org/icraf

van Noordwijk, M, *et al.* To segregate—or to integrate? The question of balance between production and biodiversity conservation in complex agroforestry systems. In Agroforestry Today 9(1): 6-7. ICRAF, See address above.

Walker, R. 1993. Attracting Wildlife for Agroforestry. Hawai'i Department of Land and Natural Resources, Division of Forestry and Wildlife, 1151 Punchbowl St. Honolulu, HI USA 96813 (808) 587-0166.

Bees and Agroforestry

Kim M. Wilkinson and Craig R. Elevitch

All fruit and seed crops need to be pollinated in order to be productive. Bees are very active and effective pollinators for many kinds of crops. The integration of bees into agroforestry systems can improve crop yield. This chapter discusses both the use of honey bees (apiculture) and the fostering of wild bees.

Honey Bees

Properly managed pollination by honey bees can result in larger, well-formed fruits, berries, vegetables, nuts, and seeds. At the same time, the honey bees produce honey and a wide range of other products that are potential sources of income.

While managed pollination by honey bees has become standard for large-scale agriculture in temperate areas, innovative beekeeping practices are springing up throughout the tropics. The subject has wide appeal to tropical farmers because beekeeping does not require large amounts of labor, land, or capital, but enhances productivity and contributes to sustainability of farming systems. Beekeeping can be practiced successfully on a part-time basis, and yields a wide array of high-value products that can increase a farmer's income by 40–60%.

Beekeeping is being practiced in tropical orchards, home gardens, plantations, and many agroforestry systems including coconut, coffee, pineapple, and others. Beekeeping is also a relatively low-impact activity that can increase local people's income from native forest or conservation areas.

Bee products

When most people think of beekeeping, they think of honey production. Honey is an important product that fetches a high market price in many parts of the

Bees provide valuable services and many products. (photo: C. Elevitch)

Tropical agroforestry trees which are a good source of nectar for honey bees

Acacia confusa (formosa koa)	*Citrus species* (citrus trees)	*Mangifera indica* (mango)
Acacia holosericea (holosericea)	*Cocos nucifera* (coconut)	*Melia azedarach* (chinaberry)
Albizia adianthifolia	*Eucalyptus species* (eucalyptus)	*Morus nigra* (mulberry)
Albizia chinensis	*Dalbergia sissoo* (sissoo rosewood)	*Pimenta dioica* (allspice)
Albizia lebbeck (Tibet tree)	*Gliricidia sepium* (madre de cacao)	*Pithecellobium dulce* (Manila tamarind)
Albizia saman (rain tree, monkeypod)	*Gmelina arborea* (white beech)	*Prosopis species* (kiawe, etc.)
Azadirachta indica (neem)	*Grevillea robusta* (silk oak)	*Psidium guajava* (guava)
Cajanus cajan (pigeon pea)	*Hibiscus rosa-sinensis* (hibiscus)	*Sesbania sesban* (sesban)
Calliandra calothyrsus (calliandra)	*Inga vera* (inga, ice cream bean)	*Syzygium cumini* (java plum)
Cassia spectabilis (golden shower tree)		

world, but there are many other products from bee keeping that can be equally if not more lucrative than honey. "Apitherapy," or the use of bee products for health and healing, is growing in the world market. Apitherapy products include natural bee pollen, raw propolis, fresh royal jelly (currently selling for US $70–$100 per kilogram), and bee venom (currently selling for over $100 per gram in China). Other products from bees include bee wax, which is used for candles and in many crafts, including batik work. Honey can be processed into honey cider-vinegar and honey wine (also known as mead). Honey and bee products are also being used in soaps and beauty products.

Multipurpose Tropical Trees and Shrubs for Bees

If you are wondering if your current agroforestry system will benefit from and support bees, look at these examples of tropical agroforestry trees and shrubs that all provide nectar for bees. The improved pollination by the bees enhances production of seeds or fruits of these plants as well:

Fostering Wild Bees

Honey bees have become a key element in food production, especially for pollination. While the food supply is becoming dependent on one kind of bee (*Apis mellifera*), there exist over 20,000 species of

wild bees, and many other pollinators including moths, birds and bats. Our need for an expanding food supply and managed farming systems must be balanced by an awareness of future possibilities, and particularly the need to make room for species that may not currently have recognized economic importance.

The risks of dependence on one kind of bee for crop production is already becoming clear. Problems from diseases, pests, and invasion from the Africanized honey bee are jeopardizing beekeeping in some parts of the world. For example, in the northwestern United States, honey bee populations have been severely depleted (in some areas by 40%) by pests such as the honeybee tracheal mite. In order to get adequate pollination of home orchards, the native, solitary Blue Orchard Mason Bee (*Osmia lingaria*) is now being encouraged in the area by increasing the availability of nest-holes, and several gardening suppliers now sell Mason Bees and their nests.

Wild bees, while not as abundant pollinators as the honey bee, can play important economic roles, and should be protected in their own right. In many areas of the world, small-scale growers depend on wild and feral bees, rather than managed honey bees, for pollination. Wild bees represent a tremendous diversity of forms and adaptations. Many wild bees do not live in hives, but are instead solitary. Some burrow in the ground; others bore into wood to build nests. Agroforestry systems provide ample opportunities to mingle managed and unmanaged environments, with room to preserve and encourage wild bees.

A number of factors have contributed to the decrease in the wild bee population. These include the destruction of the native bees' habitat for urbanization and large-scale agriculture; the use of pesticides, to which bees (including honey bees) are very sensitive; modern tilling practices, which destroy ground nests; and the decreased floral diversity of cropping systems.

Ways to foster wild bees in agroforestry systems:

- leave hedgerows or unmanaged areas in crop areas as nesting sites
- utilize more diverse crop plantings (to feed diverse pollinators);
- utilize no-till systems (to preserve ground nesting sites);
- plant alternative forage adjacent to agricultural areas; and
- reduce pesticide use, or at least shift the timing of sprays to minimize impact on feral bees.

These steps will increase diversity and abundance of wild bees. The movement to develop other bee species as managed pollinators will also be important for the future.

References

Orion Magazine, Autumn 1993. Special edition on wild bees. Orion Society, 195 Main Street, Great Barrington, MA 01230; Fax:413-528-0676; Web: http://orionsociety.org/magazines/orionmag/orion.html

FAO. 1987. A Beekeeping Guide. Tropical and Sub-Tropical Apiculture, FAO Agricultural Services Bulletin 68, MF 32-773. FAO and UNIPUB.

Mizrahi, A., and Y. Lensky (eds). 1997. Bee Products: Properties, Applications, and Apitherapy. Plenum Publ.

Original Source

This chapter was originally published as *The Overstory #40*.

Pest Prevention through Ecological Design

Craig R. Elevitch and Kim M. Wilkinson

Agroforestry and Biodiversity (page 98) covered the advantages of biologically diverse farming systems, including a more balanced insect flora. This chapter expands on this concept for establishing systems that are inherently less susceptible to insect pest problems.

Pest Prevention through Ecological Design

"An ounce of prevention is worth a pound of cure."—old adage

Native forest ecosystems in the tropics teem with insects that co-exist with thriving and productive plants. However, modern forestry and farming arranges plants in patterns of human design, usually large monocultures, which creates ecological imbalance. These plantings often give rise to high populations of "pest" insect species, who feed on concentrations of their food source and interfere with production. For over 60 years, a sophisticated arsenal of insecticides has been routinely employed in the attempt to control pest insect populations. However, insects evolve quickly, and become resistant to the poisons—and new insect pests appear regularly as agricultural trade globalizes. As a result, insecticide-based management tends to become increasingly expensive over time, as more and newer chemicals are developed. Many insecticides are not selective in their targets, and also eliminate predators of pests, which ultimately worsens the pest problem. After decades of all out warfare against insect pests, it is now apparent that fighting pests is a losing battle. It is time for a different approach entirely.

The alternative is to develop carefully planned ecologically-based agricultural systems which are inherently less susceptible to attack by insect pests. Such systems minimize the necessity of reacting to pest infestations with intensive management practices. Instead, the system as a whole is designed and developed so that, like a natural ecosystem, pest populations are regulated through the checks and balances of nature. Ultimately, the need for human intervention to moderate insect populations can be greatly reduced.

In this system, if and when serious pest problems appear, the judicial use of botanical pesticide products (like neem) and intensive pest management strategies like IPM (integrated pest management) are brought in as a last resort, and then only with the long-term goal of creating a healthy system with a naturally balanced population of pests and predators. [Below we include some references for integrated pest management (IPM), although the focus of the article is on setting up systems so that minimal IPM intervention is required.]

Providing habitat for pest predators is part of ecological design

Pest prevention through ecologically based design is a complex subject that warrants more attention and research. There are thousands of different kinds of insect pests, and many complicated interactions between the structure of the landscape, the behavior of the species, and the connections between pests and their predators that should be better understood to maximize the effectiveness of this model. There are some general guidelines that are recognized as valuable, which are outlined below.

Two Keys to Pest Prevention

Healthy plants

Keeping plants healthy is important to deterring pests, as healthy plants are less likely to be attacked.

When a plant is stressed it is more susceptible to pest problems. Drought, injury, nutrient imbalances, and other factors can reduce a plant's ability to resist damage, just as a person who eats well and is in optimum health is more likely to withstand exposure to a virus than someone who is stressed and has a poor diet. Remember, too, that the appearance of a plant can be deceiving—sometimes a plant may look lush and healthy to a human eye, when in reality it is stressed due to excessive water, fertilizer, or shade. The kinds of naturally fertilized plantings in a stacked agroforestry system, providing appropriate niches and microclimates for many species, can be helpful in contributing to plant health.

These are some tips for fostering a system with healthy plants:

- Select plants that are well adapted to your site
- Select plants that genetically retain natural defenses, and are not overly bred by people
- Fertilize through use of added organic matter, not soluble fertilizers or large amounts of uncomposted manure

Diversity

Diversity of plant species can go a long way in reducing susceptibility of plantings to insect pest problems. Monocultures concentrate the food source of the pest species, and hence give rise to high populations of that pest. By using a patchwork of species, there is reduced concentration of food source for pests, and some pests may not be able to readily identify their food source in the mixture. A mixture of species also provides diverse habitat for pest predators. A balance of pests and predators is a key to natural pest management. Predators include other insects, as well as spiders, birds, frogs, reptiles, and other predators. There are some specific elements you can add to your planting that will help attract predators such as ponds or water sources (to attract frogs, birds, and reptiles); trees which provide habitat, and certain flowering plants (to attract predatory wasps, etc.). It should also be noted that in diverse plantings, if a serious pest problem arises, there are diversified crops to support the economic survival of the farm or forest.

Tips for diversity:

- Use a diversity of species which have roles in windbreaks, shade, commercial crops, etc.
- Use plant materials for each species with diverse genetic make-up—avoid excessive use grafted/cloned plants
- Use modern selections as well as heirloom varieties
- Use native and exotic species
- Limit contiguous plantings of a single species through the use of patchwork plantings

Original Source

This chapter was originally published as *The Overstory #23*.

Further Reading

Fukuoka, M. 1978. The One Straw Revolution, Rodale Press. Documents pest management based on observation of nature. This title is out-of-print, but is very much worth looking for in used bookstores.

Meitzner, L.S. and M.L. Price. 1996. Amaranth to Zai Holes: Ideas for Growing Food Under Difficult Conditions, ECHO, N. Fort Myers, FL. Contains excellent biocontrol resources:
http://www.echonet.org/tropicalag/az-text/azch8.htm

Animals in Agroforestry

Craig R. Elevitch and Kim M. Wilkinson

The integration of animals can be a controversial topic. Animals such as cattle, goats and sheep are often associated with ecological degradation and deforestation. There is no doubt that the inappropriate use of animals and poor management leads to many environmental problems. However, this does not necessarily have to be the case.

If planned and managed properly, the appropriate kinds of animals can be key components in sustainable farming systems. Agroforestry systems that incorporate animals with tree crops can enhance important cycles of nature such as nutrient cycling and balancing of insect populations while reducing energy intensive management techniques. The key is to integrate the natural needs, behaviors, and products of animals with the environment provided by the agroforestry system in a way that maximizes the benefits to the animals and to the system as a whole.

The right animal in the right place at the right time can provide many beneficial services

As a part of their normal behavior, animals forage for plant foods and/or insects, spread manure, and dig and/or scratch in the earth. Many of the products and behaviors of animals, for example manure, are considered problems or pollutants in industrial production of e.g. poultry and livestock. Industrial systems of raising animals separate animals from their natural environment. In these systems, many of the cycles of nature which are beneficial to both animals and their environment are broken. However, these animals can perform many beneficial functions when integrated into an agroforestry system.

Some products and services of animals for agroforestry:

- grazing/weed maintenance (livestock, poultry)
- insect control (poultry)
- cleaning of fallen fruit/nuts, other organic wastes (livestock, poultry)
- spreading nutrients in the form of their manure (livestock, poultry)
- scratching and digging to prepare for planting (pigs, chickens, turkeys, etc.)

Similarly, agroforestry systems can have an excess of weedy undergrowth, fallen fruit or nuts and insect populations. Often these excesses are controlled through human intervention—weed cutting, insect control, etc. Animals, when selected carefully for the right agroforestry system can carry out many of the maintenance functions through their normal behavior.

Some products and services of agroforestry systems for animal husbandry:

- favorable habitat
- access to a diverse diet
- access to medicinal plants and insects
- natural population densities

Bill Mollison's "Chicken and egg" example from the Permaculture Designer's Manual is a classic approach to systems thinking as it pertains to animals. In most commercial production systems, chickens are caged in large facilities. Food, water, and grit is provided to them via a massive, energy-intensive infrastructure of farming and transportation. In this unnatural and crowded environment, chickens are often stressed, and producers therefore also supply them with medication from the pharmaceutical industry. The manure from these factory-like facilities is in many cases considered a pollutant, and in some cases is contaminated. The resulting products of eggs or meat are questionable in quality in the eyes of many consumers. (In fact, consumers gaining a greater understanding of the environmental impacts and health conditions of these kinds of animal factories are limiting their intake of animal products.) The chickens are deprived of their natural activities and a healthful environment, and the humans must work very hard to supply the chickens with food and medicine and dispose of their waste. As Mollison asks: "Who is working for whom?"

In an integrated system, by comparison, chickens are raised in managed habitats where they have regular access to a diverse diet rich in plants and insects, as well as their other needs such as shelter and water. In return, the chickens control understory growth through foraging and scratching, eat large quantities of insects, and return the nutrients back to the system through their manure. In such a managed system, the chicken's behaviors and wastes play their natural role in what is a complex natural system. By using the natural cycles, raising chickens in an agroforestry system can reduce human inputs to both the chickens and the plants.

Examples of animals in agroforestry systems:

- Chickens in garden systems, orchards and forest
- Ducks in aquatic environments, such as rice paddies
- Geese to control grasses in orchards
- Livestock in forest plantations (silvopasture)

Of course an animal in the wrong place at the wrong time can create problems, not solve them. For example, the wild pigs prevalent in Hawai'i destroy new plantings, damage trees, and spread weedy exotic species throughout native forest. The same pigs have been used successfully for decades in traditional Hawaiian farm forestry in controlled paddocks to graze and consume farm residues, and to provide meat for sustenance. In another example, chickens (and other poultry) are notorious for damaging new plantings, especially gardens. Once an area is prepared and planted, it is essential to exclude the chickens (or other poultry) until the plants can hold their own against them.

Advantages of integrating animals:

- Less reliance on outside inputs
- Reduced human maintenance
- Better plant health through natural fertility cycling

Disadvantages:

- Animals must be carefully selected for particular systems
- Animals require tending and management
- Food and water may need to be supplemented
- Health care required
- Requires a special set of skills and knowledge

The Right Animal in the Right Place at the Right Time

The introduction and management of animals must be carefully thought out, to ensure that the right kinds of animals are introduced to the right place, and at the right time. Some environments, like savannas, are naturally suited for certain types of grazing animals; in other areas smaller animals and birds might be more appropriate. For some very fragile ecosystems, animals may not be appropriate at all.

Also, the type of animal is important for the environment, and farmers should not feel they have to limit themselves to conventional animals. All over the world, farmers are branching out to incorporate animals that are more appropriate to their local environment, culture, and market demands. Examples of alternative animals being used successfully include iguanas, small forest deer, and ostriches.

Commingling the right animals with the right agroforestry system can create highly productive systems that require less human intervention for maintenance and control. In this way, animal production can be sustainable.

Original Source

This article was originally published as *The Overstory #35*.

Further Reading

Mollison, B. 1990. Permaculture: A Practical Guide for a Sustainable Future, Island Press, Washington, DC. Covers many systems which integrate animals.

Pell, A. 1999. Animals in Agroforestry in the Tropics. In: Agroforestry in Sustainable Agricultural Systems, Louise Buck, *et al*, (eds) offers a more scientific approach to nutrient cycling.

Board on Science and Technology for International Development (BOSTID). 1991. Microlivestock: Little-known Small Animals with a Promising Economic Future. National Academy Press, Washington, DC.

Lee, A. 1994. Chicken Tractor, The Permaculture Guide to Happy Hens and Healthy Soils. Good Earth Publications. Shelburne, Vermont.

Gutteridge, R. and M. Shelton. 1994. "Animal Production Potential of Agroforestry Systems." In: J.W. Copland, A. Djajanegra, and M.Sabrani, (eds). Agroforestry and Animal Production for Human Welfare." ACIAR Proceedings No.55 1994. ACIAR, Canberra.

Salatin, J. 1996. Salad Bar Beef. Chelsea Green Pub Co. An enthusiastic portrayal of integrating beef cattle into farm systems for profit.

Silvopasture

USDA National Agroforestry Center

The previous chapter introduced the integration of animals as a key component in forestry and agroforestry systems. This chapter introduces the specific case of integrating livestock and forestry, called "silvopasture."

Silvopasture as an agroforestry practice is specifically designed and managed for the production of trees, tree products, forage and livestock.

Silvopasture results when forage crops are deliberately introduced or enhanced in a timber production system, or timber crops are deliberately introduced or enhanced in a forage production system. As a silvopasture, timber and pasture are managed as an integrated system.

Silvopastoral systems are designed to produce a high-value timber component, while providing short-term cash flow from the livestock component. The interactions among timber, forage and livestock are managed intensively to simultaneously produce timber commodities, a high quality forage resource and efficient livestock production. Overall, silvopastures can provide economic returns while creating a sustainable system with many environmental benefits. Well-managed silvopastures offer a diversified marketing opportunity that can stimulate rural economic development.

Planning Considerations

Before new silvopastoral systems are established, implications of merging forestry and agricultural systems should be explored thoroughly for economic and environmental considerations along with local land use, zoning, cost-share program and tax regulations. Environmental requirements (e.g., planting trees, stream-side protection, wildlife habitat maintenance) also may vary with land use.

Plant Considerations

When making tree and forage crop selections, consider potential markets, soil type, climatic conditions, and species compatibility. The timber component should be:

• marketable

• high quality
• fast growing
• deep-rooted
• drought tolerant, and
• capable of providing the desired products and environmental services.

Select and use trees and planting/harvesting patterns that are suitable for the site, compatible with planned silvopastoral practices and provide desired economic and environmental returns.

The forage component should be a perennial crop that is:

• suitable for livestock grazing
• compatible with the site (soil, temperature, precipitation)
• productive under partial shade and moisture stress
• responsive to intensive management, and
• tolerant of heavy utilization.

Livestock Selection

Potential livestock choices include cattle, sheep, goats, horses, turkeys, chickens, ostriches, emu, rhea or game animals such as bison, deer, elk, caribou, etc. The selected livestock system must be compatible with tree, forage, environment and land use regulations. In general, browsing animals such as sheep, goats or deer are more likely to eat trees while large grazing animals such as cattle or elk are more likely to step on young trees. Younger livestock are more prone to damage trees than are older, more experienced animals. Livestock are more likely to impact broadleaf trees than conifers.

Design and Establishment

Silvopastures can be established on any land capable of simultaneously supporting tree and forage growth. However, silvopastoral systems can require a relatively large land base to sustain timber and livestock production continuity. A source of local technical assistance is essential to develop a silvopastoral system matched to local conditions and landowner objectives. Appropriate establishment methods depend on:

Integrating pasture, trees, and livestock can improve overall yield. Here sheep control weeds in a coffee plantation. (photo: C. Elevitch)

- woodland/forest type (e.g., site conditions, and tree species, age, pattern and spacing) or existing pasture situation;
- whether even-aged or uneven aged forest stands are anticipated; and
- landowner objectives (e.g., timber products, environmental benefits, wildlife, etc.).

Tree pattern is an important factor for silvopasture success. Trees can be evenly distributed over the area to optimize growing space and light for both trees and forage. Alternatively, grouping trees into rows or clusters concentrates their shade and root effects while providing open spaces for pasture production. Trees are typically pruned to increase light penetration and develop high-quality sawlogs.

Management

A successful silvopasture requires understanding forage growth characteristics and managing the timing and duration of grazing to avoid browsing of young tree seedlings. Livestock should be excluded from tree plantings during vulnerable periods. Im-

proper management of silvopastures can reduce desirable woody and herbaceous plants by over-grazing and soil compaction. Thus, intensive management of livestock grazing is the key to success.

Available management tools include:

- tree harvesting, thinning and pruning
- fertilization to improve both forage and tree production
- planting legumes for nitrogen fixation and forage production
- multi-pasture, rotational grazing
- rotational burning
- supplemental feeding
- developing water sources (e.g., stock tanks, windmills, photovoltaic pumps, hydraulic rams, ridge reservoirs, etc.) locating salt/mineral licks and walkways to encourage uniform livestock distribution
- fencing (e.g., standard or electric), tubing, plastic mesh, repellents, and seasonal livestock exclusion to reduce damage to young seedlings

Benefits of Silvopasture

Economic Benefits

Integrating trees, forage and livestock creates a land management system to produce marketable products while maintaining long-term productivity. Economic risk is reduced because the system produces multiple products, most of which have an established market. Production costs are reduced and marketing flexibility is enhanced by distributing management costs between timber and livestock components.

Comprehensive land utilization in silvopastoral systems provides a relatively constant income from livestock sale and selective sale of trees and timber products. Well-managed forage production provides improved nutrition for livestock growth and production. Potential products of the tree component include: sawtimber, veneer logs, pulpwood, firewood, pine straw, posts and poles, harvested game, nuts, fruit, ornamental flowers and greenery, tree sap products, mushrooms, organic mulches, and other secondary products.

Woodland and Forage Benefits

Grazing can enhance tree growth by controlling grass competition for moisture, nutrients and sunlight. Well managed grazing provides economical control of weeds and brush without herbicides, maintains fire breaks and reduces habitat for gnawing rodents. Fertilizer applied for forage is also used by trees. In addition, livestock manure recycles nutrients to trees and forage.

Livestock Benefits

Some forage species tend to be lower in fiber and more digestible when grown in a tree-protected environment. Trees that provide shade or wind protection can have a climate-stabilizing effect to reduce heat stress and windchill of livestock. Protection from trees can cut the direct cold effect by 50% or more and reduce wind velocity by as much as 70%. Livestock require less feed energy, so their performance is improved and mortality is reduced.

Environmental and Aesthetic Benefits

Silvopastures can increase wildlife diversity and improve water quality. The forage protects the soil from water and wind erosion, while adding organic matter to improve soil properties. Silvopastures provide an attractive landscape with an aesthetically pleasing "park-like" setting. In contrast to concentrated livestock operations, silvopastoral systems are less likely to raise environmental concerns related to water quality, odors, dust, noise, disease problems and animal treatment.

Original Source

This article was reprinted with the kind permission of the US Department of Agriculture National Agroforestry Center. The unabridged version of "Silvopasture: An Agroforestry Practice" and references can be viewed at:

http://www.unl.edu/nac/silvopasture.html

This excerpt was originally published as *The Overstory #36*.

Further Reading

Reid, R. and G. Wilson. 1985. Agroforestry in Australia and New Zealand. Goodard and Dobson, 486 Station Street, Box Hill, Victoria 3128, Australia.

Gutteridge, R.C. and H.M. Shelton (eds). 1994. Forage Tree Legumes in Tropical Agriculture. CAB International, Oxon, UK.

Productivity of Animals in Agroforestry Systems

Ross C. Gutteridge and H. Max Shelton

This is the third chapter in a series on animals in agroforestry. Animals in Agroforestry (page 105) covered the advantages and disadvantages of integrating animals with agriculture and forestry. Silvo-pasture (page 107) introduced the integration of livestock in forestry systems.

This chapter summarizes examples of several important agroforestry systems which incorporate animals

Plantation crop systems

The principal plantation crops where integration of livestock is possible are rubber, oil palm and coconuts. In the past, most attention has focused on the integration of cattle with coconuts and this system has the greatest potential for further development. The unique quality of coconuts, compared to most other plantation crops, is the relatively constant and bright light environment over the life of the crop (60–80 years). Consequently, understorey pastures can be grazed on a semi-permanent basis. Liveweight gain potential can be quite high and is influenced by a number of factors but particularly light level. Improvement is possible through the use of shade-tolerant pasture species.

There is increasing interest in the grazing of sheep in rubber and oil palm plantations. In Malaysia, the productivity of sheep under rubber has been extensively investigated. Experiments showed that productivity was moderate under young rubber (2–5 years) provided palatable leguminous cover crops were grazed, but low under mature rubber where light levels had fallen to less than 20% transmission of light. There is potential to increase productivity by using shade-tolerant forage species and by altering the conventional rubber planting system to a hedgerow system.

Forestry systems

Successful forest grazing systems based on *Pinus radiata* and sheep have been developed for the temperate regions of southern Australia and New Zealand. Sheep are preferred because they are less inclined to browse the trees than cattle. Stocking rates vary between 12 and 25 animals/ha in the early stages of tree

the crop while all or part of later prunings can be

development, but need to be reduced by at least 50% by year 10.

In the tropics, forest grazing systems have been less successful. In the Solomon Islands, pastures and cattle under *Eucalyptus deglupta* plantations at densities of 130 stems/ha could not be sustained in the long term. In a young plantation (trees 23 years old), a stocking rate of 2.5 beasts/ha, giving liveweight gains of 0.45 kg/hd/day was achieved; however, by year 7 with almost complete tree canopy cover, stocking rates had to be reduced to less than 1 beast/ha, producing only 0.25 kg/hd/day liveweight. Substantial damage to the trees due to bark stripping by the cattle also occurred.

Animal production in forest plantation is therefore transient unless the trees are widely spaced, permitting ample light penetration to the pasture.

Horticultural systems

A number of other tree crop species such as mangoes, kapok, tamarind, cocoa and cashews have some potential for integration with livestock as they are usually planted on a wide spacing (10 x 10 m or 8 x 8 m) which promotes food light penetration especially in young crops.

The animal production potential from these systems, although not well documented, would not be high because of the precautions necessary to prevent damage to the often palatable leaves of the crop and the low light profile when the trees reach maturity.

A specialized agrosilvopastoral horticultural system in Bali is vanilla production under coconuts—the vanilla orchid is supported and shaded by the tree legumes *Gliricidia sepium* or *Erythrina* sp. The shade level is regulated by lopping the branches of shade trees which are fed to livestock.

Livestock and Alley farming

The inclusion of livestock into alley farming systems necessitates that farmers change their tree management and foliage use practices. The daily demands of animals for feed require tree pruning at times unnecessary for cropping. Thus in alley farming, prunings taken at or near crop planting are used as mulch for used for animal feed.

Cattle grazing under coconuts. Tongatapu, Tonga. (photo: C. Elevitch)

At Ibadan in Nigeria, Reynolds and Atta-Krah suggested that the surplus foliage from 1 ha of *Leucaena leucocephala* and *Gliricidia sepium* from alley farming could provide half the daily fodder requirements for 29 goats. In the dry season fallow period, livestock can be allowed direct access to the cropping area to graze crop residues and browse the trees. In Malawi, a 0.25 ha leucaena alley farm produced enough leaf material to feed three dairy cattle 3 kg/DM/hd/day during the dry season.

In lowland humid regions of the tropics where farm size is often small, the amount of forage generated from alley farming is very low. However, in semi-arid regions, the additional forage from both prunings and crop residues may be the major incentive attracting farmers to use the alley farming technique.

Trees in cropping systems

In the more intensive agricultural areas of Asia and Africa where land is scarce and livestock are raised in small numbers by smallholder farmers, forage tree legumes are planted as "fodder banks" along border or fence lines, and on rice paddy bunds or in home gardens. Foliage from these trees is usually harvested under a cut-and-carry system and is a principal source of high quality fodder to supplement low quality fodder such as crop residues. In China, the leaf of the deciduous tree *Paulownia*, grown over an area of 1.8 million ha of cropping land, is collected in autumn and fed to cattle, sheep and pigs.

In parts of Africa, the incorporation of tree legumes in cropping areas has been described as "the bedrock of traditional agroforestry systems in Africa." The trees are occasionally lopped for feed and are grazed in the dry season. Animal productivity is generally low. In the Batangas region of the Philippines, a 2 ha area of *Leucaena leucocephala* grown in association with the fruit tree *Anonna squamosa* was able to supply the forage requirements of 20 growing cattle over a 6-month period.

Three strata systems

The three strata forage system is an integrated agroforestry practice developed in Bali, Indonesia. It enhances crop and livestock production through the provision of forage, to supplement crop residues from the cropping area, from a combination of pastures, shrubs and trees. The system comprises three tiers or strata of forage grown as borders in an upland cropping system.

The system aims to produce a constant high quality feed supply throughout the year. The first stratum of herbaceous grasses and legumes supplies forage from the early wet to the early dry season; the second stratum of tree legumes provides forage for the early dry to the mid-dry season while the third stratum of taller trees covers the period mid-dry to early wet.

Results indicated that the three strata system produced 90% more feed and carried a 29% higher stocking rate in the wet season and 46°%, higher stocking in the dry season compared to the traditional system. The growth rate of animals from both systems was similar. Although crop production was reduced slightly in the tree strata system, an economic analysis of both systems indicated that profitability was higher and risk more widely spread in the three strata system.

This system would appear to have wide applicability outside the Bukit Peninsula where it was tested. The environmental conditions there (1000 mm rainfall, long dry season 7–8 months) are similar to many other regions of the semi-arid tropics.

Summary and Conclusions

There is substantial potential for animal production in animal-based agroforestry systems and a number have been designed specifically to improve or enhance animal productivity. High levels of production are only possible through the use of high quality fodder-tree legumes when livestock production is the major economic activity. Further evaluation of the existing tree legume varieties will broaden the resource base available and enable the expansion of these systems into a wider range of environments.

The animal production potential of forest and plantation crop grazing systems is relatively low and improvements in these systems will come largely from the identification and selection of herbaceous forage species tolerant of lower sunlight conditions. Improvement is also possible through changes in plantation management practices such as tree spacing and pruning regimes.

In all systems the service role of the trees in providing shade and shelter must be taken into account as this aspect is often undervalued in assessing the productivity of agroforestry systems.

Original Source

This article was adapted from the original Animal Production Potential of Agroforestry Systems by Dr. Ross Gutteridge and Dr. Max Shelton, from Proceedings entitled, "Agroforestry and Animal Production for Human Welfare" J.W. Copland, A. Djajanegra and M.Sabrani, (eds). ACIAR Proceedings No.55 1994. ACIAR Canberra. Kind permission to reprint this excerpt was granted by the Australian Centre for International Agricultural Research (ACIAR):

http://www.aciar.gov.au

This excerpt was originally published as *The Overstory #37*.

Further Reading

Forest, Farm and Community Tree Network. (FACT Net). 1998. Nitrogen Fixing Trees for Fodder Production - A Field Manual. FACT Net, Winrock International, 38 Winrock Drive, Morrilton, Arkansas 72110-9370 USA Tel: 501-727-5435, Fax: 501-727-5417; Email: forestry@winrock.org; Web:

http://www.winrock.org/forestry/factnet.htm

Gutteridge, R.C. and H.M. Shelton (eds). 1994. Forage Tree Legumes in Tropical Agriculture. CAB International, Oxon, UK.

Fodder Tree Establishment

James M. Roshetko and Ross C. Gutteridge

Livestock play an important role in small-scale farming systems throughout the world. Most often livestock graze fallow fields, pastures and woodlands deriving most of their sustenance from crop residue, grasses and other herbaceous plants. A smaller but important component of livestock diets comes from tree fodder. Farmers harvest tree fodder from natural forests, savanna and woodlots. Additionally, they often deliberately propagate trees on their farms to expand fodder resources. Many of the most important fodder trees are nitrogen fixing species. This article covers the propagation, establishment, and maintenance of this important group of nitrogen fixing trees used for fodder.

Site Preparation

To minimize weed growth and competition, site preparation should occur immediately before fodder tree establishment. Removal of vegetation can be achieved by manual, mechanical, chemical or a combination of means. To assure adequate establishment of nitrogen fixing fodder trees, it is necessary to practice thorough site preparation. This is particularly important in grass ecosystems, where fodder trees are often planted. The objective of site preparation is a seed bed with limited weed competition, where tree seedlings can thrive. At a minimum, remove all vegetation within 50 cm of the position where seedlings or seed will be planted. Both above ground and below ground plant biomass (i.e., stems and roots) must be removed. If rows of fodder trees are being established, meter-wide seed beds the length of the rows must be prepared. For individual fodder trees, seed beds one meter-diameter are sufficient.

A few precautions are warranted. The use of burning as a site preparation method is not recommended, unless experienced personnel are present. The removal of 100% of the vegetation from a site is not advisable. Complete removal of the vegetation is costly and leaves the site vulnerable to soil erosion. Furthermore, some of the existing vegetation may provide useful fodder, mulch, fuel or other products.

Seed Preparation

Nitrogen fixing fodder trees are usually established by directly sowing seeds or by transplanting seedlings. The seed of many of fodder species have hard, waxy or thick seedcoats that inhibit water absorption and delay germination. Under natural conditions, seedcoats are degraded by exposure to sun, rain, wind and animals.

Uniform seedling size can be achieved through seed scarification—a process designed to penetrate the protective seedcoat and allow seed to absorb water and germinate at a uniform rate. The most common scarification treatments are cool water, hot water, acid and nicking.

Cool water Seeds are soaked in cool, room-temperature water until they swell. The volume of water should be five times the volume of seeds. Soaking time is 12–48 hours depending on species, provenance, age and quality of seed. This treatment is appropriate for seeds with a thin or soft seedcoat, recently harvested seed, seed of small-size, and large quantifies of seed.

Hot water —Boiling water is poured over the seeds at a volume five times the volume of seeds. The seeds must be stirred gently during the 2–5 minute soak. Hot water can kill the seed—it is important not to soak the seed for too long! Pour off the hot water, replace it with cool water and soak for 12 hours. This treatment is appropriate for seeds with hard or thick seedcoats, old seed, and large quantities of seed. It is best to treat a small quantity of seed first to make sure your technique is correct before attempting to treat large quantities of seed.

Acid (**CAUTION**—Very dangerous—for laboratory professionals only) Cover seeds with sulfuric acid for 10–60 minutes. Seed should be completely submerged but just below the surface of the acid. Acid can kill the seed—do not soak the seed for too long! Gauge the length of acid treatment by the appearance of the seed. The waxy gloss of the seedcoat should be replaced by a dull appearance. A pitted appearance indicates damage—remove the seeds before this occurs. Remove seed from acid, rinse with water for 10 minutes and soak in cool water for

12 hours. Do not pour water into the acid or a violent reaction will occur! The acid can be used several times. This treatment is appropriate for seeds with hard and thick seedcoats. Acid treatment can be dangerous! In most circumstances it is not recommended!

Nicking Cut or scrape a small hole in the seedcoat. A knife, nail clipper, file, sand paper or sanding block can be used for this operation. To avoid damaging the seed embryo, cut or scrape the seedcoat opposite the micropyle. Soak the nicked seed in water for 12 hours. This treatment is appropriate for all types of seed, although nicking seed by hand is time consuming and only feasible for small quantities. Large quantities of seed may be nicked using a meat grinder, gristmill or thresher.

No treatment Some seeds germinate quickly without treatment. Application of the above methods may be impractical, make seed difficult to handle or decrease viability. No treatment is needed for tiny seed (i.e., *Desmodium* spp.); seeds with thin or incomplete seedcoats; and recalcitrant seed (i.e., *Erythrina edulis*).

The length of the initial soak in cool water, hot water or acid will vary according to species, provenance, age and quality of the seed. If large numbers of seedlings will be produced, or nursery operations will last for several years, it is recommended that several soaking times be tested in order to determine the most suitable time length for local conditions. As noted, with all methods the last process is to soak seed in cool water for 12 hours. This final process allows seed to absorb water, results in visible swelling and further hastens germination. To improve this process, and thus germination, this period may be increased up to 48 hours. Once removed from the final soaking sow seed immediately! If sowing is delayed, the seed will dehydrate resulting in decreased seed viability and weak seedlings. The table below summarizes appropriate seed scarification methods for common nitrogen fixing fodder trees.

Seed scarification treatments for selected nitrogen species (Revised from Macklin et al 1989). (Key: A—Hot water; B—Acid; C—Nicking; D—Cold water; E—No treatment)

Species	Treatments	Species	Treatments
Acacia acuminata	C; D	Chamaecytisus palmensis	A for 4 min.
Acacia aneura	A; C	Dalbergia spp.	D
Acacia angustissima	C; D	Desmodium spp.	E
Acacia holosericea	A for 1 min.; C	Enterolobium cyclocarpum	C; D
Acacia leucophloea	A; B for 10–30 min.; C	Erythrina edulis	E (recalcitrant seed)
Acacia melanoxylon	A; B for 15 min.; C	Erythrina poeppigiana	D; C
Acacia nilotica	A; C; D	Erythrina variegata	A
Acacia polyacantha	D	Faidherbia albida	A; B for 20 min.; C; D
Acacia saligna	A; C	Flemingia macrophylla	A; B for 15 min.; D
Acacia senegal	C; D	Gliricidia sepium	C; D; E
Acacia seyal	A; B; C	Leucaena spp.	A; B for 5–15 min.; C
Acacia tortilis	A; C; D	Ougenia dalbergioides	D for 24 hours
Adenanthera pavonina	A for 1 min.; B	Paraserianthes falcataria	A; B for 10 min.; C
Albizia lebbeck	A; C; D	Pithecellobium dulce	C; E
Albizia odoratissima	A for 1 min.; D	Pongamia pinnata	E
Albizia procera	A; C	Prosopis spp.	A; C
Albizia saman	A; C	Robinia pseudoacacia	A; B for 20–60 min.; C
Cajanus cajan	D; E	Sesbania grandiflora	C; D
Calliandra calothyrsus	A; C; D	Sesbania sesban	A; C; D

Two common scarification methods: nicking seed coat (left) and treatment with near-boiling water (right). (photos: C. Elevitch)

Rhizobium Inoculation

The seed of nitrogen fixing trees should be treated with *Rhizobium* inoculum after scarification and prior to sowing. *Rhizobium* bacteria and NFTs form a symbiotic relationship that enables the trees to "fix" atmospheric nitrogen into a form useful for plant growth. This relationship allows NFTs to grow on infertile or degraded soils where available nitrogen is in low supply. The nitrogen fixation process occurs in nodules formed by the bacteria on the tree roots. To determine the health of nodules cut them open. A red or pink color indicates nodules are fixing nitrogen. Green, brown or black nodules are not fixing.

There are many strains of *Rhizobium* bacteria. These strains and NFTs often exhibit exclusive preferences for each other. Some bacteria will form nodules with some NFTs but not others. Likewise, trees may form nodules with many strains or just a few. A successful match will produce healthy nodules. If an NFT is native or naturalized in an area, the soil will likely contain appropriate *Rhizobium* strains. However, if the tree does not occur locally, or the site is degraded, populations of the appropriate *Rhizobium* strains may be too low to form healthy nodules.

To assure an effective *Rhizobium*-NFT match, it is best to use a *Rhizobium* inoculant. Inoculants are produced in laboratories and contain 1000 times the bacteria found in most soils. The bacteria in the inoculants are alive. They are sensitive to heat, dehydration, direct sunlight and low temperatures. It is best to use inoculants when received—viability decreases greatly after 6 months. When storage is nec-

essary, the inoculant should be placed in an airtight bag (being sure to exclude all air) and stored in a moist, cool and dark place. When ordering inoculants be sure to specify the NFT species you plan to inoculate.

To apply inoculants, first cover seeds with a sticker solution. Place seeds in a plastic bag or bucket and cover them with a solution made of gum arabic, sugar or vegetable oil. Either dissolve 40 g of gum arabic in 100 ml of hot water and allow to cool, or dissolve 1 part sugar in 9 parts water. Combine 2 ml of one of these mixtures, or 2 ml of vegetable oil, with 100 g of seeds and shake or stir until the seeds are well coated. Then add 5 mg of inoculant and shake or stir until the seeds are well covered with inoculant. Allow the inoculated seeds to dry for 10 minutes to eliminate any stickiness and sow immediately. Do not store inoculated seed—the bacteria will die.

Seedlings can also be inoculated in the nursery after germination. Mix inoculant in cool water and irrigate the seedlings with the suspension. Keep the mixture well shaken and irrigate until the inoculant is washed into the root zone. A 50 g bag of inoculant is sufficient to inoculate 10,000 seedlings. For more information on the NFTs-*Rhizobium* relationship and inoculation methods consult Keyser (1990), Postgate (1987) and Somasegaran and Hoben (1985).

It may not always be possible to obtain laboratory-produced inoculant. At such times, soil containing the appropriate bacteria can be gathered from under trees of the same species being grown in the nursery. Choose healthy trees that are growing well and have abundant red or pink nodules. Some of this soil can be mixed with nursery potting mix or added to planting pits. Inoculation by this method assures that the bacteria will be appropriate for the tree species and the local environment. However, this approach may not be as effective as using a correct laboratory-produced inoculant.

VAM Inoculation

Like *Rhizobium*, vesicular-arbuscular mycorrhizal fungi (VAM) are soil organisms that invade the roots of NFTs and other plants to form symbiotic relationships. Plants provide VAM food in the form of carbohydrates. VAM infection improves plant survival and growth by enhancing the root's ability to absorb moisture, macro-nutrients and micro-nutrients from the soil. Increased access to phosphorus is a specific advantage of VAM symbiosis. This relationship helps plants to colonize infertile or degraded sites. Unlike other mycorrhizae, VAM does not produce visible external hyphae; its branched hyphae are mainly contained within the infected root. The spores of VAM are formed near infected roots in the organic layer of the soil. They are large and are not disseminated by wind like the spores of other mycorrhizae. To assure the VAM plant association, seedlings or seed should be inoculated in the nursery. Inoculation is particularly important when trees are to be planted on degraded sites where the organic soil has been removed.

VAM inoculation is usually accomplished by incorporating the organic soil from beneath a healthy host-plant into the nursery soil at a rate of 5–10% per volume. This method is simple and appropriate for most farm-level or community nurseries. However, it entails moving large amounts of soil and may transfer pathogens from forest soils to the nursery. It is not possible to sterilize forest soils because the process will also kill the VAM. For larger nurseries, a second option is to construct a "VAM production bed." First, collect infected soil as described above and completely fill a nursery bed. Next, sow seed of the appropriate host plant at a close spacing. Once well established, the roots of the infected plants, and VAM, will permeate the soil in the nursery bed. Remove the soil and roots, and then finely chop and mix them into the nursery soil as an inoculant at a rate of 5–10% per volume. This method, while more expensive and management intensive than collecting soil beneath a healthy host-plant, is appropriate if many seedlings are to be produced over a number of years.

Healthy host-plants should be maintained in the VAM production bed to assure continued supply of VAM inoculant.

Recent advances in technology have made laboratory production of VAM inoculants practical. Several commercial inoculants are available which are appropriate for NFTs. Readers interested in more information on VAM and inoculation are encouraged to consult Casetellano and Molina (1989), Ferguson and Woodhead (1982), and Malajczuk *et al* (undated).

Seed Sowing

As previously mentioned, seed can be sown in the nursery or directly in the field. In either case, the seed bed or nursery soil should be well cultivated and free of weeds. Seeds should be sown in the soil to a depth of once or twice their width. In field plantings where rapid soil drying is likely to occur, the depth of sowing can be increased to 10 times the width of the seed. The seed should be covered with soil, sand or mulch. When using mulch, be sure it does not contain weed seeds! For most species germination will occur within 1–3 weeks. Young germinants are sensitive to dehydration, weed competition and insects. Care must be taken to guard against these dangers.

For nursery production, standard local nursery methods are recommended. Further information on nursery practices and management is available in standard texts on the subject. Depending on the species, seedlings are ready for transplanting to the field after 6–16 weeks in the nursery. Seedlings should be "hardened" in direct sunlight for at least one week before transplanting, preferably at the beginning of the wet season. Because of the large number of trees planted in most fodder production systems, establishment is usually achieved by direct sowing. This method is more cost-effective than nursery production, however, there is less control over the planting site. Direct sowing operations should be conducted only during the rainy season.

Vegetative Propagation

Some nitrogen fixing fodder species can be established from vegetative cuttings. Propagation techniques differ greatly from species to species but generalizations are possible. *Gliricidia sepium* and most *Erythrina* species are commonly propagated by large cuttings 1–3 meters in length. *Albizia* spp. and *Dalbergia* spp. and *Ougenia dalbergioides* are also reproduced by small stem cuttings 15–20 cm in length and 1.0–1.5 cm in diameter.

Straight and healthy stems, branches, coppice growth or roots are recommended for vegetative propagation. Branch cuttings may retain their original morphology resulting in crooked trees. While crooked trees are not aesthetically pleasing, their morphology has no negative effect on fodder production or quality. Cuttings are usually harvested at the end of the dry season or beginning of the rains. The use of sharp clean tools will produce healthy undamaged cuttings. The cuttings of some species can be stored for up to 15 days before planting. Storage should be in a cool, dry and shady place with good aeration. Do not pile cuttings directly on the ground. Large cuttings should be stored vertically.

Water accumulation on the tips of cuttings can cause stem rot. To avoid this problem the apical (top) end of cuttings should be cut at a 45 degree angle. Rooting is promoted by scarring the lower portion of the cutting which will be buried. Scarring should be done with a sharp knife and should penetrate the cambium. If available, treat scars with a rooting hormone. Cuttings should be planted, not pushed into the ground causes damage to the bark and result in weak roots. Large cuttings should have 30% of their length buried in the soil. Small cuttings should have 50–75% of their length buried.

It should be noted that cuttings generally produce shallow root systems without a strong, deep taproot. Shallow root systems leave trees vulnerable to drought and blow-down during windstorms. Also, while cuttings provide quick establishment, time-and labor-costs per plant are greatly increased. Therefore in most fodder production systems, propagation by seed is preferred.

Field Management

After germination or transplanting, the top growth of most nitrogen fixing fodder seedlings is slow. Initially, the seedling's growth energy is allocated to root system development. While this growth pattern aids long-term tree survival, it does not assist young seedlings become established among pre-existing vegetation—even where adequate site preparation has been completed. In most ecosystems, competition for sunlight, soil moisture and soil nutrients is intense and young slow-growing trees are often the losers. Competition is particularly intense when trees are planted in grass ecosystems. Grasses, and other herbaceous plants, have intensive root systems

Even fast-growing nitrogen fixing trees benefit greatly from weed control, especially during establishment. This *Acacia koa* is stunted by pasture grass competition. (photo: C. Elevitch)

with many fine roots which densely permeate the upper soil layers. By contrast, trees have extensive root systems with thick roots which sparsely penetrate large volumes of soil. Grasses and trees are ecologically antagonistic, once present, grasses often prevent the establishment of trees.

When trees are small, grass and other weed competition must be controlled. While management regimes differ by site and species, a good recommendation is to remove all vegetation within 50 cm of the trees every 2–4 weeks. The objective is to deny weeds the opportunity to impede tree growth. As trees gain size, the frequency of weed control operations can be reduced. However, weed control must be maintained until the trees achieve a dominant position and begin to suppress competing vegetation. This usually occurs within 6–12 months of tree establishment. It is not necessary or desirable to remove 100% of the weed competition. Some vegetation—particularly grasses—are valuable fodder and improve the overall productivity of the fodder production system.

Fertilizer application can improve fodder tree growth and survival. However, little information is currently available concerning appropriate fertilization regimes for most fodder trees. A detailed study undertaken at the University of Queensland in Australia indicated that *Leucaena leucocephala* has a high requirement for phosphorus and calcium. On infertile soils, growth responses will occur at rates up to 225 kg P/ha and 230 kg Ca/ha. However, if the *L. leucocephala* plants have formed an association with VAM much lower rates of phosphorus fertilizer give the same response.

When fertilizers are applied it is essential to practice thorough weed control. The intensive root systems of herbaceous weeds respond quickly to fertilizer application. Trees respond more slowly. Left unchecked, weeds will suppress trees. Fertilization without adequate weed control results in decreased fodder tree survival and growth. In rural areas, fertilizers can be expensive or unavailable. For these reasons, fodder trees on small-scale farms are generally not fertilized.

The longevity of fodder trees is increased when the first harvest is delayed until trees are 9–21 months old. Actual age at first harvest depends on environmental conditions and tree growth. Under arid or poor soil conditions, growth will be slow and the first harvest should be later. When growth is fast, the first harvest can be sooner. The goal is to allow trees to establish deep roots. The resultant healthy plants will have ample carbohydrate reserves to resprout quickly and vigorously after harvesting. Fodder production per harvest and long-term fodder production both increase when the first harvest is delayed. The first harvest, whether by cutting or grazing, may terminate the downward growth of the roots. This is an important consideration, particularly in arid and semi-arid environments.

Fodder trees are a valuable crop that can sustain or increase livestock production. They should be managed intensively. Most often fodder trees are established in integrated systems with grasses or other fodder crops. While trees and herbaceous plants are ecologically antagonistic, their fodder products are complementary, together forming well-balanced livestock diets. Fodder trees should be managed to improve the livestock production system, not necessarily to maximize tree growth or tree fodder production.

References

Castellano, M.A. and R. Molina. 1989. Mycorrhizae. In: T.D. Landis, R.W. Tinus, S.E.

McDonald, and J.P. Barnett, eds. The container tree nursery manual, Volume 5. Washington DC, USA: USDA Forest Service, pp 101–167.

Ferguson, J.J. and S.H. Woodland. 1982. Production of endomycorrhizal inoculum: A. Increase and maintenance of vesicular-arbuscular mycorrhizal fungi. In: N.C. Schenck, ed. Methods and principles of mycorrhizal research. St. Paul, Minnesota, USA: American Phytopathological Society, pp 47–54.

Keyser, H. 1990. inoculating tree legume seed and seedlings with rhizobia. Paia, Hawaii, USA: Nitrogen Fixation in Tropical Agricultural Legumes (NifTAL) Center, 2 pp.

Liegel, L.H. and C.R. Venator. 1987. A technical guide for forest nursery management in the Caribbean and Latin America. General Technical Report SO-67. New Orleans, Louisiana, USA: USDA Forest Service, Southern Forest Experiment Station, 156 pp.

Macklin, B., N. Glover, J. Chamberlain, and M. Treacy. 1989. NFTA Cooperative Planting Program establishment guide. Morrilton, Arkansas, USA: Forest, Farm and Community Tree Network (FACT Net), Winrock International, 36 pp.

Malajczuk, N., N. Jones, and C. Neely. Undated. The importance of mycorrhiza to forest trees. Land Resources Series—No. 2. Washington, DC, USA: The World Bank, Asia Technical Department, 10 pp.

Postgate, J.R. 1987. Nitrogen fixation, second edition. The Institute of Biology's studies in biology. London, UK: Edward Arnold LTD, 73 pp.

Shelton, H.M. 1994. Establishment of forage tree legumes. In: R.C. Gutteridge and H.M. Shelton, eds. Forage tree legumes in tropical agriculture. Wallingford, UK: CAB International, 139 pp.

Somasegaran, P. and H.J. Hoben. 1985. Methods Legume—Rhizobium Technology. Paia, Hawaii. NifTAL Center, 367 pp.

Original Source

With the kind permission of the authors and publisher, this article is excerpted from:

Roshetko, J.M. and R.C. Gutteridge (Editors). 1996. Nitrogen Fixing Trees for Fodder Production: a field manual. Forest, Farm, and Community Tree Network (FACT Net), c/o Winrock International. Morrilton, Arkansas, USA.

A hardcopy of this book is available for purchase from: Winrock International FACT Net 38 Winrock Drive Morrilton, AR 72110-9370 USA; Tel: 501-727-5435; Fax: 501-727-5417; Email: forestry@winrock.org;

Web: http://www.winrock.org/forestry/factnet.htm

This excerpt was originally published as *The Overstory* #91.

Tropical Forage Tree Legumes

Max Shelton

"It is a humbling fact for grass pasture experts to realize that probably more animals feed on shrubs and trees, or on associations in which trees and shrubs play an important part, than on true grass-legume pastures." —CAB Publication No. 10 (1947)

Much has been written on the role of forage tree legumes. The literature abounds with reports, scholarly papers, conference proceedings, and books which describe traditional uses of indigenous species and new opportunities with exotic species. Tree legumes offer many benefits. Apart from their value as feed for livestock, tree legumes are recognised for their multipurpose contributions to the productivity of farming systems, to the welfare of people and to the protection of the environment. But it is the flexibility of their uses that makes them especially significant; they can be found on farms ranging from small-holder subsistence to large-scale commercial.

The most well known species, *Leucaena leucocephala* (leucaena), was once referred to as the miracle tree. This label did great damage to perceptions of the value of leucaena, especially after the movement of the psyllid insect around the world. Following this event, great hardship was suffered by those who depended on this species for their livelihood. Its limitations are now more clearly understood (Shelton and Jones 1995) and have led to a worldwide study of alternative species; both those currently in use, as well as new, but not yet domesticated species.

Traditional Use

The worldwide interest in forage tree legumes may seem relatively recent probably because publications and promotion of tree legumes have greatly increased over the past 15–20 years. In reality, the use of tree legumes in tropical farming systems dates back to the beginning of domestic agriculture, although early use was not for forage. Indigenous peoples had excellent knowledge of the multipurpose value of the various species available.

In Mexico and Central America, where many of our most useful forage tree species originate, there was no tradition of tree forage use. For example, Mesquite (*Prosopis* spp.) pods were a component of diets of inhabitants of the United States and Mexican border lands for several thousand years, and later on were consumed by the white pioneers of the 1800s (Ibrahim 1992). Its use as a browse has been more recent.

There is evidence of indigenous use of unripe *Leucaena* pods and seeds for human consumption in the Tehuacan Valley in Mexico since the first domestication of agriculture. Archaeological studies have located *Leucaena* fragments in prehistoric cave settlement sites dating back to 6800 BC and it seems that *Leucaena* cultivation may have begun about 2000 years ago (Hughes 1998). It continues to be cultivated for human consumption in Mexico today, but rarely for forage.

In another contrast with present day fodder use, the genus *Calliandra* has its centre of origin in Central America, where it has little significance for any agroforestry purpose (Arias and Macqueen 1996).

The Spanish conquerors of Mexico observed local people using and cultivating *Gliricidia sepium* (gliricidia) for a number of non-forage purposes (Stewart *et al* 1996). From this time, gliricidia was transported around the world in several waves of introductions, beginning with Spanish colonization in the 1600s, to provide shade for plantation crops (coffee, tea, cacao). The Spanish are thought to have introduced it to the Philippines and to the Caribbean. Later in the 1800s, it was introduced to Sri Lanka and other Southeast Asian countries and finally to West Africa in the 1900s (Stewart *et al* 1996).

There are some examples where the principal indigenous use of tree legumes was and is for forage. These tend to be in the drier regions of the world, e.g., the Sahel and North Africa. Even today, in these arid and semi-arid zones, tree legumes, principally *Acacia* spp., continue to provide a proportion of total herbage intake, and most of the protein intake, for livestock. This increases during dry periods (Baumer 1992).

More recent movements of tree legume germplasm (over the last 50 years) have largely been for agroforestry purposes, of which forage use was one of the primary proposed objectives.

Benefits and Species

Many benefits are claimed for forage tree legumes. Apart from their value for livestock, they are recognised for their contributions to farming systems, the welfare of rural populations, and protection of the environment. There are now many species and varieties available for farm use with a wide range of ecological adaptation. However, no single species delivers all stated benefits, and there is no single species suited to the entire range of conditions. Therefore, we must be realistic in our goals when selecting forage trees for farming systems. Choice of species will depend on the specific requirements of the farming system in which they are to be grown. It is important to reconcile need, environment, and sustainability with choice of species. Multiple objectives or multiple habitats will necessitate an integrated approach using several species.

Whilst forage is just one of the many uses of tree legumes, it is concluded that forage use offers the best opportunity for commercial enterprise provided livestock markets exist. Most other uses are of semi-subsistence value or have an environment focus, thus limiting economic opportunity. It is significant that both small and large-scale operators are finding relevant applications for tree legumes.

Exotic Versus Native Species

"Too often in extension work, a few exotic species have been strongly promoted without any attention being given to the rich indigenous flora and local knowledge of it." (Bekele-Tesemma *et al* 1993).

Over recent years there has been increasing interest in indigenous species as an alternative to introducing exotic species, and debate concerning the appropriateness of introducing exotic species into indigenous ecosystems. There are many reasons for this trend:

1   Farming communities have very detailed knowledge of the use and value of indigenous species, and often this has not been documented, assessed or verified (B. Calub, personal communication, Schrempp *et al* 1992).

2   There are clear ecological advantages in using a diversity of indigenous species, compared to a monoculture of exotics.

Brahman cattle graze grass pasture planted with hedgerows of *Leucaena*. (photo: M. Shelton)

3 Concern, sometimes for nationalistic and patriotic reasons, about preserving and conserving indigenous germplasm.

4 A reduced emphasis on promotion of exotic species and greater in situ use of local tree diversity, may reduce risk of unwanted weed invasion and genetic pollution through hybridisation (Hughes 1994).

There is no simple answer to this debate and decisions have to be made on individual merit. There are arguments on both sides. Combined use of native and exotic species may have merit.

Often exotic species are more vigorous and produce higher yields than indigenous species. This was the case in Malawi where *L. leucocephala*, *Cassia spectabilis* and *Gliricidia sepium* have been promoted over the indigenous *Faidherbia albida* which is slow growing (Cromwell *et al* 1996). In fact, there are many regions where exotic species have made invaluable contributions. It has been estimated that 150 to 200 M people use gliricidia worldwide, the majority of whom live outside its native range (Simons 1996). Leucaena is now naturalised in the Philippines where it is the principal source of tree fodder and of fuelwood. This species underpins a sustainable, highly productive beef cattle production system in northern Australia (Middleton *et al* 1995).

In India, fast growing, multipurpose exotic tree species introduced with the relatively slow growing *Acacia nilotica* (an indigenous tree) enhance biomass production. However, competition reduces growth of the indigenous tree. Careful planning and thoughtful species selection was recommended before implementation of exotic large-scale afforestation programmes (Neelam-Bhatnagar *et al* 1993).

Sometimes indigenous species are better adapted to difficult soils. In Costa Rica, native leguminous species had more potential for reforestation and agroforestry on acid soils high in aluminum and manganese than exotic species (Tilki and Fisher 1998). In contrast, in the mountainous area of Minas Gerais, Brazil, where acid infertile soils predominate, the exotic species *Acacia mangium* and *A. auriculiformis* achieved faster growth than indigenous species when introduced into an existing *B. decumbens* pasture (Carvalho 1997).

Accessing High Quality Seed

Many farmers are unable to access high quality seed of the best varieties e.g., new releases with insect and disease resistance, or greatly improved productivity. Greater attention is required to educate the distributors of seed (private and institutional) on the importance of using the best germplasm of known genetic quality. More formalised distribution protocols may be needed to protect farmers against receipt of poor quality or unnecessarily expensive planting material. There needs to be greater emphasis placed on both institutional and private investment in the establishment of seed and clonal orchards to ensure that sufficient quantity of the best materials are available for distribution to farmers.

The current recommendation for selecting seed from a native range, is to obtain seed from at least 25, and preferably 50 trees, with sufficient distance between them (50 m) to minimise the likelihood of co-ancestry (Allison and Simons 1996). This simple approach was not appreciated when the first introductions were made.

Weediness

A number of introduced tree legumes have become serious weed pests. Given the large number of introductions to many new environments, this is not surprising. Weediness of introduced exotic trees has generally occurred when:

• The purpose for the introduction has failed, or results in only partial use of trees,
• Seedlings and trees are protected from grazing by thorns, or low palatability,
• Trees have abundant, precocious seed production,
• Seeds are only partially digested by ruminant grazers, and viable seeds are spread in faeces,
• Seed is spread on the hoofs of animals, or transported by flood waters,
• Seeds are long-lived in the soil,
• Young plants grow and colonise rapidly, and tolerate drought, grazing and fire,
• Trees are long-lived,
• There are disturbed areas nearby suitable for invasion,
• There is unpredictable growth as trees perform beyond expectations away from natural predators, or in new climatic, edaphic or management environments.

These conditions have been partially met by a number of introduction events e.g., *Acacia nilotica* was introduced to provide shade and fodder for sheep in western Queensland but now infests 6 M ha of Astrebla grasslands (Carter 1994).

Over the past 80–100 years, mesquite (*Prosopis* spp.) has become an aggressive invader of desert grasslands in the southwest United States (Ibrahim 1992) due to interference in the natural ecological balance by man and his activities. Strategies for control and management of this problem are still not available. Grazing livestock and reduced occurrence of fire were key factors in the increase in density of mesquite. The original movement of *Leucaena leucocephala* subspecies *leucocephala* around the world commencing in the 1600s has lead to this inferior but seedy variety becoming a weed in many tropical environments (Hughes 1994).

The question of weed risk raises many difficult questions with few easy answers. Some suggest that only indigenous species should be considered in agroforestry programs as a way to avoid possible invasion of natural ecosystems by exotic introductions. But this is an unrealistic constraint on farming systems and indeed the environment. Tree legumes are becoming increasingly more important in our livestock industries and our communities. It is imperative that we actively pursue environmentally responsible objectives. Whilst biological control measures have been partially successful (e.g., the bruchid beetle in leucaena), as always, the key is to use preventative rather than remedial measures. It is important to carefully evaluate the level of risk, rejecting high risk introductions, and then to carefully manage introductions to minimise the chances of weed outbreak.

When introducing new species to an environment it may be necessary to first:

1   Review risk of spread by assessing seed production, seed longevity, seed dispersal mechanisms,

2   Review potential methods of control such as susceptibility of seedlings and trees to grazing (thorns, toxins, anti-palatability will reduce animal access); susceptibility to fire, chemical and mechanical methods; and occurrence of insect predators and pathogens in the native range,

3   Study climatic and soil characteristics, in relation to habitat preference of introductions, to predict potential areas susceptible to invasion,

4   Ensure that farmers have been informed as to how to manage and make full use of the introductions. There are many examples of apparent weediness occurring because villagers may be unaware of the many uses of new plants,

5   After introduction, install long-term monitoring and rapid action systems,

6   In improvement programs, investigate opportunity to breed sterile varieties e.g., the sterile triploid in *Leucaena* breeding programs.

A number of these strategies can be combined to reduce weed risk. Nevertheless, tree legumes should not be introduced where risk is high, or where nearby disturbed vegetation might be ecologically threatened.

Forage Quality

Forage quality is essential in tree species used for commercial livestock production. Whilst there is sufficient chemical composition data on tree legumes, this can be misleading. Detailed information on the most important nutritional characteristics (intake of digestible dry matter, production of animal product) is not available for most species.

Low palatability (animal preference) is an issue for many species, yet our understanding of palatability is only partial. Educational programs are required to inform researchers, extension workers and farmers of methods to overcome the reluctance of inexperienced animals to consume new materials. There is opportunity to mix both livestock and plant species and match plant palatability characteristics with livestock preference, to achieve both acceptance of the feed and nutritional advantage.

Many genera contain high levels of tannins which will reduce forage quality. Levels above 5–6% appear to reduce digestibility and the release of protein for ruminants use. Some species in the genera *Acacia*, *Calliandra*, *Prosopis*, *Leucaena* and *Flemingia* have particularly high levels (>10%) although, there is great variation in tannin levels both between and within species, and therefore opportunity for selection of lower tannin varieties.

It is concluded that species in genera, such as *Acacia*, *Prosopis*, *Flemingia*, *Calliandra*, *Erythrina*, whilst important, can be regarded as lower in forage quality. In contrast, key species from *Leucaena*, *Gliricidia*, *Sesbania* and *Chamaecytisus* (Osuji *et al* 1997) are generally of higher quality. Nevertheless, there can still be significant inter- and intra-specific variation, as was found in *Leucaena*, and this offers scope to seek higher quality varieties in some genera.

The Main Species

There are several hundred species of leguminous trees with potential for forage listed in the literature

(Houérou 1980, Atta-Krah 1989). Most have not been investigated and few are in current use in any significant way. Of the 5000 known nitrogen fixing woody species, Brewbaker (1986) suggested that only about 80 leguminous tree and shrub species may have potential multipurpose agroforestry roles, including fodder, in tropical farming systems. Roshetko et al (1996) listed 46 species suitable for fodder, but many fewer have found significance in world animal production systems as key sources of forage supply.

The species and key references are given in the table below. There may be additional species which have forage potential, and within each species there is genetic variation which can be exploited. However, in this brief review only those species in significant use for forage are listed. Selection for membership of this list was a subjective process although fodder value was the pre-eminent selection criteria.

Other species have potential but are not yet in significant use. Examples include the *Leucaena pallida* x *L. leucocephala* KX2 hybrid, *L. collinsii* and *L. trichandra*, the latter species for the high altitude tropics (Shelton et al 1998).

Most-used tree legume species for forage purposes

Higher quality species	Lower quality species
Albizia lebbeck	*Acacia aneura* *
Chamaecytisus palmensis	*Acacia nilotica*
Cratylia argentea	*Acacia tortilis* *
Desmodium rensonii	*Albizia chinensis*
Desmanthus virgatus	*Albizia saman*
Gliricidia sepium	*Calliandra calothyrsus*
Leucaena leucocephala	*Erythrina spp.*
Leucaena diversifolia	*Faidherbia albida* *
Sesbania grandiflora	*Flemingia macrophylla*
Sesbania sesban	*Prosopis juliflora*

* Principal application is in indigenous semi-subsistence systems

References

Allison, G.E. and Simons, A.J. (1996). Propagation and husbandry. In: Stewart, J.L., Allison, G.E. and Simons, A.J. (eds), Gliricidia sepium—Genetic resources for farmers. Tropical forestry Paper 33. Oxford Forestry Institute. pp. 49–71.

Arias, R.A and Macqueen, D.J. (1996). Traditional uses and potential of the genus Calliandra in Mexico and Central America. In Evans, D.O. (ed) International Workshop on the Genus Calliandra. Forest, Farm and Community Reports Special Issue, 1996. Winrock International. pp. 108–114.

Attah-Krah, A.N., Sumberg, J.E. and Reynolds, L. (1986). Leguminous fodder trees in farming systems—an overview of research at the humid zone programme of ILCA in Southwestern Nigeria. In: Haque, I., Jutzi, S. and Weate, P.J. (eds). Potentials of forage legumes in farming systems of sub-saharan Africa. ILCA, Addis Ababa, pp. 307–329.

Baumer, M. (1992). Trees as browse to support animal production. In: Speedy, A and Pierre-Luc Pugliese (eds). Legume trees and other fodder trees as protein sources for livestock. Proceedings of the FAO expert Consultation held at the Malaysian Agricultural Research and Development Institute (MARDI) in Kuala Lumpur, Malaysia. FAO of the United nations. pp. 1–10.

Bekele-Tesemma, A., Birnie, A. and Tengnäs, B. (1993). Useful tress ans shribs for Ethiopia. Regional Soil Conservation Unit. Swedish International Development Authority. 474 pp.

Brewbaker, J.L. 1986. Nitrogen-fixing trees for fodder and browse in Africa. In: Kang, B.T. and Reynolds, L. (eds), Alley farming in the humid and subhumid tropics. proceedings of a workshop held at Ibadan Nigeria, 10–14 March 1986, IDRC Ottawa, pp. 55–70.

Carter, J.O. (1994). Acacia nilotica—a tree legume out of control. In: Gutteridge, R.C. and Shelton, H.M.(eds), Forage Tree Legumes in tropical Agriculture. CAB International, pp. 338–351.

Carvalho, M.M. (1997). Asociaciones de pasturas con arboles en la region centro sur del Brasil. Agroforesteria en las Americas 4, 5–8.

Cromwell, E., Brodie, A. and Southern, A. (1996). Germplasm for Multipurpose Trees: Access and Utility in Small-Farm Communities. Case studies from Honduras, Malawi, & Sri lanka. Overseas Development Institute. 93 pp.

Hughes, C.E. (1994). Risks of species introductions in tropical forestry. Commonwealth Forestry Review, 73, 243–252, 272–273.

Hughes, C.E. (1998a). Leucaena. A genetic resources handbook. Oxford Forestry Institute, Tropical Forestry Papers No. 37. 274 pp.

Ibrahim, K.M. (1992). Prosopis species in the south-western United States, Their utilisation and research. In: Dutton, R.W., Powell, M. and Ridley, R.J. (eds), Prosopis species—Aspects of their value, research and development. Proceedings of Prosopis symposium held by CORD, University of Durham, UK. pp. 83–115.

Middleton, C.H., Jones, R.J., Shelton, H.M., Petty, S.R. and Wildin, J.H. (1995). Leucaena in northern Australia. In: Shelton. H.M., Piggin, C.M. and Brewbaker, J.L. (eds), Leucaena—Opportunities and Limitations. Proceedings of workshop held in Bogor, Indonesia. ACIAR Proceedings No. 57, pp. 214–221.

Neelam Bhatnagar; Bhandar, D.C., Promila Kapoor; Bhatnagar, N. and Kapoor, P. (1993). Competition in the early establishment phases of an even aged mixed plantation of Leucaena leucocephala and Acacia nilotica. Forest Ecology and Management, 57, 213–231.

Osuji, P.O., Odenyo, A.A., Acamovic, T., Stewart, C.S. and Topps, J.H. (1997). The role of legume forages as supplements to low quality roughages—ILRI experience. Selected papers from an international conference on Evaluation of forages for ruminants in the tropics, Harare, Zimbabwe, 28 August–1 September 1995. Animal Feed Science and Technology, 69, pp. 1–3, 27–38.

Roshetko, J.M., Dagar, J.C., Puri, S., Khandale, D.Y., Takawale, P.S., Bheemaiah, G. and Basak, N.C. (1996). Selecting species of nitrogen fixing trees. In: Roshetko, J.M. and Gutteridge, R.C. (eds), Nitrogen Fixing Trees for Fodder Production—A Field Manuel. Winrock International, Morrilton (AR), USA. pp.23–23.

Schrempp, B., Tato, K. and Hurni, H. (1992). Non-conflicting multipurpose tree integration: a case study in the Harerge Highlands, eastern Ethiopia. Soil conservation for survival. A selection of papers presented at the 6th International Soil Conservation Organisation held in Ethiopia and Kenya. pp. 109–117.

Shelton, H.M. and Jones, R.J. (1995). Opportunities and limitations in leucaena. In: Shelton. H.M., Piggin, C.M. and Brewbaker, J.L. (eds), Leucaena—Opportunities and Limitations. Proceedings of workshop held in Bogor, Indonesia. ACIAR Proceedings No. 57, pp.16–23.

Shelton, H.M., Gutteridge, R.C., Mullen, B.F. and Bray, R.A. (eds) (1998). Leucaena—Adaptation, Quality and Farming Systems. Proceedings of workshop held in Hanoi, Vietnam. ACIAR Proceedings No. 86. 358 pp.

Simons, A.J. (1996). Seed orchards and breeding. In: Stewart, J.L., Allison, G.E. and Simons, A.J. (eds), Gliricidia sepium—Genetic resources for farmers. Tropical forestry Paper 33. Oxford Forestry Institute. pp. 119–125.

Stewart, J.L., Allison, G.E. and Simons, A.J. (1996). Gliricidia sepium—Genetic resources for farmers. Tropical forestry Papers 33. Oxford Forestry Institute. 125 pp.

Tilki, F. and Fisher, R.F. (1998). Tropical leguminous species for acid soils: studies on plant form and growth in Costa Rica. Forest-Ecology-and-Management, 108, 175–192.

Original Source

This article was adapted with permission of the author and publisher from:

Shelton, M. Tropical Forage Tree legumes: Key Development Issues. FAO Rome.

Web: http://www.fao.org/ag/AGP/AGPC/doc/Present/Shelton/default.htm

The original source is a publication of the Grassland web site of the Food and Agriculture Organization of the United Nations located at:

http://www.fao.org/ag/AGP/AGPC/doc/pasture/pasture.htm

This excerpt was originally published as *The Overstory* #107.

Animal Tractor Systems

Andy Lee

When planned and managed properly, animals can be key components in sustainable farming systems, enhancing important cycles of nature such as nutrient cycling and balancing of insect populations. A well-designed system with animals can also greatly reduce the human labor required to care for the animals and to prepare and maintain crop areas.

Animal tractor systems are a sustainable, cost-effective, and humane way to integrate animals into an agricultural system. Although the term "tractor" can be confusing, animal tractor systems do not involve draft animals.

Animal tractors are shelter-pen systems where animals such as chickens, turkeys, geese, ducks, pigs, or goats become integral parts of agricultural environments. In animal tractor systems, the animals are managed for productivity of eggs, milk, or meat. At the same time, the scratching, pecking, tilling, and manure spreading behavior of animals is used to prepare, clean, or maintain planting areas.

This chapter describes animal tractors for many purposes, including market garden operations, orchard settings, pond preparation, land clearing, and pasture improvement/diversification.

Animal Tractors

The key to creating an effective animal tractor system is to integrate the needs, behaviors, and products of the animals with the farm system as a whole. An animal tractor locates animals where its food is abundant, where the animal enjoys relative freedom, and where the natural behaviors of the animal are put to best use. By having an animal in the right location, the need to be fed, watered, and cared for by humans is minimized.

Animal tractors bring into harmony the relationships between farmers, the agroecosystem, and animals. The animal provides a handy tillage tool with its continual scratching, pecking, or rooting behavior. It becomes a biomass recycler, consuming excess weeds, grasses, insects, etc. The manure returns to the earth as fertility for the crops.

Orchard maintenance

Animal tractor systems can be very effective for ground cover maintenance, and work well with orchard or tree crops. In an orchard animal tractor system, the animals are rotated through the orchard, either in movable pens or in a series of fixed paddocks. When at the proper density, the animals clean the area between and under the trees of grasses, weeds, and weed seeds, scavenge wastes and windfall fruits, and eat insects and their larvae. At the same time, the animals add their manure to help fertilize the crops. When the pen area has been cleared and fertilized by the animals, they are moved on to the next section of orchard.

A well-planned chicken tractor lets chickens prepare and maintain garden areas naturally

With the appropriate combination of animals and crop trees, this system has been effective with chickens, guinea fowl, turkey, pheasant, quail, sheep, and pigs. On a healthy mixed diet from the orchard, animals tend to have less disease problems.

Lighter animals such as chickens or other poultry can be rotated permanently through an orchard system. More intensive animal tractor systems, for example with pigs, can be very useful in orchard establishment as well as for seasonal maintenance. The system can be further adapted to be more productive by mixing tree species that provide additional food for the animals; for example papaya, banana, and inga (ice cream bean).

Market Gardens

Poultry such as chickens and turkeys are excellent for preparing and fertilizing garden areas. In such systems, the poultry are confined to an area in sufficient density to remove virtually all green matter, fallen fruit, insects, etc. When an area is grazed clean, the animals are moved to a fresh area.

In our case, we use turkeys to fertilize and prepare our market gardens. At the end of each garden season in the Fall we herd turkeys into our enclosed gardens to graze. They eat crop residue and weeds right down to bare ground in no time. Then we harvest the turkeys for the holidays and unroll round bales of hay to mulch the gardens for the winter. The following spring we transplant our garden crops right into the mulch.

To establish a new garden site we use a tractor-powered spading machine to work up the plot. In following years we rely solely upon the turkeys for clean up and fertilizing, and the mulch for soil stability and weed control. Underneath the mulch the soil stays wonderfully loose, sopping up rain and providing a great habitat for soil dwellers and plant roots. Our yields are always well above national averages, and our soil gets richer year by year.

Portable tractor systems are also very effective with chickens. For household production, 120 sq. foot (11 sq. meter) pasture pens are just fine for up to 30 layers or 80 broilers. On a commercial scale, such small pens are too costly and labor intensive for the number of birds each can house. We use a portable ranging system, where we house the birds at night and enclose them in a 1700 sq. foot (160 sq. meter) area during the day inside a portable electric netting. This way we can double or even triple the number of birds per shelter, and still be able to move them easily on a daily or weekly basis.

Preparing Pasture

Removing deep rooted woody weeds requires the power of a pig tractor. A pig tractor works much the same as poultry tractors. Instead of scratching, it is the rooting behavior of the pigs which is used. Pig tractors can be used to prepare land for permanent tree crops or rotated seasonally to clean up crop wastes or fallen fruits.

A small, easily movable chicken tractor with 2-4 chickens can be used to clean up weedy areas in home gardens. By moving every day or two, a small tractor can be used to "mow" the lawn. (photo: C. Elevitch)

My father used pigs to root out a pasture in a cut over wood lot on our farm in Southwest Missouri. To encourage the pigs to root at the stumps, he dug holes around the roots of oak and hickory and filled them with shell corn. He then turned in the hogs.

In a few months the stumps were rooted out and the ground was completely churned up. After taking out the stumps, the bare ground was disc harrowed and planted to permanent pasture with scattered trees. The whole process took about a year, but the results were excellent. I returned to my father's farm forty years later, and found the pasture is still thriving, with cattle grazing amongst the trees that offer shelter and shade.

Pond Preparation

Another application for the pig tractor is in pond preparation. In this case the wallowing and rooting behavior of the pigs, along with their manure and trampled crop residue combine to make a watertight pond bottom.

In my family's case, we have had very good results turning boggy garden areas into ponds. First, we turn feeder pigs into the garden and let them eat crop residue and weeds. The pigs love to wallow and root in the boggy areas. After the area is thoroughly worked over by the pigs, we use a grader to scoop out the pond. We then return the pigs to wallow some more.

The combination of compaction and gleying (similar to gluing) of manure and plant residue creates a perfect pond bottom that holds water for years. Any time the pond starts to leak, we'd just put a pig or two in there for a few days. Ponds usually leak at the water level, and that's where the pigs do the most good. Half in and half out of the water they lay there for hours just slicking the pond side to a impermeable surface, fixing leaks we can't see.

Pasture Improvement and Diversification

Animal tractors can be used very effectively to revitalize and diversify pasture. Using pig and chicken tractors in mobile enclosures can greatly enhance the pasture.

We use beef cattle followed by a chicken tractor to improve our pasture. We only raise a few cattle inside portable electric sheep netting (7000 sq. ft. or 650 sq. meters). We stock the enclosures so that the cattle daily chew the grass down low enough for the chickens to graze on it. The chickens follow the cattle by a week. The time between gives the manure pats time to dry out, for seeds to germinate, and for parasites to become larvae. The chickens scratch the cow pats completely apart, spreading the fertility of the cow pat over a much larger area and eliminating the large cow-pats found in conventionally grazed fields. At the same time, the chickens sanitize the pasture by eating weed seeds and grain that passed through the cows, and eating the parasite larvae. This breaks up the parasite cycle and makes it safe to graze the cattle across the field in controlled rotations without concern for reinfecting them with stomach parasites.

We also use pig tractors in our permanent pasture. Each tractor occupies 130 sq. feet (12 sq. meters), and is roofed and enclosed on one end with sheet metal roofing to shelter the pigs. The pig tractor is on wheels so we can move it easily each morning when we do chores. Leaving the pigs at any one place for just one day churns up a small area of pasture. As soon as we move the pig tractor to its next spot we throw grass and clover seed on the rooted up area to diversify the pasture vegetation.

Land Preparation

Various animals can be used to prepare land, depending on the condition of the vegetation. For lightly vegetated land prone to erosion, a movable poultry tractor works well to quickly remove the tops of weeds and lay down a light coat of manure, in preparation for planting permanent ground covers such as grass, legumes or other protective plants.

Where vegetation is too rough for poultry, pigs, goats or cattle can be used to prepare land for production. For example, on parts of our land crowded with red cedar and black locust sprouts, Virginia creeper, honeysuckle and multi-flora rose, we use goats to clean up the vegetation (Boar meat goats). We use the goats to prepare the land ahead of the chickens, again relying on the poultry to spread the manure and break up parasite cycles.

Conclusion

Here at Good Earth Farm in Central Virginia, USA, our livestock and poultry are reclaiming a 40-acre Shenandoah Valley farm. The results we are seeing are gratifying, especially knowing that we have not spent any money on fertilizer, and in all likelihood we'll never have to, as long as we keep rotating the animals to where they are needed.

The livestock and poultry are also our cash income, to pay for the land and house, and to keep us clothed. Without them we would both have to work off the farm to make ends meet. Instead, we live the kind of life we have always dreamed about, and look forward to sharing our knowledge with others who are ready to learn.

Original Source

This article was originally published as *The Overstory* #50.

Further Reading

Lee, A. 1994. Chicken Tractor, The Permaculture Guide to Happy Hens and Healthy Soils. Good Earth Publications. Shelburne, Vermont. A thorough reference on chicken tractors and enjoyable to read.

Mollison, B. 1990. Permaculture: A Practical Guide for a Sustainable Future, Island Press, Washington, DC. Describes many systems which integrate animals.

Morrow, R. 1993. Earth User's Guide to Permaculture, Simon & Schuster, Intl. Presents a good introduction to animal tractors.

Salatin, J. 1996. Pastured Poultry Profits. Chelsea Green Pub Co. Step-by-step guide to raising chickens on pasture.

Protecting Land from Wind, Erosion, Intruders, and Noise

Animals, plants, soil and people benefit from shelter from the elements. Tree buffers, barriers, and hedges provide protection from harmful winds, salt spray, snow, fire, pesticide drift, noise pollution, damaging animals, and erosion.

Section Contents

Soil and Water Conservation

Meine van Noordwijk and Bruno Verbist

What Is Soil Conservation?

Soil conservation means a way of keeping everything in place, literally as well as in a more abstract sense of maintaining the functions of the soil in sustaining plant growth. Soil conservation practices involve managing soil erosion and its counterpart process of sedimentation, reducing its negative impacts and exploiting the new opportunities it creates. Young (1989) defined soil conservation as a combination of controlling erosion and maintaining soil fertility. In the past the focus has often been on trying to keep the soil at its place by plot-level activities only. Currently, the attention has switched to landscape level approaches where sedimentation is studied along with erosion, and the role of channels (footpaths, roads and streams) is included as well as the "filters" that restrict the overland flow of water and/or suspended sediment.

Why Bother With Soil Conservation?

Erosion concerns differ widely between human interest groups in the uplands and those who live downstream. Erosion is part of the long-term geological cycles of mountain formation and decline, occurs in any vegetation and is an essential part of soil development. Efforts to reduce erosion to zero in humanly used landscapes are doomed to failure, but perceptions of the optimum degree of soil conservation differ between interest groups (stakeholders).

Concerns on soil conservation for agriculturally used lands, especially those recently converted from forest, are usually based on a combination of:

1   On-site loss of land productivity,
2   Off-site concerns on water quantity (Annual water yield, peak (storm) flow, and dry season base flow)
3   Off-site concerns on water quality, as erosion leads to sedimentation on lowlands, siltation of lakes and reservoirs and/or the eutrophication of water.

Concerns b and c are mainly valued by lowland interest groups who perceive changes when natural (for-est) vegetation is converted into agriculture, whereas aspect a is mainly an upland issue. The combination of those three concerns led to a widespread concept of erosion as the major contributor to loss of productivity of uplands as well as the cause of lowland problems with water quantity and quality.

Soil conservation measures will not address all concerns such as loss of land productivity (a), water quality (b) and water quantity (c) to the same degree. We have to differentiate between them in evaluating environmental impacts of land-use or land cover change and in considering options for maintenance of "forest functions" in agricultural landscapes.

Some Key Principles (Modified from FAO and IIRR 1995)

- The farm household should be the focus of every soil conservation program, as they take the daily decisions that shape the landscape; communal action at local level can be an important entry point for outside soil conservation programs.
- Farmers cannot ignore the short-term benefits of the land use decisions they make. Only those production strategies have a chance to be adopted that will provide a reasonable return on the labour and other resources a farmer has to invest. Conservation strategies or technologies that do not meet this criterion are doomed to fail.
- Lack of secure land tenure maybe a major cause of low farmer interest in environmental conservation. Improving tenure security may be the main intervention needed for farmers to adopt reasonable soil conserving technologies.
- Soil conservation programs have often led to "pseudo-adoption" if strong social pressure, subsidies or other government incentives (including tenure security) were used to support adoption of practices that required substantial labour and other resource investment.
- Loss of soil productivity is often much more important than the loss of the soil itself, as the soil on the move tends to be rich in organic matter and nutrients, relative to the remaining soil.

- Loss of soil productivity is not easy to assess, because impoverished zones of net erosion may be accompanied by enriched zones of net sedimentation and the farmer may decide to grow different crops in these two environments.
- In upland systems, plant yields are reduced more by a shortage or excess of soil moisture (especially for tuber crops) or nutrients rather than by soil losses per se. Therefore, there should be more emphasis on rainwater management, particularly water conservation, and integrated nutrient management and less on soil conservation. Agronomic process such as tillage and mulching that maintain infiltration rates are more useful than mechanical measures blocking the path of water flowing at the soil surface in preventing erosion and runoff.
- Erosion is a consequence of how land and its vegetation are managed, and is not itself the cause of soil degradation. Therefore prevention of land degradation is more important than attempting to develop a cure afterwards.
- Most past soil conservation programs focused more on land degradation than on the land user (the farm household), and used a top-down approach in "dissemination" and "extension" of "best-bet" practices. Top down programs have tended to focus primarily on the symptoms of erosion through subsidised terracing, promotion of hedgerow intercropping systems or other measures which have had mixed success when introduced by outside agencies, rather than through farmer-led adoption.
- Soil conservation programs that aim to reduce land degradation problems through treatment of causes, require a long term, bottom-up approach supporting farmers who generally have detailed knowledge of their farm, know a wide range of potential interventions (although they can still learn new ideas from experiences elsewhere) and choose between these interventions on the basis of the resources and pressures on the farm household.

What Soil Conservation Techniques Are Common?

A risk of accelerated erosion exists on cultivated land from the moment trees, bushes, grass and surface litter are removed. Erosion will be exacerbated by attempting to farm slopes that are too steep, cultivating up-and-down hill, continuous use of the land without any rotation of different crops, inadequate input of organic materials, compaction due to footpaths or heavy machinery used for tillage and removal of harvest products etc. Erosion control depends on good management, which implies establishing sufficient crop cover and selecting appropriate practices to maintain infiltration with or without soil tillage. Thus soil conservation relies strongly on agronomic methods in combination with a realistic soil management whilst mechanical measures play only a supporting role.

A range of well-illustrated examples can be found in FAO-IIRR, 1995. We just would like to highlight examples of those three main groups of soil conservation strategies that involve agroforestry:

Agronomic or biological measures utilise the role of vegetation in helping to minimise the erosion by increasing soil surface cover, surface roughness, surface depression storage and soil infiltration. Some examples are:

Strip cropping/alley cropping/hedgerow intercropping

Contour hedgerow systems using nitrogen fixing trees/shrubs have been widely promoted to minimise soil erosion, restore soil fertility, and improve crop productivity (Kang and Wilson 1987, Young 1997; Sanchez, 1995; Garrity, 1996, Friday KS, Drilling and Garrity, 1999). Hedgerows of trees or shrubs (usually double hedgerows) are grown at intervals of 4–6 m along the contours. The strips or alleys between the hedgerows are planted with food crops. The hedgerow trees are regularly pruned to minimise shading of food crops, the pruned biomass can be used as green manure or as mulch *in situ*, or as fodder. Through time, natural terraces can form at the base of the hedgerow trees, and thereby minimise soil erosion and surface run-off Terrace formation can be rapid if the soil is ploughed, but slower in no-till or manual tillage systems.

This technique has been recommended as a common feature of extension programs for sustainable agriculture in Asia. But this innovation has not been widely adopted outside of direct project intervention areas by upland farmers despite the positive results reported in a number of experimental and demonstration sites. The positive and negative ecological interactions between (hedgerow) trees and food crops are discussed more in detail in the Tree Crop Interaction lecture note (van Noordwijk and Hairiah, 2000). However, the major problem in practice is the large amount of labour needed to prune and maintain woody hedgerows. ICRAF (1996) estimated that the amount of labour required to prune leguminous-tree hedgerows was about 31 days per hectare, or 124 days annual labour for four prunings in the Philippines. There is a need for simpler, less labour intensive but effective contour hedgerow systems.

One can state that on flat land hedgerow intercropping is not interesting because of the high level of labour input needed. On sloping land, the improvement of soil fertility, stabilising crop production, may in principle pay off the labour inputs, but real farmer interest probably requires that the soil fertility accumulated in the hedgerows be used for profitable trees, crops or fodder.

Improved fallow systems (IFS)

In the uplands, arable areas are planted with food crops for some years and then the land is fallowed for some time to allow the soil to rejuvenate. To shorten the fallow period, the area can be seeded with leguminous trees. Once the soil has been rejuvenated, the trees are cleared for crops. This can be considered as an improved version of the traditional shifting cultivation practice. More information on fallow management, which was initiated, tested, proved and developed by farmers can be found in the lecture note on Indigenous Fallow Management (IFM) (Burgers, Hairiah and Cairns, 2000).

Example: the native *Leucaena* is used in a fallow system in Naalad, Naga, Cebu (the Philippines). The trees are cut and the branches are piled along the contours to form a barrier structure known locally as *balabag*, which traps the eroding soil. Through time, natural terraces are gradually formed, thus stabilising the steep slopes. Other advantage of this system is the reduction of the amount of nitrogen (N_2) needed as fertiliser because of N-fixation by *Leucaena*. The pruned leaves and branches can be used as fodder.

Natural Vegetative Strips (NVS)

The use of natural vegetative strips (NVS) has proven to be an attractive alternative because they are so simple to establish and maintain. NVS are attractive as they mainly consist of no intervention. When land is ploughed along contour lines, certain strips of 40–50 cm wide are left unploughed, across the field on the contour. These strips are spaced at desired intervals down the slope and can be marked

beforehand. The recommended practice for spacing contour buffer strips has been to place them at every one meter drop in elevation, but a wider spacing may be acceptable.

Soil management is concerned with ways of preparing the soil to promote dense vegetative growth and improve the soil structure so that it is more resistant to erosion. Some techniques included in this group are: minimum tillage, crop rotation (food/cover crops), manure, sub-soiling and drainage.

- Minimum tillage/zero tillage. In this system, simple farm equipment such as hoes and digging sticks are used to prepare land and plant food crops. Spraying herbicide kills weeds, and all plant residues (including weeds) are returned into the soil. Farmers in swidden systems traditionally are familiar with minimum tillage practices. While more intensive tillage generally increases porosity of the topsoil and reduced barriers to infiltration of the soil surface, it normally interrupts the continuity of the macro-pores in the soil and can reduce deep infiltration, especially if a plough-pan is formed. No till systems that are implemented on soils that have never been ploughed or compacted by the use of heavy machinery generally maintain the high infiltration rates of forest soils. Transitions from ploughing to minimum tillage systems often involve a number of years of reduced infiltration, before new continuous macro-pore system is re-established by the activity of earthworms and other soil engineers.

- Crop rotation is common practice for smallholder farmers in SE-Asia. It is a system with various crop species grown in sequence on the same plot. Example: maize grown at the first season and groundnuts in the second season. Groundnuts can replenish N (via N-fixation) which was extracted by maize. The different rooting pattern of different crop species planted may help on soil structure formation and improve water percolation. These cropping pattern can vary from year to year depending on market price or on soil/weather condition, but they are chosen for the same purposes: better soil physical and nutrient condition, interrupts life cycle of weed/pest/ plant disease.

Mechanical or physical methods can be viewed as an attempt to control the energy available for erosion (rain splash, runoff). These methods depend on manipulating the surface topography by installing terraces, ditches. Examples are:

Bench terraces consist of a series of alternating shelves and dykes and are used on sloping land up to 40% with relatively deep soils to retain water and control erosion. The dykes are vulnerable to erosion and are protected by a vegetation cover (e.g., *Cajanus cajan*, *Sesbania grandiflora*, *Sesbania sesban*, *Gliricidia sepium* or fruit trees such as banana (*Musa* spp.) and sometimes faced with stones or concrete. The plant spacing (6 x 6 m) of bigger fruit trees as mango (*Mangifera indica*), jackfruit (*Artocarpus heterophyllus*) etc., is generally too wide to be effective for dyke protection, but it increases economic revenue on those terraces. The terraces are normally constructed by cutting the soil to produce series of level steps or benches, which allow water to infiltrate slowly into the soil. Bench terraces are suitable mainly for irrigated rice-based cropping systems.

Soil traps (more commonly known as sediment traps) are structures constructed to harvest soil eroded from the upper slopes of the catchment. Common types of soil traps are check dams and trenches. They slow down the water flow and allow heavier soil particles to settle. It prevents widening and deepening of gullies and promotes the deposition of nutrient-rich, highly fertile sediments. Afterwards this area can be used for growing crops. The accumulated soil can also be returned to the field, but that is quite laborious.

The size of the check dam depends on the size of the drainage or gully to be protected. Check dams can be built of stakes (e.g., from *Gliricidia*), bamboo, loose rocks, logs or other locally available materials. They should be permeable, as they are meant to slow down the speed of the water to increase sedimentation. They are not meant to stop or divert the flow of the water.

A combination between agronomic measures and good soil management can influence both the detachment and transport phases of the erosion process, whereas mechanical methods are effective in controlling the transport phase but do little to prevent soil detachment.

Conclusion

To conclude with a word of caution: Most soil conservation measures require a lot of labour investment, while it is not always obvious who will benefit from it. Before an attempt is made to introduce soil conservation measures, some time should be spent to "read the landscapes." This means that some time should be spent on trying to answer the following questions, before any activity is undertaken:

- Is soil erosion a real problem? Who perceives soil erosion as a problem: the uplanders, the people downstream or other stakeholders?
- Are there any elements in the landscape, which are currently reducing soil erosion?
- If the different stakeholders see lack of soil conservation as a problem, how and to what extent will the person executing the soil conservation measures also benefit from his/her work? If the one who is supposed to carry out the job will not benefit in the short and long term, chances of failure are large.
- If soil erosion is seen as a downstream problem, then a discussion should be held between downstream and upstream stakeholders to find a reasonable solution, which could include compensation paid to farmers upstream to carry out soil conservation measures.
- If it is clear that those who will do the soil conservation also benefit from it, only then one can start thinking about different technical measures.

References

Coughlan KJ, Rose CW, eds. 1997. A new soil conservation methodology and application to cropping systems in tropical steeplands. ACIAR Technical Reports 40, Australian Centre for International Agricultural Research, Canberra.

FAO, IIRR. 1995. Resource management for upland areas in SE-Asia. An Information Kit. Farm field document 2. Food and Agriculture Organisation of the United Nations, Bangkok, Thailand and International Institute of Rural Reconstruction, Silang, Cavite, Philippines. ISBN 0-942717-65-1: p 207.

Friday KS, Drilling ME and Garrity DP. 1999. Imperata Grassland Rehabilitation Using Agroforestry and Assisted Natural Regeneration. Bogor: ICRAF, Southeast Asian Regional Program. p 167.

Garrity DP. 1993. Sustainable land-use systems for sloping uplands in Southeast Asia. In: Technologies for Sustainable Agriculture in the Tropics. American Society of Agronomy Special Publication 56 Madison, Wisconsin, USA

Garrity DP. 1996. Tree-Soil-Crops interaction on slopes. In: Ong CK, Huxley P. eds. Tree-Crops interactions: a physiological approach: CAB-International. p 299–318.

Garrity D, Stark M, Mercado A. 1999. Natural vegetative strip technology: A "NO COST" paradigm that may help transform tropical smallholder conservation. Paper presented on Bioengineering meeting.

ICRAF. 1996. Annual Report for 1995. International Centre for Research in Agroforestry, Nairobi, Kenya.

Morgan RPC. 1986. Soil erosion and conservation. Longman Group UK. p 296.

Sanchez PA. 1995. Science in agroforestry. Agroforestry systems 30(1):5–55.

van Noordwijk M, van Roode M, McCallie EL and Lusiana B. 1998. Erosion and sedimentation as multiscale, fractal processes: Implications for models, experiments and the real world. In: De Vries P, Agus F and Kerr J, eds. Proc. Int. Workshop on Soil erosion at multiple scales. CAB Int. Wallingford, UK. p 223–253.

Young A. 1997. Agroforestry for soil management. CAB Int. Wallingford, UK. p 320.

Original Source

This edition of *The Overstory* was excerpted with permission of the publisher from:

van Noordwijk, M. and B. Verbist. 2000. Soil and Water Conservation. International Centre for Research in Agroforestry, Bogor, Indonesia.

Publisher contact: International Centre for Research in Agroforestry Southeast Asian Regional Research Programme P0 Box 161, Bogor, Indonesia Tel: +62 251 625415; fax: +62 251 625416; Email: icraf-indonesia@cgiar.org;
Web: http://www.icraf.cgiar.org/sea

Printed copies of the original can be purchased from: http://www.icraf.cgiar.org/sea/ICRAFPubsList/Bookstore/BookStoreNew.htm#Lect   ure-Notes

This excerpt was originally published as *The Overstory* #104.

Buffers: Common Sense Conservation

USDA Natural Resources Conservation Service

Conservation buffers are a common-sense way to protect a most valuable asset— land—and demonstrate a personal commitment to conservation.

Best described as strips or small areas of land in permanent vegetation, conservation buffers help control potential pollutants and manage other environmental concerns. Filter strips, field borders, grassed waterways, field windbreaks, shelterbelts, contour grass strips, and riparian (streamside) buffers are all examples of conservation buffers.

Conservation buffers can be especially helpful in maintaining a productive, profitable, and responsible farming or ranching operation. Farms and ranches today produce more than crops and livestock. They also produce environmental benefits. Conservation buffers can help you protect soil, air, and water quality; improve fish and wildlife habitat; and demonstrate a commitment to land stewardship.

Conservation buffers can be used along streams and around lakes or wetlands. They can also be installed at field edges or within fields. Buffers are most effective, of course, if they are planned as part of a comprehensive conservation system.

To maximize their effectiveness and your overall conservation program, buffers should be combined with other proven conservation practices, such as conservation tillage (or no-till systems), nutrient management, and integrated pest management. Working together, these practices will provide an effective yet profitable conservation program.

The Value of Buffers

Chances are you are already using some form of conservation buffer in your farming or ranching operation. When used as part of a well-planned and properly implemented conservation farming system, buffers can play a big role in conservation plans.

Buffers slow water runoff, trap sediment, and enhance water infiltration in the buffer itself. They trap fertilizers, pesticides, bacteria, pathogens, and heavy metals, minimizing the chances of these potential pollutants reaching surface water and ground water sources. Buffers also trap snow and reduce blowing soil in areas with strong winds. They protect livestock from harsh weather, offer a natural habitat for wildlife, and improve fish habitat. Wooded buffers can provide a source of future income.

Properly installed and well-maintained buffers help diversify the "look" of a farm, adding to its beauty, recreational opportunities, land value, and even air quality. All of these benefits add up to make buffers a visible demonstration of one's commitment to common-sense conservation.

Types of Buffers

There are many different types of buffers. While these practices may be called different names in different regions of the country, their functions are much the same—improve and protect ground water and surface water quality; reduce erosion on cropland and stream banks; and provide protection and cover for livestock, wildlife, and fish. Some examples follow.

Shelterbelts/Field Windbreaks A row or rows of trees, shrubs, or other plants used to reduce wind erosion, protect young crops, and control blowing snow. Shelterbelts also provide excellent protection from the elements for wildlife, livestock, houses, and farm buildings. Field windbreaks are similar to shelterbelts but are located along crop field borders or within the field itself. They may also be called hedgerow plantings in some areas.

Living Snow Fences Similar in design to field windbreaks/shelterbelts, living snow fences serve the additional function of being used to help manage snow deposits to protect buildings, roads, and other property. They can be designed and placed to help protect nearby areas for livestock, provide wildlife cover, and collect snow to enhance soil moisture and nearby water supplies.

Contour Grass Strips Narrow bands of perennial vegetation established across the slope of a crop field and alternated down the slope with strips of crops. Properly designed and maintained contour grass strips can reduce soil erosion, minimize transport of sediment and other water-borne contaminants, and provide wildlife habitat.

Riparian Buffers Streamside plantings of trees, shrubs, and grasses that can intercept contaminants from both surface water and ground water before they reach a stream and that help restore damaged streams.

Filter Strips Strips of grass used to intercept or trap field sediment, organics, pesticides, and other potential pollutants before they reach a body of water.

Grassed Waterways Strips of grass seeded in areas of cropland where water concentrates or flows off a field. While they are primarily used to prevent gully erosion, waterways can be combined with filter strips to trap contaminants or field sediment.

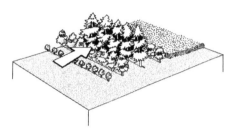

Windbreaks are a common kind of buffer

Salt-Tolerant Vegetation Special areas planted to vegetation capable of growing in high-saline environments and capable of reducing saline seepage.

Cross-Wind Trap Strips Rows of perennial vegetation planted in varying widths and oriented perpendicular to the prevailing wind direction. Cross-wind trap strips can effectively prevent wind erosion in cropping areas with high average annual wind speeds.

Shallow Water Areas for Wildlife Areas of shallow water within or near cropland that are protected by permanent shrubs, trees, and grassed areas. These areas are vital to enhancing wildlife habitat.

Wellhead Protection Areas Land within a maximum 2,000-foot radius from a public well, as designated by the Environmental Protection Agency (EPA) or a State-designated agency, can be enrolled in the continuous CRP sign-up. Circular-shaped areas can be "squared off" to eliminate odd-shaped corners to a maximum of 367 acres.

Other Types of Buffers Include:

Field Borders—Grass-seeded areas along the edges or ends of cropland.

Alley Cropping—Crops planted between rows of larger mature trees, or between hedgerows of fast-growing (usually nitrogen fixing) trees.

Herbaceous Wind Barriers—Perennial vegetation established in rows across the prevailing wind direction.

Vegetative Barriers—Narrow, permanent strips of dense, tall, stiff, erect perennial vegetation established parallel and perpendicular to the dominant slope of the field.

Stream bank Plantings—Plants, shrubs, and/or trees placed to protect streambanks.

Original Source

This article was excerpted from the original published as *Buffers, Common-Sense Conservation* published at http://www.nhq.nrcs.usda.gov/CCS/Bufrs-Pub.html.

This excerpt was first published as *The Overstory* #73.

Vegetative Erosion Barriers

Michael Pease

The problems of retaining soil, water and plant nutrients where they can support timber growth and fruit production are critical to productive agroforestry. Yet we are steadily losing our soil resource and much of our water and plant nutrients is lost in run-off.

Previously, solutions to problems of soil erosion and to soil and water run-off have been sought mainly from earthworks and engineered constructions. However, such structures often prove to be costly, ineffective, and unsustainable. The solution lies in permanent, vegetative barriers planted on the contour. There is an upright, tufted, deep-rooted and very dense grass that is proving to be one of the prime tools in providing a solution to these problems, particularly in tropical countries. It is called *Vetiveria zizanioides* or vetiver grass.

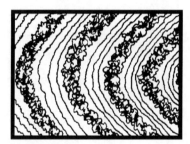

Plan view of vegetative contours

Highlight of Vetiver Grass

Vetiver has been grown in various countries for many centuries but principally for the value of the essential oil that is produced from its roots rather than for its soil conservation properties. Vetiver grass originates from Northern India. Within the past 15–20 years it has been planted in some 100 countries. Erosion control barriers using vetiver grass is a low-cost, simple and effective technology, proven by much practical application and research data.

Vetiver can survive extremes of drought, heat, water logging, pH, and, to some extent, cold. It is insensitive to photo period and grows year-round where temperatures permit. It does not harbour pests and diseases to any significant extent. Most importantly,

most cultivated varieties of vetiver do not produce viable seed as has been shown in trials in a number of countries including Hawai'i. So it is not a weed and not invasive. Any reader interested in growing vetiver grass should check carefully that the plants are of a genotype (genetic selection) that either produce no seed, or produce only sterile seed.

Vetiver is a bunch grass with very rapid growth in warm, moist conditions growing to more than 2m in height and with a remarkably dense and vertical rooting system descending for 3–5m. It is a very strong plant, its roots having a tensile strength equivalent to one sixth of mild steel, and when planted on the contour as a hedge presents a virtually impenetrable barrier through which soil can hardly pass and through which water only passes with much reduced velocity. As silt builds up behind the plant it is capable of shooting from the nodes and rising above the deposited silt to form a natural terrace. Weeds and undesirable foreign grasses, are unable to penetrate through a well-established hedge. It is cheap and easy to plant and maintenance is minimal. Overall, it is not detrimental to crops or forestry grown between hedgerows due to the vertical nature of its rooting system.

Vetiver is tolerant to a wide range of climatic and soil conditions. For instance it has been shown to flourish in temperatures from -9°C to 50°C and in areas with rainfall as low as 300mm per annum or as a high as 6,000mm per annum. It survives pH levels as low as 3.3 and as high as 10.6. It has been successfully grown to stabilise soils on the slimes surrounding mining sites in South Africa and tin mine wastes in Malaysia and Australia where it tolerates very high levels of heavy metals. It has also been used for degraded wasteland rehabilitation. It will grow in saline and sodic conditions and even in acid sulphate soils or pure laterite. It survives fire well, pushing out new green shoots shortly after fire has ravaged an area. Consequently, when in its green state, it can be used as a firebreak. Whilst vetiver is growing effectively at 40° North in some countries its primary area of growth is in the tropics and sub-tropics. It is commonly grown to control soil erosion and retain water on slopes in excess of 45 degrees.

Vetiver acts as a pioneer plant growing where other plants would not survive and providing microclimatic conditions where native species may become established. A good example of this is in Murcia region of Spain where vetiver has been successfully established to control erosion under conditions of 300mm annual precipitation and on very poor soils.

At a time when there is much concern regarding global warming and CO_2 emissions, 18,000 ha of land protected by vetiver grass hedgerows will provide a CO_2 sink for the CO_2 produced by 100,000 automobiles travelling 20,000 km per annum!

In the United States, the National Research Council reviewed the potential of the grass and reported that, "vetiver hedges were a cheap, safe, and effective technique to slow erosion and retain soil moisture."

Vetiver stabilizing an orange orchard in Jiangxi Province, China. The leaves are cut for mulching. (photo: D. Grimshaw)

Multiple Uses of Vetiver

Vetiver has a myriad of on-farm and other uses besides those mentioned above, including, for example, use as a living fence and boundary marker. The leaves and roots of vetiver can be used for an extensive range of handicrafts and are excellent for thatching. The young leaves are palatable to livestock and have about the same nutritive value as Napier grass (*Pennisetum purpureum*). It is used domestically in cooking and insect control and also has medicinal properties.

Vetiver in Agroforestry: Fruit, Timber, and Mixed Systems

There are conflicting views as to how best to use vetiver hedges to aid increased production from fruit trees. As a semi-circle around fruit trees, about 3m from each tree on the down-hill side, it has been shown to be an effective technique with lychees in Thailand where increased yields exceeding 20% were recorded. (However, if the hedge forms a complete circle round the tree it prevents moisture reaching the tree rather than retaining it for use by the tree's roots.) The technique provides a windbreak that benefits young tree growth in the early stages. Using vetiver hedges planted on the contour with the fruit trees also planted on the contour between the hedges is probably the most dependable method. Competition between the vetiver and adjacent fruit trees is minimal because of the vertical nature of the vetiver rooting system as has been shown

Vetiver protecting a pine planting in Malawi. (photo: D. Grimshaw)

in Vietnam. In Trinidad's Maracas Valley it was noted that mango trees benefited from the presence of vetiver hedge barriers due to increase in soil organic matter and moisture. In the Philippines vetiver was shown to be tolerant to heavy shade, but the converse is reported elsewhere. In Malaysia, under rubber and oil palm, it was shown that vetiver is tolerant to moderate levels of shade intensity. Vetiver is only tolerant to heavy shade if it has first been established in full sunlight before being shaded out, as is the case in sugarcane closing over the hedge.

In trials in China it has been shown that vetiver planted in citrus orchards increased soil organic matter from 0.4% to 1.8%. Soil bulk density decreased whilst porosity, organic matter, various trace elements and some 20 amino acids increased. Vetiver hedgerows have also been effectively demonstrated in citrus plantations in Costa Rica. Overall, where vetiver hedges are planted in fruit tree orchards increased yields can be expected due to reduced run-off, the retention of organic material and run-off behind the hedges and protection of tree seedlings against wind.

In the case of timber production it is best to plant the vetiver hedge barriers at the same time or before planting the trees. This allows the vegetative barriers to become well formed and for erosion to be controlled and soil moisture retained to benefit the young tree growth. It is possible that eventually the tree canopy may become so dense that the vetiver will die due to lack of sunlight. However, by then it will have done its work and its initial planting will have been justified through increased timber or fruit production. As a rough "rule of thumb" it can be said that vetiver will take at least 50% shade after establishment, though this figure is regarded as very conservative by Dr. Julio Alegre, Coordinator at ICRAF in Peru. Over time, silt will build up behind the vetiver hedge and this should be taken into consideration when planting the nearest row of trees above the hedge.

In eucalyptus and teak plantations for example, where run-off is high, plantation layout could be so designed as to allow unshaded vetiver hedges to be sited at strategic points to break the velocity of rainfall run-off. Essentially, the vetiver hedge will provide an understory that complements the tree production.

In areas of high rainfall intensity such as Peru, which may receive in excess of 400mm in a month, ICRAF is promoting the agroforestry practice with farmers of planting each row of fast-growing native tree species such as *Inga*, *Erythrina*, *Gliricidia* and *Cassia* combined with another row of vetiver at an interval of 4-6m, depending upon slope. Resultant terrace formation is fast and farmers can grow crops between the rows that benefit from the build-up of silt and plant nutrients.

At this early stage in the development of Vetiver Grass Technology (VGT) data is scarce regarding increased timber production resulting from the establishment of vetiver hedge barriers. However, it stands to reason that with increased soil moisture, retention of plant nutrients and reduction in erosion tree growth will be more rapid and overall production will be higher.

Vetiver produces an excellent long-lasting, absorbent mulch which, when placed around fruit trees reduces evaporation and aids in the long-term, build-up of mycorrhizae. The leaves are unattractive to insects. In India it was recorded that 90% of tree seedlings survived when mulched with vetiver as against 30% in an untreated control nursery.

In Guangdong Province, China, an experiment in eucalyptus plantations was commenced in 1991 and observations recorded over a 50 month period by Dr. Liao Baowen of The Research Institute of Tropical Forestry. Two rows of trees were inter-planted, one with vetiver and the other with *Stylosanthes guyanensis*; a third plot was left as control with trees only. The results indicated that the surface liquid run-off in the vetiver plot was 15.7% lower than the stylo and 18% lower than the control plot. The surface solid run-off on the vetiver plots was 30.3% less than the stylo and 54.6% less than control. A subsequent measurement of five-year old eucalyptus showed a 15.9% increase in diameter at breast height, compared to control. Overall, increased tree growth as a result of the vetiver hedge barriers may be as much as 20%.

As mentioned above, vetiver is a pioneer plant but this role can be enhanced when it is planted in conjunction with tree species. In China it has been shown that such practices:

The slope area in the foreground was seeded with vetiver and did not take well nor is erosion controlled. In the middle ground some vetiver was planted below a badly engineered drain outflow and was partially washed away. In the background vetiver is well established and the slope is not eroding and has been stabilizing. Tree seeds will establish naturally between the vetiver hedgerows and eventually the road fill will be forested. (photo: D. Grimshaw)

- assist in the stabilization of slopes;
- alleviate sheet erosion, especially under storm conditions;
- provide a more aesthetically pleasing effect than vetiver on its own and;
- result in greater economic benefits.

References

Newsletters produced by The Vetiver Network, 15 Wirt St. N.W., Leesburg, VA, 20176 USA, Web: http://www.vetiver.org, Email: vetiver@vetiver.org

Board on Science and Technology for International Development. 1993. Vetiver Grass - A Thin Green Line Against Erosion. National Research Council, Washington DC.

Baowen, L., Z. Dezhand and Z. Songfa. 1991. "Studies on the effects of soil and water conservation of vetiver grass in eucalyptus plantations" Research Institute of Tropical Forestry of Chinese Academy of Forestry.

Tam, T.T., T. Phien, N. Tu Siem. "A promising grass for soil conservation in Vietnam." National Institute for soils and fertilisers, Vietnam.

Hin Som, K. "Study on cultivation of vetiver grass to maintain moisture for fruit crops." Royal Development Study Centre, Thailand.

Le, L.C., G. Zhenyan, L. Shizong, X. Hanping. 1995. Forest Research Institute, Guangdong province, China.

Grimshaw, R.G. and L. Helfer. 1995. Vetiver Grass for soil and Water Conservation, Land Rehabilitation and Embankment Stabilization. World Bank Technical Paper No 273, Washington DC.

Hanping, X., A. Huixiu, L. Shizhong, and H. Daoqian. South China Institute of Botany, Academia Sinica, Guangzhou, China.

Private communications from: R.G. Grimshaw, P. Truong, C. Elevitch, J. Greenfield, and J. Alegre.

Original Source

This chapter was originally published as *The Overstory* #45.

Windbreak Design

Steven Burke

People, plants and animals thrive in sheltered environments. Creating a sheltered environment is an important farm management objective. The only practical way to provide shelter for broadscale agriculture and pasture is by establishing windbreaks. Farmers and other land managers increasingly recognize the value of shelter, and windbreaks are more and more a feature of rural areas throughout the world. Windbreaks have a place on almost every farm.

Key Design Criteria

A drive through the countryside often reveals many poorly designed and haphazardly established windbreaks. Faults are difficult to correct after planting. A little thought and care in the design of your windbreak will result in a valuable long term asset and improve a farm's productivity and profitability.

Height

Maximising windbreak height is generally the most important windbreak design consideration.

The area protected by a windbreak is directly proportional to its height. In other words, by doubling the height of a windbreak you double the area protected. Increasing the average windbreak height in a windbreak system increases the distance between the windbreaks required to provide the same level of protection.

Windbreaks therefore should be designed and established to make sure they reach the maximum mature height possible. The most important design issue is to include at least one row of the tallest shelter trees capable of growing on the site. Also use good quality plants of species and provenances (local varieties) known to grow well in your locality. Provide good conditions for plant growth by following recommended site preparation and establishment procedures.

As well as the final mature height, other factors to consider when selecting the species in the tallest rows are their growth rate and the life span. Fast growth to the maximum height means the maximum extent of shelter is achieved earlier. Long-lived species increase the time span that this is maintained.

Length

The length of a windbreak and the presence of gaps also greatly influences windbreak performance.

Short windbreaks tend to be very ineffective because the wind curls around each end due to turbulence. This results in a narrower area being protected than the length of the windbreak. It's best to make windbreaks as long as possible. A common rule of thumb is to make windbreaks at least 10 times as long as their mature height.

Gaps in windbreaks should be avoided if at all possible, as they decrease windbreak effectiveness. Wind speed in front of a gap is increased due to concentration and funneling of winds.

Gaps however are sometimes necessary due to the need for gates and access through windbreaks. If this is the case, wind funneling problems can be kept to a minimum. A small island shelterbelt just in front of the gap is one solution. In multi-row windbreaks, the gap can be angled at 45 degrees to the prevailing wind direction.

Porosity

Porosity is the degree to which wind can pass through a windbreak.

There is a strong relationship between windbreak porosity and the minimum wind speed produced on the lee side. Denser (or less porous) windbreaks reduce wind speed to a lower level immediately in their lee and the point with the lowest wind speed occurs is located closer to the windbreak. Very dense (<20% optical porosity) windbreaks are desirable where a small area of high quality shelter is required, such as livestock havens or around houses.

A significant problem with these dense windbreaks is the greater turbulence they create in their lee. Turbulence generally decreases with increased porosity. This increased turbulence is felt at ground level beyond a quiet zone of reduced turbulence which extends to about eight times the height (8H). Hence significant wind turbulence can be expected in the zone extending beyond 8H for dense windbreaks.

Ironwood (*Casuarina cunninghamiana*) windbreak planted in a double row at 2 x 2 m spacing offers good protection against trade winds. Waimea, Hawai'i. (photo: C. Elevitch)

The vertical distribution of porosity is also important. In general, the usual aim is to have uniform porosity from ground level to the top of the windbreak. The most common mistake is to not provide low shelter down to ground level, either due to poor windbreak design or maintenance. The effect of this is funneling of winds underneath the windbreak creating a narrow zone of increased wind speed immediately in the lee. Clearly this zone has the potential for adverse effects on crops, livestock and exposed soil. Beyond this, these windbreaks still provide an extended area of valuable shelter.

The type of trees in the windbreak greatly affects its porosity. Different species have greatly different foliage density and therefore produce windbreaks of different porosity. For example, eucalypts tend to have more open crowns whilst introduced cypresses have very dense foliage. Windbreak porosity is also reduced by decreasing the spacing between trees within rows and increasing the number of rows.

Number and spacing of rows

Single row windbreaks can provide very good shelter, providing they consist of tree species which re-tain foliage down to ground level. These windbreaks use the least area, but they are susceptible to problems caused by gaps and non-uniform growth. Frequently the maximum height obtained is less than for multiple row windbreaks. These problems can be overcome by increasing the number of rows at the small expense of more space used. Given the significant investment in establishing and double fencing a windbreak, compromising on the number of rows is often a false economy.

It is usually a good idea to have multiple row windbreaks. Belts with several rows give a better opportunity to use tall tree species which naturally lose their foliage near ground level (or are pruned for timber production) in conjunction with lower shrubby species. Good permeability and height can often be obtained from 2–4 rows with one or two rows of tall trees. Narrow windbreaks of 2–4 rows are generally optimal in terms of minimising the area of land removed from agriculture whilst providing maximum shelter benefits.

Other benefits can be provided by further increasing the number of rows. Rows of fast growing species can be included to provide rapid shelter which will later either die out or be removed. Wildlife habitat is usually enhanced. Stock can be moved into fenced, broad, multi-row windbreaks at critical times when maximum shelter is needed. Tree and shrub species which are more susceptible to the wind may be inappropriate in narrow windbreaks, however can be included in the protected inner rows of a broad multi-row windbreak. In very exposed climates, such as in coastal areas, a larger number of rows can assist tree survival and growth due to greater mutual support.

More rows in windbreaks are particularly recommended for dry regions, because growth rates are generally slow and survival rates more variable than in wetter areas.

There is some evidence that very broad windbreaks produce an aerodynamically less efficient barrier to the wind than narrower ones. This should be considered before unnecessarily including a very large number of rows in a windbreak.

Valuable timber can also be grown if one or more rows of timber producing tree species are included. In New Zealand, a system of timber producing windbreaks called "timberbelts" has been developed and is being widely adopted in Southern Australia and elsewhere. Here a row or rows of high-pruned, timber producing species is planted alongside a row of low growing shelter species. More timber rows can be included if greater timber production is desired at the expense of less land available for crops or pastures.

Rows can be varied from 1.5–5 m apart to allow adequate room for the development of the trees and shrubs. In general, the fewer the rows, the closer they may be spaced.

There should be two and preferably three metres between the outside row and the fence to prevent stock browsing off too much low level foliage. Loss of low foliage results in undesirable increases in wind speed close to the windbreak due to wind funneling. This distance can be reduced slightly with electric fencing. Leaving an adequate distance between the outside row and the fence leaves space for the trees to grow. It greatly reduces stock pressure on the fence and the likelihood that it will fail. An extra metre either side of a windbreak only occupies 0.2 ha per km of windbreak, a small price to pay for significantly enhanced windbreak performance.

Rows of low growing trees and shrubs should be located on the outside of the windbreak to prevent them being shaded out by taller species.

Cross-sectional profile

A common misconception in windbreak design is to aim for a sloping cross-section or profile. A sloping aerodynamic profile actually reduces windbreak effectiveness. Steep sided windbreaks create a more effective barrier to wind flow and therefore shelter a greater area. Multi-row windbreaks should if possible have their tall rows on the windward side and the lower growing rows to leeward.

If shade is desired from the windbreak, then place the tallest rows so that they cast the maximum shadow at times when shade is most needed (e.g. in mid afternoon).

Spacing of trees and shrubs within rows

Spacing should be sufficient for the windbreak to provide the required porosity in a reasonable amount of time. Too great a spacing leads to an excessive period of time before the gaps close between the trees. Too small a spacing can lead to insufficient porosity and results in higher establishment costs.

Tree spacing should be varied according to the types of tree being used and the site to be planted. The average spacing for medium to tall trees is 2.5–6 m and for small trees and large shrubs is 2–4 m. Compact low shrubs are commonly planted at 1.5–3 m spacing. In general, trees and shrubs should be more closely spaced in narrower windbreaks and can also be closer in wetter, more fertile areas.

An alternative approach is to plant trees and shrubs more closely than the final intended spacing and to thin them as they grow. This results in the faster establishment of shelter. This can be achieved in a number of ways. The simplest is to simply plant the long-term shelter species at a greater density and thin them as they develop. Another method is to alternate the planting of fast growing short-lived shrubs with slower growing long-lived species. The faster growing shrubs are thinned before they compete excessively with the long term species which will ultimately comprise the windbreak. The trees and shrubs removed can be used for firewood, fence posts or fodder.

Try to stagger the position of trees so that they are opposite spaces in adjoining rows to provide more uniform porosity, fewer gaps, faster establishment of shelter and optimal use of the space available.

Species Selection

Plant tree and shrub species which will provide the windbreak characteristics you require (particularly final height, growth rate and porosity).

The most important considerations when selecting species are:

- At least one row of the tallest species that will grow on the site should be included as previously described.
- Foliage density and crown shape. This varies greatly with species, so affecting windbreak porosity. For single row windbreaks, the species selected must provide adequate foliage density from tree-top to ground level. Where multi-rowed windbreaks are to be established, then more flexibility in species selection is possible. Use of smaller trees and shrubs in particular can reduce problems with the loss of foliage at ground level of the tallest trees.
- Growth rate. Fast early growth is desirable as it leads to the more rapid establishment of shelter. Unfortunately it is common for rapid growing species to be short-lived. Trees which grow very fast can also be less wind firm. In these cases, a row of these species can be planted on one side of the windbreak or planted alternately with slower growing species within a windbreak row. They can then be allowed to die out or thinned when they are not required. Fast growth is also advantageous where the species are selected to provide timber fuel-wood or fodder production.
- Compatibility with crops and pastures. Some species compete with adjacent crop and pasture growth to a greater extent than others. Trees and shrubs with deep, penetrating roots generally compete less for moisture than shallow spreading root systems. Some species chemically inhibit the growth of plants around them through a process called allelopathy. Conversely other trees and shrubs can have beneficial effects, for example through nitrogen fixing (particularly *Allocasuarina*, *Casuarina*, and *Acacia* species) and adding organic matter to soil.
- Ability to regenerate naturally under the environmental conditions of the site. Choosing these species creates perpetual self-sustaining windbreaks. Indigenous species are often able to regenerate most easily.
- The life span of tree species. Selecting long-lived species obviously maximises the useful life of the windbreak. Try to choose species which can live together harmoniously for a long time. By selecting species of roughly equivalent life span, impaired windbreak performance as plants gradually die out can be avoided. Be careful of the quickest growing species as these are often short-lived or prone to disease. The benefit of quick shelter may be gained at the expense of a much shorter period of effective shelter. Alternatively, closely planted nurse rows of rapid growing, short-lived shrubs or trees may be worth considering to provide early shelter for slower growing species, especially on exposed sites. The nurse rows can be removed or be allowed to die out as the windbreak matures.
- Number of species in each row. Try not to include too many, particularly for windbreaks with only a few rows, as this tends to decrease uniformity in height and permeability. Often one species per row is best. There are some exceptions to this rule, such as the alternate planting of slow and fast growing species within a row described above or the alternate planting of tall pruned timber species of tree with slow growing, shrubby shelter species within the same row.
- Fire resistance or ability to regenerate is desirable in fire-prone areas. This can save much in re-establishment costs. For example, many eucalypts reshoot from branches and trunks after being burnt. Other species respond to being burnt by fire through massive germination of seed accumulated in the soil. This is common with Acacia species. The result is rapid regrowth of the windbreak at no cost.
- Flammability of foliage. Tree and shrub species of low flammability can protect assets against the heat of fires when used as radiation shields. These should be located well away from buildings as they will still burn under extreme fire conditions.
- Landscape and wildlife. Select species which blend in with existing vegetation and landscapes. Species can also be selected to provide food and shelter for wildlife. Indigenous species (i.e., those naturally occurring in your locality) usually offer the best value for providing wildlife habitat. They are part of the local environment and local wildlife are well adapted to them.
- Timber and tree crops. Species can be selected so that timber and tree crops are produced directly from the windbreak. Timber can be grown in farm windbreaks without compromising shelter benefits. Firewood, posts and poles can be provided for on-farm use. These products, together with sawlogs and pulpwood, can be produced for sale to supple-

ment and diversify farm income. To grow usable timber, care must be taken with windbreak design, and management, as well as species selection. Trees in windbreaks can also be selected to provide other valuable tree crops such as seed, nuts, honey and broombush.

- Coppicing ability. Trees which coppice (or re-sprout from cut stumps) reduce re-establishment costs after the trees are harvested for timber or fodder. Coppicing species can greatly assist with windbreak re-establishment and renovation.
- Fodder. Low windbreaks can consist entirely of fodder species of shrubs (for example, tagasaste, saltbush or *Acacia saligna*). Alternatively a fodder row or rows can be included in a more conventional windbreak. If these are located close to the fence line, the shrubs can be simply lopped and thrown over the fence to stock.

Most important, the windbreak species must be able to grow well on your site. Two rules of thumb can be applied here. Look around your district and see what species are healthy and being successfully used in windbreaks. Secondly, plant species indigenous to your locality. They are well adapted to the local environmental conditions, having evolved there over thousands of years. Seek advice from an experienced tree grower, nurseryman or government advisory officer about the windbreak species that have performed well in your area.

Conclusion

Windbreaks are capable of providing a multitude of benefits to the landholder and the wider community. Give careful consideration to what functions a wind-break is to perform then design and plan windbreak establishment accordingly.

References

Bird, P.R. 1991. "The role of trees in protecting soils, plants and animals in Victoria". In: Papers of The Role of Trees in Sustainable Agriculture, A National Conference. Rural Industry Research and Development Corporation, Canberra, pp 77–87.

Burke, S.J.A. 1991. "Effect of shelterbelts on crop yields at Rutherglen". In: Papers of The Role of Trees in Sustainable Agriculture, A National Conference. Rural Industry Research and Development Corporation, Canberra, p89–99.

Raine, J.K. and Stevenson, D.C. 1977. Wind protection by model fences in a simulated atmospheric boundary layer. *J. Indust. Aerodyn.* 2: 159–180.

Original Source

This article was adapted with the kind permission of the author and publisher from:

Burke, S. 1998. Windbreaks. Butterworth-Heinemann, Woburn, Massachusetts, USA.

This comprehensive and well-illustrated book covers the siting, design, species selection, establishment, and maintenance of multipurpose windbreaks. It is available from the publisher at http://books.elsevier.com/ or the direct link to http://www.bh.com/bookscat/links/details.asp?isbn=075068951X

This excerpt was originally published as *The Overstory* #129.

Multipurpose Windbreaks

Kim M. Wilkinson and Craig R. Elevitch

Windbreaks are rows of vegetation, usually trees, strategically placed to protect an area from winds. Although planting windbreaks is an investment that takes some land out of production, well-designed windbreaks have often been shown to protect the health and productivity of crops enough to make the overall return positive. Farmers sometimes increase the benefits further by creating multipurpose windbreaks. A multipurpose windbreak is designed to provide multiple functions and/or products, in addition to wind protection. Multiple produces from a windbreak can include yields such as fruit, timber, animal fodder, mulch, wildlife habitat, and other economic or farm products.

Adding multiple functions or products to a windbreak plan can make the installation and management more satisfying and economically viable for the farmer. The desire for additional yields must always be balanced by the need to maintain the integrity of the wind protection.

Multipurpose windbreaks require special care in planning and management to maintain the primary function of wind protection while maximizing secondary yields. When planning a multipurpose windbreak, is best to factor in all the basic necessities for effective wind protection first. The basic design should include the appropriate orientation, placement, length, height, profile, number of rows, spacing, density, and continuity to provide effective protection. There are a number of excellent publications available in books, extension materials, and on the web that cover the specifics of form and position of effective windbreak design. Once the form and position are carefully determined, then multiple functions or products can be added.

General guidelines for multipurpose windbreak design

- The species used should be selected first for their wind tolerance and appropriateness for the site (climate, soils, etc.); the products should be a secondary consideration in selecting species.
- Windbreaks designed for multiple products should comprise of multiple rows. This affords some protection of the producing trees by the other trees in the windbreak. It also enables more flexibility in management and harvest of products without compromising wind protection by creating gaps.
- Trees yielding products such as fruit, food, fodder, or mulch should ideally be located in the interior or wind-sheltered rows of the windbreak, for maximum protection.
- A diversity of species should be used to allow for greater flexibility in management and for better resistance of the windbreak as a whole to damage from insects or disease.

A well designed windbreak can reduce losses and increase profits

Fruit or Nut Production

Incorporating fruit or nut-bearing species into the windbreak can provide increased family food or marketable produce. However, fruit trees battered by wind will usually have reduced yields resulting from poorer pollination, wind damage to flowers or young fruits, and reduced quality if the fruit falls to the ground or is bruised. In very windy areas, therefore, fruit from windbreaks is generally used just for family consumption.

To maintain the windbreak's primary function, wind-tolerant fruit tree species should be used. These should be integrated with other wind-tolerant species to form an effective windbreak. Also, keep in mind that fruit trees in a windbreak should be pruned only very sparingly, as pruning can greatly compromise wind resistance.

There are a number of things that can be done to maximize the secondary yield of fruit or nuts:

- If strong winds are seasonal, choose species that flower and bear in calmest months

- Plant fruit trees in the more sheltered areas of windbreak to maximize fruit production and quality
- Select trees which bear fruit on main branches, trunk, or interior of tree, rather than on outer branches (for example, fruits like jackfruit (*Artocarpus heterophyllus*) or jaboticaba (*Myrciaria cauliflora*).
- Know the cultural requirement of the fruit trees and care for them appropriately
- Irrigate if necessary

Example species that have been used for this purpose: coconut palm (*Cocos nucifera*), dwarf Brazilian banana (*Musa* sp.), jackfruit (*Artocarpus heterophyllus*), mango (*Mangifera indica*), longan (*Dimnocarpus longan*), cashew (*Anacardium occidentale*), macadamia (*Macadamia integrifolia*), tamarind (*Tamarindus indica*)

Timber Trees

Since planting trees for a windbreak involves a long-term investment, the idea of including trees that will be harvested for timber one day appeals to many farmers.

The main drawback of having timber as a secondary yield from a windbreak is that wind stress or damage may compromise the timber tree's form or produce timber of poor quality. Also, since windbreak trees should be pruned only sparingly or not at all, the lack of pruning may reduce timber yields on certain species that require a lot of pruning for optimal timber production.

Of all multipurpose uses of a windbreak, planning for timber harvest requires the most careful effort. Since entire trees will be removed, the planting, harvesting, and replanting must be coordinated. In some cases, the entire windbreak is harvested, and then replanted. In other cases, timber trees are integrated with permanent rows of non-timber windbreak trees.

Some farmers plan to harvest entire rows on a rotational basis; others selectively harvest in a staggered pattern. Consultation with a professional forester is recommended.

Example species that have been used for this purpose: Dunn's white gum (*Eucalyptus dunnii*), silky oak (*Grevillea robusta*), narra (*Pterocarpus indicus*), and neem (*Azadirachta indica*).

Mulch or Fodder from Nitrogen-fixing Trees

Some farmers like to integrate nitrogen-fixing trees (NFTs) in a multi-row windbreak, and prune the NFTs regularly to provide a nutrient-rich mulch for crops, or a nutritious fodder to supplement the diet of farm animals.

Although pruning should be avoided for most windbreak trees, the practice of cutting back NFTs and allowing them to resprout can be integrated with windbreak management. Pruned NFTs are much more susceptible to wind damage if they are allowed to regrow to a large size, but if they are cut regularly and the regrowth kept small they will be effective as a short row. To maintain the windbreak's primary function with this practice, it is essential to prune the NFTs regularly. Also, planting these species on the most sheltered side of the windbreak will help prevent problems and improve productivity.

Example species that have been used for this purpose: giant leucaena (*Leucaena leucocephala*), *Sesbania sesban*, *Calliandra calothyrsus*, and *Gliricidia sepium*.

Wildlife Habitat

The ability of windbreaks to provide wildlife habitat and corridors is one of the most documented, both in tropical and temperate areas. Many farmers enjoy providing important ecological benefits from their windbreak. Farmers that harbor wildlife may also enjoy other benefits, such as economic returns from wildlife or a more balanced pest/predator population in their crop area.

Keep in mind that providing wildlife habitat will harbor all kinds of animals, which may include rodents or other animals that are a problem for crops.

To maximize wildlife habitat in a windbreak:

- Create long, contiguous windbreaks that function as wildlife corridors
- Connect windbreaks to larger forest, wood lot, or wild areas if possible
- Plant known food/pollen source for target species
- Use a wide diversity of species
- Create an understory (shrubs and herbaceous plants, for shelter and foraging)
- Allow deadfall/old logs/snags for habitat (if not a safety hazard)
- Create a diversity of other niches for habitat (mulch, large trees, shrubs, etc.)

References

International Institute of Rural Reconstruction. 1990. Agroforestry Technology Information Kit. IIRR, Room 1270, 475 Riverside Dr., New York, NY 10115.

Nair, P.K.R. 1993. An Introduction to Agroforestry. 1993. Kluwer Academic Publisher. This comprehensive textbook bridges the gap between theoretical and practical knowledge in agroforestry.

Rockeleau, D. *et al*. 1988. Agroforestry in Dryland Africa. ICRAF, PO Box 30677, Nairobi, Kenya.

Agroforestry Information Service (AIS) for the Pacific Fact Sheet, "Windbreaks for the Pacific Islands," FACT Net (Farm, Community, and Tree Network); Email: forestry@msmail.winrock.org;

Web:
http://www.winrock.org/forestry/factnet.htm

Original Source

This article summarizes *Multipurpose Windbreaks: Design and Species for Pacific Islands* by Kim M. Wilkinson and Craig R. Elevitch which covers windbreak design, followed by a discussion of planning considerations for multiple-use windbreaks for timber, fruit/nut production, mulch/fodder, and wildlife habitat. Includes species table of over 90 windbreak species. Download this publication at:

http://agroforestry.net/afg/book.html

This excerpt was originally published as *The Overstory #32*.

Animal Shelter

Steven Burke

Extremes in climatic conditions can have enormous effects on the productivity of farm animals. Numerous studies indicate that the provision of shelter improves livestock performance through moderation of some of these effects.

Windbreaks can improve pasture production, which in turn provides benefits to livestock. More available feed means that animals will be heavier and healthier, or that higher stocking rates can be maintained. In addition to providing more feed, windbreaks can offer other important benefits to animals including increasing weight gain and health, and moderating the harmful and potentially lethal effects of wind, rain, sun, and cold.

Healthier and more productive animals

Animals protected by windbreaks can be healthier and more productive. Productivity of farm animals is optimal for a comfort zone of a relatively narrow temperature range. Animals experiencing excessively hot or cold conditions require more energy to maintain basic metabolism and thus have less energy available to increase body weight or to produce meat, milk or wool. In other words, more feed is required to counter environmental stresses. Under adverse conditions, livestock performance is inefficient relative to the quantity of feed consumed.

Experiments with sheep and cattle have shown that strong wind and rain double the energy requirement of animals for maintenance. One Australian study from the New England Tablelands in New South Wales showed that cold stress can depress sheep liveweight gain by 6 kg, and can depress wool growth by 25% (Lynch and Donnelly 1980). A study in Montana in the USA showed that beef cattle protected by windbreaks were on average 16 kg heavier than those in unsheltered feedlots. It is well known that dairy production is improved by providing sheltered conditions. In southern Victoria it has been calculated that the provision of shelter can increase milk production by 30%. Ten per cent of this is due to greater efficiency of conversion of feed, and 20%

due to the greater amount of feed available (Fitzpatrick 1994).

Grazing behaviour, and consequently feed intake, can also be affected. This may be partially compensated for by increased grazing when the conditions moderate. Animals under adverse environmental conditions generally graze less, and sometimes not at all.

Example: Intensive Shelter for Dairy Production

Simon Park sees a number of benefits flowing from the establishment of an intensive shelter system from his 120 ha dairy property near Wonthaggi, Victoria Australia. Simon has developed a long-term whole farm plan which features paddock subdivision and the planting of a regular series of windbreaks on the paddock boundaries. The windbreaks are generally parallel and spaced from 50–100 m apart, producing a very intensive shelter system.

Windbreaks are being established by a combination of direct seeding and planting of seedlings. Simon is convinced of the increased milk yields that can result from sheltered grazing conditions for his herd. The farm is also near the coast and very windswept, so increased pasture growth can be expected from the provision of intensive shelter.

Priority for shelter

Areas where animals are confined, such as stockyards and feedlots, should be given high priority for protection by high quality windbreaks. Sheltering these areas will reduce feed requirements, improve the weight and condition of stock, and result in improved animal health.

Although cattle are much more hardy than sheep, calves can still be susceptible to exposure, especially when newborn. On average, in Kansas in the USA, a 2% increase in calf survival is gained from the provision of windbreaks. Pigs and goats are extremely susceptible to death from exposure, even more so than sheep. This is because they do not have skin covering with the same thermal properties as greasy sheep wool. Shelter should be a high priority for these animals.

In livestock areas with large paddocks, consideration should be given to the establishment of carefully located within-paddock shelter. Observe the movement of animals in bad weather. Sheep in particular will end up in the downwind corner. Special arc-shaped windbreaks can be planted to protect these critical areas.

Special livestock havens also have considerable merit for exposed areas with no naturally sheltered areas. A livestock haven is essentially an area enclosed by windbreaks providing a very high degree of wind protection. Farms with many dispersed trees can still incur high stock losses in severe weather. The key is to have areas of high quality shelter available and, importantly, people on hand to move stock into these protected areas at critical times. Woodlots and agroforests can also be ideal areas to locate vulnerable stock in severe conditions.

Windbreaks are also extremely useful when located along passageways, as animals can take shelter in lanes during extreme conditions. For this reason, passageways protected by windbreaks can provide a very effective backbone for a shelter network.

Example: Passageway Shelter a Safe Haven

Neil and Sue Lawrence have established over the years a network of passageways across their 1,000 ha Balmoral property in western Victoria. The passageways are a tremendous labour saver when moving stock around the property. In some areas, around the house and shearing shed, red gums (*Eucalyptus camaldulensis*) have been established by direct seeding to provide shelter to the passageways and surrounding areas.

A cold southerly snap hit in December 1987 during shearing when 1,600 off-shears sheep were held in an exposed paddock near the Lawrence's house. During the wild night, they moved the sheep into a sheltered passageway. hey lost 23 sheep in the 200 m before reaching shelter, but all those that made it survived. "In the passageways it was as though a switch had been turned off a big fan. The sheep stopped dying and some even started to graze."

While the Lawrence's flock escaped almost unscathed, one neighbour lost 600 off-shears sheep and the district total was 30,000. Neil reckons that the

$200 or so that it cost him to direct seed those trees was the best investment he ever made.

Shelter from sun

Shelter trees can also provide substantial additional benefits due to the provision of shade. In warmer regions, provision of shade should also be considered to reduce stock losses (particularly for calves and lambs) from heat stress. Where these benefits are likely to be substantial, shade plantings within paddocks should be considered in addition to windbreaks.

Shade can also make a valuable contribution to animal production, particularly in hot areas, such as the semi-arid and tropical north of Australia, but seasonal benefits can also be obtained in temperate regions.

Excessive heat depresses the condition of cattle by reducing feed intake. Heat stressed cows produced fewer calves and the calves produced have a lower birth weight. Calves frequently die of heat stress, particularly in tropical northern Australia. Heat stress can also markedly affect dairy production. One Queensland study (Davison *et al* 1988) showed that the provision of shade increased milk production for each cow by 2 kg per day combined with an improvement in milk composition. European cattle breeds benefit more from provision of shade than tropical breeds.

For sheep, excessive heat is detrimental to ram fertility, and in ewes can reduce ovulation rate and conception. Heat stress in sheep can also lead to death, particularly for lambs. Ewes will assist their lambs to seek shade if this is available (Bird *et al* 1984).

Protection from cold and wet conditions

Where livestock graze in the open year round, and they may consequently become susceptible to harsh climatic conditions from time to time. Of the three factors which create exposure problems in livestock (cold, wet and wind), wind is the most practical to moderate through the provision of shelter.

The greatest reductions in mortality from exposure are produced by windbreaks designed to provide significant wind reductions when conditions of extreme exposure arise. Areas of high quality shelter created by dense windbreaks are required to achieve the maximum benefits. Alternatively, stock can be confined in paddocks with natural shelter due to topography or dispersed shelter across the paddock such as tussock grasses or shrubs.

Cold, wet and windy conditions frequently combine to produce conditions lethal to animals in the field. Wind chill is the effect of increased cooling experienced because of the combined effect of wind and low temperature. This occurs because wind increases the loss of body heat from the surface of an animal. This situation becomes even worse when the animal is wet, and heat losses due to evaporative cooling also occur. Animals in the open under these conditions can be extremely vulnerable.

For example, the most widely recognised benefit of shelter to livestock in southern Australia is the prevention of the death of newborn lambs from exposure in wet, cold, windy weather. Most lamb losses occur within three days of birth. Lambing percentages can be very low in many regions in Australia because of this problem. It has been estimated that in southern Australia, on average, as many as 15% of newborn lambs die from exposure. Several Australian studies have shown that lamb mortality in cold, wet weather can be at least halved by the provision of adequate shelter. Lamb losses can be commonly reduced from 20% to 10% by the provision of adequate shelter and stock management.

A chill index model has been developed (Donnelly 1984) which relates temperature, rainfall and wind speed to lamb mortality. This shows that by reducing wind speed from 10 m/s to 2.5 m/s through the provision of shelter, lamb mortality is at least halved. Ewes do not always seek shelter when lambing, and natural sheep camping and lambing areas are often on exposed high ridges. Unshorn ewes are less likely to seek shelter to lamb than shorn ewes. To minimise lambing losses, either dispersed shelter must be available across the paddock, the natural lambing sites must be sheltered, or the ewes must be confined to a "lambing haven," a confined area of high quality shelter. Good management is important to ensure lambing ewes are in the right place at the right time. Set stocked lambing paddocks need to contain enough feed to last the lambing period, often 6–10 weeks.

In the case of sheep, the benefits of shelter have been shown to include increased feed availability, reduced lambing losses, reduced off-shears losses, and increased efficiency of conversion of feed to meat and wool. In southern Victoria it has been estimated that these factors can combine to produce an overall increase in sheep productivity of 29% (Fitzpatrick 1994).

If high quality shelter is available for susceptible stock, it is important to plan ahead to ensure the ability to move them quickly to these areas in bad weather. It can be worth changing the location of fences to encourage stock to move to shelter in bad conditions. The location of shelter is crucial, it is often best to locate areas of maximum shelter in the downwind corners of paddocks or on high ground because sheep are often driven by high winds and it can be very difficult to move sheep into a gale.

Conclusion

The provision of adequate shelter can prevent dramatic stock losses under extremely adverse conditions. It can also provide small regular returns due to improved animal productivity. Shelter therefore produces a combination of benefits to livestock.

References

Bird, P.R., J.J. Lynch, and J.M. Obst. 1984. Effect of shelter on plant and animal production. In: Proceedings of Australia Society for Animal Production 15: 270–3.

Davison, T.M., B.A. Silver, A.T. Lisle, and W.N. Orr. 1988. The influence of shade on milk production of Holstein-Freisian cows in a tropical upland environment. In: Australian Journal of Experimental Agriculture 28:149–54.

Donnelly, J.B. 1984. The productivity of breeding ewes grazing on lucerne or grass and clover pastures on the tablelands of southern Australia; III: Lamb mortality and weaning percentage. In: Australian Journal of Agricultural Research 35:709–12.

Fitzpatrick, D. 1994. Money Trees on Your Property: profit gained through trees and how to grow them. Inkata Press, Sydney.

Lynch, J.J. and J.B. Donnelly. 1980. Changes in pasture and animal production resulting from the use of windbreaks. In: Aust Journal of Agricultural Research 31:967–79.

Original Source

This article was adapted with the kind permission of the author and publisher from:

Burke, S. 1998. Windbreaks. Butterworth-Heinemann, Woburn, Massachusetts, USA.

This comprehensive and well-illustrated book covers the siting, design, species selection, establishment, and maintenance of multipurpose windbreaks. It is available from the publisher at http://www.bh.com/sciences or http://www.bh.com/bookscat/links/details.asp?isbn=075068951X

This excerpt was originally published as *The Overstory* #85.

Live Fences

Stefan D. Cherry and Erick C.M. Fernandes

Live fences can be divided into two basic categories; live fence posts and live barriers or hedges. Live fence posts are widely spaced, single lines of woody plants that are regularly pruned back and used instead of metal or wooden posts for supporting barbed wire, bamboo or other materials. Hedges are thicker, more densely spaced fences that generally include a number of different species and usually do not support other fencing materials.

The primary purpose of live fences is to control the movement of animals and people, however, they have proven to be extremely diverse, low risk systems that provide farmers with numerous benefits. Besides their main function living fences can provide fuelwood, fodder and food, act as windbreaks, or enrich the soil, depending on the species used.

Live Fence Posts

Live fence posts are commonly found in conventional barbed wire fences. In many cases, the trees and shrubs that appear along fence lines, originate from seeds deposited by birds perching on dead fence posts and the fence wire. In other cases, farmers may deliberately plant stakes of easy to root species such as *Gliricidia sepium*, *Erythrina* spp., *Spondias* spp., and *Bursera simarouba*. The live fence posts are far more durable than traditional wooden posts as they are more resistant to attack by termites and decay fungi.

When grazing or browsing animals are part of the farming system, the only way to establish live fence posts and eventually a living fence, is to start with a conventional wire fence supported by dead fence posts and to gradually establish live fence posts to substitute for the decaying posts.

The species used for live fence posts must have the ability to rapidly form a callus and cover over the point of attachment of the wire to the post. The callus protects the wood from attack by decay fungi and wood-boring insects. Tree or shrub species that have a resin or sap that is corrosive to metal, should be avoided. Otherwise, the wire breaks a few months after being attached to the live fence post.

Gliricidia sepium is the most common live fence post species in Central America and in other tropical areas because of the ease with which large stem cuttings root and its multiple uses such as forage, green manure and its properties as a rat poison. Farmers commonly start the establishment of *Gliricidia* live fence posts by planting a few large (1.5–2.0 m) stakes in the existing conventional wire fence. These stakes normally take root within a month or so and farmers allow the shoots to grow for 6–10 months before cutting them back. After the first pruning, prunings can be carried out every 4 to 8 months. Shoot pruning at intervals of 6 to 8 months result in woody sprouts that are suitable for use as stakes. Farmers are thus able to multiply live stakes for their fence posts within a year or two after establishing the first live fence posts.

Live fence posts are strong and long lasting

Live Fences

Most resource-poor food crop farmers do not have sufficient capital to purchase barbed wire or other fencing materials. As an alternative, more and more farmers are using a number of different tree and shrub species to establish dense, often thorny, hedges to protect their crops. Another alternative often used by farmers is the combination of easy to establish live fence posts and poisonous or unpalatable species. An example southwestern Ethiopia combines *Erythrina abyssinica* with *Euphorbia tirucalli*. The latex of *E. tirucalli* is highly toxic and the plant is generally avoided by livestock. If well estab-

lished, these natural barriers can deter both animal and human trespassers from entering into the farm.

A barbed-wire fence strung on living fence posts of *Erythrina variegata* is strong enough to contain pigs. (photo: C. Elevitch)

Many farmers also use live fences as a method of demarcating their farms. Although agroforestry may not be appropriate under certain land tenure circumstances, live fences can serve as one method of securing land ownership where the law permits.

Products and Services from Live Fences

The term multipurpose tree is often used when referring to the more useful agroforestry species such as *Leucaena*, *Gliricidia* and many others. Multipurpose trees such as these when incorporated into live fences can also provide fuelwood, nutrient-rich mulch, erosion control and land stabilization, as well as other products such as food and fencing materials and a source of high quality forage for ruminants.

Seed Banks Live fences that can serve as functional seed banks. For example, in Cameroon, where an increasing number of farmers are becoming interested in experimenting with agroforestry, non-governmental organizations are buying seeds of *Calliandra calothyrsus* from farmers at a cost of 4,000 CFA (US $8) per kilogram for distribution to other farmers. Seeds

of *Tephrosia vogelii*, a biannual, leguminous shrub used for shorter-term live fences and improved fallows, can be bought in the market during most of the year within the region of the Kom ethnic group in the northwest province.

Protection of Farmland In the river valleys of eastern Sonora, Mexico, flood plain farming is dependent upon living fences. Fences of willow and cottonwood maintain, extend and enhance flood plain fields. These ecological filters also protect fields from cattle, harbor agents of biological control of pests, and provide renewable supplies of wood. Farmers often allow live fences to grow tall and serve as windbreaks to protect cropland.

Fodder and Fuelwood Leaves, branches and twigs pruned from live fences and live fence posts provide farmers with an on farm source of fodder and fuelwood. Pruning intervals of 2 to 3 months yield more leafy material than pruning intervals of 4 to 8 months which result in more woody material. This allows farmers to choose which product is of higher priority during different times of the year and adjust their management techniques accordingly. A study in Embu, Kenya found that fresh foliage of *Calliandra* *calothyrsus* increased butterfat content of milk by about 10% when fed to lactating cows. Live fences around the perimeter of the farm can act as nutrient traps, preventing loss of nutrients that could normally be lost through leaching or surface runoff.

Fruits, Flowers and Medicinal Products Farmers can also plant fruit trees to supplement their diet and provide the household with important micronutrients, often lacking in some diets. The fruit can also be sold in the market to contribute to household income. There are a number of tropical fruit trees that have been incorporated into live fencing systems in Cameroon either as fence posts or within live fence hedgerows including guava, citrus, Bush plum (*Canarium* sp.), *Inga edulis*, *Spondias mombin*, *Moringa oleifera*, and a variety of palm species. A variety of medicinal plants (*Prunus africana*, *Columbrina* spp., *Comiphora* spp., *Azadirachta indica*) are often grown in living fences.

Conclusions

Live fencing is one form of agroforestry that can provide a range of products and services on farmlands. Although live fencing systems are traditional, the extent of the many potential benefits and the number of different farmer-developed systems are currently not well understood or even well documented. We can learn a lot from farmers who have been using live fences in their various farming systems and assist in farmer-to-farmer transfer of these technologies.

Original Source

The full version of this article with excellent photographs can be viewed at: http://ppathw3.cals.cornell.edu/mba_project/livefence.html.

Financial support for the development of the original article was provided by the Cornell Agroforestry Working Group (CAWG) of the Cornell International Institute for Food Agriculture and Development (CIIFAD).

This excerpt was originally published as *The Overstory #38*.

Further Reading

A three-part video concerning live fencing presents the perspectives and management practices of small-scale farmers in Cameroon, West Africa. In the first part of the video the farmers describe crop destruction and why they have established live fences. In the second part, farmers demonstrate three main establishment practices and discuss some of the challenges related to creating a live fence. In the third part, farmers demonstrate how they maintain their own live fences and talk about tree species and how they choose which species to use. The 30 minute video is in English. The video is distributed through ECHO, 17430 Durrance Rd., N. Ft. Myers, FL 33917 USA, Tel: 941-543-3246, Fax: 941-543-5317, Email: ECHO@echonet.org;
Web: http://www.echonet.org.

Introduction to Integrating Trees into Pacific Island Farm Systems presents eight agroforestry practices that integrate trees into farm systems. Includes silvopasture (trees and livestock), windbreaks, contour hedgerows, live fences, improved fallow, woodlots, sequential cropping systems, and understory cropping:
http://agroforestry.net/afg/book.html.

Multipurpose Windbreaks: Design and Species for Pacific Islands covers windbreak design, followed by a discussion of planning considerations for multiple-use windbreaks for timber, fruit/nut production, live fence, and other uses. Includes species table of over 90 windbreak species:
http://www.agroforestry.net/afg/book.html.

Trees as Noise Buffers

US Department of Agriculture National Agroforestry Center

Noise can cause anxiety, tension, or even illness. Prolonged exposure to high levels of noise can cause hearing loss. Today we regard noise as a form of environmental pollution, and in some circles noise is considered an international health concern.

Trees to the rescue? Planting "noise buffers" composed of trees and shrubs can reduce noise five to ten decibels (reduces noise approximately 50% to the human ear). To achieve this effect, the species and the planting design must be chosen carefully.

Generalized Recommendations for Noise Buffers

Generalized recommendations to reduce noise with rows of trees and shrubs include:

1   For best results, plant the noise buffer close to the noise source (rather than close to the area to be protected).

2   Plant trees/shrubs as close together as the species will allow and not be overly inhibited.

3   When possible use plants with dense foliage. A diversity of tree species, with a range of foliage shapes and sizes within the noise buffer may also improve noise reduction.

4   Foliage of the plants should persist from the ground up. A combination of shrubs and trees may be necessary to achieve this effect.

5   Evergreen varieties that retain their leaves will give better year-round protection.

6   When possible use taller plants. Where the use of tall trees is restricted, use combinations of shorter shrubs and tall grass or similar soft ground cover as opposed to harder paved surfaces.

Example: Designing Buffers against Neighboring Engine Noise

To reduce neighboring noise from power mowers, generators, or other small engines, plant one to two continuous rows of heavy dense shrubs, having maximum density near ground level, and one to two continuous rows of medium height dense trees. Placement of the buffer is usually governed by practical considerations—normally it is placed near the lot boundary, as close to the source of noise as possible. If the noise problem is severe, the noise buffer may also include rock or masonry walls, or solid wooden fences at least 1.5 m (4.5 ft.) high, with the trees and shrubs planted on the near side of these barriers.

Example: Designing Buffers Against Road or Highway Noise

Persistent and troublesome noise pollution often comes from roads and highways. In fact, this problem was first recorded in the first century A.D., when Julius Caesar banned chariot traffic from the streets of Rome at night because citizens couldn't sleep!

To reduce noise of moderate traffic in communities:

• plant belts of trees 7–17 m (20–50 ft.) wide along roadsides
• plant the nearest edge of the belt within 7–17 m (20–50 ft.) of the center of the nearest traffic lane
• use 2–3 m (6–8 ft.) shrubs next to the road and back up tree rows a minimum of 3–7 m (15–20 ft.) tall when mature
• the length of the tree belt should be twice as long as the distance from the road to the recipient of the noise
• the buffer should also extend equal distance in both directions parallel to the road

To reduce heavy vehicle noise in suburban or rural areas:

• plant belts of trees 20–35 m (65–100 ft.) wide along roadsides
• plant the nearest edge of the belt within 20–25 m (60–80 ft.) of the center of the nearest traffic lane
• use 2–3 m (6–8 ft.) foot shrubs next to the road, and back-up tree rows a minimum of 15 m (45 ft.) tall at the center row
• the length of the tree belt should be twice as long as the distance from the road to the recipient of the noise
• the buffer should also extend equal distance in both directions parallel to the road

When planning roadside developments or when locating schools or residences adjacent to roads, natural terrain such as hills, ridges, and depressed highways can help to serve as noise screens. Existing

A dense, multirow hedge with a variety of species can dampen noise and dust from traffic. (photo: C. Elevitch)

trees, shrubs, and grass should be left undisturbed when possible, rather than replacing them with harder surfaces detrimental to noise control. Noise may also be further ameliorated by constructing land-forms, earthen dikes, masonry walls, or solid wooden fences, and planting the trees and shrubs on the near side of these barriers.

Multiple Uses

Noise buffers can also be planned to provide multiple products or uses. For example, a noise buffer oriented properly may also serve as a windbreak. When they contain native plants or habitat, noise buffers can provide wildlife corridors. Species can also be selected to provide useful products such as fuelwood, fruits, or nuts.

References

Cook, D.I. and D.F. Van Haverbeke. 1977. Suburban Noise Control with Plant Materials and Solid Barriers: A Report of a Study Conducted by the University of Nebraska and the US Forest Service. Research Bulletin EM 100. Rocky Mtn. Forest and Range Experiment Station, USDA Forest Service, University of Nebraska, Lincoln, NE, USA.

Cook, D.I. and D.F. Van Haverbeke. 1974. Tree-Covered Land-Forms for Noise Control. Research Bulletin 263. Rocky Mtn. Forest and Range Experiment Station, USDA Forest Service, University of Nebraska, Lincoln, NE, USA.

Cook, D.I. and D.F. Van Haverbeke. 1972. Trees, shrubs, and land-forms for noise control. Journal of Soil and Water Conservation, November-December 1972, Ankeny, Iowa, USA.

Original Source

The USDA National Agroforestry Center (NAC) provided the material for this article, including the primary source "Leaf the Noise Out," which first appeared in the Spring 1998 edition of the NAC's quarterly newsletter, *Inside Agroforestry*. Download original   at: http://www.unl.edu/nac/ia/spring98/index.html.

This excerpt was originally published as *The Overstory* #60.

Living Snow Fences

USDA Natural Resources Conservation Service
Idaho Resource Conservation and Development Association
USDA National Agroforestry Center, Lincoln Nebraska

In many temperate regions, blowing and drifting snow jeopardizes public safety and emergency services, interrupts businesses, and increases livestock and wildlife mortality. Snowplows can keep roads open, but annual costs are often high. When roads are subject to recurring snow blockage, a more permanent, cost-effective solution is often needed.

Structural barriers, commonly made of slated or picket fences, are a proven technique for reducing the impact of blowing and drifting snow. These are placed to interrupt blowing snow. With an action similar to a rock placed in a flowing stream, they cause an eddy effect that alters wind speed and direction, allowing snow to settle out.

However, another kind of snow fence, made of living plant materials such as grasses, shrubs and trees, can also be used and has several advantages over man-made structures. Often called living snow fences, they are actually densely planted windbreaks that have been specifically designed and planted to reduce blowing and drifting snow. Like a structural barrier, they cause blowing snow to settle in a designated area. Living snow fences are more cost-effective than structural barriers and provide a wide array of benefits beyond snow control.

Benefits

Living snow fences offer a wide range of options and will meet many objectives. These benefits continue to improve and multiply as a living snow fence grows and matures:

- Longevity
- Cost-effectiveness
- Reduced annual maintenance
- Snow and dust containment
- Wildlife habitat
- Aesthetic enhancement

Advantages of Living Snow Fences

- Service life is estimated at 50 to 75 years. The estimated life of a man-made slat snow fence is 5 to 7 years; over a 50-year span, the installation and maintenance costs would be 4 times more than a living snow fence.
- Average cost is $3 per mile per year for each unit of snow trapped compared to $185 per mile per year for a 4-foot slat fence.
- More efficient in capturing snow. When mature, a living snow fence may capture up to 12 times more snow than a slated fence.
- Provide habitat for birds to nest, eat, and escape. Small mammals—even deer—are attracted to the habitat created by a living snow fence.
- Can be designed to conserve energy for farmsteads, feedlots, and community facilities.

Some Disadvantages to Consider

- Living snow fences require more space than slat snow fences.
- New plantings must be protected from grazing.
- It takes from 5 to 7 years for living snow fences to provide effective snow control and 20 years to fully mature.
- Site conditions such as shallow soils and pH (acidity or alkalinity) may prohibit plant establishment.
- Living snow fences must be well planned and located to achieve the myriad of benefits they offer. For example, a snow fence located in the wrong place could cause snow to accumulate on the road instead of protecting it.

Ten Steps to Ensure Success

Step 1: Determine planting objectives. Your objective may be as simple as the control of blowing and drifting snow-or more complex with multiple objectives such as providing livestock protection or wildlife habitat, enhancing the beauty of the landscape, or water harvest and storage.

Step 2: Take an inventory of all on-site physical factors, including:

- Annual precipitation, average snow volume to be stored
- Topography and aspect, distance upwind available for planting
- Soil type, fertility, depth, and pH
- Current and potential land uses, land ownership, easements, restrictions

Step 3: Determine planting stock needed by species and number and who will order them.

Step 4: Decide what site preparation work is needed and who will do it.

Step 5: Determine fertilizer needed. Most windbreaks and living snow fences are not fertilized unless a deficiency shows in the growth and foliage of the trees and shrubs.

Step 6: Determine type of irrigation system needed to ensure plant establishment and survival. An irrigation system will need to be considered in areas with less than 20 inches of annual precipitation.

Step 7: Determine fencing needed to protect young plants from grazing livestock or wildlife. Decide who will install and maintain it.

Step 8: Decide what kind of weed barrier or mulch will be used and who will install it. Growth rates are significantly faster when weed barrier is used. Newly planted trees can't compete with annual weeds and grasses so make plans for cultivation, chemical weed control or mulching.

Step 9: Plan for proper maintenance

Frequent inspections of irrigation systems and fences to allow speedy repairs when needed.

Frequent inspection of plants to spot weed and pest problems to allow quick remedial action.

Prompt replacement of any dead plants.

Step 10: Make a plan by listing decisions made, date actions will need to take place, and who will carry out each action.

Who Should Be Involved in Planning?

Living snow fences often involve multiple landowners or jurisdictions that can make planning more complex. Involve key decision makers and partners early in the planning stages.

Possible partners include private landowners, county commissioners, county road departments, conserva-

tion districts, Resource Conservation and Development councils, State Department of Highways, State Department of Lands, State Forester, and federal, state, or local land managing agencies.

Living snow barrier.

Living Designs

Height, density, length, and plant protection are key elements in the proper functioning of a mature living snow fence. To avoid problems, carefully consider these factors during the design phase.

Height

Determine barrier height by the tallest row in a planting. Barrier height affects snowdrift depth and length. Snow storage potential can be manipulated by barrier height. Doubling the barrier height will increase snow storage by four times—an important economic factor to consider in species selection.

Density

Determine the density of a living snow fence by the species, number of rows, spacing between rows, and spacing of plants in a row. A 50 percent dense barrier stores the greatest amount of snow if other factors are equal. Between row spacing can vary depending on design criteria and objectives. Twin row high-density plantings are recommended. Preferred species are evergreens, shrubs, and low growing broadleaf trees.

Length

Length determines the maximum area that can be protected if winds are perpendicular to it. Snow storage at the ends of a barrier is significantly less than near the center. Barrier design must extend far enough beyond the protected area to intercept winds that deviate 25 degrees from either direction of perpendicular. Extending a snow fence 100 feet beyond the area to be protected will mitigate this "end effect."

Planting Protection

If livestock can access the site, then fencing will be necessary to plantings. Significant damage can occur from trampling, rubbing, and browsing. Fencing will avoid soil compaction as well as physical damage to the irrigation system and weed barrier.

Key Design Elements

- Orient living snow fence at right angles to prevailing winter winds.
- Doubling the height will more than quadruple the amount of snow captured.
- Vegetation with about 50% Density will capture and store the greatest amount of snow.
- Conifers are ideal species to plant because of their height and year-round foliage.
- Many deciduous trees and shrubs also work well, especially in combination with conifers.
- There are hundreds of site-specific design options

Plant Selection

Use of site-adapted plant species is critical to the success of a living snow fence. Consult your local office of the Natural Resources Conservation Service or Cooperative Extension for site-specific recommendations. Some commonly recommended species include:

Evergreen

- Eastern red cedar, Austrian Pine, Blue Spruce
- Rocky Mountain juniper and Utah juniper are very drought hardy
- Scotch pine and Ponderosa pine on soils under pH 7.90

Low Broadleafs

- Siberian crabapple, Mancharian crabapple
- Russian olive on upland sites only because species can spread in areas with high water tables

Shrubs

- Amur honeysuckle, Blueleaf honeysuckle, chokecherry, golden current, Peking cotoneaster, Western sandcherry
- American plum, common lilac, and silver buffaloberry can spread by suckering
- Fourwing saltbrush, Siberian peashrub (*Caragana*), Skunkbush sumac and Sagebrush

Original Source

This article was adapted with the kind permission of the authoring organizations from:

USDA Natural Resources Conservation Service, Idaho Resource Conservation and Development Association, and USDA National Agroforestry Center. 1999. Living Snow Fences. USDA National Agroforestry Center, Lincoln, Nebraska.
Web: http://www.unl.edu/nac/pubs.html [accessed: June 2003]

This excerpt was originally published as *The Overstory* #123.

Fire

Kurt W. Cremer

Effects of fire on plants, animals and soils are numerous, complex and important. In Australia most types of natural vegetation have evolved to cope with fire and are largely dependent on and shaped by fire. Effects of fire include:

- overheating and thus killing part or all of the above-ground portions of existing plants,
- combustion of plants and litter with the consequent release of nutrients
- loss of some of these nutrients through volatilisation and leaching
- elimination of some growth-inhibiting chemicals and microorganisms
- preparation of seedbeds suitable for germination and rapid early growth of new plants
- release of seed from standing plants
- stimulation of germination in some species such as Acacia
- removal of competing plants and hence the opportunity for new plants to become established
- better availability of nutrients and water to those plants that survive the fire with little or no damage
- exposure of the soil to erosion
- changes in water infiltration and retention
- and changes in the climate in and above the soil.

Fire is usually both beneficial and damaging, the net effect depending on circumstances and aims. This article deals only with direct health hazards—injuries caused by overheating, how to cope with them, and how to prevent them.

Background

Most plant tissues are killed at relatively mild temperatures—at 50°C after a few minutes and at 65°C after a few seconds. The temperatures produced by burning vegetation are far higher—about 400°C for smouldering combustion and up to 1000°C or more for flames. They may last from a few seconds in sparse grass to several hours in logs or deep humus.

The two main effects of overheating, scorching of foliage and fire scarring or ringbarking of stems, are discussed below under separate headings. They can occur separately or together. Branches and roots can also be overheated: branches quite commonly, but roots only if they are covered by less than 30–60 mm of mineral soil.

Foliage

Uninsulated tissue such as foliage can avoid overheating only by being either remote or shielded from the flames. Wind can serve to cool foliage and disperse or divert convected heat. The chance of foliage being scorched diminishes rapidly with height. Conversely, the height to which foliage is scorched reflects the intensity of the fire and the height of the flames. Dense foliage from lower crowns or adjacent trees can provide valuable shielding from radiation. Similarly, bark on branches is often killed only on the lower side that faced the fire and was heated by both convection and radiation.

Bark

Insulated tissues, such as the cambium of tree trunks, can escape overheating even if exposed to fire at close range, depending on the amount of insulation and the duration of the fire.

The protective value of bark depends mainly on its thickness, irrespective of type or moisture content, provided that the bark itself does not burn away. Thin stems (less than 20 mm) of all species are highly vulnerable to any fire because their bark is very thin. But as the stem thickens, so does the bark, and many species eventually become highly resistant, except where fires are very prolonged.

Duration of heating

Some experimental results (McArthur 1968) indicate that if the surface of bark is kept at 1000°C, the cambium will be killed in about 2 minutes if the effective bark thickness is 10 mm, in about 6 minutes for 20 mm thick bark and about 13 minutes for 40 mm thick bark. With lower temperatures at the surface of the bark, the cambium takes longer to heat.

In dry grass, flames persist at any one point for about 4–20 seconds and in eucalypt litter for about 60–150 seconds, depending on the quantity and arrangement of the fuels. A mound of humus or logs heaped against a tree's trunk can burn for hours.

The risk of damaging a tree's trunk is directly related to bark thickness. Thick bark of *Eucalyptus microcorys* (left) and relatively thin, smooth bark of *E. deglupta* (right). (photos: C. Elevitch)

The risk of damaging a tree's trunk thus depends as much on the thickness of its bark as on the amount and type of fuel near the trunk. Generally, trunks have to be well over 10 cm in diameter before they will stand prolonged fires, and even the thickest bark can be killed if much fuel is heaped against it.

Effects of Injury

Foliage and branches
Any direct damage to foliage will be noticeable as a grey or brown discoloration, sometimes within hours, always within a day or two after the fire. In the mildest form of damage, only parts of the leaf blade are damaged; the stalk and the supporting branch survive, but some of the associated exposed buds are killed. The leaf may be retained, or it may be shed in a few days as a result of an abscission layer formed at the base of its stalk (petiole). More severe scorching causes the whole of the leaf to turn brown. In this case, the petiole and thin twigs are also killed, abscission cannot take place, and the leaf is retained for months. The damage is most severe if the leaves and twigs are charred or even consumed. Sometimes all

levels of severity can be found on a single long crown, with the lowest foliage consumed and the topmost foliage still green.

Damage to branches does not become obvious until the bark cracks and falls away, several months after the fire. Severity of scorching of foliage provides a much earlier guide to severity of damage to branches. Limbs more than 10 cm in diameter tend to survive all but the most severe types of scorching.

Loss of foliage is rarely lethal by itself. It is the accompanying loss of buds that can be critical. If some foliage remains green, some buds will also have survived, even if the buds are unprotected; the tree will probably survive, unless it has been girdled. If all the foliage is browned or consumed, the unprotected buds will also have been killed and the tree can survive only if it possesses buds (or tissue able to produce buds) well protected within thick bark. Radiata pine and most other conifers do not have such protected buds and are killed by any complete scorching. The tops of most acacias are not much better off, but most eucalypts are.

In some situations, even trees with surviving bud tissues cannot recover from a complete scorching. This is probably because they lack the food reserves to start off new shoot growth. Such inability to recover is more likely after a complete scorching in autumn than in spring, and is most likely on sites where growth is rapid.

Many trees and shrubs have the ultimate in protection for some of their buds—insulation by soil. They can be killed right back to ground level but remain able to sprout again from buds located on stumps, lignotubers or roots well within the soil.

Loss of foliage will tend to result in a corresponding loss of growth, till the foliage is restored. This tendency may be offset by an increased availability of nutrients and water. Normally, a severe scorching with much delay in crown recovery will reduce growth for several years. The loss of limbs or part of the trunk may degrade the stem permanently.

Scarring and girdling of stems

Girdling here means that the bark is killed to the wood surface around the whole circumference of the stem. This has the same effect as ringbarking, i.e., removing a girdle or ring of bark. The food made by the leaves can no longer reach the roots, and these will starve unless other surviving trees are connected to the same root system, or new shoots sprout from below the girdle, either from the stem or the roots. Even if the roots continue to be fed from elsewhere, the top of the girdled tree will die after some months or years because water conduction past the girdle eventually fails.

Fire scars and dry sides at the butts of trees are major causes of degrade in wood, and of the eventual decline and collapse of trees. Often a fire does not kill any cambium but only reduces the effective thickness of the bark. Recovery to full bark thickness may take 3–20 years after the fire, depending on the amount of original bark lost. Frequent severe fires therefore make trees more and more vulnerable to scarring and girdling, even in species that are normally highly resistant. This is important to remember where fuels recover quickly after burning, e.g., in areas with dense bracken or bladey grass.

Preventing Fire Damage

In many environments it is rarely possible to ensure that a particular area will never be burnt. Usually a balanced judgment needs to be made on how to manage the fire risk; it is necessary for compromises to be made. Strategies may range from attempting

"total exclusion" of fires to deliberate burning every few years. In the wet forests of mountain ash (*Eucalyptus regnans*) with dense woody undergrowth, for instance, natural fires tend to occur only rarely, less than once a century, but to be extremely destructive when they do occur. The aim here usually has to be total exclusion of fires. In dry forests of jarrah (*Eucalyptus marginata*), on the other hand, the climate and nature of the undergrowth are such that fires could occur almost every 3 or 4 years, but the bigger trees are well adapted to withstand brief fires of low to moderate intensity. In this situation, the more destructive fires can be avoided by reducing fuel accumulation through deliberate burning every 5–10 years. But remember, young trees, with stems less than about 10 cm in diameter, can rarely, if ever, be burnt even by the mildest fire without suffering excessive damage.

The following discussion is about reducing the potential destructiveness of fires in farm situations by managing the fuels to reduce the intensity and duration of fires and by managing the trees to resist fire damage. Carrying out controlled burns or preventing and suppressing fires are separate major topics covered in other books, such as (Luke and McArthur 1978).

Managing the fuels

The main aim is to avoid having fuels that produce tall fires that could scorch the foliage of desirable trees, or cause prolonged fires in which the bark might be killed.

Areas that are particularly hazardous should be avoided for tree planting or should be planted with fire-resistant species and treated with special care. Variation in the natural frequency of fires is a major reason for variations in type and quality of forests in Australia. The forest types, in turn, strongly influence the likelihood of fires. These are the main hazards:

- Uncontrollable ground vegetation that produces highly flammable fuels, e.g., dense bracken, or tall dry grass.
- A likelihood of ignition (e.g., by careless people, machinery)
- A location downwind and upslope of likely points of ignition, especially on sites exposed to fire-weather winds (e.g., W to NW in southeast Australia). A doubling of wind speed tends to treble the rate of fire travel. Strong winds have the main influence on speed and direction of fire movement, but

slope is also important. On slopes of 10–20 degrees, fires travel respectively two and four times faster than on level ground, if the slope faces the wind. Conversely, vegetation located in fire "shadows" burns relatively rarely.

- Sites with difficult access (rocky, steep), which makes fuel management and fire suppression difficult.

Fuels can be reduced by grazing, mowing, cultivating, herbicide application, controlled burning or any practice that influences what grows on the site, including choice of crops or weeds and fertilising. Halving the amount of fuel in a pasture (5–10 t/ha on good to very good sites) reduces the intensity of the fire by about 50%, but may not affect its rate of spread.

The main qualities that affect flammability are moisture content, oil or resin content, salt content, and thickness of fuel "particles." Drier fuels ignite and burn more readily because less energy is needed to heat and vaporise the water. Therefore, green plants are safer than dry ones. Many plants will, however, burn when green, because of high oil content (e.g., *Eucalyptus* spp., *Melaleuca* spp.), provided the fire is supported by dry fuel. The green foliage of many conifers burns because of high resin content. High salt content (e.g., saltbush, tamarisk), on the other hand, reduces flammability. Thinner "particles" are more flammable because they dry faster, are heated to ignition point more easily, and are more accessible to oxygen. Dead grasses readily change in moisture content, and hence flammability, as the humidity of the air changes. Pastures may burn when they contain at least 50% dead material but are rarely dangerous before at least 90% of the material is dead.

Arrangement of fuels

Combustion is inhibited if the fuel particles are spaced so widely that they cannot heat and ignite each other, or if they are spaced so closely that the fire is starved for oxygen. A dense stand of grasses can burn explosively if left standing, or mildly if it is compacted by mowing or rolling.

Discontinuity in the arrangement of fuels is most important, both horizontally (as in fire-breaks) and vertically. Crown fires are rarely possible unless tall flames from ground fires support them. Trim off the lower parts of crowns, especially any dead parts (foliage, branches, bark) and be sure to remove heavy fuels from near tree stems, especially thin-barked ones.

Compaction of fuels by rolling, trampling, or mowing not only reduces their flammability but also hastens their decay.

Roads should be kept free of flammable fuels to 3 or 5 m widths. In the case of plantations on gentle topography the average compartment should be about 20 ha. There should be more roads on more difficult terrain. External roads, especially, should be located with fire control in mind.

Managing the Trees

Choice of species

Look for the following virtues, but do not expect them all in any one species. In most situations, however, productivity is a more important criterion for choice of species than flammability or resistance to fire.

- Live foliage should be difficult to burn, i.e., it should be green and moist, and it should preferably be high in salt and low in oil or resin content.
- Dead foliage, branches and loose bark should be readily shed so that fire cannot climb into the crown and produce sparks and hence spot fires.
- Foliage should preferably be shed only at safe times and decay rapidly: the foliage of temperate deciduous species falls in autumn and is mostly decayed by next summer, while the foliage of hard-leaved evergreens, such as the eucalypts, falls mainly during the fire season, decays slowly, and thus tends to accumulate, together with fallen bark.
- The bark should be thick and difficult to burn, and the species should be able to recover vigorously after loss of foliage by sprouting from buds well protected within the bark.
- The tree should be able to suppress any flammable undergrowth.
- The species should be able to survive drought and other stresses, and grow rapidly, so that thick bark and high crowns can be achieved quickly.

Rapid early growth

The sooner the bark is thick and the foliage high above the ground the better. Thinning, weeding, mulching, irrigating and fertilising promote these objectives. Pruning off the lower limbs is useful, especially if they carry dead material.

Protection Strategies

Recently planted trees

If the chance of ignition is very high, do not use flammable mulches and keep the area virtually clear of fuels by cultivating, mowing or herbicide treatment. Remove flammable debris left from previous clearing operations.

Windbreaks Choose species of low flammability and high fire resistance. Provide a firebreak upwind (road, cultivation, green grass). Minimise the amount of fuels on the ground and in the lower crowns by mowing and pruning.

Plantations

When choosing a species for a plantation, productivity is usually the prime criterion, but fire resistance should also be considered, particularly on hazardous sites. Promote rapid early growth to shorten the most vulnerable stages. Reduce the amount of ground fuels by cultivation or grazing. Pruning serves to improve access and decrease the quantity of aerial fuels. Trees at edges of plantations should probably not be pruned, to keep the wind out. In the short term, pruning increases amounts of ground fuels, but this hazard can be reduced by stacking the debris away from trunks, or by grazing. Fresh needles of radiata pine are often palatable and nutritious for sheep. Alternatively, run a slasher over the prunings to mulch them. The fuel produced by frequent light pruning is less hazardous than that from rare heavy pruning. Culls and tops produced by thinning should be delimbed, so the slash decays rapidly. Once the stem bark is thick and the foliage high above the ground, fuel reduction by deliberate burning can also be considered. Maintain appropriate external and internal firebreaks.

Further Reading

Cheney, N.P. 1985. "Living with fire." In: Think Trees, Grow Trees, Chapter 5. Dept Arts Heritage and Environment with Institute of Foresters of Australia. Aust. Gov. Publ. Service, Canberra.

Gill, A.M. 1975. "Fire and the Australian flora: A review". Australian Forestry, 38, 4–25.

Gill, A.M. 1981. "Coping with fire", in The Biology of Australian Plants eds. J.S. Pate and A.J. McComb, Chapter 3. University of Western Australia Press, Nedlands, WA.

Luke, R.H. and McArthur, A.G. 1978. Bushfires in Australia. Aust. Gov. Publ. Service, Canberra (359 p).

McArthur, A.G. 1968. "The fire resistance of eucalypts". Ecol. Soc. of Aust. Proceedings, Vol. 3, pp. 83–90.

Original Source

This article was adapted with the kind permission of the author and sponsoring organization (CSIRO) from:

Cremer, K.W. 1990. "Fire" In: Cremer, K.W. (Ed), Trees for Rural Australia, Inkata Press, Melbourne, Australia.

This excerpt was originally published as *The Overstory* #124.

Saving Water, Soil, and Fertility

Trees contribute to and benefit from the conservation of resources. Making the best use of even small amounts of rain, maximizing organic matter, and improving soil fertility can create a more sustainable and productive system.

Section Contents

Microcatchment

Craig R. Elevitch and Kim M. Wilkinson

Establishing tree plantings in dry climates presents great challenges. Infrequent rains are often too little to soak deeply into the soil. On the other extreme, occasional rainstorms generate rapid run-off, with little water absorbed by the soil. This run-off can cause erosion and other problems down slope.

Rather than resorting to expensive irrigation systems or earthworks (which may not be economically feasible) we can use nature's own models for sheltering and establishing new vegetation in dry climates. In nature, new vegetation often first takes hold in pits, cracks, crevasses, and at the base of large rocks.

These special areas act as small catchments, collecting rainfall and allowing it to soak into the ground. These are natural "microcatchments." Small amounts of rainfall which otherwise would not soak deeply enough into the ground to help plants, trickle to the bottom of microcatchments and can contribute significantly to soil moisture.

By constructing low-cost microcatchments, each tree can be given an improved chance to survive—and hopefully thrive—in dry conditions. Through simple adaptation of natural models, your planting area can be designed to harvest the limited rainfall and store

Planting pits for taro (*Colocasia esculenta*) made by lifting rocks out of the rocky lava substrate, Tutuila, Samoa. (photo: C. Elevitch)

water in the ground right where the plants are growing.

Microcatchments benefit plants in other ways. First, they provide small seedlings with much needed shelter from sun, heat, and desiccating winds. Second, they "catch" more than just water—they also collect small particles of dust, soil and organic matter carried by wind or water. In so doing, the base of the microcatchment becomes a relatively fertile spot in an otherwise infertile area.

The matter that collects in microcatchments works to increase the ability of the soil to hold onto water, like a sponge. As the soil holds more water, it can sustain plants longer between rains.

Based on nature's model of establishing vegetation in microcatchments, people have designed and constructed simple, low cost microcatchments for use in arid climates. There are many examples such as the "net and pan" (Kenya), Zai holes (Burkina Faso), and mulch pits (Pacific islands) all of which use the same basic concepts:

1   A physical structure made of soil or rocks such as furrows, ditches, pits or a combination of these, occupying an area of 0.25–3 square meters. This structure acts as a microcatchment, collecting water and sediments.

2   A small collection area where the microcatchment funnels rainfall, soil particles and organic matter to one plant.

There are many clever designs for microcatchments described in the references listed below. The technique is especially useful on sloping lands, where rapid run-off and erosion make plant establishment very challenging.

In an adaptation of the principle, mulch can be added to the base of the microcatchment which accelerates the process of soil improvement and helps retain soil moisture. Such systems can rapidly revegetate parched lands without large earthworks or irrigation systems. A sheet of roof iron or cardboard can also be used to cover the ground and funnel water to plants.

Original Source

This chapter was originally published as *The Overstory* #17.

Further Reading

Rockeleau, D., *et al*. 1988. Agroforestry in Dryland Africa. ICRAF, PO Box 30677, Nairobi, Kenya.

Morrow, R. 1993. Earth User's Guide to Permaculture, Simon & Schuster, Intl.

Lancaster, B. 1996. "The Man Who Farms Water," Permaculture International Journal No. 60., South Lismore, Australia.

Meitzner, L.S. and M.L. Price. 1996. Amaranth To Zai Holes: Ideas for growing Food Under Difficult Conditions. ECHO, 17430 Durrance Road, North Fort Myers FL 33917-2239, USA; Tel: (941) 543-3246, Fax: (941) 543-5317, Email: echo@echonet.org, Web: http://www.echonet.org

Five Fertility Principles

Roland Bunch

Understanding the relationship between nutrients in the soil and crop productivity is crucial in achieving and maintaining high levels of agricultural productivity. This understanding is especially important for productivity at the lowest possible costs, both economic and ecological. Soil fertility is not an easy concept to define. For the purposes of this paper, we use the definition of soil fertility presented by Anthony Young (Young 1989), "soil fertility...is the capacity of soil to support the growth of plants, on a sustained basis, under given conditions of climate and other relevant properties of land." Notice that this definition goes beyond the simplistic concept of soil content of available nutrients, and allows for other critical aspects of soil fertility such as physical and biological properties.

The Five Principles of Agriculture for the Humid Tropics

An increasing number of institutions involved around the world in small farmer agriculture have begun to use some or all of the following principles of soil management:

Principle 1: Maximize organic matter (organic matter) production

Frequently, small-scale farmers can dramatically increase the amount of organic matter their fields produce while maintaining yields and only increasing costs slightly, if at all. In fact, many green manure/cover crop (gm/cc) and agroforestry systems reduce the amount of labor needed for controlling weeds, thereby increasing overall organic matter production while decreasing costs.

Increases in organic matter production can be achieved by using the intercropping of either various crops or gm/cc's with annuals or tree crops (as in dispersed tree systems), by establishing two- to four-story fields and gardens, and by growing trees or gm/cc's on wasteland or during the dry season. In drought-prone areas, an increased provision of water in whatever form can also result in greater levels of biomass production.

Obviously, the more biomass we produce on site, the more we will have for applying to the soil, thereby making the provision of nutrients to the soil greater and more constant. If animals are present in the farming systems, they will also be more numerous and/or produce more manure per animal if they have more biomass to consume.

Principle 2: Keep the soil covered

Soil exposed to the tropical sun produces more weeds (which are another form of biomass, but may compete with crops and/or occasion a good deal of work). Unprotected soil also becomes very hot, causing a series of problems, including the more rapid rate of soil organic matter burn-out, the reduction in crop growth rates and the death of beneficial macro and microorganisms.

Shifting agriculture has been motivated in most places in the world by either declining soil fertility or increasing noxious weed growth. Once we maximize biomass production and keep the soil shaded, both of these problems are largely eliminated. The need to let the land lie fallow for years is thus also eliminated, as has been shown in country after country with the use of gm/cc's.

It is interesting to note that virtually all the systems of improved fallows or gm/cc's that farmers have developed on their own, have increased both soil cover and the overall production of biomass, as compared to the previous shifting agriculture systems.

Keeping the soil covered reduces the decomposition rate of soil organic matter, thereby making sure the provision of nutrients to the soil lasts longer and is more constant, even if mulches tend to lose a certain amount of N to volatilization.

Principle 3: Use zero tillage

Tillage both damages soil structure and increases the rate of soil organic matter burn-out. Furthermore, tillage exposes the soil (i.e., violates the principle of keeping the soil covered) and removes or incorporates the mulch, which violates the fifth principle below.

Many traditional agriculture systems use zero tillage. However, these systems are often not very productive over time, because, in the absence of large amounts of soil organic matter, nutrients are no longer constantly supplied to the soil and soil structure deteriorates quite rapidly. If, however, zero tillage is used in the presence of a maximum production of biomass, then both the supply of nutrients and good soil structure can be maintained. Thus, in contrast to many traditional zero till systems, those systems with plentiful biomass production can remain highly productive over decades, as a whole series of gm/cc and agroforestry systems have proven.

Often zero tillage cannot be practiced the first or second year of the transition, but as soil organic matter levels increase and the soil becomes covered, the populations of organisms that naturally till the soil increase rapidly, making further tillage by the farmer unnecessary. Scientists have shown, for instance, that earthworms alone can move more soil/ha/year than is moved with one ploughing using a tractor-pulled moldboard plough (Minnich 1977).

In conventional textbooks, zero tillage is linked with a major increase in the use of herbicides. However, if the soil is kept covered through an adequate use of gm/cc's and agroforestry, most small-scale farmers will find they never, or only very rarely, need to use herbicides.

Principle 4: Maximize biodiversity

Some gm/cc users report achieving slightly better yields with a mixed selection of gm/cc's. Nevertheless, this principle will find its primary importance not in the short run, but rather in maintaining the systems' long-term sustainability. It can also be very important in maintaining the balance of soil nutrients (Primavesi 1982).

Principle 5: Feed the crops largely through the mulch

Many humid tropical soils, with low pH (below 5.0), aluminum toxicity, and compaction layers, are not very hospitable environments for crop roots. Thus, crops will often grow much better if they can also access nutrients from a thick litter layer or mulch. Most, if not all, crops that grow in the humid tropics spread the vast majority of their feeder roots immediately under or even up into a mulch layer as long as it remains fairly moist. That is, they will feed much more readily from inside and immediately below the litter layer than from the soil itself.

Even the impact of chemical fertilizers can sometimes be greatly increased by being applied to the mulch rather than the soil. In Costa Rica, edible bean yields in the "frijol tapado" system, a traditional slash-mulch system, were not increased much at all above the traditional 500 kg/ha when chemical phosphorus was applied to the soil. However, yields rose two to three times traditional yields (to above 2 t/ha) when the inorganic P was applied directly to the mulch. Researchers in Africa have also noted that fertilizers applied to mulching materials are more efficient than when incorporated into the soil. (Thurston 1997)

Feeding plants through the mulch helps compensate for less than ideal conditions of soil structure or root growth, providing a supplemental source of readily available nutrients in small but constant quantities right at the soil surface, thereby making it less necessary for crops to develop huge root systems that extend deep into the soil profile. Obviously, plants' access to nutrients will be better if the nutrients are on the soil surface than if they are three feet below it, especially in impoverished, acidic soils with problems of aluminum toxicity.

Example Cases

These same principles may well apply not only to the humid tropics, but to the semi-arid tropics, as well. Reports from some semi-arid areas indicate that this is the case. Nevertheless, there still exist some doubts as to what extent crops can survive during, and recover after, the mulch has dried out completely due to the frequent droughts in such areas. Much more experimental evidence is needed in this case.

Small farmers and NGO's have developed a number of other simple ways that plants access to nutrients can be inexpensively enhanced during the transition period. Edwin Asante, of World Vision/Rwanda, for instance, has developed a sort of small farmer version of precision planting for potatoes. In this case, an 8 cm ball of organic matter, lime, and about one-fourth the normally recommended amount of chemical fertilizer are placed directly below the seed. Yields in impoverished soils with a pH of 3.5 have averaged 20 t/ha, as opposed to 9 t/ha without precision planting (personal communication). In Honduras, Elías Sanchez developed a type of strip tillage or in-row tillage (locally called "minimum tillage" or "labranza minima") which concentrates the organic matter in the crop row, where it is more accessible. And Dr. Erich Raddatz is developing strains of mycorrhizal fungi that can double fruit production by increasing plants' access to nutrients (personal communication).

Conclusion

These five principles, apart from having proven themselves time and time again among small farmers around the world, are the self-same principles a humid tropical forest employs to maintain its high "productivity" during millennia, even on soils with very low cation exchange capacities (CEC's). A tropical rainforest maximizes biomass production and biodiversity, keeps the soil shaded at all times, and feeds its plants largely through the litter layer. And, of course, no human being has to plough a forest to keep it growing lush and green, century after century.

Thus, the sustainability of forest ecology over the millennia provides important evidence that tropical agriculture following these Five Principles should also be sustainable over long periods of time. The small amount of scientific research done on this issue so far tends to support this conclusion.

References

Buckles, Daniel, *et al.* (1998) Cover Crops in Hillside Agriculture, Farmer Innovation with Mucuna, Ottawa, Canada, International Development Research Centre (IDRC) and International Maize and Wheat Improvement Center (CIMMYT).

Bunch, Roland (1995) "An Odyssey of Discovery, Principles of Agriculture for the Humid Tropics," ILEIA Newsletter, Vol. 11, No. 3, October.

Bunch, Roland (2001) "A Proven Technology for Intensifying Shifting Agriculture, Green Manure/Cover Crop Experience Around the World," and "Achieving the Adoption of Green Manure/Cover Crops," both presented at the International Institute for Rural Reconstruction (IIRR's) Conference on "Best Practices in Shifting Agriculture and the Conservation of Natural Resources in Asia," held August 14-26 at Silang, Cavite, the Philippines. Both are soon to be published by IIRR.

Cresser, Malcolm, *et al.* (1993) Soil Chemistry and its Applications, Cambridge, UK, Cambridge University Press.

Minnich, Jerry (1977) The Earthworm Book, How to Raise and Use Earthworms for Your Farm and Garden, Emmaus, Pennsylvania, Rodale Press.

Primavesi, Ana (1982) Manejo Ecológico del Suelo, La Agricultura en Regiones Tropicales, Quinta Edición, Buenos Aires, Librería "El Ateneo" Editorial.

Thurston, H. David (1997) Slash/Mulch Systems: Sustainable Methods for Tropical Agriculture, Boulder, Colorado, Westview Press.

Young, Anthony (1989) Agroforestry for Soil Conservation, Oxon, UK, C.A.B International.

Original Source

This article was adapted with the kind permission of the author from:

Roland Bunch. 2001. "Nutrient Quantity or Nutrient Access?: A New Understanding of How to Maintain Soil Fertility in the Tropics." COSECHA, Tegucigalpa, Honduras.

Web: http://ppathw3.cals.cornell.edu/mba_project/moist/Roland.pdf

This excerpt was originally published as *The Overstory* #119.

Tropical Green Manures/Cover Crops

Roland Bunch

What are green manures/cover crops? The terms "green manure" and "cover crops" originated from practices of using primarily leguminous plants and plowing them under to fertilize soils. However, as the practice has spread to the tropics, different conditions have generated different uses, and the practice has changed. The terms remain although many tropical farmers do not use the vegetation green, nor do they normally plow it under as one would a manure. The terms now refer to a series of plants, mostly leguminous, which are used by farmers for a whole range of purposes, one of which is the fertilization and improvement of the soil by applying the vegetation to the soil surface. Here, the term green manure is used to cover both green manure and cover crops.

Advantages and Disadvantages of Green Manures for Village Farmers

Advantages
The proven advantages of green manures (gm's) are numerous. The first six of those listed below would apply to virtually all leguminous gm's, while the last two would apply only to selected ones:

Organic matter Gm's are capable of contributing up to (and occasionally more than) 50 T/ha (green weight) of organic matter to the soil during each application. This organic matter has a whole series of positive effects on the soil, such as improving its water-holding capacity, nutrient content, nutrient balance, friability and pH.

Nitrogen This organic matter also adds significant quantities of nitrogen (N) to the farming systems. Common levels of fixed N reported are about 150 kg/Ha, with some species yielding even more. This means that farmers can, even allowing for significant loss of N to the air, add to their systems quantities of N that would cost them at least US $75/ha in the forms of chemical fertilizer.

Reduced costs These additions of organic matter and N are achieved with no transportation costs; they are produced right in the field. Gm's require no

capital outlay once the farmer has purchased his/her first handful of seed.

Weed control Gm's can also be an important factor in reducing weed control costs, especially when used as mulch. Thus, the use of gm's can not only reduce the use of chemical fertilizer, they can also reduce or eliminate the use of herbicides.

Permanent cover under bananas

Soil Cover The soil cover provided by many gm's can be very important for soil conservation. A careful study has shown that farmers cultivating monocropped maize on 35% slopes with a 2000+ mm rainfall in northern Honduras are actually *increasing* the productivity of their soil year by year, with no conservation practices except for the fact that the soil is covered by velvet bean ten months out of the year.

Transition to zero-till The use of gm's allows farmers to switch to zero-till systems while maintaining productivity on land. Since plowing and weeding are two heavy operations that have always provided a major advantage to those farmers capable of mechanizing their agriculture, and since gm's are often capable of eliminating both of these operations, it is quite possible that non-mechanized and/or hill-side farmers once again have the chance of competing with their wealthier, mechanized competitors. In an age of falling trade barriers, this could mean the economic salvation of millions of the world's small farmers.

Ending migratory agriculture Gm's can be effective in ending migratory ("slash and burn" or "swidden") agriculture and agriculture burning by improving soil fertility and controlling weeds.

Food and animal fodder Gm's can also provide food for people and fodder for animals, though the latter practice will, of course, reduce its value to the soil.

Each of these advantages should be analyzed and weighed when we choose gm's. It is quite infrequent that farmers are primarily attracted by the gm's ability to increase soil fertility. Much more commonly, farmers are motivated by the gm's multiple uses, for human food, weed-control capabilities, or the possibility of no longer having to till the soil.

Disadvantages

Thousands of farmers in Honduras, Guatemala, and Mexico traditionally use gm's regularly, and the practice has often spread, gradually but spontaneously, without any outside encouragement. But, in general, and in spite of the advantages named above, the use of gm's is still surprisingly rare. Why?

- Farmers resist planting gm's where they could plant either subsistence or cash crops. This means that the land they use to grow gm's must have no known opportunity cost.
- The improvement of the soil is a long-term factor which is not immediately noticeable to the farmer. Usually, significant improvement in productivity does not occur until after incorporation, which means visible results are not apparent until well into the second cropping cycle or second year. This slow appearance of a result that is difficult to believe anyway, complicates the adoption of gm's.
- Often gm's must either continue to grow or form a mulch during the dry season. Grazing animals, agricultural burning, termites and a host of other problems may prevent their lasting very long during this period.
- Conditions such as extreme drought, extreme infertility, extremes in pH, severe drainage problems, and other problems common on poorer village farms, will affect gm's almost as much as traditional crops, thereby reducing the impact of gm's. In an increasing number of cases, we can overcome such problems (for instance, we have just heard that Desmodium triflorum is flourishing in soils with a pH lower than 4.0 in Belize), but often such solutions are achieved at the cost of

reduced biomass production, reduced N fixation, and/or reduced number of niches in which the gm's can fit.

Promising Species

Although these species are the best known to date, we should all be constantly looking for alternatives.

For low elevations (0-1500 meters) or warm weather

Velvet bean (*Mucuna pruriens*) This is by far the most popular of the gm's used both by Central American traditional systems and development programs worldwide (Central America, Brazil, Africa, India, etc.), and for good reasons. Of the legumes, it is one of the best N-fixers (150 kgs/Ha), and one of the best weed suppressors. It grows well in very poor soil and resists both drought and heavy rains quite well. Its biggest problems are that it is an aggressive climber (must be pruned often, or associated with maize, and cannot be grown at all among shorter-stature crops); it is already too widely used; we must avoid its becoming so widely spread and frequently used that it develops major insect or disease problems; it is perhaps not advisable for human consumption; and the seed must be boiled for most animal consumption.

Lablab bean (*Dolichos lablab* or *Lablab purpureum*, also widely known as "hyacinth bean") The lablab bean has a whole series of advantages over the velvet bean: it is edible and good tasting without any special processing; it grows just as well as the velvet bean and produces nearly as much biomass; it is the palatable for animals of all the gm's we use, with a 23% protein content; it is perennial, often staying green and producing seeds through four or five months of drought; and it is significantly more drought-tolerant than the velvet bean. Nevertheless, in some cases (perhaps in the absence of rhizobia bacteria) the lablab bean has been fairly demanding of good soil fertility, and in others has suffered insect attacks that have significantly retarded biomass production.

Jack beans (*Canavalia ensiformis*) or Sword beans (*C. gladiata*) By far the most hardy of the known gm's, the jack bean will grow where either the climate is so dry or the soils so poor that virtually nothing else will grow. For either of these conditions, it is an excellent beginning gm. It also fixes more N than the velvet bean (230 kgs/ha) and is perennial. And the tender pods can be eaten like string beans. Furthermore, there are both bushy and climbing varieties, although all the bushy varieties we know of do some climbing when grown under shade. In some areas of Honduras, farmers who started with velvet bean intercropped with maize are now converting to jack beans in order to avoid the pruning work. However, jack beans produce about 10% less biomass than velvet bean and do not control weeds as well. Also, jack beans plants and seeds are not palatable for animals, nor is it advisable to use jack beans for human consumption, unless heavily boiled.

Vigna species Various local vignas are used traditionally and as introduced gm's, and their use should be promoted.

Other legumes Used in many areas are various crotalarias (e.g. sunn hemp), the pigeon pea (*Cajanus cajan*), and many others. We are not yet using perennial soybeans and perennial peanuts (*Arachis pintoi*), because farmers in Nicaragua and Brazil complain about not being able to get rid of them.

Shade-tolerant legumes Under trees (either bananas, oil palms, citrus, etc.) another series of legumes are useful. Usually these are slower growing perennials that climb less vigorously. Among these the most prominent is the tropical kudzu (*Pueraria phaseoloides*) which is used widely to control weeds and provide N in Central America under fruit trees of many kinds. Tropical kudzu *must not* be confused with the common kudzu (*Pueraria lobata*). The latter should probably *never* be introduced anywhere, as it rapidly becomes a very serious pest.

For intermediate elevations (1500 to 3000 meters)

Much less is known about these species, although there are a good number of them:

Scarlet runner bean (*Phaseolus coccineus*) is grown as an intercrop in maize by farmers from northern Mexico and into Honduras. It requires about 5 to 6 months to grow, but reseeds itself naturally and does not need to be pruned.

Sweet clover (*Melilotus alba*) has been found to be a very good soil improver and forage crop, and can be intercropped well with maize. However, it is difficult to get rid of, so we are not promoting it heavily as yet.

Choreque (*Lathyrus nigrivalvis*) and other Lathyrus species Choreque is used traditionally in one part of the Guatemalan highlands as an intercrop for maize which then grows exuberantly

throughout the six-month dry season. It produces more biomass than any other gm we know and is excellent for dry season fodder production, but is severely limited by its environmental requirements: it needs a very fertile soil, does poorly the first years it is grown in a given soil, and requires cold climate but cannot withstand frost. Thus it can only be grown in quite fertile soils 1800–2100 meters in elevation.

Other cool-weather gm's Used in many areas are two non-leguminous gm's that have become popular, the forage turnip (*Raphanus sativus*) and various kinds of oats (*Avena* spp.). Other gm's from this region include peas (*Pisum sativum*) and *Vicia* species (especially *V. sativa* and *V. villosa*)

To sum up, green manure plants are usually valued for their multiple uses, especially for food, and secondarily for their long-term effects on maintaining or improving the productivity of the land. Experience leads us to believe that, with the possible exception of very intensive farming systems such as irrigated vegetables and rice, green manure and cover crops systems can probably be introduced into many, if not most, of the world's small-scale farming systems.

Original Source

The above text was summarized with kind permission of the author from the following article by Roland Bunch of COSECHA, Honduras: The Use of Green Manures by Villager Farmers: What We Have Learned to Date, Technical Report No. 3, 1995, CIDICCO, Apdo. Postal 4443, Tegucigalpa MDC, Honduras C.A., email: cidicco@gbm.hn.

This excerpt was originally published as *The Overstory* #29.

Further Reading

Nonegat, C. 1991. *Plantas do Cobertura do Solo*. Claudino Monegat, Chapeco, SC, Brazil. Perhaps the best book we know on this subject.

Various authors. 1997. "Achieving Sustainability," *ILEIA Newsletter*, October 1997, PO Box 64, 3830 AB Leusden, The Netherlands, email: ileia@ileia.nl

International Institute of Rural Reconstruction. *Agroforestry Technology Information Kit*, 1990. IIRR, Room 1270, 475 Riverside Dr., New York, NY 10115.

Carbon Sequestration: Storing Carbon in Soils and Vegetation

Robert T. Gavenda, Craig R. Elevitch, and Kim M. Wilkinson

Agroforestry systems can have a beneficial influence on the global climate. This chapter describes how conserving soils and planting trees can slow or reverse the release of carbon into the atmosphere.

What is the Greenhouse Effect?

Greenhouse gases such as carbon dioxide are a natural and essential component of the Earth's atmosphere. Atmospheric gases such as water vapor, carbon dioxide, carbon monoxide, methane, and ozone. These gases also absorb heat and keep heat from radiating away from earth into outer space. This effect is much like the way glass traps heat in a greenhouse, therefore the natural warming of Earth by its atmosphere is called the "greenhouse effect."

Carbon dioxide is the most important greenhouse gas, accounting for about half of the greenhouse effect. The natural concentration of greenhouse gases (GHG) has been essential to life as we know it on earth, creating the average temperature of 15°C (59°F). Without the naturally occurring greenhouse effect, the average temperature would be minus 18°C (0°F)!

However, human activities such as burning fossil fuels, the chemical industry, and agriculture and land use changes are increasing the amount of greenhouse gases, especially carbon dioxide, in the atmosphere. Human activities have increased GHG and raised global temperature 0.5°C over the past 100 years. As a result of human-induced increases in greenhouse gasses, the temperature is projected to increase by 1–5°C during the next 100 years. While this may not sound like much, the impact could be very dramatic, if not catastrophic, on the climate. For each one degree Celsius increase in temperature, vegetation zones may change dramatically, moving toward the poles by 200 to 300 km. Each one degree Celsius of global warming will also increase water evaporation, leading to about 2% greater mean global precipitation.

Increased greenhouse gases may lead to extremes in heat waves, droughts and floods (NCRS 2000). The increased frequency of floods and droughts is significant over the last 100 years, correlating with human use of fossil fuels and drastic land use changes from forest/grassland to cropland and urban development. Increased greenhouse gases means more energy (heat) is available in the atmosphere. This energy is released in the form of intense storms and changing weather patterns causing floods, droughts, and increased fires.

Carbon Balance on Agricultural Lands

Agricultural producers can help counteract climate change by increasing the storage (or "sequestering") of carbon on agricultural lands. Both soil and vegetation act as carbon sinks, reducing the amount of carbon dioxide in the atmosphere (NRCS 2000). Wise stewardship practices can mean more carbon is sequestered in an agroforestry system than is lost to the atmosphere.

Trees store atmospheric carbon in their tissues, and add carbon to the soil

Keeping topsoils intact maintains soil quality and reduce carbon emissions into the atmosphere. Increasing vegetative cover and planting trees is also an important way to store carbon. While usually adopted for other benefits, conservation practices that conserve soil and increase vegetation also increase carbon storage. These include:

- installing permanent vegetation buffers, such as windbreaks, contour hedgerows, and riparian buffers
- converting marginal agricultural land to perennial grassland or forest
- using conservation or no-till cultivation systems
- increasing fertilizer and water use efficiency
- increasing cropping intensity
- managing woodlands to conserve soil and increase biomass
- incorporating trees into agricultural operations through agroforestry
- using cover crops (NRCS 2000 and Gavenda 2000).

Soil Quality and Global Warming

The role of soils in carbon storage has been somewhat overshadowed by tree-planting efforts. While planting trees is important to increase carbon storage, conserving soils is essential. Soils are the largest non-fossil land-based organic carbon reservoir on Earth. Global soil carbon content is:

- three times as much as in terrestrial plants and animals;
- twice the amount in the atmosphere;
- a third of the carbon in fossil fuels.

Soil erosion is a major cause of soil organic carbon loss and increasing greenhouse gas emissions. This takes place by:

1 exposing carbon locked within soil aggregates,
2 mineralizing carbon by oxidation and microbial processes, and
3 decreasing the soil's ability to support vegetation by lowering soil fertility, losing water as runoff, decreasing plant-available soil water, burying or flooding crops, and other erosion related effects.

Carbon dioxide additions to the atmosphere are caused not only by burning fossil fuel in agricultural activities, but also by soil organic carbon decomposition, and vegetation burning. Grassland and forest soils tend to lose 20–50% of the original soil organic carbon within the first 50 years of cultivation. Erosion, leaching, methane production, volatilization, and mineralization (decomposition of complex organic compounds to inorganic forms) lead to carbon loss from the soil.

Some soil processes lead to carbon storage. These include:

- deep rooting (plants or trees forming roots deep into the soil)
- humification (the formation of organic matter into humus)
- aggregation (the clustering of soil particles), and
- movement within the soil (by soil organisms and microorganisms).

Agroforestry to Sequester Carbon

Trees on farms or pastures for reforestation or agroforestry are planted for a number of benefits. They also store carbon. Some examples include (NAC 2000):

Silvopasture Timber/grazing systems managed on the same area of land can increase net carbon storage. When both the tree and grass components are properly managed, an increase in net carbon storage vs. pasture of forest alone can be achieved.

Windbreaks Vegetation windbreaks store carbon while also protecting soils farmsteads, livestock, roads, people, soils, and crops from wind. Additional CO_2 reductions may also result from improved water use efficiency.

Forested Riparian Buffers Trees grow rapidly in riparian zones due to favorable moisture and nutrient conditions. When suitable trees and shrubs grow in these moist environments they also filter out excess nutrients, pesticides, animal wastes, and sediments coming from adjacent agricultural or urban activities.

Short Rotation Woody Crops (SRWC) Low prices for traditional crops have increased the interest of farmers in fast-growing woody crops for fuel and fiber. SWRC systems provide a way of increasing on-farm income, while also being designed to treat agricultural, livestock, or municipal wastes. The rapid growth of SRWC results in high rates of nutrient uptake and large amounts of carbon storage over rotation lengths as short as 5–15 years. Net carbon benefits are realized if the wood fiber is used for solid wood products or fuel.

In some regions, agreements are in place that allow nations or corporations to offset their greenhouse gas emissions by buying credits from farmers who increase their stores of carbon in the soil or in trees

(NRCS 2000). The potential market for these carbon credits could be beneficial to agricultural producers.

Conclusion

Agricultural producers play an important role in efforts to slow or reverse the release of carbon into the atmosphere. Soil conservation is essential to this effort, as soils are a tremendous organic carbon reservoir. Planting trees and increasing vegetation can aid in conserving soil, while providing other farm benefits and increasing carbon storage.

References

Gavenda, R.T. 2000. Soils and Carbon Sequestration. Kona Soil and Water Conservation District Field Tour, Pu'u Waawaa, North Kona, February 5, 2000. USDA-NRCS, Kealakekua, Hawai'i.

USDA NAC (United States Department of Agriculture National Agroforestry Center). 2000. Working Trees for Carbon Cycle Balance/Agroforestry: Using trees and shrubs to produce social, economic, and conservation benefits. Gary Kuhn, USDA National Agroforestry Center, East Campus - UNL, Lincoln, NE 68583-0822, 402-437-5178; Web: http://www.unl.edu/nac.

USDA NRCS (United States Department of Agriculture Natural Resources Conservation Service). 2000. Growing Carbon: A New Crop that Helps Agricultural Producers and the Climate Too. Available from: the Soil and Water Conservation Society Tel: 1-888-526-3227; Email: landcare@swcs.org; Web: http://www.swcs.org.

Original Source

This chapter was originally published as *The Overstory #66*.

Forests and Water

Frank H. Wadsworth

For eons, forests have been slowing water movement and thus precipitating sediments, capturing nutrients, and building the soil. The presence or absence of forest cover may decide the ultimate fate of human society.

Forests have an intimate relationship to water supplies. The delayed release of rainwater from forested soils of the uplands are vital to lowland water supplies. Litter that accumulates on the forest floor absorbs the physical impact of torrential downpours and releases the water gently to the mineral soil beneath. This cushioning action largely prevents the water from suspending large quantities of surface soil particles and thus clogging soil pores beneath. In addition, the decaying litter enriches the water entering the soil and supports organisms that produce porous upper soil layers. These processes are the most obvious ways forests enhance water supplies. The draft on soil water is greatest under forests with their deep-rooted trees and high rates of transpiration. Between storms porous soils again become highly receptive to new water.

Storm water, generally received in torrents, may carry away the litter and surface soil if it cannot promptly percolate into the soil. Such percolation represents the lifeblood of the Tropics—it supplies the forest, and then follows subterranean pathways, reappearing gradually and continuously in springs that feed streams that in turn safeguard and support aquatic life, commerce, irrigation, and urban life downstream. This intimate relation between forests and usable water makes the Tropics habitable. Thus, tropical forests provide soil protection, a high soil infiltration rate, and, where soil is deep, substantial storage (Pereira 1967).

Even after water enters streams, it may continue to be affected by riparian forests. Tree growth on stream banks stabilizes the soil. When floods occur, the forest litter may support aquatic life important as a source of human food. Flooded streamside forests slow water movement, and thus precipitate sediments, capturing nutrients and building up the level of stream banks. At river mouths, estuaries, and along relatively protected seacoasts, mangrove forests retain sediments and provide habitats for important terrestrial, amphibious, and marine fauna.

Many rivers separate nations or run through more than one nation. Therefore, forest benefits to natural water courses are an international concern and expand the self-interest of all nations into a web of interdependence.

Part of the rainfall is intercepted by the forest canopy and evaporates. Interception by rain forest canopies varies widely with the density of the canopy and the intensity and duration of the rainfall. For short, light showers, all water may remain on and evaporate from a dense forest canopy. Measurements over time suggest that, under closed forests, about 15 to 20 percent of the rainwater is held in the canopy (Kline and others 1968, Lawson and others 1981). Whether such water benefits the ecosystem has been debated. Its evaporation cools the vegetation and the air, presumably reducing the draft on soil water for transpiration. Moist vegetation is darker in color than dry vegetation, and therefore absorbs more solar energy, suggesting that at least part of the energy required would not otherwise have been available for the ecosystem's needs (Satterlund 1972).

In the Brazilian Amazon, studies have shown that 62% of the water goes to evapotranspiration, and 90% of this is due to a delicate energy balance (Villa Nova and others 1976). Because the hydrological cycle is so intimately related to the presence of forests, general deforestation can lead to serious consequences.

Forests, Rainfall, and Soil

The relationships between forests and tropical soils are an outgrowth of forest-water relations. Humic acids picked up by rainwater as it passes through the forests accelerate weathering of parent rock and other soil-forming processes. The forest floor minimizes landslides by absorbing the shock of intense rainfall as do the dense and deep tree-root systems. Studies show the superiority of forest over other types of vegetative cover in this function (Lawson and others 1981).

The effectiveness of forests in controlling erosion varies with the climate, slope, soil condition, and the character of the forest. The densest forests, which permit few living plants in the ground layer, may be less protective than more open forests with herbs, grasses, or young trees which hold the litter in place, particularly on slopes. Many trees, and palms in particular, tend to concentrate rainfall towards their main stem. As much as 10% of the rainfall may reach the soil beneath rain forests in this manner (Lawson and others 1981). This stemflow may be rich in particulates washed from the tree bark and thus provide nutrition at the base of the tree, but the concentrated flow downslope from that point can, in extreme cases, cause severe erosion. Where these problems become serious, they can be lessened by silvicultural practices.

References

Kline, J.R., C.F. Jordan, and G. Drewry. 1968. Tritium movement in soil of a tropical rain forest (Puerto Rico). In: Science. 160:550–557.

Lawson, T.L., R. Lal, and K. Oduro-Afriyie. 1981. Rainfall redistribution and microclimate changes over a cleared watershed. In: R. Lal and E.W. Russell (Eds). Tropical Agricultural Hydrology. John Wiley and Sons. Chichester, UK.

Satterlund, D.R. 1972. Wildland Watershed Management. Ronald Press, New York, NY.

Pereira, H.C. 1967. Afforestation and streamflow in tropical highlands. Commonwealth Forestry Review. 47(4):323–327

Villa Nova, M.A., E. Matsui, and E. Salati. 1976. Estimativa da evapotranspiracao na bacia amazonica. In: Acta Amazonica. 6(2): 215–228

Original Source

This article is excerpted with the kind permission of the author from:

Wadsworth, F.H. 1997. Forest Production for Tropical America. International Institute for Tropical Forestry, USDA Forest Service, Rio Piedras, Puerto Rico.

This excerpt was originally published as *The Overstory* #80.

Effects of Trees on Soils

Anthony Young

Approaches to soil management, including problems of soil degradation and low soil fertility, have recently undergone major changes. The former view was to concentrate on achieving high levels of production from the more fertile areas, leaving the marginal lands for extensive use only. Steeply sloping and highly drought-prone areas were preferably not cultivated at all. Soil constraints were to be overcome by inputs: improved crop varieties, fertilizers, chemical control of pests and diseases, and the use of irrigation.

It had been demonstrated that crop yields could be raised by a factor of three to five times or more by the use of fertilizers, applied to the newly developed high-yielding crop varieties. This approach was successful in giving large increases in crop productivity in Western countries and Asia and moderate improvements elsewhere, but it encountered problems of many kinds. Fertilizers are costly in terms of energy resources to produce them, and continued high rates of use lead to environmental problems. Yield responses to fertilizers have declined, for example because of soil physical degradation or micronutrient deficiencies. Above all, large numbers of poor farmers simply cannot afford high levels of fertilizers and other purchased inputs, nor do they have the capital to take on the risk which these involve. Finally, the former solution of increasing the area under irrigation has run into severe constraints in the form of limits to available freshwater resources.

Aspects of this new approach include:

- find ways of making the use of marginal lands sustainable;
- reclaim and restore degraded land;
- improve germplasm to produce plant varieties which are adapted to soil constraints;
- maintain soil organic matter and biological activity, with benefits both for soil physical conditions and balanced nutrient supplies;
- improve nutrient cycling and nutrient use efficiency in agroecosystems;
- use fertilizers and other external inputs at moderate levels, seeking strategic use to overcome deficiencies that cannot otherwise be remedied;
- improve water-use efficiency.

Agroforestry can contribute to all these aspects and has a major role to play in some. The capacity of trees to grow under difficult climatic and soil conditions, coupled with their potential for soil conservation, gives agroforestry a potential in the main types of marginal lands: semiarid, sloping and those with soil constraints. There is a demonstrated potential for reclamation of degraded land. As well as crop breeding, research programmes are under way to select or, in the longer term, breed trees tolerant of adverse soil conditions. Tree litter and prunings can substantially help to maintain soil organic matter and improve physical properties and at the same time supply nutrients. The contrast between natural and agricultural ecosystems suggests a high potential for agroforestry to lead to improved nutrient cycling and hence fertilizer use efficiency. In the case of water-use efficiency, there is a known potential, as demonstrated in studies of windbreaks and contour hedgerows, although tree-crop competition for water presents problems.

Trees can improve soils and ecosystem productivity

How Do We Know that Trees Improve Soils?

Underlying all aspects of the role of agroforestry in maintenance of soil fertility is the fundamental proposition that trees improve soils. How we know that this is true?

1   The soil that develops under natural forest and woodland is fertile. It is well structured, has a good water-holding capacity and has a store of

nutrients bound up in the organic matter. Farmers know they will get a good crop by planting on cleared natural forest.

2   The cycles of carbon and nutrients under natural forest ecosystems are relatively closed, with much recycling and low inputs and outputs.

3   The practice of shifting cultivation demonstrated the power of trees to restore fertility lost during cropping.

4   Experience of reclamation forestry has demonstrated the power of trees to build up fertility on degraded land.

What Makes a Good Soil Improving Tree?

It would be useful to have guidelines on which properties of a tree or shrub species make it desirable for the point of view of soil fertility. This would help in identifying naturally occurring species and selecting trees for systems which have soil improvement as a specific objective.

Nitrogen fixation and a high biomass production have been widely recognized as desirable. However, many properties are specific to particular objectives of systems in which the trees are used. Even species that are shunned for their competitive effects may have a role in certain designs. An example is the way in which *Eucalyptus* species with a high water uptake, which adversely affects yields in adjacent crops, have been employed to lower the water table and so reduce salinization.

The properties which are likely to make a woody perennial suitable for soil fertility maintenance or improvement are:

1   A high rate of production of leafy biomass.

2   A dense network of fine roots, with a capacity for abundant mycorrhizal association.

3   The existence of deep roots.

4   A high rate of nitrogen fixation.

5   A high and balanced nutrient content in the foliage; litter of high quality (high in nitrogen, low in lignin and polyphenols).

6   An appreciable nutrient content in the root system.

7   Either rapid litter decay, where nutrient release is desired, or a moderate rate of litter decay, where maintenance of a soil cover is required.

8   Absence of toxic substances in the litter or root residues.

9   For soil reclamation, a capacity to grow on poor soils.

10 Absence of severe competitive effects with crops, particularly for water.

11 Low invasiveness.

12 Productive functions, or service functions other than soil improvement.

Not all of these properties are compatible: for example, litter of high quality is not likely to have a moderate rate of decay. The last property, the existence of productive functions, is not directly concerned with soils but is of the highest importance if the tree is to be effective in fertility maintenance. A species needs to be acceptable and desirable in agroforestry systems from other points of view, especially production. A tree might have all the desirable properties above, but, if it is not planted and cared for, it will not be effective in improving soil fertility.

Summary of Effects of Trees on Soils

The capacity of trees to maintain or improve soils is shown by the high fertility status and closed. nutrient cycling under natural forest, the restoration of fertility under forest fallow in shifting cultivation, and the experience of reclamation forestry and agroforestry.

Soil transects frequently show higher organic matter and better soil physical properties under trees. Some species, most notably *Faidherbia albida*, regularly give higher crop yields beneath the tree canopy. Trees improve soil fertility by processes which:

• increase additions to the soil;
• reduce losses from the soil;
• improve soil physical, chemical and biological conditions.

The most important sets of processes are those by which trees:

• check runoff and soil erosion;
• maintain soil organic matter and physical properties;
• increase nutrient inputs, through nitrogen fixation and uptake from deep soil horizons;
• promote more closed nutrient cycling.

Trees may also adversely affect associated crops. The effects of allelopathy (inhibition effects) have probably been exaggerated by mistaking them for, or confounding them with, other processes. Competition for water is a serious but not insuperable problem in all dry environments, whereas competition for nutrients has rarely been demonstrated.

Where the net effect of tree—crop interactions is positive, the length of the tree—crop interface, or extent of the ecological fields, should be maximized. If the net effect is negative, the aim of agroforestry system design should be to reduce the length of the interface.

A range of properties have been identified which make tree species suited to soil improvement. For many purposes, high biomass production, nitrogen fixation, a combination of fine feeder roots with tap roots and litter with high nutrient content are suitable. Tolerance to initially poor soil conditions is clearly needed for reclamation. About 100 species have been identified which are known to fulfil soil-improving functions, but there is much scope to increase this range.

Principal trees and shrubs that have been employed for soil improvement (from Webb *et al* 1984; von Carlowitz, 1986; von Carlowitz *et al* 1991; MacDicken, 1994; Young, 1989a, p. 159). Names in parentheses are synonyms formerly in use. Species marked with an asterisk (*) were not listed in the Original Source, but have been added on the basis of recent research.

Acacia auriculiformis	*Bamboo genera*	*Gliricidia sepium*	*Prosopis juliflora*
Acacia cyanophylla	*Cajanus cajan*	*Grevillea robusta*	*Prosopis tamarugo*
Acacia mangium	*Calliandra calothyrsus*	*Inga edulis*	*Schinus molle*
Acacia mearnsii	*Casuarina cunninghamiana*	*Inga jinicuil*	*Senna reticulata*
Acacia nilotica	*Casuarina equisetifolia*	*Leucaena diversifolia*	*Senna siamea (Cassia siamea)*
Acacia senegal	*Casuarina glauca*	*Leucaena leucocephala*	*Senna spectabilis (Cassia spectabilis)*
Acacia seyal	**Centrosema pubescens*	*Melaleuca leucadendron*	*Sesbania bispinosa*
Acacia tortilis	*Cordia alliodora*	*Melia azedarach*	*Sesbania grandiflora*
Albizia lebbeck	**Crotalaria* spp.	*Musanga cecropioides*	*Sesbania rostrata*
Albizia saman (Samanea saman)	*Dalbergia sissoo*	*Paraserianthes falcataria (Albizia falcataria)*	*Sesbania sesban*
Anacardium occidentale	*Dactyladenia barteri (Acioa barteri)*	*Parkia biglobosa (Parkia africana)*	*Tamarix aphylla*
Alnus acuminata	*Dendrocalamus* spp.	*Paulownia elongata*	*Tephrosia candida*
Alnus nepalensis	*Erythrina caffra*	*Peltophorum dasyrrachis*	**Tephrosia vogelii*
Alnus spp.	*Erythrina orientalis*	*Populus deltoides*	**Tithonia diversifolia*
Atriplex spp.	*Erythrina poeppigiana*	*Prosopis chilensis*	*Ziziphus mauritiana*
Azadirachta indica	*Faidherbia albida (Acacia albida)*	*Prosopis cineraria*	*Ziziphus nummularia*
Bactris gasipaes	*Flemingia congesta (F. macrophylla)*	*Prosopis glandulosa*	*Ziziphus spina-christi*

Recent Study

The soil-improving capacities of trees, and how these can be applied in practical agroforestry systems, continues to be a major focus of agroforestry. In a recent overview of agroforestry research (Nair and Latt, 1997), six out of ten review articles were concerned wholly or in substantial part with soil fertility aspects. One important recent change of emphasis is that less attention is being given to hedgerow intercropping (alley cropping), in view of the observed reluctance of farmers to adopt this system, whilst more emphasis is now placed on systems of managed tree fallows (Buresh and Cooper, 1999). An account of using trees to lower the water table, referred to above, is given by Burgess *et al* (1998). Recent successful projects in soil fertility improvement by trees are described by Rao *et al* (1998) and Niang *et al* (1999).

References

Burgess, S., *et al*. 1998. Trees as water pumps: restoring water balances in Australian and Kenyan soils. Agroforestry Today 10(3): 18-20.

MacDicken, K.G. 1991. Selection and Management of Nitrogen Fixing Trees. Winrock International, Morrilton, Arkansas, USA.

Nair, P.K.R., and Latt, C.R. (eds). 1997. Directions in tropical agroforestry research. Agroforestry Systems, Special Issue, 38: 1-249.

Niang, A. and 5 others. 1999. Soil fertility replenishment in western Kenya. Agroforestry Today 11(1-2): 19-21.

von Carlowitz, P.G. 1986. Multipurpose Tree and Shrub Seed Directory. ICRAF, Nairobi.

von Carlowitz, P.G., Wolf, G.V., and Kemperman, R.E.M. 1991. Multipurpose Tree and Shrub Database. An Information and Decision-support System. GTZ, Eschborn, Germany.

Webb, D.B., Wood, P. J., Smith, J.P., and Henman, G.S. 1984. A Guide to Species Selection in Tropical and Sub-tropical Plantations. Commonwealth Forestry Institute, Oxford, UK.

Young, A. 1989. Agroforestry for Soil Conservation. CAB International, Wallingford, UK.

Original Source

The above excerpt are adapted from Chapter 2 of *Agroforestry for Soil Management* (2nd Edition) with permission of the author and publisher. Details of the processes involved are discussed in detain in the original text.

Agroforestry For Soil Management 2nd Edition presents a synthesis of evidence from agriculture, forestry and soil science, drawing on over 700 published sources dating largely from the 1990s. These include both results of field trials of agronomy systems, and research into the plant-soil processes which take place within them. It is a valuable resource for research scientists, or for practical scientists, agronomists and foresters. The book can be purchased through the publisher CAB International at: http://www.cabi.org/bookshop/index.asp.

This excerpt was originally published as *The Overstory* #61.

Greywater for Trees and Landscape

Art Ludwig

This chapter introduces some practical ways to use water from homes (from dishes, laundry, bathing, etc., NOT from toilets) as irrigation water for trees and landscapes. Rather than contaminate usable water by combining it with sewage, greywater systems keep dish and wash water separate from sewage and reuse it in the landscape. This is a classic means of "turning waste into a resource." For specific design and installation details for greywater systems, further study is highly recommended.

What Is Greywater?

Any water that has been used in the home, except water from toilets, is called greywater. Dish, shower, sink and laundry water comprise approximately 80% of residential "wastewater." This may be reused for other purposes, especially landscape irrigation. Toilet-flush water is called blackwater. Contaminated greywater or wastewater that is difficult to handle, such as solids-laden kitchen sink water or water used to launder diapers, is sometimes called "dark grey" or blackwater. Reclaimed water (highly treated municipal greywater and blackwater, usually piped to large-volume users such as golf courses in a separate distribution system) is outside the scope of this article.

Why Use Greywater?

It's a waste to irrigate with great quantities of drinking water when plants would thrive on used water containing small bits of organic matter. Unlike a lot of ecological stopgap measures, greywater use is a part of the fundamental solution to many ecological problems and will probably remain essentially unchanged in the distant future. The benefits of greywater recycling include:

Lower fresh water use

Greywater can replace fresh water in many instances, saving money and increasing the effective water supply in regions where irrigation is needed. Residential water use is almost evenly split between indoor and outdoor. All except toilet water could be recycled outdoors, achieving the same result with significantly less water diverted from nature.

Less strain on septic tank or treatment plant

Greywater use greatly extends the useful life and capacity of septic systems. For municipal treatment systems, decreased water flow generally means higher treatment effectiveness and lower costs.

Highly effective purification

Greywater is purified to a spectacularly high degree in the upper, most biologically active region of the soil (Center for Study of Federalism 1972). This protects the quality of natural surface and ground waters.

Site unsuitable for a septic tank

For sites with slow soil percolation or other problems, greywater use may be a good alternative to a very costly, over-engineered system.

Less energy and chemical use

Less energy and chemicals are used due to the reduced amount of both freshwater and wastewater that needs pumping and treatment. For those providing their own water or electricity, the advantage of a reduced burden on the infrastructure is felt directly. Also, treating your wastewater in the soil under your own fruit trees definitely encourages you to dump less toxic chemicals down in the drain.

Groundwater recharge

Greywater application in excess of plant needs recharges groundwater.

Plant growth

Greywater enables a landscape to flourish where water may not otherwise be available to support much plant growth.

Reclamation of otherwise wasted nutrients

Loss of nutrients through wastewater disposal in rivers or oceans is a subtle, but highly significant, form of erosion. Reclaiming nutrients in greywater helps to maintain the fertility of the land.

Increased awareness of and sensitivity to natural cycles

Greywater use yields the satisfaction of taking responsibility for the wise husbandry of an important resource.

Just because

Greywater is relatively harmless and great fun to experiment with. Moreover, life with alternative waste treatment can be less expensive and more interesting.

Mulch Basins

If I had just two words to contribute to improve the world's handling of greywater they would be "mulch basin." Mulch covers the greywater and provides many other benefits.

The basin contains the water where it is needed and prevents it from escaping where it is wasted or a nuisance. The island in the middle of the mulch basin protects the delicate root crown from wet conditions and possible disease.

Mulch basins are a common feature of existing horticultural practice and could hardly be simpler to make and maintain. Don't let this fool you. Though nature takes care of their inner workings, these are fantastically complex biologically, far more complex than a municipal sewage treatment plant.

What's more, the treatment level mulch basins provide is far higher than that of a municipal treatment plant (Los Angeles Department of Water Reclamation) and instead of consuming copious electricity and chemicals to create polluted natural waters and piles of toxic sludge (Wagner and Laniox 1958) mulch basins run on sunlight and yield drinkable groundwater and fresh fruit.

Selecting Plants for Greywater Treatment/Disposal

For disposal, theoretically you don't even need plants; the bacteria on the soil particles will take care of treatment by themselves (as in a sand filter). However, you can only do better with plants. With high perk soil groundwater contamination could occur if wastewater moves through too fast. With very low

Bath house and its greywater garden in Santa Barbara, California (photo: A. Ludwig)

perk soil ponding and anaerobic conditions can occur. Plants improve physical soil conditions including perk rate, and add their own substantial contribution to getting rid of the water by transpiring it. The ideal plants for greywater disposal are:

- Tolerant of wet conditions
- Generate their own mulch or physical barrier (keeps greywater from being seen and kids or dogs from playing in it), so you don't have to
- Keep their leaves all year (so they transpire water all year)
- Look beautiful, make fruit or some other useful thing

Wetland plants also serve as solar-powered oxygen pumps. They literally pump oxygen down through their roots, maintaining aerobic conditions in mucky soil. These should be ideally suited for a heavily loaded disposal basin for this reason. Also, many form such a dense stand that the need for adding mulch is obviated; the plants themselves preclude access to the water (if there is even the tiniest area of standing water for more than a week or two, mosquitoes will hatch from it).

Selecting Plants for Greywater Reuse

Trees are the best thing to irrigate with the branched drain system. Water delivered anywhere in the root zone will benefit the whole plant. It is a heck of a lot easier to hit a few big root zones than numerous small ones. Anything smaller than a big shrub is just too small for most greywater systems, which supply only a dozen or so outlets (as compared to hundreds in a drip irrigation system). Even if it were possible to supply more outlets, an inch and a half (4 cm) pipe to every flower would be a lot of plastic.

If your fruit trees are already planted, that's what you'll be watering. If you have evergreen fruit trees, they are the priority. If your trees are not planted, then you have the opportunity to optimize the coordination between the greywater system and layout of the edible landscaping (Office of Aridland Studies).

Examples of Plants for Greywater Reuse

Bananas—Premier plant for greywater in warm climates. Make sure there is enough basin area and plants so there is no standing water; they are not wet-

land plants. Clumps will expand until they are using all available water. If they look like they need more water, chop a few down and the rest will do better. For maximum fruit production, each clump should have a mature, medium and small stalk.

Citrus

Avocado and Mango—Grow into enormous trees. Make sure you have an idea of how to water it when it is forty feet tall!

Pineapple guava—Can be maintained as a four foot hedgerow, or shaped into a twenty foot specimen tree

Fig—No paradise is complete without figs. While deciduous, there is a shorter interval between dropping leaves and growing new ones than for most deciduous fruit trees.

Apple

Plum

Peach

When Not to Use Greywater

There are a number of possible reasons not to use greywater or to use it only during certain times of year:

Insufficient space

In some situations, neighbors are too close, the yard too small or nonexistent.

Drain pipes impossible to get to

If all plumbing is entombed in a concrete slab, accessing most of the greywater won't be economical.

Unsuitable climate

In very wet climates, where using greywater for irrigation is of little benefit, better ways to dispose of it may be available. In very cold climates, freezing may prevent the use of a greywater system for part of the year.

Insufficient combined waste flow

If all greywater is reused all the time, the flow through municipal sewers may occasionally be insufficient to move toilet solids through.

Unsuitable soil

Soil that is extremely permeable or impermeable may preclude the use of a greywater system or at least require special adaptations.

Legality concerns

In most parts of the country, the legality of greywater systems is a "grey" area. However, there seems to be a general movement toward a less paranoid and more realistic official attitude regarding greywater recycling, concurrent with increased experience and improved systems (not to mention more prevalent water shortages and pollution problems) (California Plumbing Code). Authorities generally turn a blind eye toward greywater use even where illegal. In the 1970s, the state of California published a pamphlet that explained the illegality of greywater use and, at the same time, how to do it, and get a tax credit for it!

Health concerns

The main reason greywater remains illegal in many areas is concern for public health. However, in practice, the health threat from greywater has proven to be insignificant. I know of no instance in which a person in the U.S. became ill from greywater. The first actual field test by the Department of Water Reclamation in Los Angeles found that greywatered soil teemed with pathogens. However, the control soil did, as well. Their conclusion: don't eat dirt, with or without greywater! (Los Angeles Department of Water Reclamation)

Poor cost/benefit ratio

In some situations, especially when legal requirements mandate a complex system for a small flow of water, the ecological cost of the system may outweigh the benefits.

Inconvenience

So far, most greywater systems are either more expensive or require considerably more user involvement than well functioning septic or sewer systems.

Health Considerations Concerning Greywater Use

Greywater may contain infectious organisms, so keep this in mind when designing and using a system. In practice, the health risk of greywater use has proven to be minimal. It is, after all, the water you just bathed in, or residue from clothes you wore not long ago. At the same time, it's definitely poor form to construct pathways for infecting people into your design, and totally unnecessary. All greywater safety guidelines stem from these two principles:

1 Greywater must pass slowly through healthy topsoil for natural purification to occur.

2 Design your greywater system so no contact takes place before purification.

Here are examples of applying these principles to correct possible problems:

- Direct contact or consumption. SOLUTION: Carefully avoid cross connections and label greywater plumbing, including greywater garden hoses. Use gloves when cleaning greywater filters.
- Breathing of microorganisms. Droplets from sprinklers can evaporate to leave harmful microorganisms suspended in the air, waiting for someone to breathe them. SOLUTION: Don't recycle greywater through sprinklers.
- Microorganisms on plants. Direct application to foliage can leave untreated microorganisms on surfaces. SOLUTION: Don't apply greywater to lawns or directly to fruits and vegetables that are eaten raw (strawberries, lettuce, or carrots, for example). Fruit trees are acceptable if greywater is applied only to the roots.
- Contamination of surface water. If greywater does not percolate through the soil, it can flow into creeks or other waterways untreated. SOLUTION: Discharge greywater underground or into a mulch-filled basin. Don't apply greywater to saturated soils. Apply greywater intermittently so that it soaks in and soil can aerate between waterings. In general, contained greywater application at least 50 feet from a creek or lake is not a problem.

Retrofitting existing plumbing for grey water collection usually involves cutting some pipes in order to separate grey water from blackwater. (photo: A. Ludwig)

- Contamination of groundwater. It is all but impossible to contaminate groundwater with a greywater system. However, property owners with wells should not irrigate with greywater any closer to the well than county regulations allow for a septic tank leach field.
- Chemical contamination. Biological purification does not usually remove industrial toxins. Toxins either will be absorbed by plants or will pollute groundwater. Many household cleaners are composed of chemicals that are unsuitable for introduction into a biological system. SOLUTION: Don't buy products that you wouldn't want in your greywater system. Divert water containing those you can't avoid to poison the sewer or septic instead.
- System overload. Greywater systems are safest when using water that is fairly clean initially. Greywater should not contain water used to launder soiled diapers or by anyone with an infectious disease; in both cases, greywater should be diverted to the septic tank or sewer. Also, DON'T STORE GREYWATER; use it immediately, before bacteria multiply. Finally, if you are having a party where 50 people are going to use a system designed for two, consider diverting greywater to the sewer for the night.

Note on Health Risks

Much fuss has been made over the potential health risk of greywater use, without comparison with the actual risk of the current practice of disposing of sewage into natural waters used for swimming, drinking and fishing. This questionable practice short circuits effective natural purification in soil and is considered one of the least desirable techniques by the World Health Organization (Wagner and Laniox 1958).

Approximately 20% of all U.S. communities still dump sewage in natural waters after primary treatment (solids removal) only. After heavy rains, even the most technologically advanced secondary treatment plants are forced to abandon all pretense of treatment and let raw sewage flood into the ocean or river.

Widespread greywater use in a population mostly unaccustomed to taking responsibility for utilizing natural systems would not be 100% risk-free. However, even with the inevitable misuses, greywater recycling as described here is safe compared to other common activities, such as kissing, dogs pooping on lawns, and swimming downstream of municipal sewers.

Cautions from the Author

The design and use of greywater systems carry legal, public health, horticultural, and ecological consequences. The author encourages people to follow common sense and local regulations for greywater treatment. Do not use greywater for food crops or lawns unless you take appropriate precautions against the possibilities of transmitting disease and contamination from household chemicals.

References

California Plumbing Code, Title 24, Part 5, California Administrative Code, Appendix J: Greywater Systems for Single Family Dwellings. Department of Water Resources, State of California, 1020 9th Street, 3rd Floor, Sacramento, CA 95814.

Center for the Study of Federalism. 1972. Green Land-Clean Streams: the Beneficial Use of Waste Water Through Land Treatment. Center for the Study of Federalism, Temple University, Philadelphia, Pennsylvania.

Los Angeles Department of Water Reclamation. "Greywater Pilot Project Final Report." Report on first quantitative field testing of greywater health safety. May be available from Hoover Ng, Los Angeles Department of Water and Power, P.O. Box 111, Room 1458, Los Angeles 90051-0100.

Ludwig, Art. 2003. Principles of Ecological Design: Integrating Technology, Economics, and Ecology. Oasis Design, Santa Barbara. URL: http://oasisdesign.net/design/principles.htm

Office of Aridland Studies, University of Arizona. Cleaners for Greywater Systems. Office of Aridland Studies, University of Arizona, Tucson, AZ 85719.

Wagner, E. and J. Laniox. 1958 (reprinted 1971). Excreta Disposal for Rural Areas and Small Communities. Monograph #39, The World Health Organization, Geneva, Switzerland.

Original Source

This edition of *The Overstory* was adapted with the kind permission of the author from:

Ludwig, A. 2000. Create An Oasis With Greywater: Your Complete Guide to Choosing, Building and Using Greywater Systems. Oasis Design, Santa Barbara, CA, USA.

and

Ludwig, A. 2001. Branched Drain Greywater Systems: Reliable, Economical Sanitary, Low Maintenance Distribution of Household Greywater to Downhill Plants without Filtration or Pumping (A supplement to Create an Oasis with Greywater). Oasis Design, Santa Barbara, CA, USA.

and

Ludwig, A. 1999. The Builder's Greywater Guide: Installation of Greywater Systems in New Construction and Remodeling (A supplement to Create an Oasis with Greywater). Oasis Design, Santa Barbara, CA, USA.

These publications can be ordered from: Oasis Design, 5 San Marcos Trout Club, Santa Barbara, CA 93105-9726, USA for $17.95 each, or $42.85 for all three, including tax & shipping, or visit the web site: http://www.oasisdesign.net.

This excerpt was originally published as *The Overstory* #102.

Restoring Land

Trees facilitate the rejuvenation of degraded lands. They can restore productivity to severely damaged land. Trees also form the first vital threads of the in- tricate web needed to recreate native forest ecosys- tems.

Section Contents

Tropical Forest Conservation

J. Louise Mastrantonio and John K. Francis

The world's tropical forests circle the globe in a ring around the Equator. They are amazingly diverse ecosystems, ranging from lush rain forests to dry forests and savannas that contain millions of species of plants and animals. Tropical forests once covered some 15.3 billion acres (6.2 billion ha). In recent times, however, they have been cut to make room for agriculture and to obtain their many valuable products. Between 1985 and 1990, 210 million acres (85 million ha) of tropical forests were destroyed.

This guide shows how modern forest practices can help stem the tide of forest destruction while providing valuable forest products for people. In Puerto Rico, for example, the forests were abused for centuries and were severely depleted by the early 1900's. In more recent times, widespread abandonment of poor agricultural lands has enabled natural reforestation and planting programs to create a patchwork of private, Commonwealth, and Federal forests throughout the island. The Luquillo Experimental Forest, a research facility of the International Institute of Tropical Forestry, USDA Forest Service, is a model for research and forestry practices that could improve the condition of tropical forests worldwide.

Types of Tropical Forests

About half of all the world's forests are in the tropics, the area between the Tropic of Cancer and the Tropic of Capricorn. This region is best known for its rain forests—lush, steamy jungles with towering trees, epiphytes, and dense under stories of smaller trees, shrubs, and vines. But tropical forests are surprisingly diverse. In addition to rain forests, there are mangroves, moist forests, dry forests, and savannas. Such classifications, however, give only a slight indication of the diversity of these forests. One study by the Food and Agriculture Organization (FAO) of the United Nations, that considered 23 countries in tropical America, 37 in tropical Africa, and 16 in tropical Asia, identified dozens of types of tropical forests including open and closed canopy forests, broadleaf trees and conifer forests, closed forests and mixed forest grasslands, and forests where agriculture has made inroads.

Rain Forests

The largest remaining areas of tropical rain forests are in Brazil, the Congo, Indonesia, and Malaysia. In these areas, precipitation generally exceeds 60 inches (150 cm) a year and may be as high as 400 inches (1000 cm). Lowland rain forests are among the world's most productive plant communities. Giant trees may tower 200 feet (60 m) in height and support thousands of other species of plants and animals. Montane (mountain) rain forests grow at higher elevations where the climate is too windy and wet for optimum tree growth.

Mangrove forests grow in the swampy, intertidal margin between sea and shore and are often considered part of the rain forest complex. The roots of mangrove trees help stabilize the shoreline and trap sediment and decaying vegetation that contribute to ecosystem productivity.

Dry Forests

Large areas of tropical dry forests are found in India, Australia, Central and South America, the Caribbean, Mexico, Africa, and Madagascar. Dry forests receive very low rainfall, as little as 20 inches (50 cm) a year, and are characterized by species well adapted to drought. Trees of dry tropical forests are usually smaller than those in rain forests, and many lose their leaves during the dry season. Although they are still amazingly diverse, dry forests often have fewer species than rain forests.

Savanna is a transitional type between forest and grassland. Trees are often very scattered and tend to be well adapted to drought and tolerant of fire and grazing by animals. If fire is excluded, trees eventually begin to grow and the savanna is converted to dry forest. With too much fire or grazing, however, dry forest becomes savanna. This vegetation type has fewer species of trees and shrubs but more grasses and forbs than other forest types in the tropics.

Value of Tropical Forests

All forests have both economic and ecological value, but tropical forests are especially important in the global economy. Tropical forests cover less than 6

Mangrove forests are often considered to be part of the rainforest, growing along the edge of intertidal areas. *Rhizophora samoensis* growing along stream in Samoa. (photo: C. Elevitch)

percent of the earth's land area, but they contain the vast majority of the world's plant and animal genetic resources. The diversity of life is astonishing. The original forests of Puerto Rico, for example, contain more than 500 species of trees in 70 botanical families. By comparison, temperate forests have relatively few species. Such diversity is attributed to variations in elevation, climate, and soil, and to the lack of frost.

There is also diversity in other life forms: shrubs, herbs, epiphytes, mammals, birds, reptiles, amphibians, and insects. One study suggests that tropical rain forests may contain as many as 30 million different kinds of plants and animals, most of which are insects.

Wood and Other Products

Tropical forests provide many valuable products including rubber, fruits and nuts, meat, rattan, medicinal herbs, floral greenery, lumber, firewood, and charcoal. These forests are used by local people for subsistence hunting and fishing. They provide income and jobs for hundreds of millions of people in small, medium, and large industries.

Tropical forests are noted for their beautiful woods. Four important commercial woods are mahogany, teak, melina, and okoume. Honduras mahogany (*Swietenia macrophylla*), grows in the Americas from Mexico to Bolivia. A strong wood of medium density, mahogany is easy to work, is long lasting, and has good color and grain. It is commonly used for furniture, molding, paneling, and trim. Because of its resistance to decay, it is a popular wood for use in boats. Teak (*Tectona grandis*) is native to India and

Southeast Asia. Its wood has medium density, is strong, polishes well, and has a warm yellow-brown color. Also prized for resistance to insects and rot, teak is commonly used in cabinets, trim, flooring, furniture, and boats. Melina (*Gmelina arborea*) grows naturally from India through Vietnam. Noted for fast growth, melina has light colored wood that is used mainly for pulp and particleboard, matches, and carpentry. Okoume (*Aucoumea klaineana*) is native to Gabon in the Congo in West Africa. A large fast-growing tree, the wood has moderately low density, good strength-to density ratio, and low shrinkage during drying. It is commonly use for plywood, paneling, interior furniture parts, and light construction.

Other Economic Values

Tropical forests are home for tribal hunter-gatherers whose way of life has been relatively unchanged for centuries. These local residents depend on the forests for their livelihood. More than 2.5 million people live in areas adjacent to tropical forests. They rely on the forests for water, fuel wood, and other resources and as an ever-shrinking land base for agriculture. For urban dwellers, tropical forests are the source of water for domestic use and hydroelectric power. In addition, their scenic beauty, educational value, and opportunities for outdoor recreation support tourist industries.

Many medicines and drugs come from plants found only in tropical rain forests. Perhaps the best known are quinine, an ancient drug used for malaria; curare, an anesthetic and muscle relaxant used in surgery; and rosy periwinkle, a treatment for

Teak plantation. Chiang Mai, Thailand. (photo: C. Elevitch)

Hodgkin's disease and leukemia. Research has identified other potential drugs that may have value as contraceptives or in treating a multitude of maladies such as arthritis, hepatitis, insect bites, fever, coughs, and colds. Many more may be found. In all, only a few thousand species have been evaluated for their medicinal value.

In addition, many plants of tropical forests find uses in homes and gardens: ferns and palms, the hardy split-leaf philodendron, marantas, bromeliads, and orchids, to name just a few.

Environmental Benefits

Tropical forests do more than respond to local climatic conditions; they actually influence the climate. Through transpiration, the enormous number of plants found in rain forests return huge amounts of water to the atmosphere, increasing humidity and rainfall, and cooling the air for miles around. In addition, tropical forests replenish the air by utilizing carbon dioxide and giving off oxygen. By fixing carbon they help keep the atmospheric carbon dioxide levels low and counteract the global "greenhouse" effect.

Forests also moderate stream flow. Trees slow the onslaught of tropical downpours, use and store vast quantities of water, and help hold the soil in place. When trees are cleared, rainfall runs off more quickly, contributing to floods and erosion.

Deforestation

Before the dawn of agriculture about 10,000 years ago, forests and open woodland covered about 15.3 billion acres (6.2 billion ha) of the globe. Over the centuries, however, about one-third of these natural forests have been destroyed. According to a 1982 study by FAO, about 27.9 million acres (11.3 million ha) of tropical forests are cut each year—an area about the size of the states of Ohio or Virginia. Between 1985 and 1990, an estimated 210 million acres (85 million ha) of tropical forests were cut or cleared. In India, Malaysia, and the Philippines, the best commercial forests are gone, and cutting is increasing in South America. If deforestation is not stopped soon, the world will lose most of its tropical forests in the next several decades.

Reasons for Deforestation

Several factors are responsible for deforestation in the Tropics: clearing for agriculture, fuel wood cut-

ting, and harvesting of wood products. By far the most destructive is clearing for agriculture. The practice of shifting agriculture, sometimes called "slash-and-burn," has been used for centuries. In this primitive system, local residents cut a small patch of forest to make way for subsistence farming. After a few years, soil fertility would decline and the people moved on, usually to cut another patch of trees and begin another garden.

In the abandoned garden plot, the degraded soil at first supports only weeds and shrubby trees. Later, soil fertility and trees return, but that can take decades. As population pressure increases, the fallow (rest) period between cycles of gardening is shortened, agricultural yields decrease, and the forest is further degraded to small trees, brush, or eroded savanna.

Conversion to sedentary agriculture is an even greater threat to tropical forests. Vast areas that once supported tropical forests are now permanently occupied by subsistence farmers and ranchers and by commercial farmers who produce sugar, cacao, palm oil, and other products.

In many tropical countries there is a critical shortage of firewood. For millions of rural poor, survival depends on finding enough wood to cook the evening meal. Every year more of the forest is destroyed, and the distance from home to forest increases. Not only is the land degraded, but people suffer by having to spend much of their time looking for wood. Damage is greatest in dry tropical forests where firewood cutting converts forests to savannas and grasslands.

The global demand for tropical hardwoods, an $8-billion-a-year industry, also contributes to forest loss. Tropical forests are usually selectively logged rather than clear-cut. Selective logging leaves the forest cover intact but reduces its commercial value because the biggest and best trees are removed. Selective logging also damages remaining trees and soil, increases the likelihood of fire, and degrades the habitat for wildlife species that require large, old trees—the ones usually cut. In addition, logging roads open up the forests to shifting agriculture and permanent settlement.

In the past, logging was done primarily by primitive means. Trees were cut with axes and logs were moved with animals such as oxen. Today, however, the damage is accelerated by the use of modern machinery. Chain saws, tractors, and trucks make logging easier, faster, and potentially more destructive.

Endangered Wildlife

Forests are biological communities—complex associations of plants and animals that have evolved together over millions of years. Because of the worldwide loss of tropical forests, thousands of species of birds and animals are threatened with extinction. The list includes many unique and fascinating animals, among them the orangutan, mountain gorilla, manatee, jaguar, and Puerto Rican parrot. Although diverse and widely separated around the globe, these species have one important thing in common. They, along with many other endangered species, rely on tropical forests for all or part of their habitat.

Orangutans (*Pongo pygmaeus*) are totally dependent on the small and isolated patches of tropical forests remaining in Borneo and Sumatra, Indonesia. Orangutans spend most of their time in the forest canopy where they feed on leaves, figs and other fruit, bark, nuts, and insects. Large trees of the old-growth forests support woody vines that serve as aerial ladders, enabling the animals to move about, build their nests, and forage for food. When the old forests are cut, orangutans disappear.

The largest of all primates, the gorilla, is one of man's closest relatives in the animal kingdom. Too large and clumsy to move about in the forest canopy, the gorilla lives on the forest floor where it forages for a variety of plant materials. Loss of tropical forests in central and western Africa is a major reason for the decreasing numbers of mountain gorillas (*Gorilla gorilla*). Some habitat has been secured, but the future of this gentle giant is in grave danger as a result of habitat loss and poaching.

The jaguar (*Leo onca*), a resident of the Southwestern United States and Central and South America, is closely associated with forests. Its endangered status is the result of hunting and habitat loss.

The Puerto Rican parrot (*Amazona vittata*), a medium-sized, green bird with blue wing feathers, once inhabited the entire island of Puerto Rico and the neighboring islands of Mona and Culebra. Forest destruction is the principal reason for the decline of this species. Hunting also contributed. Today, only a few Puerto Rican parrots remain in the wild and their survival may depend on the success of a captive breeding program.

In addition to species that reside in tropical forests year round, others depend on these forests for part of the year. Many species of migrant birds travel 1,000 miles or more between their summer breeding grounds in the north and their tropical wintering grounds. These birds are also threatened by forest destruction.

The Practice of Forestry

Forestry—defined as the systematic management and use of forests and their natural resources for human benefit—has been practiced for centuries. Most often, forestry efforts have been initiated in response to indiscriminate timber cutting that denuded the land and caused erosion, floods, or a shortage of wood products.

Ancient Forestry Practices

In ancient Persia (now Iran), forest protection and nature conservation laws were in effect as early as 1,700 B.C. Two thousand years ago, the Chinese practiced what they called "four sides" forestry, meaning trees were planted house side, village side, road side, and water side. More than 1,000 years ago, Javanese maharajahs brought in teak and began to cultivate it. In the African tropics, agroforestry (growing of food crops in association with trees) has been practiced for hundreds of years.

In the Yucatan Peninsula of southern Mexico, the ancient Mayas cultivated fruit and nut trees along with such staples as corn, beans, and squash. Bark, fibers, and resin were obtained from plants grown in fields, kitchen gardens, and orchards. Early in their civilization, the Mayas practiced slash-and-burn agriculture. As their population grew, they found more efficient methods of growing crops. They terraced hillsides, learned how to decrease the time between "rotations" of agricultural land with native forests, dug drainage channels and canals to move water to and from cultivated areas, and filled in swampland to plant crops.

The agricultural sophistication of the Mayas enabled their civilization to grow and flourish. What brought about their demise about 820 A.D. is not fully known, but some believe that as their society developed, the Mayas over-used their natural resources to the point that their society could not be sustained.

Relatively little is known about tropical forestry before the mid 1800's in most places. At that time, the European colonial empires, notably the Dutch, English, and Spanish, brought modern forest management practices to Indonesia, India, Africa, and the Caribbean. Centers for forestry and forestry research were established, and more careful records were kept.

Sustainable Forestry

Modern forestry has its basis in 18th century Germany. Like the Chinese and the Mayan forest practices, German forestry is essentially agricultural. Trees are managed as a crop. Two concepts are important: renewability and sustainability. Renewability means that trees can be replanted and seeded and harvested over and over again on the same tract of land in what are known as crop "rotations." Sustainability means that forest harvest can be sustained over the long term. How far into the future were foresters expected to plan? As long as there were vast acres of virgin (original) forests remaining, this question was somewhat academic. Today, however, sustainability is a key issue in forestry. Most of the world's virgin forests are gone, and people must rely more and more on second-growth or managed forests. Perhaps we now face, as never before, the limits to long-term productivity.

In the German forest model, forestry is viewed as a continual process of harvest and regeneration. Harvest of wood products is a goal, but a forester's principal tasks are to assure long-term productivity of the timber "crop." That is achieved by cutting the older, mature, and slow-growing timber to make way for a new crop of young, fast-growing trees.

Harvest-Regeneration Methods

Three examples of timber harvest-regeneration methods (silvicultural systems) illustrate how foresters manage stands to produce timber on a sustained basis.

Selection In individual harvest, Individual trees or small groups of trees are cut as they reach maturity. Numerous small openings in the forest are created in which saplings or new seedlings can grow. The resulting forest has a continuous forest canopy and trees of all ages. Such systems favor slow-growing species that are shade tolerant.

Clearcutting In clearcutting, an entire stand of trees is removed in one operation. From the forester's point of view, clearcutting is the easiest way to manage a forest, and the most economical. Regeneration may come from sprouts on stumps, from seedlings that survive the logging operation, or from seeds that germinate after harvest. If natural regeneration is delayed longer than desired, the area is planted or seeded.

Clearcutting systems are often used to manage fast-growing species that require a lot of light. Resulting stands are even-aged because all the trees in an area are cut—and regenerated—at the same time. Clearcutting has become controversial in recent years because it has the potential to damage watersheds and because it tends to eliminate species of wildlife dependent on old growth trees. If clearcuts are kept small and the cutting interval is long enough, however, biological diversity may not be impaired.

Shelterwood In shelterwood systems, the forest canopy is removed over a period of years, usually in two cuttings. After the first harvest, natural regeneration begins in the understory. By the time the second harvest is made, enough young trees have grown to assure adequate regeneration. Shelterwood systems favor species that are intermediate in tolerance to shade. Such systems are difficult to use successfully and are the least used of the three silvicultural methods described.

Multiple-Use Forestry

Gifford Pinchot, the first Chief of the U.S. Forest Service, was also America's first professional forester. Pinchot advocated the use of forest resources—all resources, not just timber—for human benefit. Pinchot was a strong and charismatic leader, and his ideas helped shape the course of forestry in the United States. Pinchot had a vocal opponent in John Muir, a young naturalist from California who believed that public lands should be preserved rather than used. Eventually Muir and Pinchot became rivals for public opinion. Oddly enough, there was no loser in this early conservation battle. Muir's preservation ethic became embodied in the philosophy of the National Parks, and Pinchot's concept of wise use became the guiding principle of the National Forests.

National Forests are still managed under the concepts of multiple-use and sustained yield. The dominant uses of National Forests are considered to be wood, water, wildlife, forage (for domestic cattle and wildlife), and recreation. Extraction of minerals and other valuable products is also a legitimate use of National Forests. Because Pinchot's philosophy left room for the "highest and best use" of a given area, the National Forests now include a wilderness system of more than 32 million acres (13 million ha) in which timber harvest is not allowed.

Today it is generally thought that most, if not all, nondestructive uses of forests are valid. Some areas may be set aside as parks, others for wildlife habitat or as wilderness. Still others will be managed for timber harvest or multiple benefits. Now conflicts arise primarily over where these different uses will be dominant. In the National Forests, such decisions are made through a land-use planning process in which the public has ample opportunity for input and involvement.

Forestry Research

In the early 1900's, very little was known about the world's forests or how to manage them. In the United States, foresters were quick to recognize the value of information about forests and the Forest Service established a branch of research in 1915. Early research was done primarily in support of reforestation efforts, but as forestry grew in size and complexity, so did the research.

Today, the USDA Forest Service has six regional experiment stations located in important forest regions. Each experiment station has several field laboratories generally with specialized assignments for a geographic region or a specific subject area, and numerous sites for field research. In addition, the Forest Products Laboratory in Madison, WI, serves as a nationwide center for research and development of new technology relating to wood, including tropical woods. Two laboratories are dedicated exclusively to tropical forest research: the International Institute of Tropical Forestry in Puerto Rico and the Institute of Pacific Islands Forestry in Hawai'i.

Research is an essential component of modern-day forestry. Today's foresters require vast quantities of data and a thorough knowledge of the local ecology. They must understand not only the parts of ecosystems but how different parts of the environment interact. Scientific investigations are conducted in support of all kinds of forestry activities: silviculture, forest insect and disease control, wildlife habitat management, fire prevention and control, range and watershed management, forest products utilization, forest survey, reforestation, ecology, and economics.

Tropical Forestry

As we have seen, timber harvest in the tropics has seldom been followed by regeneration. Conversion to agriculture is often permanent and results in severe soil depletion or loss. Timber harvest contracts have usually been short term and have provided little or no incentive for timber companies to replant. So little reforestation has been done in the tropics, in fact, that many people believe that tropical forests

cannot be restored. This is not true, however. There are many examples of successful reforestation in India, Indonesia, and the Caribbean.

In the tropics, as elsewhere, forestry is a mixture of ancient techniques borrowed from local tradition combined with modern innovations. Forest reserves have been established for timber harvest, wildlife habitat, scenery, outdoor recreation, or watershed protection. In the Tropics also, agroforestry—tree growing combined with agricultural cropping—is much more common than in other parts of the world.

Plantation Forestry

In the tropics, trees are often planted and grown in plantations for wood production. Often, many species must be tried to determine which will grow best. Plantations must also be supported by major investments in forest management and research. Forest

Research is an essential part of today's forestry. Pictured: Nick Dudley. (photo: C. Elevitch)

nurseries must be established, and planting techniques and cultural practices (spacing and thinning, pruning, fertilization, insect and disease control, and genetic improvement) must be developed.

Extensive pine plantations have been established in the moist tropics, mainly in South Africa and Australia. Species most often planted include Caribbean pine (*Pinus caribaea*), ocote pine (*P. oocarpa*), slash pine (*P. elliottii*), and benguet pine (*P. kesiya*). Pines are popular plantation trees because they are generally fast growing, have good survival rates, and are adapted to a wide variety of environments, including degraded forest sites.

Eucalypts, including species such as *Eucalyptus grandis*, *E. deglupta*, *E. tereticornis*, *E. globulus*, and *E. camaldulensis* are favored for the same reasons. Eucalypts are commonly grown for pulp, fuel, and lumber. Other species commonly planted include teak (*Tectona grandis*), Honduras mahogany (*Swietenia macrophylla*), melina (*Gmelina arborea*) beefwood (*Casuarina equisetifolia*), and Mexican cypress (*Cupressus lusitanica*).

Forest Reserves

There are many reasons for establishing tropical forest reserves. They can restore watersheds and wildlife habitat, improve scenic beauty and opportunities for outdoor recreation, and produce wood and other products for local use and export. Many forest products contribute to the sustenance and income of local people: wildlife and fish, fire wood, rubber, fruits and nuts, rattan, medicinal herbs, floral greenery, and charcoal.

Perhaps the most famous of these reserves is the 5,600 square mile (14,500 km²) Serengeti National Park in Tanzania. With its vast herds of grazing ungulates (hoofed animals) and predators, including several endangered species, the Serengeti is a showcase of a savanna ecosystem that has long been protected and managed for wildlife and other natural resources. Although plagued with poachers, the Serengeti promotes the cause of wildlife conservation to the many thousands of "ecotourists" who pay to experience nature each year.

Another type of forest reserve is the "extractive" reserve, a forest dedicated to the production of useful products. Large reserves of this type have been established in Brazil. Local residents use them for tapping rubber, for gathering fruits and nuts, for hunting, and for harvesting wood on a sustained yield basis. Such uses provide a sustainable income while maintaining the ecological integrity of the forest.

Agroforestry

The practice of growing of trees in combination with agricultural crops is fairly common in the Tropics. It is possible to grow food crops year around in many forested areas, and the rural poor depend on this source of food as nowhere else on earth.

Taungya System

Various systems have been developed for combining forestry with agriculture. "Taungya" is a Burmese word meaning cultivated hill plot. This system of agroforestry was developed in Europe during the Middle Ages and probably grew up independently in a number of places in the tropics. After existing forest or ground cover is removed by burning, trees are planted along with agricultural crops. Both are cultivated until the tree canopy closes. Then the area is left to grow trees, and another site is located for combined forestry-agriculture.

Shade Cropping

An overstory of trees is often used to provide shade for agricultural crops. A common practice is to grow tree species such as guaba (*Inga vera*) in combination with coffee. In Puerto Rico, many forests developed where coffee was once grown in this manner.

Support Crops

Trees can be planted to provide support, and sometimes shade, for vine crops. Vines such as pepper and vanilla need support, and are commonly grown this way.

Alley Cropping

Nitrogen-fixing trees are planted in hedges in widely-space parallel rows along the contour of slopes. Food crops are grown in the "alley" between the rows. The trees add nitrogen and organic matter, protect the soil from erosion, and provide wood and animal forage.

Living Fences

Green fence posts that will root and sprout often are planted in a closely spaced rows. When they sprout, they create a "living fence" that provides shade and forage for cattle.

Windbreaks

Trees are often planted as windbreaks for agricultural crops, farms, or home sites. Such plantings can eventually contribute wood products as well as shelter. Food trees such as citrus, rubber, and mango can also provide fuel, lumber, and other wood products when they have outlived their original purpose.

New Directions in Tropical Forestry

The conservation issues of the past seem simple compared with those of today. Since the latter part of the 20th century, people have become increasingly concerned about global warming, deforestation, species extinction, and meeting the rising expectations of societies. Growing populations must be fed, clothed, and sheltered, and people everywhere want higher standards of living. All this places greater demands on the world's forests.

Global Warming

Warming of the earth's atmosphere is a major environmental issue. Air pollution, deforestation, and widespread burning of coal, oil, and natural gas have increased atmospheric concentrations of carbon dioxide, methane, nitrous oxide, and chlorofluorocarbons. These gases trap heat from the sun and prevent it from radiating harmlessly back into space. Thus, a "greenhouse" or warming effect is created.

Because of natural variations in climate, it is difficult to measure warming over large areas. Scientists agree, however, that increases in atmospheric concentrations of greenhouse gases will cause higher temperatures worldwide. Even an increase of a few degrees could cause melting of the polar icecaps, a gradual rise in sea level, disruption in normal weather patterns, increase in forest fires, and extinction of species.

Role of Forests

Trees, the largest of all land plants, act as a kind of environmental "buffer" for the ecosystem they dominate. They help ameliorate the extremes of climate (heat, cold, and wind) and create an environment where large land mammals, including people, can live comfortably. Trees complement animals in the global environment. Mammals take in oxygen from the air and exhale carbon dioxide. Plants use carbon dioxide in their growth processes, store the carbon in woody tissues, and return oxygen to the atmosphere as a waste product. This process, known as photosynthesis, is essential to life. Carbon captured from the atmosphere by photosynthesis is eventually recycled through the environment in a process known as the "carbon cycle." Because of their size and their dominance of ecosystems, trees have an especially important role in the carbon cycle. Tree leaves also act as filters to remove atmospheric pollutants from the air, especially important in urban areas.

Forestry Issues

Two key issues will dominate forestry in the years ahead: (1) maintaining long-term productivity of managed forests, and (2) preventing further loss of tropical forests. Both require new approaches to forest management.

Traditionally, forestry has focused on growing trees in plantations or in managed natural stands. In this "agricultural model" of forestry, other benefits of forests such as watershed protection, wildlife habitat, climate moderation, and outdoor recreation, have received less attention than wood production.

Perhaps more importantly, the sustainability of the full range of forest benefits has not been measured. There is no question that trees can be grown for crops of wood in managed stands. With intensive management—short rotations, species selection, genetic improvement, fertilization, thinning, and other cultural treatments—more wood can be produced in less time than in natural forests. But for how long? And at what cost to other resources?

As more and more of the world's original forests have been cut, the ecological value of forests has come to be more appreciated. In recent years, increased emphasis has been put on what some are calling "ecosystem management." In this model of forestry, the health and long-term stability of the forest are paramount, and timber production is considered a by-product of good forest management rather than the principal product.

In Puerto Rico, for example, wood production is a relatively minor aspect of forestry. Since the 1930's when timber harvests were curtailed, the forests have been managed primarily for watershed protection, wildlife habitat, and outdoor recreation.

There are no easy solutions to the problem of tropical forest destruction. Most expert agree, however, that the problems cannot be solved by locking up the forests in reserves. The forests are just too important to local people for that to be a workable solution. There is no doubt that tropical forests will be cut. It is better for them to be cut in an ecologically sound manner than to be cleared for poor-quality farmland or wasted by poor harvest practices.

The only real long-term solution to forest problems in the tropics is threefold: (1) practice more efficient agriculture on suitable farmland, (2) initiate more efficient forestry practices including plantations, and (3) establish reserves to protect species and ecosystems. Many forestry experts believe that we have only begun to tap the potential for wise use of tropical forests. And we are only starting to learn the value of tropical forests for medicine, house and garden plants, food and fiber, tourism, and natural resource education.

Original Source

This article is excerpted with kind permission of the authors from "A Student Guide To Tropical Forest Conservation" by J. Louise Mastrantonio and John K. Francis. This excellent introduction to forest conservation can be viewed at: http://www.fs.fed.us/global/lzone/student/tropical.htm.

This excerpt was originally published as *The Overstory* #77. It was revised by the lead author in June 2004 for publication in this volume.

Foster Ecosystems

Imants Pone

One of the biggest challenges for tropical agroforesters is the restoration and revegetation of lands that have been degraded or cleared. This chapter introduces the concept of "foster ecosystems"—using tree plantations to facilitate the natural regeneration of native species in their understories. Findings from Puerto Rico, Amazonia, and the Philippines illustrate how plantations can be used to foster the reintroduction of native species.

Creating Foster Ecosystems to Accelerate Tropical Forest Regeneration

Moist tropical forests are some of the most productive areas on Earth, but since most nutrients and biomass are stored above ground, cleared land quickly loses its productivity. What is left are open fields dominated by shrubs and grasses in which the forest is slow to regenerate. The methods described in this paper are designed to accelerate natural regeneration in cleared tropical forests through the use of plantations as "foster ecosystems."

Factors affecting regeneration

The creation of foster ecosystems focuses on improving conditions for natural succession and overcoming barriers to regeneration. When land is degraded for a period of time, natural processes are disturbed and barriers form which block the natural pathways of forest succession. Barriers to be taken into account are low availability of native seeds and other propagules on-site, seed and seedling predation, seasonal drought, root competition, and poor soil conditions. These barriers need to be ameliorated before a restoration project can be attempted.

Minimizing barriers to seed survival, germination, and growth

A major barrier to natural regeneration of forests is that conditions in open lands are unfavorable to seed survival, germination, and growth of tropical forest species. Abandoned clearings are quickly overgrown by invasive grasses and shrubs, which in turn provide excellent habitat for seed predating ants and rodents. A study by Nepstad (1991) in the Paragominas region of Amazonia found that predation of native seeds placed in abandoned clearings is very high, as is predation on germinants. This same study also found that root competition in such cleared areas is a serious deterrent to the development of seedlings. Young tree seedlings growing in open areas suffered dramatically stunted growth, mainly due to root competition from thick grasses, while he same kinds of seedlings planted in treefall gaps grew almost four times as quickly.

Plantation trees can be planted to alleviate the problems of seed predation and competition. Although tropical systems are complex and different situations may require different approaches, *Albizia lebbeck*, *Pinus caribaea*, and *Swietenia macrophylla* have worked well as "foster" trees in Puerto Rico. Established trees shade out invasive grasses and shrubs under their canopies. Ant and rodent habitat and thus predation is decreased. Because the ground vegetation has been reduced, root competition for emerging seedlings is also greatly reduced. This makes conditions for seed survival, germination and growth more favorable under the canopies of plantation trees.

Accelerating soil improvement and natural seed dispersal

Most of the nutrients and organic matter of a tropical rainforest are stored in above-ground biomass. When the trees are removed from a site which is then grazed or farmed, soil conditions can become degraded. Soil conditions can be improved by using plantations of selected tree species. Leguminous, nitrogen-fixing species grow well under difficult conditions and produce nutrient rich litter. In a plantation, soil nutrients and organic matter can be increased by nitrogen fixation and litter fall. In addition, trees can help by reducing the bulk density of soil with their roots, conserving moisture in their shade, and providing conditions favorable to a healthy population of soil microorganisms.

The last and probably most important factor in a successful regeneration is the availability and dispersal of seeds and other propagules of the native tree species. Many tropical trees can propagate by roots, by residual seeds, or by seeds disseminated from an adjacent forest. In the open conditions of a clearing, much of the residual propagative material is destroyed or is unable to germinate and survive. Rather than giving humans the work of disseminating native seeds, the presence of plantation trees can attract seed disseminating bird and mammal species to do the job of dispersing seeds naturally. Appropriate plantation species should provide perches and/or food for disseminating birds and bats. Fruit-eating birds and bats will be attracted to the tree to perch or eat its fruit. In the process, they disseminate seed from previously eaten fruit. Nepstad (1991) found 400 times more seeds under tree crowns than in open field conditions.

Plantation strategies

Pastures and abandoned croplands become open grass and shrub fields when pathways of tree invasion are blocked. Because they reduce the barriers to tree invasion, plantation trees emerging in the open fields improve the probability that other plant species will invade. A study by Parrotta (1993) in Puerto Rico on an *Albizia lebbeck* plantation found that after 4.5 years, 42 different species of trees, shrubs, vines, and other plants were present on the site. By comparison, a site left to natural processes and not planted with trees contained only one species of vine, fifteen species of grasses and forbs, and no trees or shrubs.

When creating a foster plantation, steps may be taken to improve the speed and efficiency of native forest regeneration. The pattern in which trees are planted is important. The ideal method would be to plant trees evenly throughout the field, allowing disseminators to penetrate deep into the field from the forest edge. If funds are limited, forested strips (corridors) or islands may be effective and more economically feasible. Planted forest strips should extend from the edges of natural forest stands at intervals easily transversed by disseminators (20-30m). Plantation islands are trees planted together in groups. Islands should also be planted so they are 20–30m from forest edges and other islands. For both the strip and island methods, it is expected that as these systems develop, they will spread outwards and eventually overlap, creating a continuous forest.

Conclusion

Because of the complexity of tropical forest ecosystems, different sites require different restoration techniques. Restoration managers should have a good understanding of plant and animal life histories, seed ecology and dispersal characteristics, germination microhabitat requirements, and habitat requirements of potential seed dispersing birds and mammals. Managers then have the ability to adapt their techniques to changing conditions. All researchers agree that a greater diversity of plantation species improves chances for a successful regeneration. This also allows natural selection processes to decide on the best species composition on a site.

Contrary to management intensive restorations, restorations using foster ecosystems rely on natural regeneration processes. Refining "foster ecosystem" techniques help regenerate large areas of deforested land. It will be important that such efforts are documented so that others can learn and adapt their efforts for their specific sites. Without proper documentation, it will be difficult to develop this promising technique.

References

Lugo, A.E. and P.G. Murphy. 1986. Nutrient dynamics of a Puerto Rican subtropical dry forest. In: Journal of Tropical Ecology, 2: 55-72.

Lugo, A.E. 1988. The future of the forest. In: Environment, 30(7): 17-20, 41-44.

Nepstad, DC, et. al. 1991. Recuperation of a degraded Amazonian landscape: Forest recovery and agricultural restoration. Ambio, 20(6): 248-255.

Parrotta, J.A. 1993. Secondary forest regeneration on degraded tropical lands. In: H. Lieth and M. Lohmann, Restoration of Tropical Forest Ecosystems, Kluwer Academic Publishers, 69-73.

Parrotta, J.A. 1992. The role of plantation forests in rehabilitating degraded tropical ecosystems. In: Agriculture, Ecosystems and Environment, 41: 115-133.

Rabor, D.S. 1981. The role of wildlife in forest regeneration in Southeast Asia. In: Biotrop Special Publication, 13:187-200.

Godt, M.C. and M. Hadley. 1993. Ecosystem rehabilitation and forest regeneration in the humid tropics: Case studies and management insights. In: H. Lieth and M. Lohmann, Restoration of Tropical Forest Ecosystems, Kluwer Academic Publishers, 25-36.

Original Source

This article was excerpted from the original "Creating Foster Ecosystems to Accelerate Tropical Forest

Regeneration" with the kind permission of the author. To view this article in its unabridged form with full references, please see:

http://www.hort.agri.umn.edu/h5015/97papers/pone.html.

This excerpt was originally published as *The Overstory* #27.

Further Reading

A.B. (Ed). 1992. Alternatives to Deforestation: Steps Toward Sustainable Use of the Amazon Rain Forest by Anderson, Columbia Univ Pr.

Lieth, H. and M. Lohmann (eds). 1993. Restoration of Tropical Forest Ecosystems: Proceedings of the Symposium. Kluwer Academic Pub.

Jones, L., L.J. Sauer, and I. McHarg. 1998. The Once and Future Forest: A Guide to Forest Restoration Strategies by Leslie Jones. Island Press.

Holmgren, D. 1993. Trees on the Treeless Plains - Revegetation Guide to Central Victoria. Holmgren Design Services, Hepburn, Victoria, Australia. Order through Permaculture International Journal, PO Box 6039, South Lismore, NSW 2480, Australia, Tel: +61 66 220020, Fax: +61 66 220579.

Pioneering Difficult Sites

Craig R. Elevitch and Kim M. Wilkinson

Pioneering is a natural process that takes place in the first stage of succession after land is disturbed. Natural pioneering begins on land that is newly formed or newly exposed, such as lava flows or land exposed after a glacier retreats, when there is no organic matter, seeds, or vegetation on the site. On these sites, nature has to start from scratch. Pioneering can also be observed following severe man-made or natural disturbances, such as deforestation, fire, landslides, etc. On these kinds of sites, there are still some (usually minimal) resources such as certain seeds, some organic matter and soil microbes.

People can help nature heal degraded lands

The best place to learn species and techniques you can use to restore your area is to start out by observing how nature pioneers land in your area. Here on the Island of Hawai'i (also known as The Volcano Island), we have the privilege of observing first hand the natural processes that occur on new lava flows. Because there are lava flows of many different ages bordering one another, one can observe how bare expanses of lava are converted to a forest. The process of pioneering on lava flows is instructive for pioneering other areas.

Lava flows in Hawai'i are always colonized by plants (except at extremely high elevations). The kind of plants and length of time in which colonization takes place depends mainly on rainfall and elevation, and, of course, which plants are present in the area. There is a succession of plants involved in the process of forest establishment. Initially without plant cover, the lava field lays exposed to sun and wind, and presents a very hostile environment for most plants.

Certain plants such as lichens, ferns and certain native tree species can tolerate these harsh conditions and often appear first on the lava. These early pioneers establish themselves in the most sheltered pockets and crevasses, where they can gather scarce moisture and nutrients.

The early colonists begin to form deposits of organic matter in the lava, laying a foundation for other plants to get a foothold. Organic matter plays an essential role in lava: it is the basis for soil fertility and moisture retention. Soon, a sparse litter layer appears in the protected pockets, consisting of the residues of early pioneers. Over time, other plants will find their way to these fertile niches and become established underneath the cover of the original plants. This represents the beginning of the forest, when plants begin to grow in layers, each succeeding plant making use of the increased fertility and protection offered by earlier pioneers, until a forest is established.

The key players in the process of succession described above are pioneering plants. These plants have the ability to establish themselves in harsh, difficult conditions. Pioneers lend shade and fertility to the environment, altering it and ultimately facilitating the establishment of plants that can thrive in the improved conditions. Eventually, as the more tender plants become established and the environment continues to diversify and improve, the pioneers will be succeeded.

Pioneering is a pattern of nature, and it can be aided and accelerated by people to restore productivity to damaged or degraded lands. If you are starting from a cleared or damaged area or young lava flow, you may encourage this process by planting species which are natural pioneers. Such species tend to have common characteristics: they grow rapidly, tolerate poor soils, are often drought tolerant, are relatively short lived, prefer full sun, and can survive in rocky, exposed soils. There are no universal pioneer species—instead of going by a list, we suggest using the species that grow spontaneously in your area.

Pioneer plants change the environment by:

- adding organic matter

- regulating temperatures (less extremes of hot/cold)
- providing shade
- protecting from winds
- breaking up physical barriers to extensive root growth (rock and hard pan)

Original Source

This chapter was originally published as *The Overstory #22.*

Further Reading

Young, A. 1998. Agroforestry for Soil Management, 2nd Edition. CAB International, Wallingford, UK. Presents a synthesis of evidence on the effects of trees on soil from agriculture, forestry and soil science.

Reforestation of Degraded Lands

U.S. Congress Office of Technology Assessment

Degradation of tropical land is a physical, chemical, and biological process set in motion by activities that reduce the land's inherent productivity. This process includes accelerated erosion, leaching, soil compaction, decreased soil fertility, diminished natural plant regeneration, disrupted hydrological cycle, and possible salinization, waterlogging, flooding, or increased drought risk, as well as the establishment of undesirable weedy plants. There is a strong relationship between inappropriate land-use practices and land degradation. In some places, degradation is manifest (e.g., desertification), where in others it is inferred (e.g., declining crop yields).

Deforestation in mountainous regions is one of the most acute and serious ecological problems today. Disturbance of vegetative cover on montane areas with thin soil and steep slopes results in land instability (e.g., landslides) and soil erosion. Excessive erosion not only impairs site productivity but may also adversely affect other sites or water bodies farther down the watershed.

Conversion of tropical moist forest into farm or grazing land commonly results in rapid depletion of the soil's plant nutrient supply and accelerated soil erosion. In some places the degradation process leads to takeover by persistent, aggressive weed species of low nutritive value. Often the combined problems of low soil fertility and weed infestation become so great that the land is abandoned. Such lands are subject to frequent uncontrolled fires and are often covered by coarse grasses. Whenever the vegetation is burned, erosion may increase and productivity may be reduced further.

In many arid and semiarid open woodlands, overgrazing and repeated fires have converted the vegetation to a degraded fire climax stage. Consequently, soils become dry and little woody plant regeneration occurs. Fire-tolerant vegetation—commonly unpalatable to animals—persists leading to a desert-like state. Over 20.5 million ha of tropical arid lands become desertified every year (Wood *et al* 1982).

Each year, over 500,000 ha of excessively irrigated lands become saline or alkaline as a result of inadequate drainage or use of salty irrigation water. Capillary action draws moisture to the soil surface where it evaporates, leaving salts in or on the topsoil. In some cases, salts can be leached from upland soils and bedrock, raising the salinity of runoff from deforested slopes. The increased runoff harms agricultural soil in lowland areas by causing temporary or lasting waterlogging and salinization.

The best solution to such problems is to prevent inappropriate land-use practices on forested lands. Where it is too late for this approach, reforestation is an alternative. Trees planted on degraded lands will not give such high yields as trees planted on rich, fertile lands. However, it may be the only way to raise the productivity of the most degraded lands. Furthermore, in many countries, fertile sites are reserved for agricultural activities. Given the dwindling reserves of good land and the increasing amount of degraded tropical lands, reforestation is a technology with potential to rehabilitate soils and to provide many goods and services. For example, fuelwood plantations can alleviate the worsening shortage of firewood in some areas and prevent shortages from occurring in others.

Technologies

This section summarizes the mechanics of reforestation and focuses on pertinent issues and problems that may prevent reforestation success.

Land Preparation

Many degraded sites need some type of preplanting preparation, such as clearing stumps and competing weedy vegetation. Under some circumstances, site cultivation controls weeds and improves soil aeration, soil biochemical activity, percolation of water, pH regulation, nutrient application, and surface evenness. The degree and type of land preparation depends on several factors: site and soil conditions, vegetative cover, species to be planted, and available capital and labor.

Land preparation can be done by hand or by machine. Manual methods are less constrained by the rainy season, they require few skills, and the capital cost is relatively low. They also provide temporary employment to laborers and cause minimal damage

Inappropriate land use has lead to severe degradation of lands that were once forested. This land was formerly used for sugarcane cultivation and in certain areas has lost meters of top soil to erosion. Hamakua, Hawai'i. (photo: C. Elevitch)

to soil. A disadvantage of manual clearing, however is the need to recruit, manage, and provide logistical support in remote areas for large numbers of laborers. Mechanical clearing, on the other hand, requires high capital inputs for equipment maintenance supplies of fuel and spare parts, and operator training and supervision. And heavy machines degrade the site through topsoil disruption. Yet, in general, mechanical clearing is cheaper than manual clearing (Evans 1982). The choice between manual and mechanical land preparation must be made on a case-by-case basis, determined by all these considerations.

Sometimes, artificial barriers of brushwood or other materials constructed in a grid or contour pattern, or grasses (such as vetiver) and trees planted in a similar pattern, can be used to immobilize drifting sand. Plowing the soil surface to increase water infiltration, ripping across the slope to retain water, plus construction of bench terraces on steeper slopes, and funneling moisture onto a smaller area are all conservation measures used to maximize planting success. Minicatchments built to concentrate water into

the rooting zones of individual trees are a particularly important technique in arid zones.

It may be necessary to add nutrients during land preparation. Several techniques exist including mulching with organic matter, planting nitrogen-fixing trees, applying green manure (especially herbaceous legumes), and commercial fertilizers. Mulching suppresses weeds, improves soil moisture conditions, and augments soil organic matter, but it may increase problems with rodents or other pests. Nitrogen-fixing trees can improve soil with their ability to produce nitrogen fertilizer. Foliage dropped by legumes is nitrogen-rich and will augment soil fertility as it decays.

Other measures may also be used, such as the addition of small amounts of commercial fertilizers and amendments. Nutrient levels and fluxes in plantations should be monitored to determine the prospective benefits and cost effectiveness of soil amendments. One of the less obvious soil deficiencies, occurring particularly in eroded soils in the drier climates is the lack of necessary micro-organisms. An ancient and effective method to add micro-organisms is to inoculate either nursery soils or planting holes in the field with a few grams of topsoil from well-established plantations or healthy forests. The method is not practical, however, where well-established plantations and/or healthy forests do not exist.

Species Selection

Tree species selection is important to plantation success. If a tree is grown under unsuitable soil or site conditions, it will be stressed and thus become susceptible to attacks from insects or competition from weeds. Several factors influence species selection, including the objectives of reforestation, seed availability, and costs associated with reforestation alternatives. For many degraded sites, the species need to be those that can add nitrogen to the soil as well as provide products wanted by local communities.

The importance of matching tree species with site cannot be overstated. The problem of species selection is complicated in the tropics by intricate climatic and soil patterns, and in areas that have been deforested by the highly variable degree of site degradation. Inadequate information on planting sites is a major cause of tree planting failure (Wadsworth 1982). Since most tree species used in reforestation are found over broad geographic ranges, there are different land races (subdivisions of a species with heritable characteristics resulting from adaptation to a specific environmental condition). Tree species races are often described by referring to the geographic location where the race is found naturally. Thus, the species' suitability to a particular site varies depending on the races used. Increases in yield and resistances to disease can be achieved through selection and use of appropriate seeds. Only by planting species and races on the sites for which they are adapted can maximum yields be obtained.

Natives and Exotics, Monocultures and Polycultures

Plantations cannot substitute wholly for natural forests as reservoirs of germplasm or as components of the natural environment—they are really an agricultural crop. Plantations contribute to preservation of the natural environment because they concentrate wood, food, and forage production within a minimum area, thus relieving some demands on natural forests. However, where plantations are established on land with good potential for annual agricultural crops, the effect actually may be to increase pressure on the natural forests.

Most large-scale tropical industrial timber plantations use species that are exotic to the planted area (Gallegos *et al* 1982). The widespread use of exotics may be a result of the preponderance of information, experience, and research on them, especially on *Pinus*, *Eucalyptus*, and *Tectona*. Also important to their use is the abundance, availability, ease of storage, and germination of seeds of these exotic species. The use of exotic tree species involves risks, such as susceptibility to pests and diseases. Because of the high yields possible with exotic species, however, the risks will continue to be taken.

The potential of using native species in plantations has been largely ignored. Reasons for this vary from lack of familiarity with many tropical tree species to lack of seed supplies. Native species are adapted to the local environment and, thus, may be less susceptible to stress, serious disease, and pest damage. Local people are more familiar with their native plants and have more uses for them.

Forest plantations in the past usually served industrial purposes and grew only one product, usually sawtimber, pulpwood, or fuelwood. Now, with an increasing demand for food, fuel, and fodder, plantations are needed to serve a wider variety of objectives. Thus, the use of multipurpose trees and polycultural plantings (with many species of trees) is becoming increasingly important, especially in areas with high populations.

Planting Materials

To reforest lands, seeds of various species must be available in great quantities. The seed supply for species most commonly used in tropical, industrial plantations is adequate. However, the seed supply for multipurpose, agroforestry species is small.

The customary way of raising planting stock in the tropics is to grow seedlings in a forest nursery either in open beds for bareroot planting or in containers. Good nursery practices are essential to produce a hardy plant with a well-balanced, straight root system. Bareroot seedlings are susceptible to desiccation. Containerized seedlings are more costly and bulky to handle in the field and are subject to root coiling if closed-bottom containers are used. The latter can be avoided if the containers have an open bottom and are suspended above the ground.

Another technique for producing planting material is vegetative propagation—reproduction of planting stock without the use of seed. Vegetative propagation is widely used for tree crops such as rubber, coconut, tea, coffee, cacao, and oil palm. Methods include cuttings, air layering, budding, grafting, and tissue culture. Rooted cuttings remain the most popular of these. Once the technique for a particular species is developed, the production cost is modest.

Vegetative propagation has the advantage of hastening massive reproduction of genetically superior plants, ensuring that all are of the desired genetic type. It has the disadvantage of increasing plantation risks due to lack of genetic diversity.

Seedling survival and growth rates in the nursery and at the planting site sometimes can be improved by using special kinds of fungi and bacteria. For most tropical trees, associations between tree roots and mycorrhizal fungi are essential for healthy growth. The fungi are active in the transport of nutrients and water to plant roots, and in some cases are important for the release of nutrient elements from mineral and organic soil particles. Trials have shown that seedlings inoculated with fungi show improved growth and survival over uninoculated controls. Populations of mycorrhizae are found naturally in soils, but these can be depressed after long-term clearing and/or topsoil removal, making reestablishment of

vegetation on degraded lands difficult. Various methods for reinoculating damaged soils with mycorrhizal fungi are being developed.

Legume trees can grow well on degraded land because their roots can be a symbiotic host for *Rhizobium* bacteria which produce nitrogen fertilizer, an essential nutrient for plant growth. The bacteria convert nitrogen gas in the soil into a form the plant can use. Most soils contain *Rhizobium*, but degraded soils probably contain fewer types and lesser amounts of the bacteria. Thus, the appropriate type of *Rhizobium* may not be present at the site of a reforestation effort, or present in enough quantity to infect the tree roots.

Inoculants are living organisms that must be transported and stored carefully and used correctly to retain their viability. These requirements can be difficult to satisfy, especially at remote tropical sites needing reforestation.

An alternative to using seedlings in nurseries is to plant or sow the seed directly at the reforestation site. This method is feasible where seed is plentiful and where seed and seedlings mortality is low. Direct sowing of drought-resistant species is sometimes

Early maintenance to reduce competition from weeds is essential to the success of reforestation plantings. (photo: C. Elevitch)

preferred, especially for species that have long and fast-growing taproots that may be damaged in a nursery or in transfer to the field. The advantage is that no nursery is required and planting costs are low. On the other hand, seedling survival may be low because of weed competition, lack of tending, poor weather, or animal damage.

Tree Care and Maintenance

Proper care and maintenance of the planted site is essential to ensure that trees survive to maturity. Once grown, there is the problem of monitoring timber harvests and of systematic replanting. The main causes of reforestation failure, other than inappropriate technologies, are uncontrolled grazing and fires, competition from weeds, and uncontrolled cutting for fuel, fodder, poles, and lumber.

Direct protection through fencing or guards tends to be expensive. Other, less costly methods include planting unpalatable trees (e.g., *Cassia siamea*) or thorny trees (e.g., *Parkinsonia* sp.) as barriers around the plantation. The use of living fences is becoming a more widespread practice because they provide a number of auxiliary benefits including shade, fodder, windbreak, fuel, and wildlife habitat. Another alternative is subsidizing farmers with livestock feed or with cash to purchase feed during the period when trees are most susceptible to animal damage. Grazing beneath the tree canopy sometimes can be beneficial as a means of weeding. However, livestock grazing on recently reforested watersheds can be harmful because animals compact the topsoil, leading to poor tree growth and increased runoff.

Weeding is an important aspect of plantation establishment and maintenance. Weeds compete directly with seedlings for light, soil nutrients, and water. Their shade can smother and eventually kill young trees. There are three main methods of weeding—manual, mechanical, and chemical. The manual method is the most common and requires little skill or capital. Mechanical methods may be used in large plantation projects but generally are not considered profitable in the Tropics. In many tropical countries, chemical weed control techniques have been tested and found successful, but because of safety and cost problems they seldom become the main means of weed control.

Whatever the type and location of tree planting, the cooperation of local people is essential if newly planted trees are to survive. Because most trees do not yield much benefit for several years, the options offered must demonstrate explicit benefits to the people. Tree planting programs are most successful when local communities are involved and when the people perceive clearly that success is in their self-interest.

In local communities, support can be generated through local involvement in project design, demonstration plantings, commercial plantings by entrepreneurs with larger land holdings, education of community leaders, extension and training programs working directly with farmers or laborers, and direct financial assistance or provision of substitutes.

Successful reforestation requires sufficient funds, strong political will, massive popular support, and cooperation among all involved parties. Foresters and policy makers must remember that "forestry is not, in essence, about trees. It is about people. It is only about trees so far as they serve the needs of the people" (Gribbin 1982).

References

Evans, J., Plantation Forestry in the Tropics (Oxford, England: Clarendon Press, 1982).

Gallegos, C. M., Davey, C. B., Kellison, R. L., Sanchez, P. A., and Zobel, B. J., "Technologies for Reforestation of Degraded Lands in the Tropics," OTA commissioned paper, 1982.

Gribbin, J., "The Other Face of Development," New Scientist 96(1334):489–495, 1982.

Wadsworth, F., "Secondary Forest Management and Plantation Forestry Technologies to Improve the Use of Converted Tropical Lands," OTA commissioned paper, 1982.

Wood, P. J., Burley, J., and Grainger, A., "Technologies and Technology Systems for Reforestation of Degraded Tropical Lands," OTA commissioned paper, 1982.

Original Source

This article is excerpted from *Technologies to Sustain Tropical Forest Resources* (Washington, D.C.: U.S. Congress, Office of Technology Assessment, OTA-F-214, March 1984). Library of Congress Catalog Card Number 84-601018. This book is available for sale from the Superintendent of Documents, U.S. Government Printing Office, Washington, D.C. 20402. The full text of the chapter excerpted here can be viewed at: http://www.agroforestry.net/articles/refordeg.html.

This excerpt was originally published as *The Overstory* #78.

Improved Fallow

Kim M. Wilkinson and Craig R. Elevitch

Given enough time, natural processes will restore productivity to degraded or damaged land. Traditionally, farmers have used the practice of "fallow" to allow crop land to rest without crops and be rejuvenated naturally. When the fallow is enriched with fast-growing trees, shrubs or vines, the practice is called "improved fallow." Improved fallow is an agroforestry practice that has its origins in slash-and-burn agriculture.

Farmers use improved fallow to accelerate the process of rehabilitation and thereby shorten the length of their fallow periods. The technology can be applied to any agricultural land that is not under cultivation in order to accelerate recovery, increase nutrient reserves, and improve the potential for future productivity on the site.

To create an improved fallow system, farmers scatter seeds or plant seedlings of fast-growing plants after harvest of the crops from the site. Normally, nitrogen-fixing plants are used, because they are vigorous, deep-rooted, tolerant of drought, and have the ability to accumulate atmospheric nitrogen (see Nitrogen Fixing Trees, page 320). The trees and shrubs are left to occupy the site for several months or years. During the fallow period, the plants accumulate nitrogen from the air and from deep layers of the soil, and drop their leaf litter to enrich the soil and conserve moisture. When the trees are removed at the end of the fallow period, their roots remain in the soil to decompose gradually, releasing additional nutrients to the subsequent crops.

The trees and shrubs in the fallow also provide another important service to the farmer: they fill the space and impede the establishment of undesirable weeds. Many kinds of invasive and problematic weeds thrive in open, sunny conditions on vacant land, but do not spread into areas that are cooler and shadier. The plants that are part of the improved fallow create conditions that are unfavorable to most problematic weeds, making the subsequent establishment of crops easier than if the area had to be cleared of undesirable weeds.

Benefits of improved fallow:

- Improve soil fertility
- Accumulate nutrients
- Add organic matter
- Keep down undesirable weeds while land is not under cultivation
- Break up hard soil
- Regulate temperatures (less extremes of hot/cold)
- Provide shade
- Protect from winds
- Reduce erosion
- Encourage or sustain populations of beneficial soil microorganisms
- Break up physical barriers to root growth (rock and hard pan)

When the trees are removed at the end of the fallow period, they can also yield products such as firewood or poles for sale or farm use.

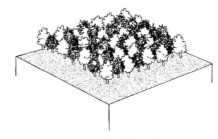

Fast growing trees restore fertility to land, given enough time

Improved Fallow Species

The effectiveness of the fallow in improving the subsequent productivity of the land depends on many factors. It is important that the land is kept in fallow long enough for the conditions to improve. The condition of the land will in part dictate the necessary length of the fallow, as severely degraded land will need more time than healthier land. The effectiveness of the species used to regenerate the land is also a key factor.

The optimal species to use for improved fallow are fast-growing, deep-rooted, tolerant of drought, easy to establish, and preferably nitrogen-fixing. There are many species that fit this description. However, in most cases it is also important that the species be easily removed or short-lived so as not to interfere with future land use. This narrows the list of appropriate species considerably.

Characteristics of species used:

- nitrogen-fixing and/or produce large amounts of organic matter hardy;
- tolerant of drought and neglect easy to establish removable or short-lived;
- will not resprout continually if cut down not weedy;
- will not spread to neighboring crop areas;
- deep rooted able to produce useful or marketable by-products such as firewood, poles, edible seeds, etc.

Improved fallow systems from around the world. Examples include:

- *Sesbania sesban* and *Tephrosia vogelii* improved fallow land between maize production in Zambia
- *Acacia mangium* improved fallow/land rehabilitation in Costa Rica
- *Gliricidia sepium* improved fallow in Southeast Asia
- Mixed species improved fallow in Amazonia

Example species used for improved fallow

Inga edulis (Inga, or ice cream bean)	*Samanea saman* (monkeypod)
Cajanus cajan (pigeon pea)	*Gliricidia sepium* (madre de cacao)
Crotalaria sp. (sunn hemp)	*Erythrina* sp. (*E. poeppigiana*, *E. fusca*)
Sesbania sesban (sesban)	*Senna siamea* (pheasantwood)

Original Source

This chapter was originally published as *The Overstory* #42.

Further Reading

P.K.R. Nair. 1993. An Introduction to Agroforestry. Kluwer Academic Publisher.

Winrock International. 1989-1998. FACT Sheets (formerly NFT Highlights). Winrock International, 38 Winrock Drive, Morrilton, Arkansas 72110-9370 USA; Tel: 501-727-5435; Fax: 501-727-5417; Email: forestry@winrock.org; Web: http://www.winrock.org/forestry/factnet.htm. Concise summaries of many important multipurpose trees and shrubs. Many available in Spanish, French, Indonesian, Chinese, Vietnamese, and Khmer.

Direct Seeding

Julianne Venning

Sowing seeds directly onto prepared ground can be a cheap and effective method for establishing trees and shrubs over large areas. In fact, direct seeding can be up to 10 times cheaper than planting for broadscale revegetation.

The establishment of plants by this method is largely controlled by climatic conditions, soil type and weed competition. These factors have a significant bearing on soil moisture, which is vitally important to germination and early survival of seedlings in the field. Seedlings must be protected from grazing by vermin and livestock until they are beyond browsing height.

Other factors that play an important part in determining the success of the method include:

- correct choice of species, e.g., avoidance of frost-sensitive species on a site prone to severe frosts;
- ground preparation to provide a suitable seedbed;
- use of good quality, viable seed;
- correct seeding rates to ensure the required density of seedlings—too little will lead to disappointment and too much will necessitate extra work for thinning;
- sowing when soil moisture is favourable for seedling germination and establishment; and
- using the correct sowing procedure so that seed is not buried too deeply.

A willingness to experiment is essential when direct seeding, as no one method will suit all situations.

The techniques described have been developed specifically for farms and include procedures to deal with competition from crop and pasture species. All aspects of the operation can be carried out using widely accepted farming practices and readily available farm machinery.

Influence of Climate, Site Conditions and Species

Like most farming, direct seeding is a game of chance. The chances of success are determined by the local climate, site conditions, selected species and available techniques.

Climate

The amount and pattern of rainfall are very important to the germination and establishment of seedlings in the field. Where rainfall is low and irregular it is possible to get false germination of seeds. This occurs when seeds begin to germinate after rain but are not able to survive due to a lack of follow-up rains and therefore inadequate soil moisture. Direct seeding has been very successful in the wetter winter-rainfall region of Australia (e.g., the Western District of Victoria) due to the relatively reliable rainfall patterns and high rainfall. However, in the arid zone and in the drier parts of the winter-rainfall zone (e.g., marginal farming areas in southern Australia) the method has had mixed success due to the less reliable rainfall patterns and low rainfall.

Site conditions

Where weeds are difficult to control it is best not to use direct seeding to establish trees. Poor results are invariably obtained with this method where there is dense weed competition. The introduced grasses and broad-leaved weeds compete aggressively for soil moisture, nutrients and light.

Species

It is important when selecting species to consider not only the potential of the site and the suitability of the species for the site but also the suitability of the species for direct seeding. Some species (e.g., acacias) are well suited to direct seeding. They produce large quantities of seed that are easy to collect and they establish readily from seed sown on site. Species that cannot be propagated readily from seed will need to be established by planting seedlings that have been raised in a nursery.

Site Preparation

Site preparation involves weed control, fencing, vermin control around the planting site and ground preparation to provide a suitable seedbed. It must be stressed that without due care with the initial step of site preparation it can be a waste of time and money to sow the seed.

Regeneration of cleared farmland on a calcrete plain at Mantung in the Murray Mallee of South Australia where rainfall averages 250 mm. Left: Site in 1987 with eucalypt seeding in foreground. (photo: G.C. Bishop) Right: Site in 2002. (photo: C.R. Harris)

Some weed control methods incorporate ground preparation. For example the fine tilth created by cultivation is ideal for sowing seeds provided the surface is firm and level. Where chemical means of weed control are used, ground preparation may be required to prepare a suitable seedbed just before sowing.

The time needed to achieve adequate weed control before seeding depends on the type of weeds present and the means of control used. Where persistent perennial weeds are present, chemical control may be necessary over two seasons before ground preparation and sowing can begin. The removal of weeds well before sowing conserves soil moisture.

However, on sites prone to erosion, complete removal of all grasses and other weeds should be avoided. On these sites weeds should be removed in strips or niches (spots) so that the areas cleared for sowing are relatively small. The weeds left adjacent to the cleared areas also provide some protection for the young seedlings.

Weed Control

The use of fertilisers and sowing of improved pastures have made direct seeding of native species more difficult on farms. The introduced pasture species are able to establish quickly on exposed, high-nutrient soils, suppressing or even preventing growth of the slower growing native species. Weed control has become essential in rural areas for successful di-

rect seeding. The method employed will be influenced by site characteristics, such as soil type and weed spectrum, and the machinery available. A variety of approaches can be used. Mechanical methods include cultivation and grading (scalping); chemical methods use a knockdown herbicide, or a mixture of a knockdown and a residual herbicide. Mechanical and chemical methods may be combined, e.g., cultivation followed by the use of pre- or post-emergent herbicides.

It has been found that cultivation, with or without pre- and post-emergent herbicides, controls weeds for only a month or two before they begin to reoccupy the site. Grading away the uppermost topsoil substantially improves early seedling survival as it removes the weed-seed reserve and therefore effectively retards weed re-invasion. Removal of the topsoil does not appear to affect growth of the seedlings.

Opportunities for weed control after sowing are limited to those situations where herbicides can be applied selectively or where herbicides that kill the weeds but not the seedlings are available.

Although cultivation has generally given poor results, it has been relatively successful at one site where the soil has good moisture-retaining properties and weed competition is limited. However, where weed competition is a problem, methods that control weed re-invasion for at least a year after seeding must be used for direct seeding to be successful.

Sowing the Seed

Pretreatment

The seed may be treated before sowing to overcome dormancy, to hasten germination or to provide inoculation. Sometimes seed is pelleted for easier sowing or to protect the seed from insect predation or fungal infection. Pelleting is recommended only if exact prescriptions are known for the species being used because fungicides and other chemicals are poisonous to germinating seed, even at low concentrations.

Although pelleting has been found to improve seedling establishment in forests, there is little conclusive proof at present to support its use for a wide range of species on farms. It is regarded by some as an extra process complicating an otherwise simple operation.

Seeding rates

When using only small-seeded species (e.g., eucalypts, bottlebrushes) rates vary from 0.1–1.0 kg/ha. However, when including large-seeded species with low viability (e.g., native pines (*Callitris* spp.)) a higher rate is required (e.g., 1–2+ kg/ha). High seeding rates add an unnecessary cost to the operation and can usually be avoided if the correct site preparation and seed treatment have been carried out.

Assessments of the quantity of seed required are generally based on the experience of the operator. However, it is possible to calculate the necessary amount of seed using the following equation:

$$\text{kg seed required} = \frac{\text{plants required/ha}}{\text{viable seed/kg} \times \% \text{ establishment}}$$

The viability of each seedlot in the seed mix should be determined. There are several techniques for testing seed viability. The simplest way is to take a sample of the seedlot and cut through each seed to determine the number of viable seed per unit weight. The contents of viable seed are usually white and fleshy.

Another method for determining seed viability is to germinate samples of seed at a temperature approximating field conditions at the expected time of sowing. The number of germinants is counted over a period of 3–6 weeks.

Conservative estimates of percentage establishment for small-seeded species would be 1% and for large-seeded species 5%. Underestimating the percentage

will result in a greater density of trees or shrubs than is required. Percentage establishment figures for eucalypts are usually 1–5% though figures as high as 38% have been recorded. Similarly, figures for acacias are usually 5–15% but again much higher figures (up to 65%) are not uncommon. Results vary widely depending on the species and site conditions and are generally difficult to predict.

Three-year old acacias and eucalypts established in trials located on an alluvial plain in the Mid North of South Australia where rainfall averages 475 mm per annum. (photo: J. Venning)

Time of sowing

The time of sowing is determined by rainfall patterns, likely occurrences of frost, optimum germination temperatures of the species used and weed problems at the site.

In Victoria and southern parts of New South Wales seed is sown in spring–early summer as soil temperatures are rising and weeds are dying. However, rainfall must be adequate to allow sufficient root development or the seedlings will not survive over the ensuing dry summer months.

Throughout most of the South Australian agricultural area spring rains are not reliable. Therefore seed must be sown as soon as possible after the break of season, generally in May–June, once weed control has been completed. Seedlings are then growing at the same time as a wide range of weeds, which can reduce seedling survival.

In the tropics, best results have been achieved when seed is sown at the beginning of the wet season, even though operations can be delayed at this time of the year by bad weather.

Optimum germination temperatures for species must be considered (Boland *et al 1980*). Species that favour low temperatures should be sown in winter and those that favour higher temperatures in spring-summer if rainfall patterns allow.

Sowing methods

Where residual herbicides have been used for weed control, seed placement should aim to avoid contact with the chemical, particularly if it is likely to impede or prevent germination. Seed can be sown in riplines where the treated topsoil has been put to one side, or, if the site is stony and cannot be ripped, seed can be sown in niches. Niches are created by pulling away the topsoil so that a shallow saucer-shaped depression is formed.

Seed is placed in the base of the depression where the soil has been lightly disturbed. This technique can also be used to simulate grading on a small scale in rocky areas. Spacing between riplines or niches should be adjusted to suit the species sown.

Where non-residual herbicides (e.g., Roundup) have been used, seed can be randomly spread over the surface. Although this method can be wasteful of seed, it does ensure an irregular placement of trees and shrubs and therefore a more natural appearance.

The equipment used to sow the seed should apply the right quantity of seed per unit area and distribute the seed correctly (e.g., not bury it too deeply). Seed can be sown using agricultural seeders (e.g., combine, drill, air seeder), by hand-operated spreaders (e.g., chest-mounted fertiliser spreader) or by hand.

In salt-affected areas seed is generally sown on raised furrows (mounds). Conversely, in sandy soils seed is sown in depressed furrows to reduce the effects of sand blasting.

Specialised machines have been developed to complete the different steps of direct seeding in one pass. These machines spray the ground, create a raised or depressed furrow along which a predetermined quantity of seed is sown at specified intervals with or without a mulch. The precision of the seed feeders ensures economical use of seed and better control of its placement, which is an advantage for shelterbelt and fodder-crop establishment.

For landholders who do not wish to do the work themselves, contractors with these machines offer an attractive alternative. Some machines are also available for hire for those who wish to save the cost of labour.

Seed can be mixed with a medium to help spread it evenly. Sand and bran are commonly used. On new farmland in Western Australia and in mine rehabilitation work, fertiliser is often used as a medium. However, on sites where weeds are prevalent the use of fertiliser should be avoided. Fertiliser serves to enhance weed growth and any benefits to the sown species can be lost due to increased weed competition.

Seed protection

Moisture retention around the seed is improved and ant and/or insect predation can be reduced

when some seed protection is provided. Optimum cover is generally considered to be 1–2 times the smallest diameter of the seed. A light soil covering can be achieved using peg harrows or dragging a chain over the site after sowing. Conventional tyne harrows can bury seeds too deeply and need to be carefully adjusted. Seed can also be compacted into the soil using a roller. Although results have been variable with compaction, it is generally better than no protection at all. Mulches can also be used to cover the seed lightly.

Insect damage and seed predation can be controlled by treating the sown area with insecticides (e.g., 2% chiordane). As it involves an extra cost it should only be applied if it is absolutely necessary. Success has been achieved on farms throughout southern Australia without the use of insecticides, but it may be required where insects are a problem.

Aftercare

A site should be visited regularly after seeding to check the progress of seedlings. This allows any plant diseases or insect infestations to be treated promptly and may reveal reasons for failures.

Seedlings established by direct seeding should require minimal aftercare provided weed control before seeding was adequate to suppress weed re-invasion for the first year and the species have been sown at the correct seeding rates. By the end of their first year the seedlings should have a well-developed root system and further weed control should not be necessary.

If percentage establishment is higher than expected, thinning may be warranted. Unwanted seedlings can be killed by touching them with a rope wick impregnated with herbicide.

It is important to keep a record of the materials and methods used and to monitor the site regularly during the first year. When results are poor it is easier to work out what went wrong if good records have been kept. There is no point in repeating the same mistakes the next year when simple corrective measures could substantially increase survival rates.

Further reading

Boland, D.J., Brooker, M.I.H. and Turnbull, J.W. (1980). Eucalyptus Seed. CSIRO, Canberra.

Clemens, J. (1980). 'Direct seeding of native woody plants.' Landscape Australia, 4/80, 279–284.

Venning, J. (ed.) (1985). Proceedings of a Workshop on Direct Seeding and Natural Regeneration Techniques, Adelaide, 27–29 March 1985. Department of Environment and Planning, Adelaide.

Original Source

This article was adapted with the kind permission of the author and sponsoring organization (CSIRO) from:

Venning, J. 1990. "Direct Seeding" In: Cremer, K.W. (Ed), Trees for Rural Australia, Inkata Press, Melbourne, Australia.

This excerpt was originally published as *The Overstory* #125.

Land Husbandry

Roland Bunch

The following summarizes three and a half decades of extension in soil and water conservation and land husbandry strategies. The most important aspect of our 35-year process of learning about land husbandry around the world has been the follow-up studies and visits made one to fifteen years after the aide programs departed. We have repeatedly visited areas where programs previously worked to observe what aspects were sustained by the farmers on their own (Bunch and Lopez, Silsoe). These visits have been very instructive—and sometimes sobering.

Land Husbandry and Soil Conservation

The evolution in terminology in the area of land husbandry and soil conservation reflects how attitudes have changed about the problems of erosion, crop production, and farmer assistance programs. At first, we talked of soil conservation, pure and simple. When we realized that the water we saved was having more impact on yields than the soil we saved, terminology changed to, "soil and water conservation." In the early 1980's, it became clear that land husbandry had to achieve more than just stop the erosion. Productivity was not going to increase much, nor farmers become very motivated, if what little topsoil was left was not also improved. So the terminology became, "soil restoration" and "soil recuperation." Later, a movement in Africa began enlarging the concept once again by calling it "land husbandry," including everything a farmer does that conserves or improves the soil (Shaxson). We prefer the term "land husbandry," but do not use it very much because of one fatal flaw—it does not translate very well into many other languages.

The concepts behind the term "land husbandry" are very important. Soil conservation and recuperation should be seen as an integral part of agricultural development, not solely an end unto themselves. That is, we should not be making terraces or hedgerows without looking at the entire farming system, without working on other practices simultaneously, or without analyzing the over-all economic and social balance sheet. Also, soil improvement as an integral part of crop management is more important than any practices designed only to conserve or improve the soil. In other words, soil conservation and recuperation should be a result of good soil use throughout a farming system, not the result of one or more technologies implemented largely for this single purpose.

An Ambitious Goal

Land husbandry efforts have been shifting strongly over the last 30 years from structural technologies (e.g., terraces, bunds and ditches) toward vegetative or agronomic technologies (e.g., hedgerows, green manure/cover crops (gm/cc's) and dispersed shade). The economics of land husbandry have become increasingly important. Heavily subsidized structural conservation efforts are very expensive, and many such projects have had more negative than positive impact over the long term. Fewer and fewer outsiders are willing to finance structural soil conservation.

We can no longer claim that soil conservation is too expensive for small farmers. Increasingly, we are finding soil conservation and recuperation technologies that can pay for themselves within the first year of their application. These include many technologies involving organic matter (organic matter) use, green manure/cover crops (gm/cc's), improved fallows and dispersed trees.

A goal is in view that all agricultural techniques that impact positively on land husbandry should more than pay for themselves within the first year after adoption. This is an ambitious goal—one that requires that constantly searching for better technologies. In our experience this goal will accelerate the shift from structural to vegetative technologies.

It is worth noting here that farmers are as economically motivated with land husbandry as they are with any other investment. One five-year after study found that farmers developed more labor-intensive land husbandry practices where they had begun growing valuable vegetable crops aimed at good, nearby markets. On the other hand, farmers who only grow subsistence crops or live isolated from good markets generally invest very little in soil quality.

Structural Technologies

The following is a brief discussion of some of the drawbacks of structural technologies.

Contour rock walls We almost never use this technology any more. It is far too expensive in labor. If the presence of rocks is a major problem of the site (the damage they cause is often overestimated), they can be placed in narrow lines every two or three rows, on a contour, and farmers can then plant the rows between them.

Contour ditches

A mainstay in Central America 25 years ago, we only promote ditches now where drainage is the limiting factor for productivity. In this case, they are given a 0.5–1.0% slope. Once again, a high labor requirement is the problem with contour ditches.

Terraces

Although this conclusion is somewhat more controversial, we feel the actual construction of contour terraces more than one (or at most two) m in width is a waste of time and effort. Note that each time you double the width of the terraces, you also double the effort needed/ha (i.e., each terrace, covering twice as much area, requires four times as much work). The problem of topsoil getting buried beyond the root zone often is even more critical than cost.

In-row or strip tillage

Sometimes called "minimum tillage," in-row tillage consists of tilling only the row (perhaps a swath 35 cm wide), while leaving the soil between the rows (65 cm?) untilled. Organic matter is then applied, only in the tilled rows.

This technology is especially attractive because it forms microterraces (each one holding one row) over a period of three or four years, using less work than just plowing the whole field. It approximately doubles the concentration of organic matter in the crops' root zone, thereby almost doubling its impact, while the effect of the residual organic matter benefits future crops (planted in the same rows year after year) rather than future weeds.

Nevertheless, three-year- and five-year-after studies have found that in-row tillage tends to be sustainable only when slopes are over 20% and either farmers

have irrigation, they can plant fairly high-value market crops on the in-row tillage or they have traditionally plowed their fields either with animal traction or by hand, and will have to do less work than normal to adopt the in-row tillage. Generally, in-row tillage is also most popular with farmers who actively farm less than 1 ha of land in a given year.

Soil traps

Farmers in several countries (e.g., Haiti and highland Guatemala) have dedicated a lot of effort to gully control by using soil traps. These farmers generally own less than 0.5 ha of land.

Contour bunds

We have had little personal experience with bunds, but the literature describing past experiences with this technology is heavily pessimistic, with sustainability reportedly close to zero. Furthermore, this technology has almost always depended on outsiders' tractors or heavy subsidization.

All of the above soil conservation structures require maintenance. If not maintained, they often make the situation worse. Studies have shown that their sustainability after program termination is almost nonexistent.

Prevention: The Role of Cover

Preventing erosion is far better than trying to stop soil that has begun moving down the hillside. One of the best ways to prevent soil erosion is to keep the soil covered, especially during the rainy season(s). I found it hard to believe when I first heard about the kinetic energy of raindrops and how the impact of a raindrop when it hits the soil is far more important in causing erosion than the flow of water over the surface. Experience has proven this point. For instance, in northern Honduras (humid tropics), an estimated 10,000 farmers use a system of growing maize year after year on the same soil that uses no structural soil conservation measures even though the average slope is 35%. One would expect heavy soil erosion. In fact, the soil in these fields, over the last 40 years, has become considerably more fertile (negative erosion?), with zero or minimal applications of chemical fertilizer. Why? First, the soil is constantly covered, year-round, by velvetbean (*Mucuna* spp.). Second, because of the tremendously high soil organic matter content has increased water infiltration. This example illustrates the two best ways to prevent erosion: vegetative cover and high soil organic matter.

More important than any other practice to control erosion are systems that are mulch-based, involving intercropping, dry-season cropping, and anything else one can do to maximize biomass production (i.e., *in situ* produced mulch material). It matters little whether trees, shrubs, vines or animals produce the biomass.

Vegetative or Agronomic Technologies

Contour hedgerows or contour vegetative barriers

Of the soil conservation practices widely used by soil conservation programs up through the 1960's, this is close to the only practice that continues to be used widely, with many positive, long-term results. Nevertheless, some important modifications in this practice have occurred.

Experience has proven that it is largely self-defeating to try to push farmers to plant hedgerows close together. Rather than planting them at 6 m intervals along the slope, as recommended in some programs, farmers much prefer planting them at 12–15 m inter-

vals. When other effective practices are in place such as in-row tillage or good vegetative cover, every other hedgerow may be removed with no adverse effects.

The closer placements of hedgerows are recommended to stop every bit of erosion with this practice alone. We must remember that barrier practices such as these, should be used only as a last-gap measure, mostly for emergencies (i.e., "extreme events"). Our first and most important line of defense against erosion should always be soil cover and other agronomic practices.

A second major change made by farmers is in the selection of species used in the hedgerows. The hedgerows we in COSECHA promoted in the Guinope region in Honduras have been expanded, albeit slowly, since the program was active there in the 1980's. But more than half the farmers have pulled out the Napier grass (*Pennisetum purpureum*) and king grass (*Pennisetum purpureophoides*) we introduced. In their place, they have planted some 19 other species (Silsoe). Among these are lemon grass (for making tea), vetiver, various fruit trees, and a few woody gm/cc and fuelwood species (rather few

Direct-seeded contour hedgerow for erosion control. (photo: C. Elevitch)

because Guinope still has a lot of communal forest). Sugarcane is the most popular species, because of its many uses (for sale, cattle, consumption, etc.).

Some of the more innovative programs now call their hedgerows "multipurpose barriers." They first ask farmers what species they most want, and in what quantities. (Why does it always take us so long to conclude that what the farmer wants matters most?) The typical farmer plants a 100 m hedgerow of Napier grass for each grazing animal, then 20 m of lemon grass, 20–40 m of vetiver for medicinal purposes or thatch, and the rest in sugarcane. Tree species, for fruit, firewood or construction, are planted at intervals in among the other species, often resulting in a dispersed shade effect. Yes, the best farmers practice intercropping, even in their hedgerows.

I have seen farmers prefer a natural vegetative strip (NVS) over single-species or two-species hedgerows, but I have yet to meet a farmer choose to let naturally-occurring species grow in his or her fields when they realized they could instead grow a whole selection of useful species there.

The application of organic matter

Even if this were only a list of soil conservation practices rather than of land husbandry practices, this practice would belong here. Why? Because erosion only occurs when all of the rainwater is not absorbed through soil infiltration. Surface runoff rarely occurs in natural forests or even fields with sufficient soil organic matter. Erosion is therefore largely a symptom of insufficient soil organic matter.

Sometimes, large amounts of organic matter are already locally available. If farmers are not using locally available coffee pulp, crop residues, sugarcane bagasse, or animal manure, they should be taught to use it. Composting may be useful for high-value species (e.g., commercial vegetables or fruits), but for most subsistence crops and grains, compost is too expensive. In most cases, we must find ways of applying this organic matter directly to the soil. For instance, coffee pulp just needs to be spread out in the sun to dry in order to become a high quality fertilizer.

Gm/cc's

The term gm/cc's (green manure/cover crops) refers to "any species of plant, often but not always leguminous, whether a tree, bush, vine or crawling plant, that is used by a farmer for one or several purposes, at least one of which is that of maintaining or improving soil fertility or controlling weeds." That is, a gm/cc can be a traditional subsistence crop (e.g., cowpea, mungbean or scarlet runner bean), a tree—from tephrosia to mother of cacao (*Gliricidia sepium*)—or even a non-legume, such as black oats, wild sunflower (*Tithonia diversifolia*) or cultivated sunflower (*Helianthus annuus*) (Monegat). What makes any of these a gm/cc or not, is whether the farmer plants that particular species in part because it will make the soil better or help control his or her weeds. As with "trap crops" or "nurse crops," the farmer's intention is a key part of the definition.

It is important to note that gm/cc does not refer here to growing a monocropped "green manure" and then burying it at the flowering stage. In most gm/cc systems, the gm/cc is grown intercropped with traditional crops, is cut down after the plant has been harvested, and is left on the soil surface as a mulch. Traditional "green manures" have been tried for centuries in developing countries, and virtually all have failed miserably.

We have found over 150 gm/cc systems in use by small farmers around the world, at least 60% of them developed by the farmers themselves. These systems involve over 70 gm/cc species. We are discovering additional systems out in the villages almost every week, and mathematical extrapolation from known systems indicates that over 500 such systems actually exist. These systems are frequently not noticed by agronomists—frequently I find such systems in countries where I have been told none existed (Bunch).

Books have now been written about gm/cc's (most are only in Spanish and Portuguese). We can't give the subject matter the space it deserves here, but I will mention a few salient points (Monegat, Calegari *et al*, Experiencias).

The gm/cc species are used for more than fifteen different purposes, but the most important, in approximate decreasing order of priority, are: human food, animal feed, weed control, sources of income, improved fallows or the elimination of fallowing, a necessary preparatory stage before using zero tillage, and the recuperation of wastelands.

The species most popular around the world are the scarlet runner bean (*Phaseolus coccineus*), pigeon pea (*Cajanus cajan*), velvetbean (*Mucuna* spp.), cowpeas (*Vigna unguiculata*) and other vignas, and the jackbean (*Canavalia ensiformis*). One should be creative in choosing species, first finding out what are farmers' highest priorities (stopping erosion or improving the soil is almost never the highest priority)

Mixed planting of mangos, coconuts and breadfruit over coffee trees. Kona, Hawai'i. (photo: C. Elevitch)

and giving preference to locally known species, especially if they are locally consumed.

The advantages of these systems are numerous. They increase soil organic matter, fix nitrogen (often between 80–120 kg of N/ha/year), frequently cost less than the value of the benefits they provide (yes, we are talking, in many cases, about essentially free organic matter), control even the most noxious of weeds, provide soil cover, maintain soil moisture, and allow zero tillage. In an age of threatened globalization of commerce, perhaps one of the most important and least appreciated advantages of gm/cc's is that they may be the only way small farmers in countries such as Paraguay or Cambodia will ever compete with the mechanized agrobusinesses of the North. Mechanization's greatest advantages come in soil preparation and weed control. Since gm/cc's can control weeds and allow zero tillage, they can eliminate both operations. Eliminating weeds is even cheaper than mechanizing their removal.

Strip cropping, crop rotations and intercropping

These are all important land husbandry technologies. I have little to say about them to add to what is already widely known.

Dispersed shade

Almost all crops grow better in the lowland tropics (under about 1,000 m) with a ten to fifteen percent shade. This allows for growing one tree about every ten to fifteen m each direction, in either cropped or grazed fields. Small farmers already use this technology in many areas around the world (Malcolm Cairns of ICRAF has found scores of such traditional systems in Southeast Asia, for instance). Those who know of these systems consider them to be probably the most promising agroforestry system known, both in terms of potential farmer acceptance and of the brute number of full-blown trees these systems could get planted around the world.

Advantages include a general increase in crop yields of about 50%. Even more important is the protection against either too little or too much rain (yields may drop 20% while neighboring farmers lose almost everything), thereby appealing to small farmers' aversion to risk. And then there is the trees' innate value—their production of high-value timber, fruit, firewood, etc. Compared, for instance, to alley cropping, this technology produces an increase in yields because the shade is distributed fairly evenly, rather than concentrated. Dispersed shade also produces a similar total tree biomass per unit area (though with fewer trees), and allows the trees to grow into full-grown trees, rather than being managed as short-stature shrubs. Dispersed tree systems have been successfully used with basic grains and pasture land, in intensive as well as extensive systems, and are found all the way from the semi-arid Sahel to Southeast Asia's rainiest rainforests.

Improved (or eliminated) fallows

The maize-mucuna system which has spread across the rainforests of Northern Honduras has allowed farmers working on poor, hillside fields under 2,000 mm of rain a year, to grow 2-ton/ha maize for forty-five years—every single year. I have also seen farmers who used a Leucaena species to grow maize 20 straight years in southern Ghana, farmers in Vietnam and Cameroon who reduced their 8-year fallows to only one year by broadcasting *Tephrosia vogelii* seed on their fields at the beginning of the fallow, and farmers all over the world who have cropped their tropical fields every year for one or two decades because of gm/cc's. Many farmers now laugh at the idea that fallows are necessary.

Improved fallows could probably single-handedly do more to solve Africa's food shortage, not to mention its problem of deteriorating soils, than any other single technology we know.

References

CIDICCO, *et al.* 1997. Experiencias Sobre Cultivos de Cobertura y Abonos Verdes, Tegucigalpa, Honduras.

Bunch, R. 2001. "A Proven Technology for Intensifying Shifting Agriculture, Green Manure/Cover Crop Experiences Around the World," In Shifting Cultivation, Towards Sustainability and Resource Conservation in Asia, International Institute for Rural Reconstruction (IIRR), Cavite, Philippines.

Bunch, R. and G. López. 1995. Soil Recuperation in Central America, Sustaining Innovation After Intervention, Gatekeeper Series No. 55, International Institute for Environment and Development (IIED), London.

Calegari, A., *et al.* 1993. Adubacao Verde no Sul do Brasil, (Second edition) Assessoria E Servicios a Projetos em Agricultura Alternativa (AS-PTA), Rio de Janeiro.

Monegat, C. 1991. Plantas de Cobertura do Solo, Características e Manejo em Pequenas Propriedades, Claudino Monegat, Chapeco, Santa Catarina, Brazil.

Shaxson, F. 1999. New Concepts and Approaches to Land Management in the Tropics with Emphasis on Steeplands (Soil Resources, Management and Conservation Service of the Food and Agriculture Organization (FAO), Rome, Italy.

Silsoe. No date. Research Institute, "Adopción de Tecnologías de Conservación de Suelos y Agua en el Distrito de Guinope, El Paraíso, Honduras."

Original Source

This is an invited article submitted by Roland Bunch to *The Overstory*. This article was originally published as *The Overstory* #111.

Suggested reference:

Bunch, R. 2002. Land Husbandry. *The Overstory* #111. Permanent Agriculture Resources, Holualoa, Hawaii. URL: http://www.overstory.org

Land Management: Caring for Resources

Anthony Young

The older approach to land management, based on the transfer of Western technologies, has been replaced by a new set of ideas. For management of the croplands, new approaches include the land husbandry basis for soil conservation, low-input sustainable agriculture, and small-scale irrigation. On open rangelands, reconciling the extreme complexity of land management needs with communal tenure raises problems which are almost insuperable. Multiple-purpose forest management has replaced the earlier focus on wood production. Agroforestry has helped to diversify farm production, and offered new means of soil management.

These new approaches have a number of ideas in common: understanding the processes in the soil, water, and plant ecosystem, as a basis for their modification; adapting management methods to the infinite variety of local conditions; and increasing production not by taking in more land nor with higher inputs, but by using soils, water, fertilizers, and plant resources with greater efficiency. Finally, it has invariably been found that best results come from a participatory approach, implementing changes through the joint efforts of resource scientists and the knowledge and skills of the local people.

The fundamental principle of land management is sustainability, the combination of production with conservation. Given the extent of poverty, the urgency of the food situation in the developing world, and the present low level of productivity of many farming systems, the priority must be to increase production. This has to be achieved in ways that do not degrade, and where possible improve, the land resource base on which production depends. The primary objective is, of course, the welfare of the people. Taking land resources as an alternative focus, however, provides a powerful means to integrate production with conservation, and so to lead towards sustainability.

A set of new ideas on land management has taken the place of the older approach, which was based on high levels of inputs and transfer of Western technologies to the developing world. The new approach has two common themes or principles. The first is to make use of external inputs, but at moderate levels and with higher efficiency. To achieve this objective means working in conjunction with processes of the natural ecosystems. The second principle is to implement changes through collaboration with the people, the approach of participatory development. Underlying these is a fundamental three-stage approach:

- to understand the functioning of the natural ecosystem, soils, water, plants, animals;
- taking this understanding as a basis, to construct a sustainable managed ecosystem, a land use system that will both be productive and conserve or improve the resource base;
- to reconcile the management needs for sustainable production with economic and social requirements and constraints.

Because the environmental conditions vary widely, standard recommendations, or extension "packages," are not enough. Management methods have to be constantly adapted to the site conditions of climate, water, soil, and vegetation, not only to their variation in space but also their changes over time. Farmers have always made such adaptations, and extension staff should do so.

Much has been learnt about land management based on these principles. It is impossible to review the whole range of land management methods, so the focus will be on selected ideas which hold promise for the future. A framework is provided by the three major production systems—croplands, rangelands, and forests—together with the new science of agroforestry which overlaps these.

Land Husbandry: The New Approach to Soil and Water Conservation

In the older, or conventional, approach to soil conservation, the objective was to reduce soil loss, measured as tonnes per hectare. This was achieved by means of earth structures: either terraces, or combinations of contour-aligned banks (often called bunds) with ditches. Water runoff was reduced either by causing it to sink in, as with terrace systems, or by diverting it into controlled waterways. Conservation of this type became a branch of civil engineering; manuals were published on how to build such structures for local conditions of rainfall, slope, and soil. Under the former system of land capability classification, only gentle slopes were classed as suitable for arable use; all steeper land was allocated to grazing, forestry, or conservation." Agricultural extension work was based on the view that soil conservation should come first, as a prerequisite for agricultural improvements. It was commonly conducted on the basis of a prohibitive policy, either by forbidding cultivation of steeply sloping land or by legally enforced requirements for the construction of conservation works.

Devised initially for farming conditions in the USA, the conventional approach to conservation is technically successful in reducing runoff and erosion. As regards adoption it had some notable successes, in Zimbabwe for example, where some landscapes of bunds, waterways, etc. looked from the air like a conservation textbook. In Asia, some extensive terracing systems were constructed, for example in Taiwan.

But, in many cases, the older approach to conservation simply did not work. A clear example of failure is the case of Jamaica. Repeated attempts were made to introduce terrace systems to the hill lands, through a series of externally funded projects. These have not been maintained, and are largely abandoned. In many countries, land shortage has enforced widespread cultivation of sloping lands, and to prohibit this is both economically and socially unrealistic. In the Ethiopian highlands, whole communities have their land on steep hillsides. In Malawi in 1960, cultivation stopped at the foot of the hills; by the mid-1970s, cultivation had extended up the hills and onto the steeply dissected rift valley scarp areas. It is difficult to enforce legislative penalties. Farmers' co-operation could not be obtained unless they could see an immediate benefit in terms of higher crop yields, and, when conservation is carried out in isolation from other improvements, no such benefits occur.

Out of the failures of the former system a new approach to conservation arose, commonly called land husbandry. Features of this approach are:

- The focus of attention is not upon soil loss as such, but on its effects on production; these arise principally through loss, in eroded soil, of organic matter and nutrients.

- More attention is given to biological methods of conservation, especially maintenance of a soil cover, including through agroforestry. Earth structures, whilst by no means excluded, receive less emphasis.

- In dry lands, there is greater integration between soil and water conservation. Farmers are able to see more immediate benefits from conserving water.

- It is recognized as politically and socially unacceptable to forbid the cultivation of sloping land. Ways have to be found to make such cultivation environmentally acceptable.

- In extension, it is recognized that conservation can only be achieved through the willing participation of farmers. For this to occur, they must be able to see benefits. It follows that conservation should not be a separate element, but an integral part of improved farming systems.

Thus there are two basic elements to land husbandry, technical and social. There is no doctrinaire reason to favour biological methods over earth structures if the latter are agreed to be the best solution, but the cost and labour involved in their construction, and more importantly maintenance, mitigate against their use. Taken to its extreme, there should be no soil conservation projects—only projects to improve sustainable production, in which conservation forms an element. In a project for the central hill lands of Jamaica, the primary, and explicit, objective is to improve production of perennial crops, coffee and cacao. More productive crop varieties, better managed, produce more leaf litter, and the only specific conservation-directed element of management is to ensure that this litter remains on the soil.

The current need is human and institutional. Existing staff of conservation departments will require retraining. Education in conservation has to be considerably broadened from its former, engineering, basis, to include skills in the use of biological methods, greater awareness of the wider problems of farming, and practical training in participatory extension. There is a need to consider how far soil conservation departments should remain separate. One solution is to abolish them, and incorporate technical conservation specialists within the general agricultural extension service. The improved opportunities which are offered by land husbandry can only achieve their potential through well-educated staff and effective institutions.

Conclusion

Land husbandry, integrated plant nutrition, small-scale irrigation, communal management of rangelands, multiple-use forest management, agroforestry—these are only a selection from the many new approaches to land resource management. There is the need to understand the functioning of natural ecosystems— soils, water, and plants—as a basis for their sustainable management. This management must be jointly for production at the present and conservation to meet the needs of the future; and, as the natural environment is infinitely variable, the best methods of management will differ from place to place. Another need is to meet requirements for increased production not by taking in new land, nor by adding higher levels of inputs, but by using resources with greater efficiency. A further theme is the active involvement of local people in land management. The participatory approach has a social value, helping to direct attention to the needs of the rural poor; it can equally well be justified on pragmatic grounds, in that no other approach to land resource management works so effectively.

Original Source

This edition of *The Overstory* was excerpted with the kind permission of the author and publisher from the original:

Young, A. 2000. Land Resources: Now and for the Future. Cambridge University Press, Cambridge, UK.

Copies of this publication can be purchased from:

Cambridge University Press at http://www.cambridge.org. Direct link for purchase: http://uk.cambridge.org/earthsciences/catalogue/0521785596/

This excerpt was originally published as *The Overstory* #103.

Hawaiian native ʻohiʻa lehua (*Metrosideros polymorpha*) pioneers pahoehoe lava. (photo: C. Elevitch)

Growing Trees for Forestry

Meeting people's needs for wood products need not involve cutting down natural forests. Cultivating trees on agricultural land can improve farm income and provide multiple benefits for the community. Products range from firewood to high-value timber.

Section Contents

Farm Forestry

Craig R. Elevitch and Kim M. Wilkinson

World demand for timber is steadily increasing, while availability of hardwoods from natural forests is decreasing. Some of the future timber supply will come from large plantations. However, timber and wood products can also be a sustainable, high-value yield from farms and agroforests.

Farm forestry is the management of trees for timber yields by farmers. Farm forestry can take many forms. Some farm forestry projects resemble small-scale forest plantations. Others are diverse agroforests, involving timber trees mixed with animals, crops, or other trees with nontimber products. Projects can range in size from very small (one acre) to very large (hundreds of acres). Farm forestry has the potential to produce quality timber products, increase farm incomes, support community development, and provide employment and environmental benefits.

Forestry on farms presents numerous opportunities for environmental and economic benefits. (photo: C. Elevitch)

Often the term "forestry" has been associated with large-scale single-species plantations managed exclusively for commercial return of a timber product. Indeed, much of the scientific and economic study of forestry has been devoted to the needs of this industrial form of forestry. The farm forester shares the goal of commercial timber returns. However, the small-scale farm forester may have a very different set of resources, needs, and objectives compared to the industrial forest investor.

Timber Trees on Farms

Some farm foresters may choose to devote all or part project to a solid stand of timber trees. These plantings usually consist of trees planted close together, uniformly spaced, and managed as small-scale timber plantations. Sometimes called woodlots or tree farms, these plantings can also be a productive use of poor, difficult, or hard-to-access farmland, such as steep slopes, river banks, or waterlogged areas.

There are many ways to integrate timber trees with other farm practices such as with pasture, windbreaks, and crops. These may improve returns and enhance environmental benefits. Integrating trees into farm systems may also have potential drawbacks. Careful planning is necessary to select appropriate species, and to prevent problems from competition and shading. Good planning helps to ensure that the interactions between the trees and other farm elements are beneficial, and result in a net gain for the farmer.

Some examples of ways to integrate timber trees with other farm elements include:

- Silvopastoral systems—trees and livestock;
- Windbreaks (also known as shelterbelts);
- Sequential cropping systems—short-term crops planted with and eventually replaced by long-term timber trees;
- Wide row intercropping—wide spacing between rows of timber trees, with crops cultivated between the rows;
- Dispersed trees—timber trees with shade-tolerant crops in a permanent arrangement.

In agroforestry systems, the return from timber will usually be lower than if the timber trees were cultivated in solid stands. However, integrating timber trees with farm systems can enable farmers to diversify their yields, and make more efficient use of land. The total return per acre over time from combined timber and nontimber products may exceed the financial yields of single-species forestry.

Some Benefits and Drawbacks of Farm Forestry

Farm forestry differs from large-scale commercial forestry in a number of important ways. Some of these differences can work in the farm forester's favor; others may be a disadvantage. In most cases, it is unrealistic to assume that the small-scale grower can hope to compete in the same markets, and with the same product line, as large-scale industrial plantations. The farmer must instead understand the advantages and disadvantages of their situation in order to optimize the potential for an economically viable forestry planting on their property.

The smaller scale of farm forestry projects and the higher level of personal involvement puts farm foresters in a position to benefit from many economic or environmental products of the forest that are not available to the industrial grower. For example, small scale operations may enable the farm forester to exploit market niches of specialty timbers for which there is a small but high-value market. Site-specific planning and species selection can allow the farm forester to make optimal use of the resources, microclimates, and conditions available on the site. Farmers may also make better economic and/or personal use of the secondary benefits of trees on their property, such as recreation, wildlife habitat/hunting, livestock shelter, aesthetic values, windbreak, watershed enhancement, etc. Integrating trees with other crops can result in diversified returns and increased net benefits.

Farm forestry also has some drawbacks compared with large-scale industrial forestry. The long-term investment required for forestry may be difficult for farmers to make. Misunderstanding or ignorance of farm forestry in government, planning agencies, funding sources, and the community at large may also be a barrier. Constraints to harvesting and marketing relatively small quantities of wood products may also be an issue. Harvesting, processing, and marketing are other areas where little is known of the critical factors influencing the economics of forestry for small land holders.

Financial Returns of Farm Forestry

Timber trees represent a long-term investment of land, labor, and resources for farmers. For this reason, it is important that the farmer/landowner care-fully consider the economic prospects. Good planning, including careful financial analysis, is essential.

However, farm forestry involves financial questions that economists, researchers, government officials, and scientists cannot presently answer with any degree of certainty. Predicting growth rates, timber volumes, prices, and markets in twenty or more years is difficult. The diverse conditions and practices of farm forestry can add to the uncertainty. For example, in mixed agroforests, interactions between timber species and other elements may be unknown and untested. On degraded lands where environmental conditions have become inhospitable to many species, the growth and yields even from well-known plantation forestry species are uncertain.

An understanding of some basic financial analysis tools can help a farm forester estimate the potential of investing in a forestry project. Financial analysis provides a means to compare different forestry scenarios. This can be used to weigh the costs and returns of investing in farm forestry against the farmer's other options for economic use of the property. Analysis tools also aid in project design, in selecting project size, budget, implementation factors and management strategies.

Financial analysis includes estimating the costs and returns of a farm forestry project. Typical costs include planning, site preparation, fertilizers, seedlings, planting and maintenance costs, thinning, pruning, and harvesting. Estimating returns can be a very uncertain process, but there are ways to conservatively determine the potential for returns, including "best-case" and "worst-case" scenarios. These scenarios can be varied to examine the possibilities of changing market conditions, risks of natural disasters, or other factors.

Farm forestry is an expanding field that is gaining appreciation from both farmers and researchers for its potential. More information is becoming available to aid the farm forester in planning a successful project. Some current resources are listed below.

References

Elevitch, C.R., and K.M. Wilkinson (eds). 2000. Agroforestry Guides for Pacific Islands. Permanent Agriculture Resources, Holualoa, Hawai'i. Web: http://www.agroforestry.net

Holmgren, D. 1994. Trees on the Treeless Plains: Revegetation Manual for the Volcanic Landscapes of Central Victoria, Holmgren Design Services, Victoria, Australia.

Reid, R., and G. Wilson. 1985. Agroforestry in Australia and New Zealand, Goddard & Dobson, Victoria, Australia.

Stephen, P., and R. Reid. 1999. Australia Master Tree-Grower Farm Forestry Economics Exercise. School of Forestry, The University of Melbourne

Sullivan, G. M., S.M. Huke and J.M. Fox (eds). 1992. Financial and Economic Analysis of Agroforestry Systems. Proceedings of a workshop held in Honolulu, HI, USA, July 1991. Web: http://www.winrock.org/forestry/factnet.htm.

Original Source

This article was originally published as *The Overstory* #48.

Integrating Forestry into Farms

Rowan Reid and Peter Stephen

Farm forestry is the commitment of resources by farmers, alone or in partnerships, towards the establishment or management of forests on their land. To realise the full potential of farm forestry, avoid the temptation to promote or accept someone else's favourite or "pet" planting models. Farm forestry design should not be "top down" or "bottom up," but rather "inside out." Farmers and their communities need to be encouraged to look for opportunities whereby forestry can help solve their immediate needs while providing the prospect of generating the products and services that others are prepared to purchase.

Introduction

Designing farm forestry opportunities begins by asking the question: "Why would you want to grow or manage a forest?" The responses in any group of farmers will vary widely but can be loosely related to their financial, environmental, agricultural, non-agricultural or personal goals:

- Financial goals: investment, diversification, deferring income, utilising unproductive land, enhancing property values, providing on-farm employment, etc.
- Environmental goals: controlling land degradation, enhancing natural habitats, screening offensive industries, improving water quality, etc.
- Agricultural goals: shade and shelter, controlling vermin and noxious weeds, recycling or fixing soil nutrients, fodder for stock, etc.
- Non-agricultural goals: enhance tourism potential, develop new skills and job opportunities, establish a forestry related on-farm business, etc.
- Personal and lifestyle goals: wishing to leave a legacy, watch a forest grow, learn about the natural environment; improve the view, etc.

Farmer participation in forestry is driven by a diverse and complex set of motivations and constrained by an equally diverse range of limitations. Identifying clear motivations is the first step to designing appropriate farm forestry options.

Whole business planning has been widely promoted within the farming community under terms such as

Whole Farm Planning or Property Management Planning. These approaches use a number of tools to help farmers define their forestry related goals and personal performance criteria. Mapping the farming enterprise using aerial photographs is one method that can help identify areas where trees or forest management may be able to contribute to the farm goals. Areas considered unsuitable for production agriculture might be identified on the map as the first step to designing farm forestry options. Another example is the boundaries between different land classes. These are often ideal locations for belts of trees for shelter and land protection.

Balancing Multiple Goals

As farmers list and prioritise the full range of objectives they are seeking from their forests, the importance of careful planning and research becomes clear. Unfortunately, multiple objectives are not always complementary. Managing a shelterbelt, riparian strip or recharge plantation for commercial timber will require strategies to avoid any unacceptable impacts of harvesting on the non-timber benefits. Good design will require some understanding of the complementary or competitive relationship between different objectives and the compromises required in order to achieve an appropriate balance.

Strategies to deal with conflicts may incur additional management costs or lower than optimal production of a particular product or service. It is common for farmers to accept these losses and costs in order to reduce the risks associated with single purpose forestry. Multipurpose designs often carry lower risk and are more adaptable as the following three examples illustrate:

1. Timber Plantations for Salinity Control

Revegetation of recharge areas is widely acknowledged as a possible means of controlling the rising water tables that contribute to dryland salinity. Hydrological surveys often identify the principal recharge areas as the cleared well-drained hillslopes where water easily penetrates. To control the recharge, farmers are often advised to establish a canopy of evergreen perennial vegetation that can dry the soils to depth or intercept subsoil drainage. The trees or shrubs do not necessarily need to be indigenous, or even native, but they must be able to grow well on the site and survive the likely droughts and other threats. The costs associated with revegetation and the subsequent loss of agricultural production from the planted area represent a real and substantial investment, whereas the environmental return is often uncertain and difficult to describe in dollar terms.

Depending on the farmer's other interests, they might consider establishing a commercial plantation on the recharge site. If an industrial forestry company is offering a commercial joint venture or lease, they may be able to negotiate for a plantation to be established on the site. To be effective for salinity control the plantation must be located correctly, remain productive and be harvested in a way that doesn't allow recharge to return to the pre-planting levels. This may mean that conventional plantation species or management methods are inappropriate. Blue Gum (*E. globulus*), for example, is susceptible to drought deaths on dry, well-drained sites so alternative, although less vigorous, species such as Sugar Gum (*E. cladocalyx*) may be more suitable. Such areas are also often difficult to access and expensive to harvest making production of low value products like pulpwood unviable, whereas sawlogs may be viable to harvest due to higher log values.

Although the site may not be ideal for production forestry, the farmer may be willing to accept a lower return in order to achieve salinity control. This may mean lower lease payments or lower prospects of deriving a profit from the timber. Where the costs of establishing a non-commercial forest are inhibitive, the multipurpose option reduces the farmer's exposure to risk while meeting their most critical environmental concerns. What is important for timber production is that the trees are viable to harvest at some time in the future.

2. Shelterbelts with a Timber Option

It is widely accepted that a conventional sheep and cattle grazing enterprise in southern Australia can increase, or at least maintain, agricultural production if trees are planted strategically over about 10% of the farm. Depending on the situation, the trees may need to be established in continuous narrow belts aligned to reduce damaging winds as well as in special areas for stock shelter during lambing and calving or immediately after shearing.

If the farmer is able to achieve these design criteria by including timber species managed for high value markets, they might be able to develop a valuable resource that can be harvested when needed. The costs of fencing, establishment, and the land itself can be justified from the shelter benefits alone. The only additional expense is some time spent researching possible timber markets and silvicultural options and the cost of a few hours extra management to ensure the trees produce a saleable product. In any event, the risks and costs are dramatically reduced because of the multiple values. If, for whatever reason, the trees are unsalable when mature, the farmer still has the shelter and other values to enjoy.

3. Forestry for Economic Diversification

Investing in forestry on the less productive parts of the farm may be a means of building income security without threatening conventional agricultural production. Agricultural returns are susceptible to poor seasons and fluctuating markets. Timber, seed and other tree products commonly have markets that are unrelated to those of the agricultural commodities like wool and beef. Some tree products, like timber, remain available for harvest even through poor seasons.

Forestry may also offer taxation, superannuation and generational transfer attractions for farmers. By investing in a long term venture that will mature well into the future, farmers may be able to ensure they have sufficient funds for their own retirement without the need to draw resources out of their children's agricultural enterprise.

A thorough diagnosis of the farm's business situation and the family's investment objectives may be required to ensure that any farm forestry project reflects their particular situation and their preparedness to commit resources to what may be a long and risky investment. The best design is the one that matches the farmer's own performance criteria without exposing them to an uncomfortable level of risk.

Boundary planting of *Flueggea flexuosa*, a durable timber and wind-tolerant tree. Samoa. (photo: C. Elevitch)

The Perfect Compromise

Many farmers will prefer multipurpose farm forestry designs in preference to "best-bets" that maximise single values. Because farmers are able to capture many of the non-timber benefits offered by forests they may, for example, accept higher costs, slower growth or lower returns from a commercial plantation if this means that it will also provide shelter or wildlife benefits. By the same token, a farmer planting trees for shelter or land protection may be willing to accept the additional labour costs associated with managing some of the trees for timber just to keep that option open.

If farmers are seeking multiple benefits they will need to clearly specify their priorities and the minimum requirements for each outcome. This is where farmers will need to do their homework. If, for example, shelter is the primary goal then understanding the principles of shelterbelt design allows the farmer to prescribe a layout that will provide sufficient shelter in the right location at the right time. Even where commercial production of forest products is not a primary concern, the farmers must be sure that their mature forests will be viable to harvest. Timber production cannot be considered a bonus if it costs more to harvest than it is worth.

When defining goals, farmers must be specific. If shelter is sought then specify what is to be sheltered (sheep, crops, pasture), when shelter is required (summer, winter, off-shears) and where (near the shed, across the whole top paddock). If expecting a commercial income from trees, note the desired investment period (10, 20 or 30 years), attitude to risk (for example, happy to aim for high return despite high risk), and any taxation or superannuation implications.

Summarise the Goals

In many cases farmers will be able to identify a range of objectives, some of which will be essential to the success of the planting and others which are desirable but not essential. It is also useful to identify the following:

- Must haves—what the project must provide to satisfy
- Like to have—extra benefits that would be welcome
- Must nots—characteristics or outcomes that must not result
- Prefer nots—characteristics or outcomes that should be avoided

These goals help highlight and prioritise the design criteria that must be achieved in order to satisfy the farmer's objectives, those that are common to different objectives and those which may initially appear contradictory.

This becomes a shopping list that can be used to compare different types of forestry before committing to a project plan. If the products or services produced by a forest are to be sold, then some market research as to the product specifications required by potential purchasers and the marketing options is required.

Markets for Products and Services

Farm forests can be designed and managed to provide a wide variety of products and environmental services for which there may be a commercial market. Timber is only one such product. Others include oils, seed, foliage and Christmas trees. Environmental services that might be saleable include carbon sequestration, improved water quality, biodiversity and recharge control. In fact, anything that an individual, organisation or government may be prepared to purchase can be considered as a potential source of income. Remember that markets for forest products and services can change. It may also be worth giving some thought to what may be considered of value in the future.

Timber is a useful example to illustrate the importance of market research. Growers must appreciate that the value of a good log at the mill door is many times that of a poor log. This will generally be reflected in the price, but may also be evident in the level of market interest and the preparedness of log buyers to undertake the sale on the farmer's terms. It is common for farmers with small forests containing average logs to find they are the last in line when it comes to arranging a harvest. Farmers should talk to timber processors in their region about what constitutes a perfect log and ask them how they see the market changing in the future.

Because harvesting and wood transport costs are affected by lot size and site conditions, it is also worth considering forest specifications. Farmers need to consider their harvesting options and then talk to contractors about what affects logging costs. Small plantations on steep sites are expensive to harvest and may only be viable if the trees are very valuable. Farmers wishing to harvest the trees themselves need to consider what skills they might require and what tree and stand specifications might affect their costs. Chainsaws and farm tractors may only be effective where log size and quality is high and the stand is open with easy access.

Silviculture—Manipulating Forest Growth

Silviculture is essentially the manipulation of forest growth through design and management. Careful species selection, planting pattern and site preparation can set a young forest up so that it has the best chance of success. Once established, the timely use of various tools such as fertiliser application, pruning, grazing, fire and thinning can help direct future growth in any number of ways.

Whatever the benefits we expect from a forest, silviculture can be used to balance or enhance them. Thinning might be a means of increasing the proportion of high value sawlogs in a native forest or enhancing biodiversity by stimulating understorey plants. Grazing can be used to reduce fire hazards while also providing shelter for stock. While site characteristics, climate and changing markets will also affect the growth and value of a forest, silviculture remains the most powerful tool of the farm forester. By the same token, poor silviculture or neglect can result in land degradation, poor productivity or low production values.

Designing and Evaluating Options

Coming up with a farm forestry project plan that is profitable and appropriate, based on the farmer's needs, constraints and opportunities, is a question of design. A useful starting point is to try and visualise what a perfect forest for the purpose might look like.

This provides a focus for deciding on the species, design and management required and may help identify risks and uncertainties. Farmers should shop around for promising options based on the experience in their region and make notes on the advantages and disadvantages of each.

In some cases it will be nearly impossible to put a dollar figure on a farmer's personal performance criteria. What value can be placed on enhancing the attractiveness or amenity value of the family farm if there is no intention of selling it? If landscape is an important consideration, try and visualise how the forest will look as it grows and then describe the farmer's preferences and dislikes. There are computer models that can help do this, but the best starting point is for farmers to visit other farms where farmers are doing similar things and make their own judgement.

By referring back to their original goals and constraints, farmers can make a final decision that they are comfortable with supported by economic analysis, risk assessment and personal preference. All farmers need to make their own judgement and appreciate that what is right for them may not be appropriate for others, even their neighbours. If it appears impossible to develop a practical and attractive design that involves an acceptable level of risk then the farmer should not proceed. This should not be seen as a failure of the process but rather a means of avoiding disappointment. If this is the case, farmers should keep an eye open for new opportunities or changing circumstances. Farm forestry is a dynamic industry with new methods and markets continually being developed.

Farmer Aspirations and Market Opportunities

Those with an interest in the products and services of farm forestry need to ensure that farmers understand their product specifications and are able to negotiate a viable sale. Where they have the knowledge and the price is right, farmers will be able to produce and sell timber, erosion control or biodiversity in the same way they sell lamb or milk. Regulations and market impositions that stifle good design and innovation must be challenged.

To be successful, farmers must own their projects, accept responsibility for the management decisions and be able to negotiate the sale of products and services in a fair market place.

Original Source

This edition of *The Overstory* was adapted with the kind permission of the authors from the original:

Reid, R. and P. Stephen. 2001. The Farmer's Forest—Multipurpose Forestry for Australian Farmers. RIRCD Publication No. R01/33. Melbourne, Australia.

Copies of this publication can be purchased from:

Australian Master TreeGrower Program Department of Forestry The Institute of Land & Food Resources The University of Melbourne Victoria 3010, Australia Tel: 61 3 8344 5011; Fax: 61 3 9349 4172 Email: rfr@unimelb.edu.au;
Web: http://www.mtg.unimelb.edu.au/farmers_fo rest.htm

This excerpt was originally published as *The Overstory* #98.

Choosing Species for Timber Production and Multiple Benefits

Kim M. Wilkinson and Craig R. Elevitch

Timber products can be a sustainable and high-value product from small farms, agroforests, and small-scale forestry projects. Like any other business venture or investment, careful planning can make a difference in terms of economic success or failure. This chapter introduces the basic steps to choose species that match the needs, goals, and site conditions of a project prior to planting.

What Species Should We Plant?

The most common question asked by those beginning a project with timber trees is: "What species should we plant?" There is no precise formula for choosing "the right" species. Instead, choosing species is a process reliant on personal knowledge, judgments, and experience, informed by literature reviews, the advice of other growers and resource professionals, and other information (Turnbull 1986). Knowledge of project goals, commercial requirements, planting site conditions, and the range of potentially suitable species is essential in the species selection process.

The steps involved in choosing suitable species for a particular site and purpose are (after MacDicken 1994):

1   What products and services are desired? Determine the end-use requirements/products and set production objectives.

2   What type of environment does the planting site have? Describe the planting site using the best available sources.

3   What is known of similar environments? Review local experiences and relevant literature with other trees and crops.

4   What timber trees grow well under these conditions? Review local experiences, relevant literature, species trials from similar conditions.

5   What land-use practices are found under similar conditions? Review literature, observe local practices.

6   Select candidate list of species based on all available data. Assemble and analyze information on end uses, environment and species requirements.

7   Narrow down species list. Conduct test plantings on intended planting sites. Plant trees from a range of seed sources in either formal or informal experiments.

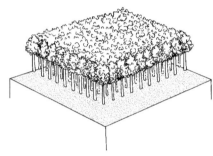

Timber trees represent a long term savings account for farms

Defining Desired End Products

As with any other business venture, planting timber trees for commercial returns must begin with the end in mind: what products are desired? The desired timber products should be defined as accurately as possible, for example, "high-value native hardwoods for furniture," "small dimension saw timber for the local sawmill," or "finely-figured woods for local crafts market."

Because of the long-term nature and unpredictability of the timber market, growers may want to keep several options open for end-product use. Additionally, some trees may be used for multiple timber products, for example large logs for saw timber and smaller remnants for crafts. If so, each potential end-product should be defined, and species that offer the greatest flexibility in end-uses may be selected.

New technologies for processing, wood preservation, and treatments may extend potential uses and market opportunities for species that do not meet specific criteria (Lemmens *et al* 1995). Nevertheless, it is recommended to specify in advance the kind of wood products desired in order to ensure that the species will be able to meet the commercial objectives of the project.

Different characteristics of trees will result in different timber products.

Example wood types

End Product	Tree Characteristics	Property Requirements
Sawn Timber	Large size, moderate to fast growth, good form, ease of pruning	Strength, stability, wood uniformity, good seasoning, working, and finishing
Sheet products/veneer	Very large size, good natural pruning, wounds cover over quickly (for few knots)	Figure, peeling or slicing quality, few knots, good adhesive bonding strength (if for plywood)
Wood chips, pulp, and paper	Rapid growth, straight stems, easy to grow, coppicing desirable	Fiber length, light color, low extractives content, density
Posts and Poles (Roundwood)	Straight stems, strong apical dominance, few or thin branches, preferably self-pruning (without knots), little taper from top to bottom, bark should strip easily.	Durable in contact with the ground or in water, capable of taking high cross-loads, have minimal spiraling, resistant to termites and wood-borers (Turnbull 1986)

Source: Evans 1992 and Turnbull 1986

Defining Desired Services

The desired services or multiple uses of the trees must also be clearly defined in advance for appropriate species selection. Suitable species must meet certain criteria, as well as be planned and managed appropriately, if they are to provide timber and serve a useful function in the farm system.

Some of the desirable characteristics for trees in certain agroforestry practices are outlined below:

Silvopastoral systems (trees and livestock)
- Tolerant of livestock impacts (resistant to damage to root systems, bark, etc.)
- Not poisonous/toxic to livestock
- Have large crowns above livestock reach
- Thin canopy (allows light to enter for pasture forage)

Windbreaks
- Wind firm root systems
- Bushy deep crown that allows some wind penetration
- Wind strong, pliable branches (not brittle or easily breakable)
- Delayed shedding of lower limbs
- Branching to the ground (if single-species windbreak is used)

- Salt-tolerant (if near coastal area)
- Rapid growth (if early protection is required)
- Long life
- Should not harbor pests of neighboring crops
- Root systems should not compete excessively for water with adjacent crops

Woodlots
- Fast-growing
- Provide useful products
- Able to coppice, resprout, or otherwise regenerate easily (if rotational harvest are desired)
- Hardy, tolerant of harsh conditions (if planted on marginal land)

Sequential cropping systems, Dispersed trees, or Wide row intercropping
- Trees not excessively fast-growing or competitive with crops
- No allelopathic effects on crops
- Canopy allows acceptable light penetration to crops
- Not damaged by cultivation or harvest of surrounding crops

Land Rehabilitation
- Tolerant of drought, poor soils, and neglect

- Fast-growing
- Deep-rooted
- Nitrogen fixing and/or produces litter with high nutrient content (for soil improvement)
- Removable, does not resprout after cutting (if area is to be planted in other crops after rehabilitation)

Defining the Site Characteristics

A description of the planting environment is essential in selecting species that will grow well on the site. The description of site characteristics should include elevation, slope, rainfall regime, maximum length of dry season, soil analysis, wind and temperature information, and so forth. Any other information that can be obtained about the site will also be valuable, including a survey of existing vegetation, a history of land use, etc. The process of evaluating the project site can be as comprehensive as desired. Growers should allow sufficient time for this process—several months to a year is not excessive. The time consumed by a detailed site evaluation is rewarded by more informed planning decisions.

Determining similar environments

The more comprehensive the understanding of the project site, the easier it will be to limit species choices to the most promising species from similar environments. In some cases, for example in the Pacific Islands, the many varied climates, soils, and management capabilities can make the task of matching species even to similar local environments complicated. Sites separated by only a few miles may have a very different soil type, wind direction, or rainfall pattern than the planting site being evaluated. Assistance may be available locally from extension agents and other resource professionals to help growers locate similar environments in the region. The successful species and practices from these environments can then be evaluated for their suitability for the project.

When considering exotic species, the most common method is to attempt use species that are successful in similar environments and latitudes elsewhere. This technique involves comparing the climate of the planting area with other equivalent climatic areas around the world. Then species can be evaluated based on their performance in species trials with similar conditions, or based on their performance in their native range (Turnbull 1986).

For certain species some of this work has already been done, and information is exchanged via data banks and other information on species (see Resources).

What Timber Trees Might Be Suited to the Conditions?

After determining the desired end-uses/services and the environmental conditions, review information about timber species. Local experiences, relevant literature, traditional practices, databases, and species trials from similar conditions can all be valuable sources of information. Species that potentially could perform well on the site and that meet the end-use and management objectives of the project create a preliminary comprehensive list of potential species. This initial list may then be narrowed down by eliminating species based on practical considerations such as availability.

Understanding Genetic Variability

There is tremendous genetic variation within a single species. As a result, there are dramatic differences in growth rates and performance from different seed sources from a single species. These genetic variations can affect productivity as much as variation among species (Wadsworth 1997). For this reason, it is wise to test several different selections of a species to determine which is optimal for the project.

Testing and Trials

The long-term nature of timber production usually precludes the possibility of testing a new species for a full rotation, from planting through to harvest and market. The most reliable information comes from species trials conducted in formal, designed experiments that examine all phases of growth (MacDicken 1994). However, since this is usually not feasible, even one or two years of informal species trials is valuable. No amount of research and advice can substitute for test plantings on the intended planting site. The trial period typically involve planting a number of species, and when possible a range of seed sources (varieties and provenances) within each species.

The performance of these species can then be observed. Some early indicators for timber production include the following (after Wadsworth 1997):

- Early height growth is a good indicator of adaptation of species to a site.
- Uniform growth of individual trees denotes favorable conditions.
- Self-pruning is a sign of a favorable site.
- Susceptibility to insects and diseases is minimal on sites to which trees are well-adapted.

The time and expense devoted to testing candidate species should be viewed as an investment. As with any other business venture, starting on a small scale and observing the results will aid in successful expansion to a larger scale planting. It is also an important form of risk-management, preventing growers from staking scarce time, land, and resources on species that do not perform as expected. One or two years of species trials will serve to eliminate more species from the list, and narrow the candidates down to those with the greatest possibility for success on the site.

References

Dawson, I., and J. Were. 1997. Collecting germplasm from trees—some guidelines. In: Agroforestry Today, Vol 9, No 2, ICRAF House, United Nations Avenue, Gigiri, PO Box 30677, Nairobi, Kenya; Email: aftoday@cgnet.com; Web: http://www.cgiar.org/icraf

Evans, J. 1992. Plantation Forestry in the Tropics: tree planting for industrial, social, environmental, and agroforestry purposes. Clarendon Press, Oxford, UK.

Lemmens, R.H.M.J, I. Soerianegara, and W.C. Wong (eds). 1995. Plant Resources of South-East Asia (PROSEA) No. 5(2). Timber Trees: Minor Commercial Timbers. Backhuys Publishers, Leiden, The Netherlands.

MacDicken, K.G. 1994. Selection and Management of Nitrogen-Fixing Trees. Winrock International, Morrilton, Arkansas, USA.

Thaman, R.R. and W.A. Whistler. 1996. A Review of the Uses and Status of Trees and Forests in Land-Use Systems in Samoa, Tonga, Kiribati and Tuvalu. South Pacific Forestry Development Programme, Suva, Fiji.

Turnbull, J.W. (Ed). 1986. Multipurpose Australian Trees and Shrubs. Australian Centre for International Agricultural Research, Canberra, Australia.

Wadsworth, F.H. 1997. Forest Production for Tropical America. USDA Forest Service Agriculture Handbook 710, Washington, DC, USA.

Original Source

This chapter was originally published as *The Overstory* #59.

Further Reading

AS Salim, A.S., *et al.* 1998. Agroforestree database: a tree species reference and selection guide. International Centre for Research in Agroforestry (ICRAF), Nairobi, Kenya. A selection guide for agroforestry trees covering more than 300 species. Valuable for field workers and researchers who are engaged in activities involving trees suitable for agroforestry systems and technologies. Available as CD-ROM from ICRAF and at: http://198.93.235.8/cfdocs/examples/treessd/AFT/AFT.htm

PROSEA. Plant Resources of South-East Asia (PROSEA) Handbooks. PROSEA Foundation. A valuable series on plant resources for Southeast Asia which is useful to all tropical regions. Order through: PROSEA Network Office, c/o Research and Development Centre for Biology (RDCB-LIPI), Jalan Ir. H. Juanda 22, P.O. Box 234, Bogor 16122, Indonesia. Tel: +62-251-322859, 370934; Fax: +62-251-370934; Email: prosea@indo.net.id; Web: http://www.bib.wau.nl/prosea/home.html.

Farm, Community and Tree Network (formerly Nitrogen Fixing Tree Association). 1989-1994. NFT Highlights. Nitrogen Fixing Tree Association, Morrilton, Arkansas, USA. Concise summary of information about multipurpose trees and shrub species: http://www.winrock.org/forestry/factpub/factsh.htm or order hardcopies from Winrock International. Many available in Spanish, French, Indonesian, Chinese, Vietnamese, and Khmer.

Coppice-with-Standards: New Forestry with Ancient Roots

Peter Bane

Coppice-with-standards is a two-story woodland management system where among cut trees or "coppice," some trees are left to grow as larger size timber, called "standards." This traditional system supports sustainable production of timber and nontimber forest products, while enhancing ecosystem diversity and wildlife habitat.

The forest-dwelling cultures of northern Europe developed cultural methods of woodland management well suited to sustaining both permanent forest and a continuous flow of woodland products to support their societies.

A permanent system of forest cultivation called coppice-with-standards evolved in the British Isles over the past thousand years, which provided a large range of products—from construction timber to fencing and furniture parts to fruits, nuts, honey, and wild game—while maintaining continuous forest

Coppice-with-standards maintained a diverse mixed-age forest while providing a continuous supply of varied wood products for the local economy (left). "Veteran" trees were left to create wide park-like spaces in the woods where in autumn and winter forest crafts were worked: bodging, carving, and the making of hurdles and charcoal (right). (photos: P. Bane)

cover. "Coppice" is the practice of cutting trees to the ground purposely to stimulate resprouting. The word also refers to the regrowth itself. "Standards" are the trees selected (often planted) to grow into large timber.

The continuous cutting of small blocks of coppice creates a mosaic of environments that offers much more diverse habitat for game animals and birds than the native forest itself. These "fells," or management blocks—usually no more than an acre in size— also provide patches of higher light intensity within the forest, which in turn stimulate a tremendous profusion of flowering and fruiting shrubs and wildflowers.

Pollarding is similar to coppicing in that the trees are regularly cut back in order to rejuvenate the tops so that small diameter fuelwood can be harvested. However, pollarded trees are cut not at the ground, but about 2m (6 feet) above the ground. This practice preserved the basic tree form and also prevented animals from browsing the tender new sprouts.

Unlike most coniferous trees, many deciduous hardwoods will resprout vigorously from the stump when cut. Although some of the roots die back when the top is cut, much of the original root mass of the tree survives. From reserves of energy in the roots, the

Coppice cutting encourages profuse regrowth and a great diversity of flowering understory plants which supported game, bees, and medicinal uses. (photo: P. Bane)

tree regrows very rapidly, often sprouting 10–30 new stems, which can grow 1–5 meters (4–15 feet) in a single season. Traditionally, most woodcutting was done during the autumn and winter, after the agricultural harvest, when attention could be put on less critical chores. Besides helping to balance the annual cycle of domestic labor, this practice had many other

As the standards mature, the canopy gradually closes and growth of the underwood slows. These standards are approaching a harvestable size. (photo: P. Bane)

advantages. Wood harvested while the trees are dormant is lower in moisture and makes both longer-lasting timber and better fuel. Winter cutting also conserved the tree's energy by matching the natural cycle of vegetative regeneration. Temperate zone root energy reserves are highest in the dark months of the year as the trees adapt to cold weather by shedding their leaves and preparing for new growth in spring.

The repeated cutting had an additional benefit that is not immediately obvious: it prolonged the life of the trees, often two, three, or four, times their "natural" span. There are ash "stools" (the stumps from which regrowth occurs) in England over a thousand years old still growing coppice. The primary design of coppice-with-standards, however, is to support the yield of many forest products from a small area.

As each fell of mature woodland was harvested, the regrowth would be graded by the woodsmen. Superior stems would be selected as "tellers," the young precursors to "standards." In addition to tellers there were two classes of standards. Older yet were the "veterans," and in the French system, the "old-bark" were yet more venerable. Inferior trees, whether slower growing, prone to disease, or mis-shapen, would be coppiced for poles, wattle (smaller pieces for weaving into a kind of movable fencing for livestock), and fuelwood. The tops and branches were sometimes fed to cattle as fodder. In modern management of coppice-with-standards, young tellers are often planted from selected stock after the harvest of mature overwood.

Fells were harvested about every six to seven years, the irregularity permitting adaptation to a variable climate: a cold summer or a dry year with poor growth could be accommodated in the system. The thinning of the tellers and of the subsequent classes of standards was done with a mind to maintaining an open canopy where about half the light came directly from the sun and the other half indirectly from the sky. The overstory was thinned to maintain optimal growth conditions both for the remaining trees and for the underwood. The regular harvest of young trees and of coppice kept timber and wood processing labor to a minimum, a factor of critical importance to a society lacking power tools or fossil fuels.

"Standards" are left to grow to a size suitable for timber. The underwood was cut on a six- to seven-year rotation. This coppice shows standards amidst one-year growth. (photo: P. Bane)

Timbers were shaped with adze and froe, by hand. Firewood and poles were cut with an axe.

A sampling of tropical and subtropical timber species which have been used in coppice systems

Albizia lebbeck	*Paulownia tomentosa*
Dalbergia sissoo	*Senna siamea*
Eucalyptus species (E. grandis, E. alba, E. saligna, E. rostrata, etc.)	*Shorea robusta*
Gmelina arborea	*Tectona grandis*

The splitting of large logs, whether for firewood or fencing, was a custom adopted by Americans in response to the conditions of their forests: vast numbers of huge trees covered the continent when the first settlers moved westward. In preindustrial Europe, the notion of growing a tree to a great size, only to chop it into small pieces, was seen as wasteful of human energy. Poles and timbers were grown to the size needed, and no more, while fire-wood was cut at just the dimension required for stoves and fireplaces.

Overstory and underwood were usually of different species. This made the woodland ecologically resilient, as canopy and ground cover exploited not only different soil layers and nutrients, but grew at different seasons. The coppice and ground covers did about two-thirds of their photosynthesis for the year before the overstory came into leaf.

Oak, ash, beech, and elm were commonly the standards, while hazel, alder, lime (linden, *Tilia cordata*), willow, and hornbeam were often grown in the understory. Hazel yielded not only edible nuts, but fodder from the young shoots, and like willow, made excellent basketry, while lime leaves were eaten and the trees usually allowed to flower before harvesting, to provide a flavored honey crop. Lime was also made into greenwood furniture, while hornbeam went for fuel, and alder (a nitrogen-fixer) bolstered soil fertility. Many of these same species have additional medicinal or craft use, providing dyes, seeds, and flowers of value.

The understory was made more complex by the retention or cultivation of many fruiting shrubs such as crab apple, rowan, service tree, wild cherry, and roses. Wide pathways through the woods made access to the forest easier, and gave a place for much of the woodcraft to take place. They also introduced more edge that increased the available light and enhanced the productivity of the woodland. After each felling there would be an explosion of wildflowers the following spring, while greenwood growth increased the forage for wild game, an important meat source.

Coppice-with-standards, and strict laws requiring the retention of at least 8–20 large trees per acre, ensured the presence of all age classes of major timber trees in a small area, while enormously increasing the diversity and productivity of the forest. The system maintained undisturbed soil cover, provided timber of the sizes required for construction with minimal added processing, gave constant employment for foresters, bodgets (greenwood craftsmen), carpenters, and herdsmen, while providing a steady stream of useful products for the household and local economies.

Coppice systems have been adapted to other parts of the world. In Korea, a system called sunchon is used to grow pine standards between rows of locust (*Robinia* sp.) coppiced for fuelwood, while in southern France, Aleppo pine is grown over evergreen oak. In India sal (*Shorea robusta*) is grown over teak, the overstory providing frost protection during cool winter months to the more sensitive teak below.

We can learn much from this ancient woodland art as we too seek to regenerate both forests and forestry.

References

Law, B. 1994. "A Permaculture Woodland." In: Permaculture Magazine (UK) #6, Summer 1994, Hampshire, UK.

Rackham, O. 1978, Trees and Woodland in the British Landscape. J.M. Dent, London.

Stanford, G. 1976. Short-rotation Forestry—Principles and Practices. Greenhills Foundation, Cedar Hill, TX.

Original Source

This article by guest author Peter Bane was originally published in The Permaculture Activist, No. 40. For subscription information write to, Subscriptions, Permaculture Activist, P.O. Box 1209, Black Mountain, NC 28711 USA. Tel: 828-298-2812, Fax: 828-298-6441, Email: pcactiv@metalab.unc.edu; Web: http://www.permacultureactivist.net/

This excerpt was originally published as *The Overstory* #47.

Further Reading

Reid, R., and G. Wilson. 1985. Agroforestry in Australia and New Zealand. Goodard and Dobson, 486

Station Street, Box Hill, Victoria 3128, Australia. Describes coppice systems with primarily Eucalyptus species.

National Academy of Sciences. 1979. Tropical Legumes: Resources for the Future, National Academy Press, Washington, DC. Covers several important hardwoods which coppice.

Wadsworth, F.H. 1997. Forest Production for Tropical America. USDA Forest Service, Agricultural Handbook 710. Excellent examples of coppicing from tropical America.

Optimizing Commercial Timber Potential from Farm Forestry

Richard Finlay-Jones

There are many ways growers can increase the commercial potential of timber stands on their land. These methods can be divided into separate areas: planning, establishment, management, and harvesting. Following harvest, marketing the product according to specific customer requirements may dictate the level of processing required and the potential for increased returns.

Planning

Plantation planning provides a good method of working out a balance between environmental and economic benefits using commercial tree species (Reid 1999, Abel 1997). This requires that the landholder to develop a property management plan, which includes having an understanding of the existing problems of the property as well as some ideas about the local timber marketplace and its potential.

What Trees Where?

This is the hardest part of the planning process. As trees may take some time to grow and develop before any commercial returns can be made, it is important to work out where the trees can be grown without creating any major problems for the rest of the property. The trees should enhance the property, its appeal and function, whilst contributing to its commercial profitability.

Species selection can be difficult and can be determined by assessing:

- presence of existing commercial tree species in the landscape;
- presence of trials and demonstrations in the local catchment;
- discussions with local timber merchants and contractors;
- product specification and quality requirements;
- landholder species preferences.

Some small scale trials may often be required before any large scale planting is carried out. These trials often serve as a guide only in their early years and best assist in decision making at harvesting.

Layout and Design

The most efficient design for commercial plantations is the uniform block woodlot. Uniform spacings and row layouts allow access for vehicles, labour and machinery, reducing labour costs and increasing efficiencies, subsequently adding to the bottom line. These designs however do not always suit all landholders and properties, so design efficiency compromises may often occur. Species layout locations may also vary with the landscape, aspect, slope and soil type.

At this stage it is also important to work out how much can be managed as part of the entire property management plan given the restrictions on labour, finances and land.

Seedling Selection

Given that the species choices have been made and the design of the plantation determined (Cole-Clark 1997, 1998, 1999), it is important that seedlings are ordered well in advance. Local provenance varieties of the desired species may result in increased local disease resistance, however this is often difficult given the amount and variety of commercial seed available. Some landholders may choose to collect their own seed and grow their own seedlings to save money. However commercial seed collectors and nurseries have developed specialised skills to do just that, and consequently the quality of seedlings grown by different sources may be variable.

Site Preparation

Establishing a good planting site for the seedlings is important to give them a good start. Deep ripping may be a useful method, depending upon the soil type and the presence of hardpan. Mounding of rows may also serve to lift seedlings from poorer draining areas as well as concentrating the topsoil for better access to nutrients. For steeper slopes, spot cultivation is an option to increase the ability of air, water and roots to penetrate the surface soil layers.

Plantation preparation in NSW Australia showing "tram tracks" which allow large machinery passes along the wider rows. (photo: GHG Management Pty Ltd)

Soil Analysis and Treatment

Soil analysis is useful to determine whether nutrients are limiting and if so which ones, whether pH is optimal or whether soil structural adjustments need to be made to the rows. It is surprising how little of this is actually carried out in practice. The process of soil treatment and/or fertilisation may be carried out in conjunction with cultivation of the rows and may serve to benefit plant growth and development.

Weed Control

Control of competitive weeds is particularly important in higher rainfall areas. Experiences to date on the North Coast of NSW suggest that herbicides remain the most efficient and effective method of controlling weeds in these areas. Some sites may require several herbicide treatments in the first few years, both pre and post planting.

Work is presently being carried out to assess the best use of grass species to reduce herbicide use and increase soil mulching potential.

Control of Browsing Animals Fencing to eliminate browsing animals is imperative. In areas where browsing animals present problems, strategies such as fences, sacrificial plantings and the use of farm dogs may prove useful.

Establishment

All this work, and we still haven't planted a tree yet!

Timing

The essential part of all this planning is timing. The site is now prepared, fenced and clear of weeds. The seedlings are just about to arrive. Where's the labour to help? Is it going to rain?

The best time to plant the seedlings is when regular periods of rain are forecast. Welcome to the risky part of establishment. Ensure the seedlings are well watered prior to planting, and that the soil is either moist or rain is due. Planting in light regular rain is ideal on the North Coast, as soils can dry out very quickly and stress the planted seedlings.

Check the Seedlings (again)

When the seedlings are picked up, or they arrive at the property, they need to be thoroughly checked for:

- health/vigour
- root:shoot ratio
- root deformations
- presence of pests or disease
- soil moisture

It may be necessary to order a few extra seedlings to allow for inspection of root development and soil mix.

Planting

Planting should be carried out by experienced planters and planting crews. This will ensure good survival rates and early growth, without problems associated with root deformation. Experienced crews also ensure more uniform planting densities and spacing between trees. In many cases, it may be cheaper to plant trees more densely and allow greater selection between trees at thinning.

Management

Plantations need to be managed for the target market(s). In some areas, such as the North Coast of New South Wales, Australia, the highest prices are being achieved for pole and veneer markets. Access to these markets is somewhat limited by distance, however where these markets are accessible the need to thin and prune the trees becomes greater.

The closer the landholder is to the mill, the better the potential for commercial returns.

Thinning

Thinning is required in densely planted plantations to remove the smaller and lower quality trees in order to allow the better trees to grow on. This ensures that the quality and growth of the entire stand is improved.

The more dense the plantation, and the better the site quality, the earlier thinning will be required. Thinning should be carried out when growth of the better quality trees is limited by the stand. This can be monitored using the diameter tape.

Models for growth rates may provide some indication as to the presence of markets for plantation thinnings. On the NSW North Coast first plantation thinnings markets are beginning to appear in the form of fibre for pulp, biomass for power generation and ethanol production although returns at this stage are limited and much of this work is in trial phase.

Pruning

Pruning to ensure a single leader (bole) and pruning to ensure clearwood production (branch) should occur early in the stand life and be carried out regularly. A balance needs to be struck between the costs of pruning and the potential economic returns from the product. Veneer logs on the NSW North Coast has be turned down to 7.5cm, indicating that this may be the desirable size of the knotty core for product destined for this market.

Less emphasis needs to be placed on branch pruning for pole markets, particularly if the species are self pruning.

Nutrition

The trees and soil should be monitored regularly for nutrient deficiencies and/or problems. Some plantation owners utilise both soil and foliar fertilisers to maximise growth rates during the plantation's life.

Pests and Diseases

Like any agricultural crop, the trees should be monitored for pest and disease invasion. Christmas beetle can have a devastating annual effect on some plantations, and some control techniques are presently being trialed. At this stage on the NSW North Coast, little work is being carried out to test the economics of pest and disease control.

Integrated Grazing and Cropping

With the plantation up and away, there may be commercial opportunities awaiting landholders within the inter-rows of the plantations. The use of shade tolerant pasture species for stock grazing is being trialed in Northern NSW, increasing the potential of land being utilised for commercial plantations.

In addition there may also be some potential for the use of the inter-rows for production of commercial vegetation species, such as shade tolerant foliage and flower varieties, although this is also very much in the trial phase.

Integrated Native Forest Management

On the NSW North Coast many private properties have an abundance of private native regrowth forest which is often underutilised as a commercial resource. The growing of plantations close to such areas can result in both commercial and environmental benefits for the landholder and the community. In NSW, native forests are vigorous competitors and can assist plantations by providing some pest and disease control mechanisms. In addition, native forests can provide a valuable seed source for vegetative regeneration following final harvest of a plantation.

Supplementary Planting

Some plantation owners are trialing the establishment of higher value rainforest species below the eucalypt canopy in order to maximise production and returns per hectare. There are some questions as to the efficiency of management, the competition for water and nutrients, and the impacts of other forms of competition from mixing species.

Harvest

Harvest time is often determined by the growth and the development of the trees, the nature of the marketplace and the attitude of the grower to risk. Harvest may be a gradual process taking many years or the single process of removal of the final crop. Harvesting to maximise commercial returns theoretically occurs at a time when product prices are high (demand is high, supply is limited).

Due to the high level of risk involved, harvest operations should be carried out by experienced and skilled contractors. Better operators will maximise commercial returns through improved economies and efficiencies whilst reducing the risk of injury to the product and property. Harvesting will normally occur in commercial lots (loads) to maximise efficiencies of transport and processing. Consequently access to the stand becomes an important influence on harvest efficiency.

Marketing & Processing

Landholders need to effectively market their wood to their customers in order to maximise profitable returns. The greater the level of value adding, the greater the potential to be a price maker instead of a price taker. If growers can tailor the end product to the precise requirements of a particular customer; then the grower will have a greater potential to increase the economic returns from the plantation.

Conclusion

Increasing the commercial potential of plantations requires sound planning, management and harvest techniques. An adequate balance needs to be met between the cost of inputs, particularly labour; and the potential value of the end product. The link between planning, management and harvest is the final product quality, the requirements of the market place and the market value. If the landholder is able to market tailored products direct to the consumer the input costs are higher, however the potential for profitable returns are far greater.

References

Abel, N., *et al*. 1997. Design Principles For Farm Forestry, RIRDC/LWRRDC/FWPRDC/ JVAP.

Cole-Clark, B. 1997. What Wood Where. NSW Dept of Land and Water Conservation.

Cole-Clark, B. 1998. Pasture Improvement of Dry Hardwood Regrowth Forest A North Coast of NSW Timber/Meat Option. In: 1998 Proceedings of Australian Forest Growers Conference, July 1998, pp 41-49.

Cole-Clark, B. 1999. Planning For Farm Forestry, A Practical Guide. NSW Dept of land and Water Conservation.

Reid, R. 1999. Have you got too many trees? A case for thinning hard and early in eucalypt plantations for sawlogs. Agroforestry News p3-5,

Sandstrom, M. (Various). Greening Australia North Coast.

Original Source

This article is adapted from *Agroforestry News*, Volume 9, Issue 1 with the kind permission of the author and publisher. *Agroforestry News* features practical and timely information for farm foresters growing timber with many examples from Australia. Address: Agroforestry News Editor, NRE Port Phillip Region, Locked Bag 3000, Box Hill, 3128 Victoria, Australia; Fax: +61-3-9296-4722;   Email: wendy.davies@nre.vic.gov.au.

This excerpt was originally printed as *The Overstory* #67.

Farm Forestry Extension

Rowan Reid

The infinite possibilities inherent in farm forestry, and the wide variation in farmers' needs, resources and aspirations mean that there are no "best-bet" species, spatial arrangements or management "recipes" suited to more than a few growers within a region. This suggests that rather than promoting particular options, the objective of farm forestry extension should be to enable farmers and other stakeholders to play an active role in the development of options that best meet their own interests and resources.

Most definitions of farm forestry focus on what the forests look like or their purpose. This has led to widespread acceptance of the notion that farm forestry is part of a continuum from large-scale monoculture plantations down to small-scale plantings. From this perspective it is easy to lose sight of what makes farm forestry unique and the need to develop specially targeted research and extension programs for this sector (Alexandra and Hall 1998). Our working definition of farm forestry emphasises the decision maker rather than the outcome: *Farm forestry is the commitment of resources by farmers, alone or in partnerships, to the establishment or management of forests on their land*. What clearly distinguishes a "farm forest" or "agroforest" from a corporate, industrial or government forest is not scale, it is ownership. Not just ownership of the land or the trees, but ownership of the decision whether or not to carry out the project, and how. Farm forestry and agroforestry are therefore about choice: farmers choosing to commit their resources to the development and management of forests for, amongst other things, commercial return.

Farmers establish and manage their forests for any combination of benefits. They may place an emphasis on a single outcome, such as timber production or biodiversity, or they may seek to balance a range of benefits in a multipurpose planting. Their priorities may vary over the farm and change over time. A forest initially established or managed for wildlife or land protection might later be harvested for timber or valued for its beauty. Forests on farms may increase agricultural production or simply displace it. They might be sustainable, even improve economic,

social and environmental capital, or they may deplete these assets. The farmer, or their partners, may profit from farm forestry or come to regret their involvement. Farm forestry is different because farmers (non-industrial, non-corporate private landowners) are different.

Research and Extension

Farm forestry research and extension becomes a process of change through *"facilitating social learning"* (King 2000) which encourages farmers, communities, industry and governments to clearly define their own interests and expectations and to acknowledge where the costs and benefits lie. Rather than simply trying to get farmers to grow forests specially designed to solve the problems that outsiders perceive as critical, the aim is to empower communities to the point that they are able to articulate, design and implement forestry practices that best meet their needs. The degree to which the outcome of such a process will also meet the needs or interests of particular industry sectors, governments agencies or conservation groups will largely depend on the degree to which there are shared goals, a capacity and willingness amongst farmers to act, adequate rewards for farmers who do provide the services or products sought by others, and the degree to which penalties are imposed for non-compliance.

Fit Forestry Into The Existing Farming Culture

Rather than try to mould farmers into the dominant forestry culture the real challenge lies in fitting forestry into a farming culture and helping farmers identify opportunities to use trees and forests to express their own attitudes and aspirations. Farming cultures vary and reflect the shared ideas, beliefs, values and knowledge within the rural communities thus forming the basis of social action and response. Cultures are dynamic but only change slowly with the passage of time, changing circumstances and changes in the population. In any event, to suggest we need to change farmer attitudes implies that their existing attitudes are inappropriate or illegitimate—a morally questionable starting point.

Although attitudes are difficult to measure or describe, behaviour might be seen as an expression of an individual's attitudes and beliefs within the context of existing knowledge, resources, opportunities and threats. The reluctance of farmers to invest in production-focused farm forestry options could be seen as an expression of their broader social, environmental and economics interests and their judicious wish to reduce risk and retain management flexibility. Rejection of profitable options or an unwillingness to manage an established forest does not necessary mean that farmers are "irrational."

Neither should we assume that farmers do not have long-term goals. To the contrary, their long-term aspirations provide a basis for short term decision making. Landowners commonly talk of passing the farm onto future generations in a better state, not exposing the farm to unnecessary risk, protecting and enhancing the productive value of the property and increasing property value (Rickenbach et al 1998, Francis 2000). Forestry is clearly a powerful and useful tool that farmers and rural communities can use to achieve these goals and express their own cultures. Is it not easier to "go with the flow" and allow these honourable environmental and social imperatives to drive revegetation than to continue to argue that good forestry requires a timber focus and a profitable DCF analysis?

Capitalise on Farmers' Comparative Advantage

Farmers, especially where they are involved in alternative enterprises, are able to capture a wider range of non-timber values than those usually available to industrial growers or even off-farm investors. They may be able to take advantage of environmental grants, existing farm machinery and possibly even idle labour to establish and manage of plantations. As farmers, they are also in a position to realise the shelter, land protection and wildlife benefits of well-designed plantations. Those living on the farm are also able to enjoy the landscape values "unseen" by corporate investors and their shareholders.

Rather than viewing these non-timber values as further reason why farmers should be interested in best-bet forestry production regimes (Grist and Burns, 2000) the real opportunity lies in assisting farmers to select and design forestry projects that focus on them

realising the easily captured, short-term values. For many farmers the motivation, resources and enthusiasm to grow trees for these values already exists (Wilson et al 1995). Further encouragement and financial support may come from communities "paying" landowners for the off-site environmental values that their forests offer as proposed in the Australian government's discussion paper on Managing Natural Resources (AFFA 1999).

Some are threatened by the devaluation of timber from its status as the primary focus of forestry. If farmers are able to justify the establishment and management of trees on the basis of their short-term non-timber values, then whether or not timber is the primary goal or is able to provide a real return on investment is not important.

Aim for a Forest that is Viable to Harvest?

Where shelter, land protection, wildlife or other non-wood values are seen as significant benefits of a growing forest it could be assumed that landowners will only consider harvesting if the return from timber covers both the costs of harvesting and compensation for the loss of non-timber values. This would suggest that as farmers place increasing emphasis on the non-timber values of forests buyers may need to pay more, not less, for the timber in order to encourage them to harvest (Dole 1993). It also suggests that the farmers are unlikely to specially design and manage their forests in order to increase the future timber value (economic rational behaviour) unless this also complements short-term non-timber values.

The protection of non-wood values might also be expected to dissuade farmers from clearfelling large areas for timber. As a result, the costs of harvesting and marketing the timber from these forests might be expected to be greater than in timber-focused plantations thereby adding to the price the landowner must receive in order to justify harvesting. In any event, any economies achieved in harvesting might be expected to be lost in the need to compensate farmers for the loss of non-wood values. This suggests that the potential for farm forestry to produce timber for industry depends on farmers achieving high standing log values and having access to appropriate scale harvesting and marketing procedures.

Whether landowner's reluctance to harvest means that log prices will need to be higher for multipurpose forestry than those sufficient to drive investment in timber-only plantations is not clear. What is certain is that those factors that commonly threaten the economic viability of timber-focused plantation options, namely rotation length and site productivity, will not necessarily be the major determinants of the viability of multipurpose farm forestry. The decision to plant or manage forests on farms is likely to be justified by the non-wood values alone, whether the forests ever contributes to the country's timber supply will largely depend on whether the forest is "viable to harvest". The current approach to identifying farm forestry options is based on whether the future returns make it "viable to plant"—the result being regimes that are of little or no benefit to farmers.

Actions that may facilitate spontaneous farm forestry development

No longer need farm forestry research and development battle against the obvious economic impediments and disadvantages facing farmers as they compete to grow full cost recovery production-focused regimes. No longer will extension program focus on the questionable task of trying to change attitudes and cultures. Neither do we have any justification to ignore the prospects of growing timber in areas considered too dry, too isolated or too small for "profitable" forestry.

The following are some examples of the types of practical research and development projects that might help increase the prospects of farmers producing timber and other forest products from multipurpose plantations:

- Social research to identify landowner motivations, resources and performance criteria rather than assuming landowners will select options on the basis of their apparent long term profitability as suggested by the Net Present Value or Internal Rate of Return;
- Low impact harvesting methods for irregular, small scale and/or diverse multipurpose plantations;
- Silvicultural management techniques for mixed species or multipurpose plantations that focus on the higher value log markets;

- Results-orientated codes of practice that encourage innovation and allow landowners considerable latitude in the way they achieve socially desirable environmental objectives (an alternative to the current prescriptive input-orientated codes);
- Wood product research into the value adding of farm grown logs to increase industry confidence and thereby increase their preparedness to pay more for logs that meet their strict market specifications;
- New product research and market development for alternative wood or non-wood products from farm trees;
- Marketing mechanisms for the sale of environmental and social services from farm forestry to ensure farmers are rewarded for off-site environmental and social benefits.
- Knowledge of the relationships between the management of trees for timber (silvicultural management and harvesting) and non-timber values highlighting opportunities for multipurpose production and agroforestry.

Fitting forestry into a farming culture is about farmers growing and managing forests that provide a wide range of values rather than simplistic production focused plantations. The time frames are too long, the risks too great and the opportunities for other values too obvious. Farmers are commonly willing to compromise the long-term focus on timber in order to ensure that other values are retained. This not only ensures early rewards but reduces the risks associated with single purpose forestry options.

References

AFFA (1999) Managing natural resources in rural Australia for a sustainable future. A discussion paper for developing a national policy. Department of Agriculture, Fisheries and Forestry, Canberra

Alexandra, J. and Hall, M. (1998). Creating a viable farm forestry industry in Australia—what will it take. RIRDC Publication No 98/74.

Anderson, J. (1998). Extension for multiple interest forestry. In: Johnson J. E. (ed) Proceedings of a Symposium—Extension Forestry: Bridging the gap between research and application. IUFRO, July 19–24, Blacksburg Virginia.

Commonwealth of Australia (1997). Plantations for Australia: The 2020 Vision, Canberra.

Costello, T. (1999) Tips from a travelling soul-searcher. Allen & Unwin, Australia

Dole, D. (1993) The economics of non-industrial private forest management. Unpublished Ph.D thesis. University of Berkeley.

Rickenbach, M.G., D.B. Kittredge, D. Dennis and T. Stevens (1998) Ecosystem management: Capturing the concept for woodland owners. Journal of Forestry April 1998 18:23

Francis, J. (2000) Extension approach needs rethink. Australian Farm Journal 9(11) 78:81

Finley, J. (2000) Writing a history on the land through stewardship. Australian Farm Journal 9(11) 31:33

Hurley, P.J. (1996). Government assistance for private forestry—the Farm Forestry Agreement Scheme in Victoria. Aust. For. 49(3) 181–188

King, C.A. (2000) Systematic Processes for facilitating social learning: Challenging the legacy. Thesis presented to the Swedish University of Agricultural Sciences.

Pearson, C., Coakes, S. and Aslin, H. (2000). Social research to support successful farm forestry. In: Socio-economic research to support successful farm forestry. RIRDC/LWRRDC/FWPRDC Joint Venture Agroforestry Program. RIRDC Publication No. 01/13.

Race, D. and Fulton, A. (2000). Strategies for improving landholder's response to farm forestry development. In Socio-economic research to support successful farm forestry. RIRDC/LWRRDC/FWPRDC Joint Venture Agroforestry Program. RIRDC Publication No. 01/13.

Race, D., Buchy, M. and Fulton, A. (2001). A dynamic context: Farm forestry extension in Australia. Paper presented at the IUFRO Working Party (S6.06–03) Symposium Forestry Extension—Assisting Forest Owner, Farmer and Stakeholder Decision-Making 29th Oct–2 Nov 2001. http://www.anu.edu.au/forestry/IUFROFE2001/index.html

Reid, R. and P. Stephen (2002) The Australian Master Tree-Grower Program1996–2001Development, delivery and impact of a national outreach and education program. A report for the RIRDC/L&W Australia/FWPRDC Joint Venture Agroforestry Program.

Grist, P. and K. Burns (2000) Plantation: Combining commercial and environmental benefits. OUTLOOK 2000 New Directions/Future Markets, Volume One 167–179.

Wilson, S.M., Whitham, J.A.H., Bhati, U.N., Horvath, D. and Tran, Y.D. (1995). Survey of trees on Australian farms: 1993–4, ABARE Research Report 95.7, ABARE, Canberra.

Original Source

This article was excerpted with the kind permission of the author from:

Reid, R. 2002. "Fitting farm forestry into a dryland farming landscape—not replacing it!—Achieving spontaneous farm forestry development." Australian Master TreeGrower Program, School of Resource Management, The University of Melbourne, Melbourne, Australia.

For more information about the Master TreeGrower Program, contact:

Australian Master TreeGrower Program
Department of Forestry
The Institute of Land & Food Resources
The University of Melbourne
Victoria 3010, Australia
Tel: 61 3 8344 5011; Fax: 61 3 9349 4172
Email: rfr@unimelb.edu.au
Web: http://www.mtg.unimelb.edu.au/farmers_fo rest.htm

This excerpt was originally published as *The Overstory* #112.

More than Trees: Understory and Nontimber Forest Products

Whether cultivated or wild, forests are much more than trees. Making good use of the understory and nontimber aspects of a forest can support economic and conservation objectives simultaneously.

Section Contents

Understory: A Unique Niche for Valuable Crops

Kim M. Wilkinson and Craig R. Elevitch

Traditionally, tropical farmers have always managed and exploited the shady environment under trees, called the understory. There are many valuable cash and subsistence crops that thrive in the shady climate under trees. When cultivated in combination with tree or forest crops, understory crops enable farmers and foresters to diversify and increase their yields while reducing labor and making more efficient use of land. The understory is a niche worth cultivating.

Plantings that take advantage of the understory range from simple systems consisting of one species in the overstory and one in the understory, to complex systems with many layers of trees, shrubs, and herbaceous plants stacked together as appropriate for their needs.

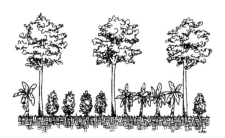

Understory crops and timber trees

A few successful examples involving a simple overstory/understory mix:

- Macadamia nut trees with coffee understory (Hawai'i)
- Native forest areas cultivated underneath for traditional medicinal or culturally valuable plants (in Hawai'i, these can include maile for leis, kava, and a variety of herbaceous medicinals)
- Timber trees (e.g., *Cordia alliodora*) with coffee or cacao underneath (Central and South America)
- Teak plantations with patchouli (an essential oil) underneath (Indonesia)
- Sesbania, a nitrogen fixing tree (for firewood, mulch, or animal fodder) supporting and shading passion fruit vines (Africa)
- Coconut plantations with taro, kava, or cattle underneath (Polynesia and Melanesia)

- Heavy-shade mixed reforestation projects with cut flowers and foliage (such as anthuriums, heliconias, etc.) underneath (Central America)

Examples of shade tolerant understory crops (some are highly shade-loving, some tolerate light shade only):

Essential oils	lemon grass, vetiver, patchouli
Spices	pepper vine, cinnamon, ginger, vanilla, cardamom, wild turmeric
Fruits	pineapple, annona species, and guava
Root crops and vegetables	taro, arrowroot, yams, long beans, and velvet bean
Herbs	oregano, basil, and chili pepper
Building/fiber materials	rattan, fan palms
Mushrooms	many culinary and medicinal fungi thrive in the understory
Others	coffee, tea, cacao, betel vine, kava

Some farmers discover that one of their current crops actually thrives in understory conditions, and rather than focus on exploiting their understory, they may look for trees to use as a canopy for their existing crop. In Kona, Hawai'i, for example, several sustainable Kona coffee farmers are experimenting with interplanting timber or nitrogen fixing trees to provide a light canopy for their coffee trees.

The understory is a unique microclimate that enables farmers and foresters to diversify, increase their yields, reduce labor, and make more efficient use of land. As with any new venture, research thoroughly, experiment carefully, and start small as you begin to explore the possibilities for your understory environment.

Further Reading

International Institute of Rural Reconstruction (IIRR). 1990. Agroforestry Technology Information Kit. IIRR, Room 1270, 475 Riverside Dr., New York,

Coffee grows as a complementary crop in the understory of macadamia nuts. Kona, Hawai'i. (photo: C. Elevitch)

NY 10115. One of the most practical references in tropical agroforestry.

Nair, P.K.R. 1993. An Introduction to Agroforestry. Kluwer Academic Publisher. This comprehensive textbook bridges the gap between theoretical and practical knowledge in agroforestry.

Clark, W.C., and R.R. Thaman (eds). 1994. Agro-Forestry in the Pacific Islands: Systems for Sustainability. UNIPUB. Very thorough treatment of agroforestry practices in the Pacific. Includes list and descriptions of many agroforestry species.

Integrating Understory Crops with Tree Crops introduces planning considerations for planting crops with forestry, orchard, or other tree-based systems. Examples of understory intercropping systems in the tropics are included, as well as a species list of over

75 trees, shrubs, and vines used as understory crops: http://agroforestry.net/afg/book.html

Original Source

This chapter was originally published as *The Overstory* #11.

Related Chapters

Integrating Understory and Tree Crops

Kim M. Wilkinson and Craig R. Elevitch

The previous chapter introduced the concept of understory crops. This chapter addresses key planning issues for integrating understory crops with trees.

Crops planted under forest, orchard, or other trees are called "understory crops." Understory crops can be vines, shrubs, herbaceous plants, or shorter trees. When integrated with tree crops, they can provide earlier returns and diversify farm yields. Understory cropping systems can also make more efficient use of land, labor, and resources, while increasing the total productivity of an area.

However, combining understory crops with tree crops is complex, and requires careful planning. The needs of the species to be planted should be well understood, as well as the effect each species will have on the other species in the system. Planning helps to avoid problems, minimize risks, and maximize benefits in crop combinations. Key practical issues in planning understory cropping systems are introduced here.

The Understory Environment

The understory is a unique environment, involving more than just shade. Shade influences air temperature, humidity, soil temperature, soil moisture content, wind movement, and more. These factors impact plants.

The shady environment in the understory can have the following effects:

- Reduces evapotranspiration (evaporation of water through the leaves and branches of the plant), conserving moisture in the plants and reducing water use
- Buffers crops from temperature extremes and fluctuations
- Protects crops from winds
- Suppresses many invasive problem weeds, which tend to prefer open conditions and full sun
- Supports a range of beneficial soil microlife that do not thrive in the open (Nair 1993).

Overstory (Canopy) Species Selection

The upper strata of a multi-layered planting is called the overstory, or canopy. The trees that make up this layer play the key role in creating the understory environment. When planning an understory intercropping system, the overstory is a crucial element. The most influential factors are canopy shape/tree form, canopy foliage type, and tree spacing.

Canopy shape The shape and form of the overstory trees is an important consideration in planning an intercropped system. Some trees have very wide, umbrella-shaped canopies. In contrast, some trees have a very narrow, columnar form. The form and canopy shape of the overstory trees should be used to help determine appropriate spacing for the trees and understory crops. In some cases, the form of the trees can be altered by pruning.

Canopy foliage Some types of tree foliage create dappled sunlight or light shade (e.g. coconut, sesbania, shower tree); others create a thick canopy with dense, heavy shade beneath (e.g. eucalyptus). Although understory crops are selected to tolerate some degree of shade, some light must be available in order for the crops to be productive. The type of foliage should be considered along with canopy shape, to determine the spacing needed to create an optimal understory environment for the crop.

Spacing The spacing of the overstory trees is important to creating the understory environment. If the standard, close spacing of single-species monocultures of forestry or orchard trees is used, usually the understory crops are phased out after few years due to competition for light and space. Compared to single-species plantings for timber or fruit trees, understory cropping systems normally involve a reduced number of trees per acre. The number of trees per acre is usually 25–75% less compared with timber or fruit trees planted alone. This wider spacing may be in a uniform pattern, or in a more random pattern of dispersed trees.

Spacing should be planned to provide an optimal environment for the understory, and minimize competition for space, light, and nutrients. The species growth rate, rooting patterns, and other factors should be taken into account when planning.

Environmental Transition of Understory

One of the important considerations in planning for an integrated understory cropping system is the rate at which the understory environment changes. As the overstory species mature, the understory environment becomes shadier, cooler, and more humid. The understory environmental transition will influence decisions in overstory and understory plant selections and plant spacing. The challenge is to predict when the optimum environmental conditions will occur and how long they will last.

Determining when the optimum environmental conditions will occur affects the understory planting schedule. For example, if understory crops thrive in shade but cannot tolerate full sun, then they should not be planted until the overstory trees have grown enough to provide sufficient shade.

How long favorable environmental conditions will last influences expectations of optimum output from understory crops, thus influencing crop selection, spacing, and scheduling. As overstory trees continue to mature, the understory conditions can be maintained by pruning or thinning the overstory trees. The net benefits of maintaining a set environmental conditions by pruning or thinning will help make decisions in scheduling (Arakaki, 2000).

Because the understory environment changes over time, some farmers may choose to change understory crop species over time. This practice is sometimes called sequential cropping (see Sequential Planting (page 259)), when short-term crops are eventually replaced by longer-term crops. Sequential cropping of understory crops optimizes the productivity of the understory as the environmental conditions change.

Understory Crop Selection

Whether the understory crop is integrated for continuous yields or in a sequential cropping system, species selection is an important consideration. When selecting species, growth and rooting habits should be understood so plants are compatible and not overly competitive for nutrients and space. Understory crops should be integrated in a way that maximizes available light, space, and nutrients, while minimizing competition.

In relation to the overstory trees, understory crops should (after Wadsworth 1997):

- tolerate partial shade
- exploit, at least partially, different soil horizons than the overstory trees
- be shorter than the overstory trees when mature (although some trees may be planned to use the shade as seedlings, but eventually overtake and become part of the upper layer)
- be less susceptible than the overstory trees to diseases they may have in common
- not involve damage to the overstory trees during cultivation or harvest of understory crops.

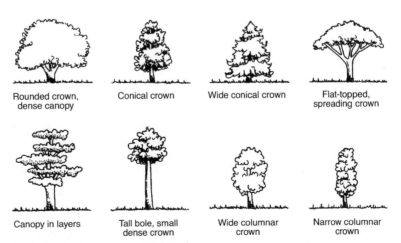

| Rounded crown, dense canopy | Conical crown | Wide conical crown | Flat-topped, spreading crown |
| Canopy in layers | Tall bole, small dense crown | Wide columnar crown | Narrow columnar crown |

Canopy shape and density are important planning considerations

Competition Issues

Understanding the rooting habits, potential allelopathic effects, and growth rates of the overstory species is part of good planning, to ensure that the trees chosen will create a beneficial environment for the understory crops. Some tree species may be too fast-growing or have allelopathic (suppressant) effects on crops, making them inappropriate for this kind of system. For example, ironwood (*Casuarina* species) have been reported to have allelopathic effects crops including sorghum, sunflower, and cowpea (Nair 1993). Other trees may simply have aggressive root systems or growth rates that are incompatible with most understory crops. Likewise, understory crops chosen should not be overly competitive with the overstory tree crops.

A Note on Varieties for Understory Crops

Much of modern agricultural research has focused on growing crops in fully exposed, monocultural (single-species) systems. In fact, many new varieties of crops have been especially selected for high light intensity tolerance and high productivity. For example, coffee trees evolved in the shady understory of tropical forests. Traditional varieties of coffee are grown under the shade of other trees, usually nitrogen-fixing trees that also add nitrogen, control erosion, recycle nutrients, and provide habitat for wildlife. Coffee has been grown intercropped with other trees for centuries (Wadsworth 1997). Agroforesters exploring potential understory crops may benefit from researching traditional varieties of crops, which may be better adapted to the understory environment than recent crop selections.

Understanding Limitations

As with any farm practice, growers should also understand the potential limitations of understory intercropping. These include:

- Shortage of scientific study and information about tree/understory crop interactions
- Risk of unforeseen competition or allelopathic effects
- Greater complexity in management of multiple species and multiple products
- Potential damage to overstory from harvest of the understory, or vice-versa
- Increased challenges of marketing diversified products.

With adequate research and good planning, many of these limitations can be overcome to effectively integrate understory crops with tree crops.

References

Arakaki, A. 2000. Personal communication. University of Hawai'i, Cooperative Extension Service, Molokai.

Nair, P.K.R. 1993. An Introduction to Agroforestry. Kluwer Academic Publisher. This comprehensive textbook bridges the gap between theoretical and practical knowledge in agroforestry.

Wadsworth, F.H. 1997. Forest Production for Tropical America. Agriculture Handbook 710. US Department of Agriculture, Forest Service.

Original Source

This chapter was originally published as *The Overstory #56*.

Sequential Planting

Kim M. Wilkinson and Craig R. Elevitch

Trees are the backbone of agroforestry plantings, but most trees represent a long-term investment. Fruit trees can take three to fifteen years to bear; timber trees usually need to grow fifteen or more years before they can be harvested. These and other long-term tree resources are valuable and necessary, but most farmers cannot afford to devote their land entirely to a crop that will not yield for many years. Sequential planting, a practice wherein short-term crops are planted with and eventually replaced by long-term trees, is a system that enables farmers to invest for the future while making a return in the present.

A classic example of sequential planting comes from farmers in Cavite, The Philippines, who have devised ways to subsist and profit off the land while their permanent tree crops become established. There are many local variations, but the basic model results in a rice paddy being converted permanently into coffee, fruit trees, and other perennials:

Sequential Planting in a Multistoried System

Year One Rice is planted. Pineapple and papaya are interplanted with the rice. Rice is harvested, phased out.

Year Two Papayas are harvested. Coffee and fruit trees are planted.

Year Three Pineapples and papayas are harvested.

Year Four Pineapples and papayas are harvested, phased out. Coffee and fruit trees begin to bear.

Some of the variations of this model increase short and long term profits even more, by incorporating bananas, corn, and other crops. This kind of system gives farmers a return from their land while they invest in long-term perennial tree crops such as fruits or timber.

There are other advantages to sequential planting, including:

- greater efficiency in land use (less land area is fallow while tree crops mature)
- increased efficiency in labor (because crop maintenance can overlap)

- enhanced farm diversity
- increased total yields over time
- greater stability, both environmental and economic
- long-term investment made economically viable through short-term yields

There are many other examples of sequential planting systems from other parts of the world. A few that are widely practiced include:

- Planting long-term timber trees into pasture, coffee, or orchards (some of these systems are sequential; others are designed to be stable over time)
- Planting orchard trees into pineapple fields or annual gardens
- Cultivating annual or short-term crops under forestry plantings until the forest canopy closes (also known as the Taungya system)

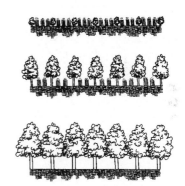

Trees replace short term crops over time

Careful planning is necessary to ensure that a sequential planting will be successful. There are a few things to watch out for in particular. One is competition—crops planted together should not have harmful effects on one another, and rooting habits should be understood so plants are compatible and not overly competitive for nutrients and space in the short-term. Planning and advanced study should also determine how long the short-term crop can be expected to bear until the long-term crop takes over by shading or root competition. Marketing of the different crops as they change from year to year is also an important factor to consider. The most effective sequential planting systems are developed over time through experience.

Sequential planting is one of the oldest agricultural practices in the world, and is a viable system for farmers or forest planters who need a short-term return as they invest in long-term tree crops.

Further Reading

Capistrano, L., J. Durno, and I. Moeliono (eds). 1990. Resource Book on Sustainable Agriculture for the Uplands. International Institute of Rural Reconstruction, Philippines. Contains a detailed description of the Cavite sequential planting systems.

Clarke, W.C. and R.R. Thaman. 1993. Agroforestry in the Pacific Islands: Systems for Sustainability. United Nations University Press, Tokyo.

Nair, P.K. Ramachandran. 1993. An Introduction to Agroforestry. Kluwer Academic Publishers and International Centre for Research in Agroforestry. The Netherlands. Describes the benefits and pitfalls of the Taungya system and other plantation/crop combinations.

Original Source

This article was originally published as *The Overstory* #10.

Nontimber Forest Products: An Introduction

Kim M. Wilkinson and Craig R. Elevitch

Nontimber forest products represent an important aspect of sustainable economic growth, conservation, and resource management. This chapter provides a brief introduction to the subject of nontimber forest products (NTFPs).

What Are Nontimber Forest Products?

Nontimber forest products (NTFPs) refers to a wide array of economic or subsistence materials that come from forests, excluding timber. Similar terms include "nonwood," "minor," "secondary," and "special" or "specialty" forest products.

There are many kinds of animal and plant resources that are derived from forests, including fruits, nuts, mushrooms, essential oils, florals, medicinal products, herbs and spices, dyes, resins, and animal products such as honey and wild game. These products are often gathered from natural forests. Others may be produced with varying degrees of cultivation and domestication, either within a forest ecosystem or as part of a planted forest system such as an agroforestry or forestry project.

NTFPs represent income opportunities from forests and forestry that do not involve cutting down trees for wood products. In forests with low timber production potential, NTFPs represent the major actual or potential source of income. In other cases, management of a forest for NTFPs does not preclude the option to harvest timber as well.

While NTFPs are traditionally used and appreciated by peoples of many cultures worldwide, the significance of these products for sustainable economic growth, cultural endurance, and environmental health is receiving increasing recognition by governments and other official agencies.

Examples of Nontimber Forest Products

A wide array of goods are classified as nontimber forest products. They include both animal and plant products. Some involve little processing, serving lo-

cal markets or family needs; others involve complex management and processing and are bound for national or international markets. Below are some examples of nontimber forest products.

Simple technology processing:
- Food (e.g. fruits, nuts, berries, root crops, sugar plants)
- Culinary herbs
- Mushrooms (e.g., for food or medicinal uses)
- Wild game
- Food insects
- Handicraft materials (e.g. rattan, bamboo, beads)
- Floral products (e.g. cut flowers, moss, vines, cut greens)

Intermediate processing:
- Herbal medicines (e.g. kava, ginseng)
- Vegetable oils
- Dyes, tannins, colorants
- Honey
- Seeds or propagative materials

Complex processing:
- Essential oils (e.g. lemon grass, vetiver, patchouli, tea tree oil)
- Pharmaceuticals and medicinals
- Herbs, spices, flavorings (e.g. vanilla, cinnamon)
- Resins, gums, saps, and oils (e.g. rubber, latex)
- Fiber plants (e.g. sisal, wauke, hau)

The Importance of Nontimber Forest Products

For millennia, nontimber forest products have been essential for subsistence and economic activities all around the world. NTFPs are also among the oldest and most long-standing of internationally traded commodities, dating back thousands of years to ancient times continuing in the present day.

According to the United Nations Food and Agriculture Organization (FAO 1997), it has been estimated that:

- 80% of the population of the developing world use NTFPs to meet some of their health and nutritional needs

- Several million households worldwide depend heavily on NTFP products for income
- The estimated total value of world trade in NTFPs is approximately US$1,100 million.

Recently, the importance of NTFPs is being rediscovered. Forests are being valued not simply for their timber, but as intricate systems capable of sustained generation of a great diversity of resources and services. NTFPs have substantial environmental, economic, and cultural impacts.

Diverse forests can yield an abundance of nontimber products

Environmental Importance

Nontimber forest products represent a way to meet environmental objectives such as conservation of forests, watersheds, and biological diversity. A growing body of scientific research suggests that NTFPs can help communities meet their needs without jeopardizing forest ecosystems. Diverse crops and diverse ecosystems are increasingly recognized as a strong foundation for sustainable economic development.

Economic Importance

Timber products have overshadowed NTFPs as major commodities in modern times. However, the important contribution of nontimber forest products to food and resource security and to financial well-being is gaining increasing recognition. In fact, in some areas, the financial impact of NTFPs may be even greater than that of forestry. For example, a study in Zimbabwe revealed that small-scale NTFP-based enterprises employed 237,000 people, compared to only 16,000 employed in conventional forestry and forest industries in the same year (FAO 1995).

In local, urban, national and international markets, forest foods and medicines contribute substantially to national economic growth. The NTFP sector is been estimated in over a billion dollars US, and is growing rapidly, perhaps faster than the timber in-

dustry. For example, the market for NTFPs has grown by nearly 20% annually over the last several years, and the related herbal medicine market at a rate of 13-15% annually (Hammet 1999). Future development of NTFPs offer good potential for increasing income, expanding opportunities, and diversifying enterprises in rural areas.

Cultural Importance

Nontimber forest products are basic cash and subsistence commodities in many cultures. Many local populations continue to have a fundamental reliance on NTFPs. In many cases these products are of far greater importance than the irregular cash income gained from commercial logging. While the preservation of NTFPs is fundamental to the maintenance and continuation of many traditional ways of life, these NTFP sources are increasingly threatened by deforestation and land development activities.

The recognition of intellectual property rights is important for many NTFPs. The fields of herbal medicine and biomedical research are growing rapidly. Often the plants, their uses, and harvesting and processing techniques were studied, selected and perfected over generations by people who used them traditionally. As these discoveries blossom into lucrative enterprises, an equitable share of the benefits are due to the people, communities, and countries from which they originate.

For Further Information

Nontimber forest products are key to sustainable economic growth and healthy rural enterprises. They also play a significant role in maintaining biological diversity, forest health, cultural well-being, and indigenous knowledge. As this important aspect of the world's forests gains increasing recognition, more information and support is being made available to people who work with NTFPs. Some useful resources are introduced below.

References

FAO. 1995. Non-wood forest products 7: Non-wood forest products for rural income and sustainable forestry. FAO, Rome, Italy.

FAO. 1997. State of the World's Forests 1997. FAO, Rome, Italy.

Hammet, T. 1999. Special Forest Products: Identifying Opportunities for Sustainable Forest-based Development. Virginia Landowner Update, Virginia Tech.

Hammett, A.L., and J.L. Chamberlain. 1998. Sustainable use of non-traditional forest products: alternative forest-based income opportunities. Proceedings, Natural Resources Income Opportunities on Private Lands Conference. 141-147.

SPC/UNDP/AusAID/FAO. 1999. A Preliminary Report on Non-Timber Forest Products in Some Pacific Island Countries. RAS/97/330, Working Paper No. 6, SPC/UNDP/AusAID/FAO, Pacific Islands Forests & Trees Support Programme, Suva, Fiji.

Thomas, M.G. and D.R. Schumann. 1993. Income Opportunities in Special Forest Products: Self-Help Suggestions for Rural Entrepreneurs. USDA ADB-666, Washington, DC.

Original Source

This article was originally published as *The Overstory* #53.

Further Reading

FAO Technical Papers: Non-Wood Forest Products Series An excellent 12 volume series on non-wood forest products (NWFPs) and their role in integrated forestry, agroforestry, and conservation. Provides useful information on the various products, and also the basics of NWFP enterprises for those products. For practitioner, policy maker, or scientist. Order from FAO in Rome (address below).

1   Flavours and Fragrances of Plant Origin, 1995
2   Gum Naval Stores: Turpentine and Rosin from Pine Resin, 1995
3   Report of the International Expert Consultation on Non-Wood Forest Products, 1995
4   Natural Colourants and dyestuffs, 1995
5   Edible Nuts, 1995
6   Gums, Resins and Latexes of Plant Origin, 1995
7   Non-Wood Forest Products for Rural Income and Sustainable Forestry, 1995
8   Trade restrictions affecting international trade in non-wood forest products, 1995
9   Domestication and commercialization of non-timber forest products in agroforestry systems, 1996
10 Tropical palms, 1998
11 Medicinal plants for forest conservation and health care, 1997
12 Non-wood forest products from conifers, 1998

Available electronically at:
http://www.fao.org/for-estry/FOP/FOPW/NWFP/pubser-e.stm

FAO. 1990. The major significance of minor forest products. Forests, Trees and People, Community Forestry Note 6. Rome, FAO. Contains a global survey of NTFP use.

Thomas, M.G. and D.R. Schumann. 1993. Income Opportunities in Special Forest Products: Self-Help Suggestions for Rural Entrepreneurs. USDA ADB-666, Washington, DC. Order from Southern Research Station, USDA Forest Service, Blacksburg, Virginia; Download this publication at: http://www.sfp.forprod.vt.edu/pubs/pubs.htm. In depth discussion of special forest products that represent opportunities for rural entrepreneurs to supplement their incomes.

W.C. Clark, R.R. Thaman (eds). 1994. Agro-Forestry in the Pacific Islands: Systems for Sustainability. 1994. Unipub. A very useful treatment of agroforestry practices in the Pacific, including lists and descriptions of many NFTP species.

Periodicals

Non-wood News is an information-rich newsletter produced by FAO's Wood and Non-wood Products Utilization Branch, providing readers with current information on nontimber forest products and their contribution to the sustainable development of the world's forest resources. Non-Wood News, Forest Products Division, Forestry Department, FAO, Viale delle Terme di Caracalla 00100 Rome (Italy), Tel: +39-06-570-52746, Fax: +39-06-570-55618. Back issues are available at:
http://www.fao.org/for-estry/FOP/FOPW/NWFP/newsle-e.stm

The ntfp-biocultural-digest is a free, international internet mailing list promoting knowledge about worldwide NTFP use:
http://www.ifcae.org/ntfp/digest/

Web Links

The FAO Forest Products Division's Non-Wood Forest Products web site has extensive information including organizational database and a broad range of publications in electronic form in English, French and Spanish:
http://www.fao.org/for-estry/FOP/FOPW/NWFP/nwfp-e.stm

The Special Forest Products web site focuses on the use and markets for special forest products: http://www.sfp.forprod.vt.edu/special_fp.htm

Institute for Culture and Ecology's Non Timber Forest Products in the United States has extensive reference information: http://www.ifcae.org/ntfp/

Free Searchable Non Timber Forest Product Bibliography Online with over 1,300 entries: http://www.ifcae.org

Rural and Agricultural Incomes with a Sustainable Environment features technical, market and regulatory information, and commercial contacts for eco-friendly products: http://www.raise.org

Conservation International's Directory of Information Resources for Non-Timber Forest Products lists many useful publications: http://www.conservation.org/library/books/ntfp.htm

Links to Web Links

Many NTFP related web sites are listed at the Institute for Culture and Ecology's links page: http://www.ifcae.org/ntfp/databases/links/

The Special Forest Products web site has an excellent list of related links: http://www.sfp.forprod.vt.edu/sfp_link/sfp_link.htm

The FAO Forest Products Division maintains a list of NTFP related sites, complete with descriptions: http://www.fao.org/forestry/FOP/FOPW/NWFP/links-e.stm

Related Chapters

Nontimber Forest Products Enterprises

Kim M. Wilkinson and Craig R. Elevitch

Nontimber Forest Products (NTFPs), also known as non-wood forest products or special forest products, represent a means for rural communities to meet their needs without endangering forest ecosystems. NTFPs are an important aspect of sustainable economic growth, resource management, and conservation.

The previous chapter introduced the subject of NTFPs. This chapter provides more practical information about starting an NTFP enterprise. Key issues that rural entrepreneurs should explore when considering on an enterprise involving NTFPs are discussed. Additional resources of books, web sites, and periodicals about NTFPs are included for further information.

Introduction

NTFPs have been traditionally important worldwide. In many areas, animal and plant resources derived from forests remain central to subsistence and local economies. The FAO estimated that 80% of the population of the "developing" world use NTFPs to meet some of their health and nutritional needs (FAO 1997).

However, the importance of NTFPs goes beyond meeting basic needs. NTFPs are also a rapidly growing market sector. The estimated total value in world trade in NTFP is approximately US $1,100 million (SPC 1999), and the market has grown by nearly 20% annually over the last several years (Hammet 1999). Future development of NTFPs offers potential for increasing income, expanding opportunities, and diversifying enterprises in rural areas.

Potential Benefits

Embarking on an enterprise involving nontimber forest products is an appealing challenge for many rural entrepreneurs. Nontimber forest products represent an opportunity for diversifying and expanding income. For small-scale farm foresters, nontimber products can also provide an earlier and sustained source of income before the timber trees are harvested. Possibilities for a variety of rural enterprises

involving not only growing and harvesting, but also value-added processing, packaging, and transport are available in the NTFP trade.

NTFP entrepreneurs may also be attracted to the prospect for other reasons. For example, indigenous peoples may use the opportunity to create cash income while maintaining and practicing a more traditional way of life. Other NTFP entrepreneurs simply value the opportunity to remain in a rural area and earn a livelihood. In some cases, the lifestyle value is a higher priority than financial gain. Some NTFP entrepreneurs, even in developed countries, choose their trade over other employment for the lifestyle benefit (Thomas and Schumann 1993).

Nontimber forest products can diversify forest income

Risks

Starting an NTFP enterprise involves a very high level of financial and personal risk. Many of the risk factors are related to the shortage of technical and practical information about NTFPs. At almost every phase in the process, from management and cultivation to marketing, harvesting, and processing, the NTFP entrepreneur may be in unknown territory. Unlike "major" commercial crops, there are usually few experts or sources of public support for NTFPs. Even where information is available, it may be difficult to apply to a new set of circumstances (New Crops News 9:1998).

Marketing information is also scarce for most NTFPs. Information such as price, the volume required by the market, and quality standards for the product is difficult to access (FAO 1995). For some NTFPs, such as essential oils or some medicinal products, buyers may have exacting specifications for the end product. Even after a crop is successfully harvested, it may not be marketable. In summary, many NTFP enterprises tend to be high risk ventures into the unknown.

Before investing time, money, and resources in a potential new venture, entrepreneurs should understand the potential pitfalls involved. Thorough research and careful planning is essential to minimize risks and develop a viable NTFP enterprise.

Planning an NTFP Enterprise: Four Evaluations

Planning and evaluating should be done up-front, before money is invested in the potential enterprise. Many small-scale NTFP ventures begin without adequate information and planning and, as a result, many of them fail. Small enterprises can enter markets selling NTFPs relatively easily, but only a small portion of these manage to adapt to the changing circumstances of supply, market demand, and competition to survive in the long-term (FAO 1995).

Prospective NTFP entrepreneurs should complete four evaluations before investing in a new venture. These include a personal evaluation, a resource evaluation, a market evaluation, and a project feasibility evaluation. Each of these is explained briefly below.

Personal Evaluation

A personal evaluation identifies and prioritizes the personal outcomes needed or wanted from the venture. These include the level of income necessary from the venture, acceptable levels of risk, and an assessment of the personal and family resources available for the enterprise (Thomas and Schumann 1993).

Resource Evaluation (Excerpt from FAO 1995)

A first step in developing any viable forest enterprise is to understand the capacity of the forest resource. It is impossible to manage the resource wisely or profitably without knowing about its natural growth and production, and the human environment that affects it.

Many people assume that harvests of NTFPs have less impact on a forest than logging. However, this assumption is unfounded. Forest ecosystems have such complex interrelationships that harvests of some non-wood resources can affect plant and wild-

life populations as negatively as logging. Without a sound knowledge of the resource and regular monitoring, harvests of certain non-wood resources can have a disastrous impact that is not noticed until it is too late to remedy. For example, overharvesting of fruits or seeds of a tree species can drastically reduce regeneration to the point of local extinction without any visible effect. Large individual trees may remain and the system might appear undisturbed. Only years or decades later, when the large trees die and no individuals replace them, will the environmental damage become evident (Peters, 1994).

Steps must be taken to understand and inventory the area's nontimber resources. Based on this, a community or enterprise can begin to prepare a plan for management.

Market Evaluation

A market evaluation is critical to the success of the project, and one of the more difficult aspects of research into NTFP enterprises. It should identify the targeted markets and locate prospective buyers. The exact specifications required by the potential buyer must also be determined, including quality, quantity, price, timing of the harvest, and other requirements. Some products have very exacting specifications. The NTFP entrepreneur must plan to meet or exceed these requirements, as well as those determined by government regulations if applicable (Thomas and Schumann 1993).

Project Feasibility Evaluation

The project feasibility evaluation examines both the technical and financial workability of the potential enterprise (Thomas and Schumann 1993). At a minimum, the financial evaluation includes a fully developed budget itemizing fixed and variable costs, and expected gross and net revenues. The amount of resources (time, money, labor, land) needed for growing, harvesting, handling, processing, transporting, and marketing the product must accounted for. The expected yield, probable price at harvest, and quality of the end product should be determined. On the technical end, the location of harvest sites, leases and permission if necessary, timing of operations, and methods of management must be addressed manner (Thomas and Schumann 1993). For NTFPs from natural forests, special attention should be given to the sustainability of harvesting the resource, and how the NTFP entrepreneur will ensure that she or he is managing in a responsible manner.

Starting Small

After careful evaluation and planning, the producer is ready to begin developing the NTFP enterprise. It is highly recommended to start small, and improve and expand over time.

There are many advantages to starting a small, pilot-scale enterprise before investing in a larger venture. Most importantly, starting small helps to minimize risk. This strategy also allows for the extra time necessary to develop good management and harvesting techniques and other effective habits of running a business. On a small scale, the impact on the environment can be observed carefully, and monitoring strategies for the future can be planned. Starting small allows for the possibility to recover from a mistake. On a larger scale, one mistake or miscalculation could jeopardize the forest resource or the finances of the producer, whereas on a small scale a mistake is more easily repaired. Also, starting small enables the producer to create a realistic time-line for future development, gauging how much of a work load is reasonable.

The following tips are offered about starting small (adapted from FAO 1995):

1   Start with one product and gradually diversify. Choose the easiest product that yields a good revenue for the time involved. Invest profits in the process required to produce a second market item. The income from the first product can also leverage credit for a larger operation.

2   Start with products for which a local market already exists. Entering an existing market allows producers to start repaying costs immediately, but creating markets for new products takes time.

3   Adopt a simple strategy. Complex production/marketing strategies permit more unforeseen difficulties.

Improving Management and Marketing (adapted from FAO 1995)

Understanding and managing currently available nontimber forest resources is an essential place to start. However, if demand for the NTFP product or pressure on these resources increases, systems and that once were environmentally sound must be adapted in order to meet needs for livelihood and income. Communities and enterprises can adapt systems for management that are culturally, economically and environmentally sustainable. Improving productivity, reducing waste in harvest, and improvement or domestication of key species are examples of ways to help increase the resource base.

The commercial options can also be improved over time. Creating niche markets, diversifying markets, and adding value locally can improve the income and security of an NTFP enterprise. It is also important to monitor and demonstrate the ecological viability of the enterprise. This helps appeal to environmentally-minded consumers, many of whom are willing to pay a premium for sustainably harvested materials.

References

The Australian New Crops Newsletter. 1998. Issue No. 9. Queensland, Australia. Web: http://www.newcrops.uq.edu.au/newslett/1-newslt.htm

FAO. 1995. Non-wood forest products 7: Non-wood forest products for rural income and sustainable forestry. FAO, Rome, Italy. Excerpts used with permission.

FAO. 1997. State of the World's Forests 1997. FAO, Rome, Italy.

Hammet, T. 1999. Special Forest Products: Identifying Opportunities for Sustainable Forest-based Development. Virginia Landowner Update, Virginia Tech.

Peters, C.M. 1994. Sustainable harvest of non-timber plant resources in tropical moist forest: an ecological primer. Biodiversity Support Program-WWF, Washington, DC.

SPC/UNDP/AusAID/FAO. 1999. A Preliminary Report on Non-Timber Forest Products in Some Pacific Island Countries. RAS/97/330, Working Paper No. 6, SPC/UNDP/AusAID/FAO, Pacific Islands Forests & Trees Support Programme, Suva, Fiji.

Thomas, M.G., and D.R. Schumann. 1993. Income Opportunities in Special Forest Products: Self-Help Suggestions for Rural Entrepreneurs. USDA ADB-666, Washington, DC.

Original Source

This chapter was originally published as *The Overstory* #55.

Further Reading

FAO Technical Papers: Non-Wood Forest Products Series An excellent 12 volume series on non-wood forest products (NWFPs) and their role in integrated forestry, agroforestry, and conservation. Of special interest for the beginning NTFP entrepreneur is Volume 7: Non-Wood Forest Products for Rural Income and Sustainable Forestry, 1995. This and the other 12 volumes are available electronically at: http://www.fao.org/for-estry/FOP/FOPW/NWFP/pubser-e.stm

Thomas, M.G. and D.R. Schumann. 1993. Income Opportunities in Special Forest Products: Self-Help Suggestions for Rural Entrepreneurs. USDA ADB-666, Washington, DC. Order from Southern Research Station, USDA Forest Service, Blacksburg, Virginia; Download this publication at: http://www.sfp.forprod.vt.edu/pubs/pubs.htm. In depth discussion of special forest products that represent opportunities for rural entrepreneurs to supplement their incomes.

The International Institute for Environment and Development's Hidden Harvest Project aims to develop approaches to local level economic assessment. Several titles in the series are available at: The Bookshop, I.I.E.D., 3 Endsleigh Street, London WC1H 0DD; Tel: 44 (171) 872 7308; Fax: 44 (171) 388 2826; Email: bookshop@iied.org; Web: http://www.iied.org/bookshop/sd_hh.html

Periodicals

Non-wood News is an information-rich newsletter produced by FAO's Wood and Non-wood Products Utilization Branch, providing readers with current information on nontimber forest products and their contribution to the sustainable development of the world's forest resources. Non-Wood News, Forest Products Division, Forestry Department, FAO, Viale delle Terme di Caracalla 00100 Rome (Italy), Tel: +39-06-570-52746, Fax: +39-06-570-55618. Back issues are available at: http://www.fao.org/for-estry/FOP/FOPW/NWFP/newsle-e.stm

Nontimber Forest Products (Temperate)

Deborah Hill

Nontimber forest products (NTFPs), also known as "nonwood," "minor," "secondary," and "special" or "specialty" forest products, involve an existing forest or woodland, and intentionally cropping something other than trees. The practice may or may not involve cultivation—the intention is to manage the forest for nontimber crops. This kind of cropping can be done in any kind of forest and has been traditional in many parts of the world. With careful planning, forest farming can be done in conjunction with other agroforestry practices.

This chapter focuses on nontimber crops of forests in the continental United States. Although the focus is primarily temperate, NTFP producers will be interested in the management techniques described for a wide variety of commercial crops. Forest farmed products include mushrooms, botanicals of medicinal or culinary value, fruits and nuts, craft materials, maple and other syrups, and baled pine straw. Other, more traditional wood products such as fence posts and fuelwood are also possibilities, while the raising of honeybees (apiculture) is yet another option.

Exotic Mushrooms

Wild mushrooms that can be found in temperate woods include morels (*Morchella* spp.), chanterelles (*Cantharellus* spp.), boletes (Boletaceae) and honey mushrooms (*Armillaria mellea*) along with several other edible species. Most of these are only seasonally available, and one must be *very* sure that the mushrooms in question are the edible ones—not look a likes that may be poisonous!

High quality mushrooms may be forest-farmed, on the other hand. These include culinary mushrooms such as shiitake (*Lentinula edodes*), maitake (Hen-of-the-woods, *Grifolafrondosa*), oyster mushrooms (*Pleurotus* sp.) Lion's Mane (*Hericium erinaceus*), King Stropharia (*Stropharia rugosoannulma*) as well as a primarily medicinal mushroom, reishi (*Ganoderma lucidum*). The majority of these mushrooms grow in wood fiber and can be inoculated into small diameter (7–12 cm (3–5 inch)) logs.

Production of these mushrooms can return enough economic benefit to justify thinning and culling forest stands to upgrade the quality and improve the health of the remaining trees. Because small logs are preferred for mushroom production, large branches can be used as well as small diameter trees.

Shiitake and oyster mushrooms are probably the most familiar of the exotic mushrooms. These, along with Lion's mane, reishi, and maitake can be inoculated into drilled holes in logs harvested during the dormant season (November-February in the central USA). The objective is to inject the active mycelium or "root" of these fungi into the wood that they will ultimately consume at a time when it contains the maximum amount of sugars. This season begins when the tree is shutting down for the winter—having shed its leaves—and runs through the time it gears up again in the spring, preparing for the new year's growth.

Trees used for this purpose must be alive at the time of cutting. Even though the fungi feed on dead wood, it is important to get the desirable mycelium into the wood before some other bacterium or fungus begins the decay process. Log lengths vary, but most people cut lengths they find easy to handle. All my experimental work has been done with logs one meter (39 inches) long, but other people have worked with logs both longer and shorter. Cutting logs shorter than 70 cm (24 inches) could create problems with the mushroom spawn drying out.

Black morels on forest floor. (photo: D. Hill)

My own experiments, as well as those of people in Ohio, Oklahoma, Minnesota, and Wisconsin, show that shiitake will grow on almost any species of hardwood tree, although oaks, especially the white oaks, are favored. It is possible to grow these mushrooms on conifers, but this has not been very successful.

Once the logs have been inoculated and sealed, they need to be placed in a relatively cool, moist environment for the fungi to grow (run) through the entire log. Ideally this would be a wooded site with some mixture of conifers (so that there is some shade year round), and near a water source. Monitoring the moisture content of the logs is important; supplemental watering may be necessary in hot, dry weather. Production usually begins 6–18 months after inoculation and continues seasonally with the right combination of moisture and temperature. The logs usually produce about 10% of their original weight in mushrooms over their productive life. Shiitake logs can be sterilized and reinoculated with oyster mushrooms when the shiitake production declines.

Markets are available and increasing in many parts of the country. If you expect to sell mushrooms, how-

ever, it is important to locate your own markets before inoculating any logs. The fungi that do not grow on logs—stropharia and morels—grow on the forest floor. Stropharia can be "seeded" into wood chip beds in the forest and watered like a garden until they begin to produce mushrooms. Even though these mushrooms can grow to remarkable sizes (big enough for a child to sit on!), they are marketed when relatively small—roughly the size of large commercial button mushrooms.

Morels are a little trickier to grow—their life cycle is known, but it is still difficult to produce them at will. Kits are available, and at least two companies are producing morels commercially under controlled indoor conditions. They too require a prepared bed on the forest floor and need to be kept moist until they produce. Under outside conditions they will only produce in season, which is late spring to early summer.

Botanicals and Medicinals

Every culture has had people in it who knew which plants to collect in the forest and how to use their dif-

Value-added ginseng cultivated under black walnut trees (left). Cultivated ginseng roots (right). (photos: D. Hill)

ferent parts to remedy various ills. Botanicals such as echinacea (purple coneflower) and St. John's wort are now available in outlets from your local pharmacy. Some of the forest-based botanicals include herbs such as goldenseal (*Hydrastis canadensis*), black cohosh (*Cimicifuga racemosa*), bloodroot (*Sanguinaria canadensis*), and blue cohosh (*Caulophyllum thalictroides*), as well as bark from such trees and shrubs as witch hazel (*Hamamelis virgimana*), slippery elm (*Ulmus rubra*) and sassafras (*Sassafras albidum*).

Probably the best known and certainly most valuable botanical is American ginseng (*Panax quinquefolium*) Ginseng grown under forest conditions, so-called woods-grown, woods-cultivated, or wild-simulated, has maintained a stable price of close to $300 per pound for some time.

Most of the herbaceous and shrubby botanicals are marketable for pennies to dollars per pound, and there an several national herb companies that will buy dried material from producers. Several of these herbs can be encouraged to grow in larger patches than occur naturally, by techniques that disturb the forest soil very little. Both herbaceous medicinals and exotic mushrooms prefer a forest canopy—usually with fairly dense (75–85%) shade, so minimal alteration of the overstory is needed. As with most plant cultivation, the problems are competition for water and nutrients, so some weeding may be necessary.

Most of these herbaceous plants, especially those with marketable leaves, seeds, and fruits, bear annually. Harvesting roots may take longer. Goldenseal, from which both root and leaves are marketable (and seed for that matter), takes two or three years to develop a large enough root mass to market. Ginseng commands a high market price because it takes five to ten years to develop the kind of root that brings top dollar.

Ginseng plants usually begin to produce seed in their third year and the seed can be a product in itself. The planting market demands both seed and 1st- or 2nd-year rootlets, so small roots can also be marketed for transplanting.

The greatest challenge in growing ginseng to fruition is keeping it until it's big enough to sell. In the central US—and the Appalachian and Ozark Mountains in particular—theft of nearly-grown ginseng is widespread. Ginseng is considered by the federal government to be a threatened plant, and its harvesting is restricted to certain months of the year and to certain ages of root, but there is considerable disregard for those laws, and little enforcement by local officials.

Trees and shrubs from which roots (sassafras) and bark (witch hazel, slippery elm) are taken for their medicinal use, require a different kind of management. Witch hazel is best managed by cutting the stems fairly close to the ground, then stripping the bark off. Cutting the stems encourages resprouting while taking the bark off the standing stems would probably kill the whole plant. Slippery elm, which can grow into a large tree, can either be managed—like the witch hazel—by coppice when young, or could bear some vertical strips of bark being removed from a mature tree, as long as most of the bark is left around the trunk to keep its circulation functioning. Some of the roots of sassafras may be removed without killing the whole tree; alternately, only the smaller shoots may be harvested, roots and all.

Fruits and Nuts

Native fruits and nuts are other options for forest farming, and can include such species as persimmon (*Diospyros virginiana*), pawpaw (*Mimina triloba*), hazelnuts (*Coryhs* spp.). pine nuts (*Pinus* spp.), and walnuts (*Juglans* spp.). Unfortunately, one of the greatest nut trees of all time, the American chestnut (*Castanea dentata*), no longer grows big enough to produce nuts. It occupied some 20% of the eastern deciduous forest and was effectively wiped out by an exotic disease in the 1920's.

As with apiculture and maple syrup production, farming of fruiting species requires adjustment of the forest canopy (more water, nutrients, sunlight) to allow for better growth of the crop trees. This usually means removing the surrounding trees whose crowns touch the crowns of the crop trees (you can then use some of the harvested wood for mushroom production, fence posts, or firewood for boiling maple syrup!).

Crafts Materials

Working crafts materials as part of forest farming ranges from collecting pine cones and gilding them for decorations, or waxing them for fire starters, to selecting odd-shaped branches or burls on trees for carving. There are many plant species at all levels, from herbs to shrubs to vines to canopy trees, that may produce something harvestable for crafts.

Grape vines are collected for fashioning into decorative wreaths, while small diameter (less than 25 cm (10 inches)) white oak saplings are the ideal size for making splints for white oak baskets. People have even made (beautiful) baskets from kudzu vines, so opportunities live greatly in the eyes of the beholder. One enterprising company injected dyes into very young pine saplings (less than 5 cm (2 in) in diameter) and then cuts the stems and branches into disks that were made into jewelry—the color already in them.

Crafts from wood are the dominant types produced in Kentucky and probably in most of the mountain regions of the central United States; they are also the most economically valuable. Greens and grasses used in the floral trades may be more valuable in areas like the Pacific Northwest. Although many of the forest resources for crafts may be obtained by collection or "wild crafting," some of the most desirable species can be "farmed" by intentionally altering the habitat to increase their production.

Maple Syrup

Maple syrup, and syrup or "beers" made from other tree saps, have been produced for centuries in North America. Native Americans figured out how to get this sweet material long before Europeans came to this continent. A "sugar bush" is simply a forest where the owner has selected for maple trees, specifically sugar maple (*Acer saccharum*). Maple syrup can be made from the sap of any maple tree species but the sugar content of sugar maple sap is higher than that of the other maples, and it therefore takes fewer gallons of sap to make a gallon of syrup (with sugar maple the ratio is about 40 to 1, so it's a lot more work to get the syrup from the others).

Management of the sugar bush requires spacing the trees far enough apart that they form large crowns (when the trees are all crowded together in a normal forested situation, the crown of any individual tree is not particularly large). Large crowns mean a lot of leaves, and a lot of leaves means high syrup production.

The expense of maple syrup production lies in the fairly substantial capital investment required for the tapping (buckets or plastic tubing), boiling, and bot-

Transporting raw maple sap from trees to sugar house. (photo: D. Hill)

tling equipment and materials. People who do this every year build a "sugar shack"—a building that houses the boiling pans, with lots of roof ventilation for the steam to escape, and a long, deep fire pit for heating the sap. Scrap wood from other forest management operations can be used to fuel the sugaring process. Labor is intensive during the production process, but the season of work is short, lasting usually four- to six-weeks in the spring—when days are beginning to warm but nights are still cool, and before bud break. The result is a very high value-added product.

Pine Straw

Pine straw is the annual needle drop of pine trees. Commercially, it is baled from under long-needled pines in the Deep South, specifically loblolly (*Pinus taeda*) and longleaf pines (*P. palustris*) This material makes excellent mulch, especially for landscaping. There have even been experiments to color the pine needles for interior landscaping so that they can match the decor of the room! Even though harvesting removes organic material from the forest floor, and thereby reduces the amount of nutrient cycling available to the stand of trees, people have found that it is possible to rake and bale the pinestraw from the same location every other year or every third year without markedly affecting the nutrient balance. Pines with long needles are preferred because these take longer to break down. The pinestraw is baled much like hay, and can return a significant short-term economic benefit while owners are waiting the 20–30 years required for the timber crop to mature. Managing for pinestraw production means planting the trees in widely-spaced rows to accommodate the movement of the straw harvesting machinery.

Fence Posts

The most desirable tree species for fence posts in the eastern United States are black locust (*Robinia pseudoacacia*) and Eastern red cedar (*Juniperus virginiana*) In the west, it is probably redwood (*Sequoia sempervirens*). These species are desirable because of their natural resistance to decay—locust posts may last for decades without chemical treatment, whereas other species, even with treatment, may not last as long. Management consists of favoring the growth of these species over others and providing access to maximum water, light, and nutrients in the

Pine straw mulch in landscaping. (photo: D. Hill)

system where they are growing. Fence posts are also an option as an intermediate product in the crop tree rows of an alley cropping system. Black locust, for example, can grow large enough to be harvested for fence posts in 12–15 years, while black walnut may take three times longer than that to reach a size that would be considered marketable.

Fuelwood

Fuelwood, or firewood, is more of a by-product of other management for forest farming than perhaps a specific activity, unless the forest is managed to encourage the growth of trees that are known to be excellent fuelwood, such as black locust or some of the less commercially desirable oaks (post oak, *Quercus stellaria*, or blackjack oak, *Q. marilandica*). Ex-

Entrepreneur's sign for selling firewood. (photo: D. Hill)

Beekeeper opening hive (left). Shelf of bee products in natural food store (right). (photo: D. Hill)

hausted mushroom logs can be used for firewood also, although they maybe punky enough that they are better ground up and used for mulch.

Apiculture

If agroforestry is "the intentional integration of agronomic crops with tree crops or livestock with tree crops," then with apiculture in forest farming, the "livestock" are very tiny! It has been estimated that one in every three bites of food we eat is dependent on active pollination of plants. The insect world, specifically bees and wasps, are the major operators in this case.

The European honeybee (*Apis mellifera*) is the best-known of these insects, although it is not a native species. It has a couple of characteristics which make it particularly valuable. One is that honeybees show species fidelity, which means that they will use the same source of nectar to make honey until source is exhausted. This enables them to make "specialty" honeys from crops such as buckwheat, tupelo, and sourwood. Another is that they collect pollen, along with nectar, and use both to raise their young, but also collect it in sufficient volume that it can be harvested without compromising the health of the hive.

Managing honeybees is not difficult, and acquiring bees and hives is neither particularly expensive nor complicated. Extracting honey from the combs is an expensive proposition (extractors are costly), but it is possible to get good equipment second-hand.

Forests can be managed to favor trees that honeybees particularly like, such as basswood (*Tilia ameri-* cana) and black gum (*Nyssa sylvatica*), providing extra light, water, and nutrients for those trees, as well as exposing the crowns to maximize surface area for flower production.

Average production for a hive is 23 kg (50 lb.) of honey per year. It is also possible for a hive to produce 23 kg (50 lb.) of pollen in a year. Products from the hive include: royal jelly (the super-rich food fed in tiny amounts to all honeybee larvae, but the exclusive diet of the queens) popular in both the health food and cosmetic markets; propolis, another product used in food supplements; and beeswax, used for candle-making and other crafts. Pollination itself is another saleable service, as hives can be transported from place to place to pollinate crops. And some alternative health practitioners use honeybees for their venom, which anecdotally is said to be extremely helpful to people suffering pain from rheumatoid arthritis, or other joint problems.

Summary

Farming the forest provides many options for annual (maple syrup, crafts, some botanicals, mushrooms) and longer-term (fuelwood, fence posts, ginseng) commodities, along with the possibility of timber crops. Production of these commodities may involve altering the forest canopy (shade for mushrooms and botanicals, crown spread for apiculture and maple syrup) or making changes in the forest floor (sowing medicinals such as ginseng and goldenseal, inoculating for morels or stropharia). Many of these options could also be implemented in the tree rows of alley crop plantations, as well as in the selection of species for windbreaks and riparian buffer strips. One or more of these options can provide annual cash flow and can be managed by various member of a family. Implementing several of them will bring greater biodiversity to the existing forest, thereby enhance its health, while supplementing annual income from the land.

Original Source

This article was originally published in *The Permaculture Activist*, No. 40. For subscription information write to, Subscriptions, P.O. Box 1209, Black Mountain, NC 28711 USA. Tel: 828-298-2812, Fax: 828-298-6441, Email: pcactiv@metalab.unc.edu; Web: http://www.permacultureactivist.net/.

This excerpt was originally published as *The Overstory #71*.

Further Reading

Persons, S.W. 1994. American Ginseng—Green Gold. Bright Mountain Books, Asheville, NC.

Hill, D.B, and L. Buck. 1998. "Forest Farming: Revitalizing and Expanding Crop-Yielding and Forest Based Enterprises." In: Agroforestry - An Integrated Science and Practice. W.J. Rietveld, H.E. Garrett, and R.F. Fisher (eds). American Society of Agronomy Special Publication.

Thomas, M.G., and R. Schermann. 1993. Income Opportunities in Special Forest Products. USDA Agricultural Information Bulletin 666.

Between Wildcrafting and Monocultures: Agroforestry Options

Wayne S. Teel and Louise E. Buck

Agroforestry is an approach to plant and animal production that intentionally integrates natural resources conservation objectives into the system. By strategically selecting combinations of woody and herbaceous plants and managing them to perform complementary agroecological roles, often with animals, the sustainability of producing multiple products with comparatively minimal external inputs can be enhanced. Environmental benefits that agroforestry systems generate often can be captured directly by the managing landowner through the creation of niches that over time favor the production of a variety of unique and profitable products.

This article explores the potential for producing nontimber forest products in agroforestry systems. By identifying options for this type of practice we aim to foster appreciation for the numerous opportunities that are present, and yet to be invented, for integrating specialty forest products into farms and rural enterprises. Expanding market demand for NTFPs provides an important incentive for landowners to invest in conservation farming practices through agroforestry. Such practices can serve also to limit the overexploitation of nontimber forest products from their native habitats.

Enthusiasm for designing and managing NTFPs in agroforestry systems is growing. Such practice is complex and uncertain, however, and experience has not been widely shared. Success will depend on a constellation of factors. Strategies for investing in NTFP production through agroforestry need to consider technical, economic, social, and institutional feasibility within particular cultural and ecological settings. We draw attention to key issues that influence the potential effectiveness of agroforestry approaches to producing NTFPs and suggest some means of addressing them that may help to unblock current constraints.

Wildcrafting and the Problems of Nontimber Forest Products

According to legend, when the English colonizers of North America arrived, a squirrel could travel from the Atlantic to the Mississippi without ever touching the ground. Forests were, and remain, the dominant ecosystem in some parts of North America. European colonists, with a strong agrarian cultural tradition, never really learned to live in or with American forests, which were used as a source of timber, fuel, and fertilizer in the form of potash. Occasionally a special forest product such as naval stores—the sap from longleaf and other pine trees (primarily used for caulking in wooden sailing vessels)—became a key resource in support of the emerging imperial economy in Great Britain. No attempt was made to conserve this resource, and converting even longleaf pine to farmland signaled the "advance of civilization" (Williams 1992).

In the colonial process of usurping land and rights to the land of native peoples, much indigenous knowledge acquired by Native Americans over the millennia was lost. But Native Americans held and continue to hold an abundance of knowledge about native vegetation and technology for its use. A notable example is the sugar maple *(Acer saccharum)*, which is a major tree species of the forests in the Northeast, from Kentucky to Minnesota and Maine and on into Ontario, Quebec, and the Maritime Provinces in Canada. Indigenous people in this region knew the sweet quality of the sap and developed ways to condense the sap into syrup using stone bowls and hot rocks (Nearing and Nearing 1950), technology that over time was adapted by white people to eventually create today's maple sugar and syrup industry.

Indians taught colonists about the medicinal uses of slippery elm *(Ulmus rubra)* and coneflowers *(Echinacea* spp.) (Missouri Dept. of Conservation 1993). They also identified the value of black cohosh *(Cimicifuga racemosa)* for treating the symptoms of menopause. Black cohosh, a herbaceous perennial forest understory plant, is the main ingredient in *Remifemine,* an over-the-counter botanical packaged in Germany and sold in health centers. These are just four in a wide array of so-called nontimber forest products, or special forest products (SEPs), that have modern-day international markets.

Foresters have long overlooked the value of these plants and have directed their efforts to silviculture and timber extraction, and more recently to rotational production of timber in monocultures or mixed stands. Another group of forest users has tapped the resources of the understory, often without the knowledge and consent of the landowners, whether the U.S. Forest Service, timber companies, or private landlords. In the eastern mountains of North America, these folk learned to derive an income from the land in niches ignored by the mainstream (Krochmal, Walters, and Doughty 1971; Crellin and Philpott 1990). Wildcrafters, as this group is sometimes called, glean the forests for roots, fruits, bark, branches and sap, or other products that they then sell to middlemen or processors. Some wildcrafters also actively manage sections of land for production, though not necessarily in a systematic fashion (Emery 1998).

Many plants of economic or cultural value are potentially at risk and alternative production systems should be considered. Determining ways to propagate and cultivate these plants in an economically viable way is essential. New ways of managing and harvesting plant populations will be situated somewhere between wild grown stock and open field monocultures.

Ginseng: A Model for NTFP Development?

Of all NTFPs, American ginseng *(Panax quinquefolius)* stands out as one of the best understood, arguably the most endangered, and certainly one of the most economically valuable. Ginseng acquired its status by virtue of its role in Chinese medicine. The Chinese species *(Panax ginseng)* has long been valued as a tonic for increasing energy and virility. Men chew pieces of roots, which look like tiny, misshapen carrots, the best having a human-like appearance. Due to the overexploitation of Chinese forests and expanding populations, Chinese ginseng production no longer comes close to meeting demand. American ginseng has achieved status as a valuable re-

placement, though it is not considered an exact substitute (Foster *1995).*

Wildcrafted American ginseng of acceptable quality, as determined principally by age and shape, may sell to the collector for over $500 per pound. When prices rise to such dizzying heights, more people consider expanding domesticated production. Both in China and the United States, growers have made strides in producing ginseng under artificial shade. Shade-grown ginseng is an ingredient in many products now sold in the United States: herbal teas, soft drinks with ginseng, and a variety of herbal supplements. This type of ginseng, however, does not fill the same market niche as the wildcrafted ginseng in high demand by the Chinese market. Monocropped product sells for between ten and twenty dollars a pound, hardly a profitable price, because the roots do not possess the shape, age, or color characteristics desired in the Chinese market (Hankins 1997).

Since truly wild ginseng is becoming increasingly rare, and mono-cropped, artificially shaded ginseng does not bring a high price in conventional markets, searches are under way for alternative production strategies. One such method is called wild-simulated production. This process involves preparing seedbeds in the plant's natural habitat, sowing seed or one-year-old rootlets, and letting nature do the rest. Producers claim that the wild-simulated product will be comparable to wildcrafted roots and sell in that high-priced market (Beyfuss 1998).

Producers have tried other methods of growing ginseng in the forest understory with more intensive production techniques. Instead of simply preparing beds, landowners like Bill Slagle in West Virginia prepare an entire section of understory after thinning a hardwood stand and then plant the area with ginseng (Temperate Agroforester 1999). This mixed hardwood and ginseng production system, combined with the growing of shiitake mushrooms on the thinned oak logs, is a prime example of an agroforestry system designed for an on-farm forest. Sustaining ginseng production via Slagle's intensive method, however, depends upon the use of substantial quantities of chemical inputs, which may impair the long-term viability of this currently highly profitable strategy.

Agroforestry Examples

There are four main characteristics of agroforestry systems:

- First, they are intentional. Conscious efforts are made to incorporate trees into farming systems to improve the overall productivity and health of the farm, including the on-farm forest.
- Second, such systems are *intensive*. When these systems are in place, the overall complexity and diversity of spatial or temporal use of land rises, as does the type of management interventions.
- Third, agroforestry systems are *interactive*. Relations between the trees and crops are manipulated, enhancing the production of more than one product while simultaneously providing conservation benefits such as erosion control or expanding wildlife habitat.
- Fourth, these systems are *integrated*. The trees and crops are not seen as separate units but are managed together to increase productivity and protect the farm's soil and water.

Though all agroforestry systems share these characteristics, the practices themselves are highly variable, depending on the ecology of the farm, the types of products the farmers wish to grow, and the ability to market them. Until recently, some NTFPs have not been considered major components of these systems, while others have been part of some systems from the earliest stages. There are five categories of agroforestry systems that vary regionally across the continent but have similar spatial characteristics. These are considered in turn, with examples of appropriate NTFP management.

Forest Farming

"Farming the agroforest" generally refers to turning the understory region of a forest environment into a production zone for NTFPs in an intentional, intensive, and integrated fashion. Forest farming involves manipulating forestlands to create conditions that are conducive to introducing agricultural or cropping techniques into the forest system (Hill and Buck 2000). Many farms have some woodland. These areas traditionally were sources for fuelwood, fence posts, and building material from selected woody species and sometimes provided a haven for farm animals from temperature extremes. Farm woodlands occasionally were sources for wild berries or fruits as well but for the most part were left unmanaged and underutilized.

Each region of the country will feature different understory crops. Any location with the potential to sustain a forest, however, will likely have a healthy selection of herbs, botanicals, fruits, mushrooms, and more that can be managed in the understory among the trees. An example from the southeastern United States is saw palmetto *(Serenoa repens),* a low-growing palm that occurs as a major understory plant in pine *(Pinus clausa)* scrub and savanna throughout Florida and northward into parts of South Carolina and Mississippi. This endemic plant is important to many species of wildlife for nesting and protective cover and as a food source (Tanner, Mullahey, and Maehr 1995). Human interest in the plant has grown as "enviroscaping" has expanded, saw palmetto being naturally drought- and insect-resistant and requiring no fertilizer. Landscapers have found it difficult to transplant the species from the wild and have it survive, thus nurseries specializing in native species have begun to raise plants from seed to supply this market demand (Tanner, Mullahey, and Maehr 1995). The medicinal value of the saw palmetto fruit for relief of prostate gland swelling has led to its commercialization, and in 1995 its economic value began to make the news when the price for raw fruit exceeded three dollars per pound. A strong projected demand for the fruit by European pharmaceutical companies can supply an added economic value to the pine-dominated landscape from which it originates.

Alleycropping

In years after the term agroforestry was coined, alleycropping received more research and extension attention than any other agroforestry practice. As the name implies, alleycropping involves alternating rows of trees and crops in a cultivated setting. Tree rows may be straight or follow contours. Spacing between rows differs based on the types of benefits desired from the trees. In tropical settings, one benefit sought was enhanced soil stability and fertility, using deep-rooted trees, commonly nitrogen-fixing, to stabilize soils and add nitrogen through leaf litter to the cropped area of the field. In this system, trees are closely planted in rows that are spaced from ten to thirty feet apart depending upon conditions. Frequent pruning of the trees is required for nutrient release and to reduce light competition. These systems have tended not to be popular with farmers due to the high levels of labor and management required to control competition and obtain their multiple benefits. Alleycropping in developing countries tends to be most successful in contour hedgerow configurations where controlling erosion is important and in commercial, cash crop situations on relatively high-potential lands.

In North America, alleycropping, or intercropping with trees, is focused less on nutrient cycling benefits and more on producing an annual crop on producing an annual crop from the tree itself. The predominant species in these systems is black walnut (*Juglans nigra*), with research on its value in field settings conducted by various institutions from Missouri to Ontario. The tree has two major sources of value: the nut, harvested annually from trees that are fifteen years old or more, and timber, especially from veneer-quality logs derived from well-pruned and managed plantations (Garrett *et al* 1991). Trees are planted in rows between forty and sixty feet apart to allow for use of farm equipment and thinned and pruned in the rows to an eventual density of approximately thirty trees per acre.

Opportunities for managing NTFPs in alleycropping systems will change as the tree component matures. During the establishment stage, a sun-loving herb such as echinacea might be grown in the alleys between rows of young trees. A shade-loving plant such as ginseng or goldenseal might be planted within the rows of trees even at an early stage in the development of the system. As the trees mature and cast more shade over a wider area, increasingly shade-tolerant species could be cultivated in the alleys. There are a number of multipurpose trees that might be used in these systems such as willow for floral displays, or pine for pins rope or pine straw. Presently, however, there is little experimentation or information upon which to evaluate the potential of this type of practice. Most alleycropping efforts emphasize nut production from black walnut, pecan (*Carya illinoensis*), or various cultivars of American hazelnut (*Corylus americana*), some hybridized with the common European hazelnut (*Corylus avellana*).

Shelterbelts and Windbreaks

Shelterbelts and windbreaks have been part of North American farming systems for a long time. One or more rows of trees planted perpendicular to prevailing winds reduce wind speed, prevent or limit snowdrifts, decrease evaporation, and increase infiltration of water in properly designed systems. Although often providing secondary products, such as fence posts and firewood, windbreaks are seldom-considered product production sites. Through the 1970s and 1980s, U.S. agricultural policies promoted efficiency in farm equipment, and commodity prices encouraged many farmers to take out windbreaks and shelterbelts. With crop prices down and incentive programs like the Conservation Reserve Program

encouraging them to take erodible land out of production, farmers again are considering these practices. Many express interest in also using these sites for producing additional products.

Developing a marketable product from plants growing in field borders and shelterbelts has precedents. A company called Minnesota Wild developed a line of products from wild chokecherries (*Prunus virginiana*) commonly found in fencerows and other farm sites. Now many farmers manage the chokecherry for fruit production rather than as an opportunistic invader of a field border. Probably the key lesson from the chokecherry is that market development pulls production more readily than surplus production can push marketing.

Riparian Buffer Zones

Probably no agroforestry land use has received more recent research support than the riparian buffer zone. The need to protect streams from erosion, nutrient loading, chemical pollution, and other forms of degradation associated with agriculture and urban sprawl spurs this research. Resources available to address these problems are large and growing (Tjaden 1998).

Tjaden (1998) lists a number of items that could grow in riparian zones for a profit. These include aromatic herbs, Christmas trees and greens, cooking wood, decorative cones, ginseng (upper flood plain only), nuts, shiitake mushrooms, and weaving and dyeing materials. To this list we could add poplars and willows for harvest as fuel or wood shavings to use as animal bedding, various riparian florals like pussy willow or curly willow, and medicinal plants such as slippery elm. Slippery elm (*Ulmus rubra*) has an exceptionally wide range of traditional and medicinal uses by Native American groups throughout much of North America. Growing naturally in river bottoms and on low fertile hills from southern Newfoundland to central Florida, its ecological range extends west across much of North America. It is the white, inner bark of this forty- to fifty-foot tree that is used as an aromatic as well as for a variety of medicinal purposes (Harding 1972).

Silvopastoral Systems

Upon first consideration, integrating animals with special forest products may not seem a good idea. Given unrestricted access to forestland, animals will graze the understory down to bare soil, trample roots, and often browse or strip tree boughs and bark. In a silvopastoral system grazing needs to be carefully managed, which does not mean that the productivity of the animal component of the system must suffer. In fact, there is strong evidence that intensive, rapid rotation grazing actually increases the carrying capacity of the land as well as stimulating understory and grass growth. Much of the information on such practices comes from the work of Allan Savory (1988) on holistic resource management.

The basic theory is that cattle and other grazing or browsing animals in their natural state are always on the move. They move to avoid predators, keep ahead of flies, and pursue fresh fodder. Placing animals in a single field for long periods induces selective overgrazing and promotes degradation. By making fields smaller, moving cattle regularly, and providing alternative watering systems, the animals tend to concentrate on grass and herbaceous material, do less trampling damage, and eat less woody growth. This approach can increase the survival of an established tree component and permit the harvest of tree-grown products, although understory products would suffer from periodic grazing.

Regional and Agroecological Variations in NTFP Resources for On-farm Situations

A strategy to intentionally cultivate nontimber forest products raises a number of questions. Plant geneticists have not selected for cultivars of most NTFP species under cultivation or studied the factors affecting their growth. The economic potential of NTFP species is also poorly understood, and high demand for a wild-grown product does not necessarily translate into cultivars reaping the same profits. In addition, social impacts occur after domesticating a new crop, and these can be difficult to forecast. Finally, a sophisticated network of government agencies, commercial enterprises, and private consulting firms already serves industrialized agriculture in North America by helping farmers cope with selection, cultivation, and marketing questions. Similar services are not readily available for entrepreneurial landowners interested in new-to-market NTFPs.

The table below presents a list of NTFPs found in the four predominantly forested regions, arranged by product type. Some products are widely known, others less so, but all are expected to have market potential soon. Despite considerable regional overlap,

especially in the East, cultivation practices in different regions may require the development of different cultivars that are adapted to regional conditions.

Decoratives

Pacific Northwest: Bear grass; Western juniper; Western red cedar; Incense cedar; Christmas trees; Hybrid poplar; Noble fir (boughs); Salal; Willows

Midwest: American bittersweet; Black walnuts; Christmas trees; Corkscrew willow; Hybrid poplar; Red osier dogwood; Russian olive; Witchhazel

Northeast: American holly; Bankers willow; Birch; Black ash; Boughs (fir and pine); Christmas trees; Corkscrew willow; Willow

Southeast: Pacific Northwest Christmas trees; Easter red cedar; Grape vines; Pine straw; Pine rope; Spanish moss; *Smilax smallii*

Mushrooms

Pacific Northwest: Boletes; Matsutake (pine mushrooms); King Stropharia; Chanterelles; Morels

Midwest: King Stropharia; Oyster; Shiitake

Northeast: King Stropharia; Oyster; Shiitake

Southeast: Morels; King Stropharia; Shiitake; Truffles

Food: Nuts, Fruit

Pacific Northwest: Berries (variety); Hazelnuts; Huckleberries; Wasabe (horseradish); Honey

Midwest: Black walnuts; Chestnuts; Chokecherries; Hazelnuts; Maple syrup; Pawpaw; Honey

Northeast: Berries; Black walnuts; Chokecherries; Hazelnuts; Maple syrup; Honey

Southeast: Black walnuts; Chestnuts; Pawpaw; Pecans; Persimmons; Honey

Herbal Medicinals

Pacific Northwest: Buckthorn; Devil's club; Oregongrape; Pacific yew

Midwest: Black cohosh; Blue cohosh; Ginseng; Goldenseal

Northeast: Black cohosh; Blue cohosh; Ginseng; Goldenseal

Southeast: Black cohosh; Goldenseal; Saw palmetto; Slippery elm

Conclusion

Agroforestry is an important land use option for many landowners, particularly farmers who seek to diversify their operations ecologically and economically. Agroforestry practices can provide a variety of services such as crop protection from wind, riparian zone protection, soil conservation, and habitat for pollinators and pest predators. They also can provide products for additional income, such as fence posts, firewood, foods, herbs, nursery plants, and others. NTFPs can fit into agroforestry systems to improve overall productivity, diversity, and ecological health.

Agroforestry, however, is not a simple solution. Such practices tend to require careful planning and design and knowledge-intensive management. Nor is agroforestry development a rapid process. Most NTFPs take time to establish and may require several years to bring a significant return. In the long run, however, agroforestry systems that include NTFPs can contribute importantly to sustainable agricultural development and to forest quality improvement while generating significant economic returns to the landowner (Buck, Lassoie, and Fernandes 1999). Accepting this challenge over more conventional pathways to crop development through monocropping is a mission that can help bind natural resources professionals and practicing land managers in their quests for innovative solutions to the imperatives of natural resources conservation and sustainable economic development.

References

Beyfuss, R. 1998. *The Practical Guide to Growing Ginseng.* Freehold, NY: Robert Beyfuss.

Buck, Louise E., J. P. **Lassoie,** and E. C. F. Fernandes. *1999. Agroforestry in Sustainable Agricultural Systems.* Boca Raton, FL: CRC Press.

Emery, Marla R. 1998. "Invisible Livelihoods: Nontimber Forest Products in Michigan's Upper Peninsula." Ph.D. diss., Rutgers University.

Foster, S. 1995. *Forest Pharmacy: Medicinal Plants in American Forests.* Durham, NC: Forest History Society.

Garrett, H. E., J. E. Jones, J. K. Haines, and J. P. Slusher. 1991. "Black Walnut Nut Production under Alleycropping Management: An Old but New Cash Crop for the Farm Community." In The Second Conference on Agroforestry in North America, ed. H. E. Garrett, pp. 159–165. Columbia: University of Missouri School of Natural Resources.

Hankins, A. 1997. "Wild-Simulated Ginseng Cultivation." Temperate Agroforester. January.

Harding, A. R. 1972. Ginseng and Other Medicinal Plants. Columbus, Ohio: A. R. Harding.

Hill, D. B., and L. E. Buck. 2000. "Forest Farming." In North American Agroforestry: An Integrated Science and Practice, ed. H. E. Garrett, W. J. Rietveld, and R. F. Fisher. Madison, WI: American Society of Agronomy.

Krochmal, Arnold, Russell S. Walters, and Richard M. Doughty. 1971. A Guide to Medicinal Plants of Appalachia. Washington DC. U.S. Forest Service.

Missouri Department of Conservation. 1993. Missouri Special Forest Products Project: Final Report. Corvallis, OR: Mater Engineering.

Savory, A. 1988. Holistic Resource Management. Washington, DC: Island Press.

Tanner, G., J. J. Mullahey, and D. Maehr. 1995. "Saw Palmetto: An Ecologically and Economically Important Native Palm." Circular WEC-109. Gainesville: University of Florida, Institute of Food and Agricultural Sciences, Range Science Program. (http://www.wec.ufl.edu/research/range/sawpalm/default.htm).

Tjaden, R. 1998. "Real and Potential Income Opportunities for Riparian Areas." In Natural Resources Income Opportunities for Private Lands: Conference Proceedings, April 5–7, 1998, ed. J. S. Kays, G. R. Goff, P. J. Smallidge, W N. Grafton, and J. A. Parkhurst, pp. 199–208. College Park: University of Maryland Cooperative Extension Service.

Williams, Michael. 1992. Americans and Their Forests: A Historical Geography. Cambridge, UK: Cambridge University Press.

Original Source

This article was excerpted with the kind permission of the authors and publisher from:

Teel, W.S. and L.E. Buck. 2002. "Between Wildcrafting and Monocultures: Agroforestry Options." In: Nontimber Forest Products of the United States, Jones, E.T., R.J. McLain, and J. Weigand (eds). University Press of Kansas. Copies of this publication can be purchased from:

University Press of Kansas 2501 West 15th St., Lawrence, KS 66049 Tel: 785-864-4155; Fax: 785-864-4586;

Web: http://www.kansaspress.ku.edu/jonnon.html

A special thanks is extended to The Institute of Culture and Ecology http://www.ifcae.org/ who co-edited and contributed several chapters to Nontimber Forest Products of the United States.

This excerpt was originally published as *The Overstory* #117.

Medicinal and aromatic plants in agroforestry systems

M.R. Rao, M.C. Palada and B.N. Becker

Medicinal and aromatic plants (MAPs) play an important role in the health care of people around the world, especially in developing countries. Until the advent of modern medicine, man depended on plants for treating human and livestock diseases. Human societies throughout the world have accumulated a vast body of indigenous knowledge over centuries on medicinal uses of plants, and for related uses including as poison for fish and hunting, purifying water, and for controlling pests and diseases of crops and livestock. About 80% of the population of most developing countries still use traditional medicines derived from plants for treating human diseases (de Silva 1997). China, Cuba, India, Sri Lanka, Thailand, and a few other countries have endorsed the official use of traditional systems of medicine in their health care programs. For example, the Indian systems of medicine "Ayurveda," "Sidha" and "Unani" entirely, and homeopathy to some extent, depend on plant materials or their derivatives for treating human ailments (Prajapati *et al* 2003). People in villages and remote areas primarily depend on traditional medicines as the modern system is out of reach and expensive. Many among the educated in Asian and African countries use traditional medicines for reasons of firm belief that they are more effective than modern medicine for certain chronic diseases, they do not have side effects of some of the modern medicines, and/or for economic reasons. Thus, in many societies, traditional and modern systems of medicines are used independently.

About 12.5% of the 422,000 plant species documented worldwide are reported to have medicinal value; the proportion of medicinal plants to the total documented species in different countries varies from 4.4% to 20% (Schippmann *et al* 2002). About 25% of drugs in modern pharmacopoeia are derived from plants and many others are synthetic analogues built on prototype compounds isolated from plants. Up to 60% of the drugs prescribed in Eastern Europe consist of unmodified or slightly altered higher plant products (Lancet 1994). These drugs carry important therapeutic properties including contracep-

tives, steroids and muscle relaxants for anesthesia and abdominal surgery (all made from the wild yam, *Dioscorea villosa*); quinine and artemisinin against malaria; digitalis derivatives for heart failure; and the anti-cancer drugs vinblastin, etoposide and taxol. These compounds cannot be synthesized cost-effectively, which means that their production requires reliable supplies of plant material (van Seters 1997).

The global importance of MAP materials is evident from a huge volume of trade at national and international levels. During the 1990s, the reported annual international importation of MAPs for pharmaceutical use amounted on average to 350 000 Mg valued at over USD 1 billion. A few countries dominate the international trade with over 80% of the global import and export allotted to 12 countries each. Whereas Japan and Korea are the main consumers of medicinal plants, China and India are the world's leading producing nations. Hong Kong, United States and Germany stand out as important trade centers. It is estimated that the total number of MAPs in international trade is around 2500 species worldwide (Schippmann *et al* 2002).

Medicinal Trees in Traditional Agroforestry Systems

Many plants in traditional agricultural systems in the tropics have medicinal value. These can be found (either planted or carefully tended natural regenerations) in homegardens, as scattered trees in croplands and grazing lands, and on field bunds (Table 2). Many *Acacia* species found in Africa such as *Acacia nilotica*, *A. seyal*, *A. senegal* and *A. polyacantha*, as well as several species in African croplands (e.g., *Faidherbia albida*, *Vitellaria paradoxa*, *Adansonia digitata*, *Markhamia lutea* and *Melia volkensii*) have medicinal value (ICRAF 1992). Similarly, "arjun" (*Terminalia arjuna*) in India, chinaberry (*Melia azedarach*) in Asia and *Erythrina* species in Latin and Central America combine many uses including medicinal. Holy Basil or "tulsi" (*Ocimum sanctum*), drumstick (*Moringa oleifera*) and curry leaf (*Murraya koenigii*) are backyard plants in many Indian households and they are routinely used for common ailments or in food preparations. A number of plants used as live fences around home compounds such as henna (*Lawsonia inermis*) in India (Singh et a. 1996), *Ipomoea carnea* ssp. *fistulosa* in Bolivia and Asian countries (Frey 1995) and *Euphorbia tirucalli* around crop fields in Africa (ICRAF 1992) have medicinal values. Although the medicinal value of these plants is "exploited" locally, they are seldom used for commercial purposes (except in the case of commercially exploited neem). In fact, many of these species are valued for poles, fuelwood, fodder, fruit, shade, and/or boundary demarcation and their medicinal value is secondary.

Forests and Forest Plantations

MAPs growing in forests require (or tolerate) partial shade, moist soils high in organic matter, high relative humidity, and mild temperatures. Cultivation of such MAPs can be taken up in thinned forests and cleared forest patches, and as intercrops in new forest plantations. In China, cultivation of medicinal plants has been an age-old practice under the name of "silvo-medicinal" systems. In northeast China, ginseng (*Panax ginseng*) and other medicinal plants are grown in pine (*Pinus* spp.) and spruce (*Picea* spp.) forests; in central China, many medicinal plants are planted with *Paulownia tomentosa* and in southern China medicinal herbs are often planted in bamboo (*Bambusa* spp.) and Chinese fir (*Cunninghamia lanceolata*) forests (Zou and Sanford 1990). In Yunnan province, China, traditional "Dai and Jinuo" agroforestry systems involve the medicinal crop *Amomum villosum* in the forest areas cleared of undergrowth (Saint-Pierre 1991). The forest is thinned to give 30% to 40% shade and seedlings or cuttings are planted, which produce an average dried fruit yield of 375 kg/ha per annum (Zhou 1993). Gupta (1986) listed a number of indigenous understory herbs and shrubs that can be produced as part of forest farming or in new forest plantations to improve economic returns from forests in India. Indigenous people living in the Himalayan forest margins in Uttaranchal, India, are known to have conserved and cultivated several medicinal species for centuries (Kumar *et al* 2002).

A farmers' cooperative in the northern lowlands of Costa Rica has successfully demonstrated cultivation of the medicinal herb "raicilla" (*Cephaelis ipecacuanha*) in natural forests for export to the Netherlands and Germany (Hager and Otterstedt 1996). American ginseng (*Panax quinquefolium*), a medicinal herb exported to China from the United States and Canada is grown as an understorey in red maple (*Acer rubrum*) forests (Nadeau *et al* 1999) or deciduous hardwoods such as black walnut (*Juglans nigra*) and sugar maple (*Acer saccharum*), instead of growing under artificial shade with considerable expense (Hill and Buck 2000). Indeed, cultivation of ginseng and several other medicinal plants in the forests is a common and growing form of forest-farming practice of agroforestry in North America (Table 1). Light demanding understory species (e.g., *Echinacea* sp.) may be intercropped initially to provide early returns from plantations and after canopy closure, shade-tolerant species such as ginseng and goldenseal can be intercropped (Teel and Buck 2002). Studies in New Zealand have indicated that the American ginseng can be successfully grown under *Pinus radiata* with best growth under a tree stand of 130 stems/ha (Follett 1997). In addition to providing shade, the trees may also benefit the understory component from hydraulically lifted water. Fungal diseases are a major concern in forest farming but the application of fungicide can be detrimental to the forests' health, therefore proper spacing and mixed cropping is recommended (Cech 2002). Mechanical cultivation may not be feasible under forested conditions so labor availability needs to be considered as a constraining factor (Hill and Buck 2000).

As in the taungya system, newly established forest plantations can be intercropped with MAPs similar to food crops until the trees cover the ground. The participation of the local people with right to share benefits of the plantations, especially ownership to crops, has helped governments to establish and protect large-scale tree plantations without conflict with the local people in many Asian countries (Nair 1993). The same approach can be employed for the cultivation of MAPs in the new plantations. In the rehabilitation of degraded forestlands, participatory planning and implementation with local communities and economic benefits from an early stage onwards will ensure commitment of the people (Rao *et al* 1999).

Homegardens

Homegardens are complex agroforestry systems involving many plant species characterized by different morphology, stature, biological function and utility,

Morinda citrifolia grows under coconuts on pahoehoe lava, South Kona, Hawai'i. (photo: C. Elevitch)

practiced mostly in the humid and subhumid tropics (Kumar and Nair 2004). Food, fruit and timber species may dominate the homegardens and occupy the middle and upper strata, but medicinal plants, spices and vegetables occupy the lower stratum. Three categories of medicinal plants could be noted in homegardens: species used exclusively for medicine, horticultural or timber species with complementary medicinal value, and "weedy" medicinal species. While the first two categories are deliberately planted the latter group is part of spontaneous growth. The species composition, plant density and level of management vary considerably depending on the soil, climate and market opportunity and cultural background of the people. Homegardens of individual holdings generally cover small parcels of land and are established around homesteads. Although these systems in the past were mostly seen to meet the home needs of small-scale farmers in the forest margins, increased urbanization, transport and market opportunities in recent times are helping to produce cash value crops. Multistrata systems involve fewer species (three to 10 species) than in homegardens in definite planting arrangement and can be designed for home consumption as well as commercial production.

Medicinal plants are an invariable component of homegardens, whether they are in the Peruvian Amazon (Lamont *et al* 1999), on the slopes of the Mt. Kilimanjaro in Tanzania (O'Kting'ati *et al* 1984), or in the humid and semiarid Cuba (Wezel and Bender 2003). The species composition differs depending on cultural background, distance from markets and influence of tourism. Medicinal plants accounted for about 27% of total plant species in the homegardens in Amazon (Padoc and de Jong 1991), 56% in northern Catalonia (Iberian Peninsula) (Agelet *et al* 2000) and 45% in the floodplains of the river Jamuna in Bangladesh (Yoshino and Ando 1999). In the Soqotra Island, Yemen, endemic medicinal plants such as *Aloe perryi*, *Jatropha unicostata* and *Commiphora ornifolia* are cultivated in homegardens (Ceccolini 2002). On St. Croix and St. Thomas, U.S. Virgin Islands, the medicinal trees neem, moringa, and noni (*Morinda citrifolia*) have become popular in homegardens (Palada and Williams 2000).

Riparian Buffer Zones

An agroforestry system that has received considerable attention in North America is riparian buffers zones (Schultz *et al* 2004). Riparian buffer zones can improve water quality and protect streams and rivers from degradation by nutrient loading and chemical pollutants from agriculture and urban areas, from erosion by attenuating peak flows and provide habitat for wildlife. NTFP production can help defray the cost of buffer zone installation and maintenance. Slippery elm (*Ulmus rubra*), harvested for its aromatic and medicinal inner bark, is commonly found in riparian areas in North America (Teel and Buck 2002). Riparian buffer zones are an ideal location for the production of this species, which suffers from commercial over-exploitation and the Dutch elm disease.

Intercropping of MAPs

Two types of intercropping systems can be distinguished involving MAPs: (1) medicinal plants as upper story trees and (2) MAPs as intercrops in other tree crops.

Medicinal plants as overstory trees

Coffee (*Coffea arabica*), cacao (*Theobroma cacao*) and tea (*Camellia sinensis*) are traditionally grown under shade offered by multipurpose trees that produce timber, fruit, flowers, nuts, palms etc. Medicinal tree species that grow tall and develop open crown at the top can also be used for this purpose, for example *yongchak* (*Parkia roxburghii*) in India, the protein rich seeds of which are used to treat stomach disorders (Balasubramanian 1986) and *Ginkgo biloba* in China, the nuts of which are used in Chinese medicine and fetch high value (Shen 1998). In Ivory Coast, 19 of the 41 tree species planted as shade trees in coffee and cacao provide pharmaceutical products for traditional medicine (Herzog 1994). New plantations of coffee, tea, and cacao offer scope for cultivation of forest medicinal trees that are under demand. However, research needs to identify the medicinal trees that can be grown in association with these plantation crops and develop management practices for them. Tall and perennial medicinal trees that need to be planted at wider spacing such as *Prunus africana*, *Eucalyptus globulus* (for oil), sandalwood (*Santalum album*), ashok (*Saraca indica*), bael (*Aegle marmelos*), custard apple (*Annona squamosa*), amla (*Emblica officinalis*),

drumstick or moringa (*Moringa oleifera*) and soapnut tree (*Sapindus mukorossi*) can be intercropped with annual crops in the early years until the tree canopy covers the ground. Some of the medicinal trees may allow intercropping for many years or on a permanent basis depending on the spacing and nature of the trees. The intercrops give some income to farmers during the period when the main trees have not started production.

Medicinal Plants as Intercrops

Many tropical MAPs are well adapted to partial shading, moist soil, high relative humidity and mild temperatures (Vyas and Nein 1999), allowing them to be intercropped with timber and fuel wood plantations, fruit trees and plantation crops. Some well known medicinal plants that have been successfully intercropped with fuel wood trees (e.g., *Acacia auriculiformis*, *Albizia lebbeck*, *Eucalyptus tereticornis*, *Gmelina arborea*, and *Leucaena leucocephala*) in India, include safed musli (*Chlorophytum borivilianum*), rauvolfia (*Rauvolfia serpentina*), turmeric (*Curcuma longa*), wild turmeric (*C. aromatica*), *Curculigo orchioides*, and ginger (*Zingiber officinale*) (Chadhar and Sharma 1996; Mishra and Pandey 1998; Prajapati *et al* 2003). Only 10 out of 64 herbaceous medicinal plants tried in intercropping with two-year old poplar (*Populus deltoides*) spaced 5 m apart gave poor performance (Kumar and Gupta 1991), indicating that many medicinal plants can be grown in agroforestry systems. The trees may benefit from the inputs and management given to the intercrops. Short stature and short cycle MAPs and culi-

Banisteriopsis caapi, a medicinal vine from the Amazon, grows well in mixed forest systems. (photo: C. Elevitch)

nary herbs are particularly suited for short-term intercropping during the juvenile phase of trees. Wherever markets are established, MAPs are remunerative alternative intercrops to the traditionally grown annual crops (Maheswari et al 1985; Zou and Sanford 1990). The number of years MAPs can be intercropped with a given tree species depends on the size and intensity of its canopy shade, tree spacing and management, especially pruning of branches and nature of the MAPs. Shade-tolerant and rhizomatic MAPs can be grown on a longer-term basis in widely spaced plantations.

Intercropping of medicinal plants in coconut (Cocos nucifera) and arecanut (Areca catechu) stands is an age-old practice in India and other parts of south- and southeast Asia. These palms allow 30% to 50% of incident light to the underneath, which is ideal for some MAPs, including cardamom (Elettaria cardamomum). Kacholam or galang (Kaempferia galanga)—a medicinal herb—is traditionally intercropped in mature coconut gardens in Kerala, India. Kacholam intercropped in a 30 year-old coconut plantation produced 6.1 Mg/ha of rhizomes compared with 4.8 Mg/ha as a sole crop (Maheswarappa et al 1998). Twelve-year old coconut trees did not adversely affect the growth and yields of a number of medicinal species grown as intercrops compared to the yields in the open (Nair et al 1989). In Karnataka and Kerala states, India, arecanut palm is commonly intercropped with ginger, turmeric, black pepper (Piper nigrum) and cardamom (Korikanthimath and Hegde 1994). Some of these intercrops may cause small reduction in arecanut yields but the combined returns from both the components are greater than from arecanut alone. Another plantation crop intercropped with MAPs is rubber (Hevea brasiliensis), for example with Dioscorea floribunda in the state of Assam in India (Singh et al 1998) and with Amomum villosum in Yunnan province of China (Zhou 1993). In Sikkim, India, large cardamom (Amomum subulatum) is grown under 30 different shade tree species (Patiram et al 1996). In Fujian Province, China, Cunninghamia lanceolata—an important timber tree—is intercropped with a variety of cereals, cash and medicinal and oil-producing crops (Chandler 1994). Many of the medicinal herbs commonly grown in thinned forests can also be grown intercropped with trees (Zhou 1993).

In the Caribbean islands, there has been increased interest on alternative crops that have better economic potential than traditional crops. For example,

in the U.S. Virgin Islands, a number of farmers are now opting for specialty crops such as the West Indian hot peppers (Capsicum chinense), thyme (Thymus vulgaris) and chives (Allium schoenosprasum) instead of vegetables (Crossman et al 1999). The prospects of growing indigenous MAPs such as "japana" (Eupatorium triplinerve), worrywine (Stachytarpheta jamaicensis), inflammation bush (Verbersina alata) and lemon grass (Cymbopogon citratus) in association with the medicinal trees noni (Morinda citrifolia) and moringa have been explored at the University of the Virgin Island, St. Croix, (Palada and Williams 2000). These local herbs are commonly used as bush teas and very popular in the Caribbean. Medicinal plants and herbs in intercropping produced similar yields to those in sole cropping at the first harvest, but they tended to be lower than in sole cropping at subsequent harvests (Palada and Williams 2000).

Conclusion

Traditional systems of medicine in most developing countries depend primarily on the use of plant products either directly or indirectly. Besides serving the health care needs of a large number of people, medicinal plants are the exclusive source of some drugs even for modern medical treatment. The use of plant products as nutrition supplements and in the cosmetic and perfume industry has increased the value of medicinal and aromatic plants in recent years. The over dependence on forests, natural woodlands and long-term fallows for extraction of MAPs is threatening the survival of many valuable plant species. It is imperative therefore that such endangered species are cultivated outside their natural habitats to ensure their regular supply for human needs as well as to preserve the genetic diversity. Cultivation is an important strategy for conservation and sustainable maintenance of natural stocks, but few MAPs are actually cultivated. Lack of basic knowledge on biology, ecology, propagation methods and cultural practices for the concerned species is an important constraint.

References

Agelet A., Bonet M.A. and Valles J. 2000. Homegardens and their role as a main source of medicinal plants in mountain regions of Catalonia (Iberian Peninsula). Econ Bot 54: 295–309.

Balasubramanian M.A. 1986. Yongchak as shade tree. Planters' Chronicle 80(4): 134.

Ceccolini, L. 2002. The homegardens of Soqotra island, Yemen: an example of agroforestry approach to multiple land-use in an isolated location. Agroforest Syst 56: 107–115.

Chadhar S.K. 2001. Six years of extension and research activities in Social Forestry Division Jhabua (M.P.). Vaniki Sandesh 25(4): 6–10.

Chandler P. 1994. Adaptive ecology of traditionally derived agroforestry in China. Hum Ecol 22: 415–442.

Chech R.A. 2002. Balancing conservation with utilization: restoring populations of commercially valuable medicinal herbs in forests and agroforests. p. 117–123. In M.M. Iwu and J.C. Wootten (eds), Ethnomedicine and drug discovery. Elsevier Science B.V., The Netherlands.

Crossman S.M.A., Palada M.C and Davis A.M. 1999. Performance of West Indian hot pepper cultivars in the Virgin Islands. Proceedings Caribbean Food Crops Society 35: 169–176.

de Silva T. 1997. Industrial utilization of medicinal plants in developing countries. p. 38–48. In G. Bodeker, K.K.S. Bhat, J. Burley and P. Vantomme (eds.) Medicinal Plants for Forest Conservation and Healthcare. Non-Wood Forest Products No. 11, FAO, Rome.

Follett J. 1997. Ginseng production in NZ forests: experiences from Tiketere. New Zealand Tree Grower 18(3): 19–21.

Frey R. 1995. *Ipomoea carnea* ssp. *fistulosa* (Martius ex Chiosy) Austin: Taxonomy, biology and ecology reviewed and inquired. Trop Ecol 36: 21–48.

Gupta R. 1986. Integration of medicinal plants cultivation in forest and forest plantations of North-Western Himalaya. p.59–67. In Agroforestry Systems: A New Challenge. Indian Society of Tree Scientists, Solan, India.

Hager N. and Otterstedt J. 1996. Coope San Juan, a farmers' cooperative. Sustainable use of the natural forest-past and future: a minor field study. Working Paper No. 302. International Rural Development Centre, Swedish University of Agricultural Sciences, Uppsala, Sweden. 59 pp.

Herzog F. 1994. Multiple shade trees in coffee and cocoa plantations in Coted'Ivoire. Agroforest Syst 27: 259–267.

Hill D.B. and Buck L.E. 2000. Forest farming practices. p. 283–320. In H.E. Garrett, W.J. Rietveld and R.F. Fisher (eds.) North American Agroforestry: An Integrated Science and Practice. American Society of Agronomy Inc., Madison, WI, USA.

ICRAF 1992. A Selection of Useful Trees and Shrubs in Kenya: Notes on their Identification, Propagation and Management for Use by Farming and Pastoral Communities. International Centre for Research in Agroforestry, Nairobi, Kenya, 226 pp.

Korikanthimath V.S. and Hegde R. 1994. Cardamom and arecanut mixed-cropping systems. Indian Cocoa, Arecanut and Spices J 18(4): 109–112.

Kumar A., Bisht P.S. and Kumar V. 2002. Traditional medicinal plants of Uttaranchal Himalayas. Asian Agri-History 6: 167–170.

Kumar B.M. and Nair P.K.R. 2004. The enigma of tropical homegardens. In: P.K.R. Nair, M.R. Rao, and L.E. Buck (eds). NEW VISTAS IN AGROFORESTRY: A Compendium for the 1st World Congress of Agroforestry 2004. Kluwer Academic Publishers, Dordrecht, The Netherlands.

Kumar K. and Gupta C. 1991. Intercropping of medicinal plants with poplar and their phenology. Indian Forester: 535–544.

Lamont S.R., Eshbaug W.H. and Greenberg A.M. 1999. Species composition, diversity and use of homegardens among three Amazonian villages. Econ Bot 53: 312–326.

Maheswarappa H.P., Hegde M.R. and Nanjappa H.V. 1998. Kacholam (*Kaempferia galanga* L.)—a potential medicinal-cum-aromatic crop for coconut gardens. Indian Coconut J 29(5): 4–5.

Maheswari S.K., Dhantonde B.N., Yadav S. and Gangrade S.K. 1985. Intercropping of *Rauvolfia serpentina* for higher monetary returns. Indian J Agri Sci 58: 108–111.

Mishra R.K. and Pandey V.K. 1998. Intercropping of turmeric under different tree species and their planting pattern in agroforestry systems. Range Manag Agroforest 19: 199–202.

Nadeau I., Oliver A., Semard R.R., Coulobe J. and Yelle S. 1999. Growing American ginseng in maple forests as an alternative land use system in Quebec, Canada. Agroforest Syst 44: 345–353.

Nair G.S., Sudhadevi P.K. and Kurian A. 1989. Introduction of medicinal and aromatic plants as intercrops in coconut plantations. p. 163–165. In S.P. Raychauduri (ed.), Recent Advances in Medicinal, Aromatic and Spice Crops. Today and Tomorrow's Printers and Publishers, New Delhi, India, Vol. 1.

Nair P.K.R. 1993. An Introduction to Agroforestry. Kluwer Academic Publishers, Dordrecht, The Netherlands, 499 pp.

O'Kting'ati A. Maghembe J.A., Fernandes E.C.M. and Weaver G.H. 1984. Plant species in the Kilimanjaro agroforestry system. Agroforest Syst 2: 177–186.

Padoc C. and de Jong W. 1991. The house gardens of Santa Rosa: diversity and variability in an Amazonian agricultural system. Econ Bot 45: 166–175.

Palada M.C. and Williams M.E. (eds.) 2000. Utilizing Medicinal Plants to Add Value to Caribbean Agriculture. Proceedings of the Second International Workshop on Herbal Medicine in the Caribbean. University of the Virgin Islands, St. Croix, U.S. Virgin Islands. 217 pp.

Patiram, Bhadauria S.B.S. and Upadhyaya R.C. 1996. Agroforestry practices in hill farming of Sikkim. Indian Forester 122: 621–630.

Prajapati N.D., Purohit S.S., Sharma A.K. and Kumar T. 2003. A Handbook of Medicinal Plants. Agribios (India), 553 pp.

Rao K.S., Maikhuri R.K. and Saxena K.E. 1999. Participatory approach to rehabilitation degraded forest lands: a case study in a high altitude village of Indian Himalayas. Int Tree Crops J 10: 1–17.

Schippmann U., Leaman D.J. and Cunnningham A.B. 2002. Impact of cultivation and gathering of medicinal plants on biodiversity: global trends and issues. *In* Biodiversity and the Ecosystem Approach in Agriculture, Forestry and Fisheries. Ninth Regular Session of the Commission on Genetic Resources for Food and Agriculture. FAO, Rome, Italy, pp. 1–21.

Schultz R. C., Isenhart T.M., Simpkins W.W. and Colletti J.P. 2004. Riparian forest buffers in agroecosystems: Lessons learned from the Bear Creek Watershed Project in Central Iowa, USA. In: P.K.R. Nair, M.R. Rao, and L.E. Buck (eds). NEW VISTAS IN AGROFORESTRY: A Compendium for the 1st World Congress of Agroforestry 2004. Kluwer Academic Publishers, Dordrecht, Netherlands.

Shen L. 1998. Management considerations and economic benefits of intercropping tea with *Gingko biloba*. J Zhejiang Forest Sci Technol 18(2): 69–71.

Singh U., Wadhwani A.M. and Johri B.M. 1996. Dictionary of Economic Plants in India. Indian Council of Agricultural Research, New Delhi, India. 288 pp.

Teel W.S and Buck L.E. 2002. Between wildcrafting and monocultures: agroforestry options. p. 199–222. *In* E.T. Jones, R.J. McLain. and J. Weigand (eds.) Non-Timber Forest Products in the United States. University Press of Kansas, Lawrence, KS, USA.

Vyas S. and Nein S. 1999. Effect of shade on the growth of *Cassia angustifolia*. Indian Forester 125: 407–410.

Wezel A. and Bender S. 2003. Plant species diversity of homegardens of Cuba and its significance for household food supply. Agroforest Syst 57: 39–49.

Yoshino K. and Ando K. 1999. Utilization of plant resources in homestead (*bari-bhiti*) in floodplain in Bangladesh. Japanese J Trop Agric 43: 306–318.

Zhou S.Q. 1993. Cultivation of *Amomum villosum* in tropical forests. Forest Ecol Manag 60: 157–162.

Zou X and Sanford R.L. 1990. Agroforestry systems in China: a survey and classification. Agroforest Syst 11: 85–94.

Table 1. Examples of commercially valuable medicinal plants under cultivation or that can be produced as understory component(s) in forests and tree plantations (Source: Gupta (1986); Saint-Pierre (1991); Rao et al 1999; Garrett and McGraw (2000); Hill and Buck (2000); Teel and Buck (2002).)

Latin name	Common name	Plant type	Parts used	Medicinal use	Location
Aconitum heterophyllum	Atis	Tall herb	Rhizomes	Hysteria, throat diseases, astringent	Alpine and sub-alpine Himalayas
Amomum subulatum	Large cardamom	Perennial herb	Seeds	Stimulant, indigestion, vomiting, rectal diseases	Sub-Himalayan range, Nepal, Bhutan,
Amomum villosum	Saren	Perennial herb	Seeds	Gastric and digestive disorders	China
Caulophyllum thalictroides	Blue cohosh	Perennial herb	Roots	Gynecological problems, bronchitis	North America
Cimicifuga racemosa	Black cohosh	Perennial herb	Roots	Menses related problems	North America
Chlorophytum borivilianum	Safed musli	Annual herb	Tubers	Male impotency, general weakness	India
Costus speciosus	Crepe ginger	Cane	Leaves, stem, rhizomes	Purgative, depurative and as a tonic	India
Dioscorea deltoidea	Himalayan yam	Vine	Tubers	Source of saponins and steroids	India, Pakistan
Echinacea purpurea	Coneflower	Perennial herb	Roots, rhizomes	Enhancing immune system	North America
Hydrastis canadensis	Goldenseal	Perennial herb	Rhizomes	Tonic	North America

Table 1. Examples of commercially valuable medicinal plants under cultivation or that can be produced as understory component(s) in forests and tree plantations (Source: Gupta (1986); Saint-Pierre (1991); Rao et al 1999; Garrett and McGraw (2000); Hill and Buck (2000); Teel and Buck (2002).)

Panax ginseng	Ginseng	Herb	Roots	Tonic	China, Korea, Japan
Panax quinquefolium	American ginseng	Perennial herb	Roots	Tonic	North America
Cephaelis ipecacuanha	Raicilla, Ipecac	Shrub	Roots	Whooping cough, bronchial asthma, amoebic dysentery	Brazil, India, Bangladesh, Indonesia
Rauvolfia serpentina	Rauvolfia	Shrub	Roots	Hypertension and certain forms of insanity	Sub-montane zone, India
Serenoa repens	Saw palmetto	Shrubby-palm	Fruits	Swelling of prostrate gland	Southeastern USA

Table 2. Tree species reported to have medicinal values grown in traditional agroforestry systems in the tropics

Tree species (Common name)	Agroforestry system	Medicinal use	Reference
Acacia nilotica (babul)	Field bunds, scattered trees in croplands, woodlots and grazing lands in East Africa and Indian sub-continent	Gum used for treating diarrhea, dysentery, diabetes, sore throat, bark used to arrest external bleeding	Pushpangadan and Nayar (1994)
Azadirachta indica (neem)	Woodlots, scattered trees, shelterbelts in Africa and India	Digestive disorders, malaria, fever, hemorrhoids, hepatitis, measles, syphilis, boils, burns, snakebite, rheumatism	Singh et al (1996)
Erythrina spp.	Shade tree in coffee, live fence	Different *Erythrina* species have different uses.	Russo (1993)
Parkia biglobosa (neré or locust bean tree)	Parklands in West Africa	Piles, malaria, stomach disorders, jaundice	Teklehaimanot (2004)
Prosopis cineraria (khejri)	Scattered trees in croplands in arid to semiarid areas mostly in northwestern India	Flowers for blood purification and curing skin diseases. Bark against summer boils, leprosy, dysentery, bronchitis, asthma, leucoderma and piles	Pushpangadan and Nayar (1994)
Tamarindus indica (tamarind)	Field bunds and scattered trees in croplands in semiarid India and Africa	Fruit pulp is used in Indian medicine as refrigerant, carminative and laxative. It is also recommended in febrile diseases and bilious disorders	Singh et al (1996)

Original Source

Rao, M.R., M.C. Palada and B.N. Becker. 2004. "Medicinal and aromatic plants in agroforestry systems." In: P.K.R. Nair, M.R. Rao, and L.E. Buck (eds). NEW VISTAS IN AGROFORESTRY: A Compendium for the 1st World Congress of Agroforestry 2004. © Kluwer Academic Publishers, Dordrecht, The Netherlands.

Publisher information:
Europe, Asia, Africa, Australia:
Kluwer Academic Publishers
Customer Service Department
P.O. Box 989
3300 AZ Dordrecht
The Netherlands
Tel: (+31) 78 657 60 50
Fax: (+31) 78 657 62 54
Email: services@wkap.nl

North and South America:
Kluwer Academic Publishers
Customer Service Department
P.O. Box 358, Accord Station
Hingham, MA 02018-0358 U.S.A.
Tel: (781) 871-6600; Toll free: (866) 269-9527
Fax: (781) 681-9045
Email: kluwer@wkap.com

This chapter was originally published as *The Overstory* #135.

The Hidden Bounty of the Urban Forest

Paul Jahnige

Have you ever picked berries from the edge of a forest in a city park? Made a holiday wreath from wild grapevine growing in your backyard? Collected the nuts of a Chinese chestnut street tree? Or harvested pokeweed growing in an abandoned lot? Many people do collect such products—and others—in cities. These urban nontimber forest products (NTFPs) represent important economic, nutritional, biological, educational, and cultural resources for a diversity of urban residents (Community Resources 2000).

Within the past ten years, people have increasingly recognized nontimber forest products for the important cultural, subsistence, and market values that they add to rural forests and individual households worldwide. Nearly all ethnic groups around the globe rely on NTFPs for household income, food, medicine, construction supplies, and materials for decorative and ceremonial purposes. These resources are especially important during times of economic hardship or during lulls in agricultural production (Saxena 1986).

Despite increasing use and recognition of NTFPs, they continue to be thought of as "rural" resources collected from rural areas and important to rural people (Guijt *et al* 1995). At the same time, research on the benefits of urban trees and forests typically includes beauty, increased property values, reduced noise pollution, improvements to water and air quality, and reduced energy costs but makes little or no mention of urban forest products (Moll and Young 1992; McPherson *et al* 1994).

Defining "Urban Forest" and "Urban NTFPs"

Some definitions of the urban forest account for all elements (biotic, abiotic, and social) of our urban ecosystems, while others refer only to large, closed-canopy forested areas. We define the urban forest as all trees and associated plants and animal species that live in our cities. This definition includes single street trees, yards, vacant lots, and landscaped areas as well as "forested" areas. We define an urban nontimber forest product (NTFP) as "any (nontimber)

product collected, cultivated, or derived from the urban forest."

Sources of Urban NTFPs

People collect urban NTFPs from diverse sites that span a range of ownership and management regimes—from public to private and from highly managed to unmanaged. Some products are collected from a variety of sites. For example, pokeweed is collected from yards, vacant lots, and roadsides. Other products are unique to a certain type of site. Peaches and figs appear mostly in private yards, and morels are found in closed-canopy forests. Generally, urban collection sites include:

- Street trees—publicly owned and tended, single trees planted in sidewalks and grass strips. These often include nut- and seed-producing trees, such as ginkgos, oaks, and walnuts.
- Yard trees and plants—privately owned and highly managed plant resources in front, side, or back yards. These often include fruiting plants, such as apples, pears, and berries. Yard and street trees often include exotic and ornamental plants.
- Vacant lots—publicly, privately, or community-owned lots, whether managed or wholly unmanaged. Species collected from lots include a variety of perennial and biennial plants, such as pokeweed and chicory.
- Open-grown park trees—publicly owned and managed, single trees grown in open park areas. These often include fruit- and nut-producing trees, as well as a variety of evergreen species providing decorative greens and cones.
- Open-grown trees on institutional properties—similar to open-grown park trees except that large private-sector businesses and institutions, including business parks, cemeteries, schools, and colleges, often own or care for the trees.
- Roadside and forest edge plants—both publicly and privately owned, and often unmanaged plant species growing along roadsides and forest edges. These plants often include berries, vines, and medicinal plants. Many urban roadside species are invasive.

• Closed-canopy forest plants—woodland trees, shrubs, herbs, and mushrooms that grow in both publicly and privately owned, usually unmanaged forest areas.

Use and Markets for Urban NTFPs

People collect urban NTFPs primarily for personal use. They pick berries as they walk through parks, collect chestnuts or edible mushrooms as ingredients for a special dinner, cut grapevines from roadsides to decorate their houses in the fall, or gather and can fruit for the winter.

Many people collect urban NTFPs to give as gifts and share their harvest bounty with neighbors or friends. Sharing and gift giving is an important form of social reciprocity and an example of how urban NTFP collection can help build connections between people in urban communities.

Another prevalent use for urban NTFPs is to raise funds, both for organizations and for individuals. For example, the holiday greens sale is a common fund-raiser for churches, senior centers, garden clubs, and other organizations. In some cases, people gather greens from private neighborhood yards. but they also collect and gather NTFPs from parks, cemeteries, and hospital grounds. For fund-raising, many environmental nonprofit organizations sell seedlings at festivals. In some cases, organizations raise seedlings from seeds collected in local parks, and in other cases, people may dig up seedlings from yards or roadsides where seedlings are not wanted or are likely to be mowed or otherwise lost.

Finally, some collectors bring urban NTFPs to various markets for sale. Some make holiday wreaths and other natural decorations to supplement seasonal incomes. Recreational beekeepers also sell their product locally to offset their costs. Some ven-

Urban landscaping using coconut and pandanus, two very useful trees. Apia, Samoa. (photo: C. Elevitch)

dors include collected products as a part of their inventory at local farmers' markets. For example, in Baltimore, Maryland, people report locally collected walnuts and chestnuts brought to market, while osage orange is sold as a roach repellant in the St. Louis farmers' market. Others sell products such as pokeweed, wineberry, grapevine, and pinecones to various wholesale and retail vendors including greengrocers or specialty craft outlets. Frequently, individuals sell collected products, such as mushrooms and figs, directly to restaurants or other consumers.

Urban NTFP Collectors

Collectors of urban forest products are, in many ways, as invisible as collectors of forest products elsewhere. In fact, many urban harvesters do not identify themselves as collectors.

Urban forest product collectors come from diverse socioeconomic and ethnic groups, and the products collected often reflect their socioeconomic and cultural heritage. For example, Korean collectors gather chestnuts and ginkgo nuts both because they are important ingredients for Asian cooking and because collecting is a traditional family activity. African Americans, with roots in the South, collect pokeweed as a traditional green. Many families of Greek descent grow figs, grapes, and other fruits in their backyards.

Urban collectors come from inner-city communities and suburban developments, from poor neighborhoods and wealthy neighborhoods, and from probably every ethnic group that resides within a given city. In Baltimore, there are Italian collectors who traveled from well outside Baltimore to gather chestnuts inside the city, inner-city residents who collect and can fruit from trees on vacant lots, New Englanders who made special trips to find ripe berries, and Native Americans who collect craft materials from city forests to make dream catchers.

Also in this region, anecdotal evidence points to the particular importance of urban NTFPs for certain immigrant populations, especially eastern European, northeast Asian, and southeast Asian immigrants. People suspected to have more recent connections to rural life (for example, first-generation migrants to cities) are more likely to collect urban NTFPs than are long-term urban dwellers; however, this trend is not always the case. Many Baltimore urbanites reported "rediscovering" collection as a new connection to the urban natural world as well as many recent migrants who said they were wary of urban collection.

A few people use the collection of urban forest products to boost their income. These include artisans, farmers' market vendors, and nature enthusiasts. In most cases, these folks are adding significant value to urban NTFPs through artistry, processing, education, and tourism.

The Value of Urban NTFPs

Economic Value

First and foremost, urban NTFPs provide economic values to harvesters. A product collected for personal use is a substitute for one otherwise purchased or is unique and cannot be purchased. Homemade or locally collected gifts have values that similar store-bought gifts do not capture. People selling urban NTFPs, either at fund-raisers or at local markets, earn cash from their products.

Nutritional Value

Edible urban NTFPs provide important nutritional benefits to collectors (Guijt, Hinchcliffe, and Melnyk 1995). Urban NTFPs are collected and consumed fresh, and locally collected products may taste better than store bought items. Urban NTFPs are often difficult or impossible to find in stores and thus represent greater product diversity and expanded consumer choices. Products such as fresh figs, berries, apricots, mushrooms, and nuts are excellent sources of vitamins, minerals, and proteins while being very low in fat.

Educational Value

Searching for, collecting, and using forest products promotes a greater understanding of natural environments and the human connections to them. The educational value is particularly important in cities where many residents may not know nonurban environments. Urban NTFP harvesting can build and strengthen a sense of connection, as harvesting is often a multigenerational activity in which older family members teach younger ones about the natural world, family history, and their cultural heritage. One collector taps sugar maples and collects berries with his two-year-old daughter as a way to teach her about how trees work and where food comes from. Another person uses harvesting to teach his child about poisonous plants and berries. Others use collection to teach about traditional foods and nutrition.

Recreational Value

There is significant recreational value in collecting and in bringing home the harvest. Who does not enjoy chancing upon a patch of ripe berries? Or picking apples to take home for pie? Or bringing in fresh-cut blossoms to decorate the house? Collecting is fun. People will travel thirty or forty miles just to find a farm where they can pick their own produce. Many people share harvesting and harvests with family and friends. Because people perceive these products to be scarcer in the city and urban dwellers happen upon them less often, this recreational value is often greater for urban residents.

Health Issues

Many people raise questions about health risks from using urban NTFPs. Some of the concerns include air pollution from automobile and industrial exhaust accumulating on or in edible products; lead and other heavy metals in soils from old paint, car exhaust, or illegal waste dumping; toxic chemicals from spraying insecticides or pesticides and from industrial contamination; and poisoning from eating misidentified products, especially mushrooms.

Some general guidelines for avoiding health risks include (Brill 1994): wash or peel all plants before eating them; don't collect within fifty feet of a major roadway; don't collect along railroad rights-of-way; don't collect water plants unless you have the water tested; always be sure about your plant or mushroom identification (or avoid altogether); know which parts of edible plants are edible and in what season; and collect only the plants you intend to use (Brill 1994). Uncertainty exists about serious health risks from air pollutants and heavy metal uptake by plants.

Urban Advantages

- Season extension—Urban "heat island" effects may make urban forest products available several weeks earlier in the spring and later in the fall than in adjacent rural areas. For example, cherries in Baltimore come into season about two weeks before other local cherries. This means that urban cherries are available when market prices are still relatively high at about five dollars a pound.

- Diversity—The urban forest contains diverse introduced species, many of which produce goods valued by a variety of ethnic groups and otherwise not available outside of the cities. For example, ginkgo trees, Chinese chestnuts, and figs are commonly found in the urban forest but are mostly absent in rural areas.
- Public management of single forest trees—Urban trees are managed as individuals, which makes them relatively easy to manage for product production.
- Access to products and markets—Urban NTFPs grow where many people live and shop. Very little travel time lowers costs for either collecting or selling these products.

Conclusion

As we all work to better understand and promote the sustainable use of our forest resources, it is important to remember that the urban forest is an important component. In conclusion:

1   Diverse people collect many products from the urban forest.

2   Urban NTFPs have important economic, nutritional, educational, recreational, and cultural values.

3   Urban land and forest planners and managers should consider forest product collection and collectors as they work with communities, develop planting plans, and implement forest management strategies.

4   Further investigations can help people better understand urban NTFP issues, such as empowering harvesters, collector conflicts, health risks, and ecological and management issues in the urban context.

References

Brill, "Wildman" S. 1994 Identifying and Harvesting Edible and Medicinal Plants in Wild (and Not So Wild) Places. New York: Hearst Books.

Community Resources. 2000. "Working Paper: Exploring the Value of Urban Non-timber Forest Products," at www.communityresources.org.

Guijt, I., F. Hinchcliffe, and M. Melnyk. 1995. The Hidden Harvest: The Value of Wild Resources in Agricultural Systems. London: International Institute for Environment and Development.

McPherson, E.G., D.J. Nowack, and R.A. Rowntree, eds. 1994. Chicago's Urban Forest Ecosystem: Results of the Chicago Forest Climate Project. General Technical Report NE-i 86. Radnor, PA: USDA Forest Service, Northeastern Forest Experiment Station.

Moll, G., and S. Young. 1992. Growing Greener Cities. Los Angeles: Living Planet Press.

Saxena, S. 1986. "Desert Plants Used as Human Food during Scarcity and Famines." In: Desert Environment: Conservation and Management, ed. K.A. Shankernarayan and V. Shaker, CAZRI pub. no. 26, Jodhpur, India.

Original Source

This article was excerpted with the kind permission of the publisher from:

Jahnige, P. 2002. "The Hidden Bounty of the Urban Forest." In: Nontimber Forest Products of the United States, Jones, E.T., R.J. McLain, and J. Weigand (eds). University Press of Kansas.

Copies of this publication can be purchase from: University Press of Kansas 2501 West 15th St., Lawrence, KS 66049 Tel: 785-864-4155; Fax: 785-864-4586 Web: http://www.kansaspress.ku.edu/jonnon.html

A special thanks is extended to The Institute of Culture and Ecology (http://www.ifcae.org/) who co-edited and contributed several chapters to Nontimber Forest Products of the United States.

This excerpt was originally published as *The Overstory* #106.

Urban Forestry

Guido Kuchelmeister and Susan Braatz

Although trees have been an important part of human settlements throughout history, only recently has their full value to urban dwellers been recognized. Trees and green spaces play an important role in improving city living conditions. In the past, urban forestry in developed countries was considered almost exclusively on the basis of its aesthetic merits. Now, a closer look is being given to the environmental services and quantifiable economic benefits they provide. This article discusses the role of trees in and around densely populated areas.

Introduction

Urban forestry has as its objective the cultivation and management of trees for their present and potential contribution to the environmental, social, and economic well-being of urban society. Urban forestry is a merging of arboriculture, ornamental horticulture and forest management. It is closely related to landscape architecture and park management. In its broadest sense, urban forestry embraces a multifaceted managerial system that includes municipal watersheds, wildlife habitats, outdoor recreation opportunities, landscape design, recycling of municipal wastes, tree care and the production of wood as a raw material.

Urban forestry includes activities carried out in the city centre, suburban areas and the "urban fringe" or interface area with rural lands. Forestry activities can differ significantly according to the zone. In central areas, the potential for significant new urban forestry efforts are relatively limited in most cities. Here, it is mainly an issue of maintaining or replacing trees planted long ago.

In the suburban areas, more scope exists for tree planting, as the availability of land is greater than in the city centre. The land is more likely to be privately owned than in the peri-urban or fringe area and the people more settled, thereby having a greater vested interest in tree protection and care.

There are many differences between the management of trees in an urban environment and "traditional" rural forestry. In many cities, trees are a minor part of the landscape, particularly in the centre.

Cities present harsh conditions for tree growth. Even in those which have large tree cover in their central urban area and/or suburban areas, management is complicated by the fragmentation of green space. The objectives of tree planting, the location, the configuration of planting and the management of the trees in urban areas differ from those in rural areas. Socioeconomic conditions and requirements can be quite different and more variable in a city than in the countryside. In addition, the availability of technical information on which management decisions or urban/peri-urban forestry can be based is still limited, particularly in developing countries (Kuchelmeister, 1991).

Urban Forestry Through History

The planting of trees in human settlements and as an integral part of landscape architecture is not new; it has its roots in ancient Chinese, western Asian and Greek civilizations (Jellicoe, 1985). A number of ancient cities had highly developed parks, gardens and other green spaces—the most notable being Babylon, "the mother city of gardens," dating back more than 3,000 years. The Assyrian civilization and, much later, the classical Persian and Greek civilizations arising in the fifth century BC, also had such a tradition, based on amenity as well as cultural and religious beliefs. In Europe in the seventeenth and eighteenth centuries, municipal and crown forests were managed for recreational hunting. Later, the elite developed urban gardens and parks as visual amenities in many European cities, particularly Italy, France, Austria and England. The practice of urban amenity plantings subsequently spread to colonies in Africa and Asia. Spanish colonization introduced into Latin America the concepts of interior patios in houses and public plazas in urban centres. Throughout history, the planting and management of trees and forests has been based much more on aesthetic and spiritual values than on utilitarian benefits.

The Value of Urban Forests

The list of goods and services that urban forestry can provide is impressive. Trees and green spaces help

Traditional homegardens in Samoa contain at least one breadfruit tree (*Artocarpus altilis*), as well as numerous other edible and useful trees. Apia, Samoa. (photo: C. Elevitch)

keep cities cool, act as natural filters and noise absorbers; improve microclimates and protect and improve the quality of natural resources, including soil, water, vegetation and wildlife. Trees contribute significantly to the aesthetic appeal of cities, thereby helping to maintain the psychological health of their inhabitants. Beyond ecological and aesthetic benefits, urban forestry has a role in helping resource-poor populations meet basic needs, particularly but not exclusively in developing countries.

Tangible Benefits

Beyond their aesthetic and ecological value, trees can contribute to the satisfaction of energy requirements as well as the daily food requirements of urban dwellers, particularly in the case of the poorest elements of society.

Food production

Urban agriculture is common in many cities in Asia, Latin America and Africa (Yeung, 1987; Sanyal, 1985; Streiffeler, 1987; Ninez, 1985; Skinner, 1981). Who and how many people practice it as well as what form it takes differ greatly from place to place. It is most often practiced in the urban fringe area by low-income families but, in places such as Africa and the Pacific Islands, urban agriculture is widespread within cities. Although in most places the emphasis is not on the production of staple foods, through the production of vegetables, fruits and condiments, urban agriculture can contribute to the improvement of the nutritional value and variety of city dwellers' diets.

Fruit trees are often an important component of urban home gardens. In some places, trees are planted to help supplement fuelwood and fodder needs and even to provide raw materials for handicrafts. The role of agroforestry in improving productivity and diversifying production should be examined—it is a field that should become much more important in the future.

In many developing countries, particularly in Africa and Latin America, about half the low- and moderate-income households moving into cities will be headed by women. Urban agroforestry will not only be important to household nutrition but may offer a source of income while allowing women to stay at home.

Fuelwood

Wood fuel provides between 25 and 90 percent of urban household energy supplies; it is particularly important as a source of energy in smaller urban centres in developing countries, especially in dry zones (Kuchelmeister, 1998). Poor urban households spend a significant proportion of their cash income in obtaining wood energy. If the urban poor population continues to grow, an increase in the consumption of traded wood fuel is likely to be a consequence. Under favourable circumstances, fuelwood from non-rural forests and agroforestry systems can contribute significantly to fuelwood supply.

Timber

Availability of an adequate timber supply is a problem for a growing number of households in developing countries. Principle sources of timber in urban areas are plantations, street trees, shelterbelts or windbreaks and greenbelts, parks and gardens. In many cities timber harvesting is combined with intensive outdoor recreation activities. Systematic planting of street trees for timber production is widely practised in China and Malaysia (Webb, 1998). Some cities in industrialized countries offset the costs of tree care through harvesting of trees.

Environmental Services

As a result of the predominance of concrete buildings, asphalt and metal as well as the concentration of transport systems and industrial activities in and around urban areas, the median temperature is higher (the "heat island" effect), the air is drier and often polluted, rainfall is less efficiently absorbed and the environment is generally noisier than in a rural setting.

Cleaning the air

One of the major problems in urban areas is poor air quality. Plants help remove pollutants from the air in three ways: absorption by the leaves or the soil surface; deposition of particulates and aerosols on leaf surfaces; and fallout of particulates on the leeward (downwind) side of the vegetation because of the slowing of air movement.

Research on the removal of airborne pollutants by vegetation shows that plants are effective sinks for pollution. Trees absorb sulfur dioxide very efficiently. Keller (1979) has quantified an 85 percent reduction in lead behind a shelterbelt of trees. Soil effectively absorbs gaseous pollutants, including carbon monoxide, sulfur dioxide, nitrogen oxides, ozone and hydrocarbons. Trees intercept dust: a belt of trees measuring 30 meters in width has been found to intercept almost all dust in the air. Trees also often mask fumes and disagreeable odours by replacing them with more pleasing scents or by actually absorbing them. Trees also help to increase the relative humidity of urban air through evapotranspiration.

Modifying temperature extremes

Trees, shrubs and other vegetation help to control temperature extremes in urban environments by modifying solar radiation. The shade of one large tree may reduce the temperature of a given building to the same extent as would 15 air conditioners at 4000 British thermal units (BTU), i.e., 4220 kJ, in a similar but unshaded building. Energy saving through tree planting around houses ranges from 10 to 50 percent for cooling and from 4 to 22 percent for heating (NAA/ISA, 1991).

Noise reduction

Noise is often referred to as invisible pollution. Excessive noise levels in most major cities contribute to both physical and psychological damage. Trees can help both by absorbing and refracting or dissipating noise such as that produced by the heavy vehicular traffic which characterizes urban areas.

Water use, reuse and conservation

Urban forests can help in the protection of urban water supply, wastewater treatment systems and storm water management. Most poor cities face significant wastewater treatment challenges and could integrate stabilization ponds into park systems and reuse wastewater for urban forestry. Reusing city wastewater not only recharges aquifers but also reduces the demand exerted on scarce water reserves. The greatest potential of wastewater reuse is in arid zones in developing countries (Braatz, 1994; Kuchelmeister, 1998).

Protection of the suburban and rural areas that serve as the source of cities' water is a traditional urban forestry linkage, but to be successful such projects must be integrated into urban planning.

Soil conservation

Trees and forests are a means of soil conservation, preventing landslides in fragile ecosystems with steep terrain, little vegetation and harsh seasonal rains, and thus protecting people's lives and homes.

Biodiversity

Green areas have a vital role in urban biodiversity. Suburban wetlands can be some of the most productive natural ecosystems and can provide important habitats for fauna. Incorporating green areas in networks will improve biological conservation and biodiversity; greenbelts and greenways (linear parks) can serve as biological corridors (IUCN, 1994).

Social Benefits

Improving the aesthetic quality of urban areas

It is the aesthetic and recreational value of trees, forests and parks that is most directly identified by most urban dwellers, in developed and developing countries alike. Trees fulfill certain psychological, social and cultural needs of the urban dweller (Dwyer,

Trees enhance the health and well-being of people in urban environments. (photo: C. Elevitch)

Schroeder and Gobster, 1991). They play a very important social role in easing tensions and improving psychological health; people simply feel better living around trees. One study has demonstrated that hospital patients placed in rooms with windows facing trees heal faster and require shorter hospital stays (Ulrich, 1990). When appropriately selected and placed, trees are effective in screening out undesirable views and ensuring privacy while permitting free visual access to the rest of the landscape. Parks provide easily accessible recreational opportunities for people.

Health

Parks and green areas provide opportunities for healthy physical activity. In addition, the passive benefit to physical and mental health of an urban landscape with trees has been documented in industrialized countries (Ulrich, 1984); enjoyment of green areas may help people to relax or may give them fresh energy.

Improving air quality through the planting of vegetation certainly has an impact on health, with such obvious benefits as decreased incidence of respiratory illnesses. Urban forests can also contribute to food security, as discussed above.

Employment

Tree planting and especially urban agroforestry systems can be labour intensive and provide work opportunities which may be especially important in poorer cities. In wealthier countries arboriculture is a significant business. Urban forests and green areas also provide opportunities for many kinds of formal and informal enterprise related to recreation.

Education

Urban forests are increasingly appreciated in environmental education. A number of cities both in industrialized and developing countries have botanical gardens, zoos, nature trails and visitor information centres that can inform people about flora and fauna. Easily accessible trees and woodlands provide a vital facility for both formal and informal learning.

Recreation

Urban forests greatly enhance outdoor recreation. Lower income residents tend to frequent city parks more than wealthier citizens do because they lack the financial means and leisure time to reach more distant recreation sites. To be useful to low income people, forests and green areas must be within an affordable traveling distance and must have the amenities that people desire.

Community building and property value improvement

Public involvement with trees in towns can help strengthen neighbourhood communities by providing people with an opportunity to work together for the benefit of the local environment (NUFU, 1998).

Studies have shown an increase in house prices where property is associated with urban trees, for example up to 5 percent in Hong Kong (Webb, 1998) and in the Finnish town of Salo (Tyrvainen, 1999) and up to 18 percent in the United States (Morales, Micha and Weber, 1983). In Singapore and Kuala Lumpur it has been recognized that a tree-rich urban landscape is an important attraction for new businesses and investors (Kuchelmeister, 1998).

References

Braatz, S. 1994. Urban forestry in developing countries: status and issues. In: C. Kollin, J. Mahon & L. Frame, (eds). Growing greener communities. Proceedings of the sixth National Urban Forest Conference, Minneapolis, Minnesota, USA, 14–18 September 1993, p. 85–88. American Forests, Washington, DC.

Dwyer, J.F., Schroeder, H.W. & Gobster, P.H. 1991. The significance of urban trees and forests: toward a deeper understanding of values. J. Arboriculture, 17(10): 276–284.

FAO. 1989. Arid zone forestry: a guide for field technicians. FAO Conservation Guide No. 20. FAO, Rome.

IUCN. 1994. Putting plans into action. Report of Metropolitan Open Space Systems (MOSS) International Conference, Durban, South Africa, 9–11 February.

Jellicoe, G.A. 1985. The search for a paradise garden. In IFLA Yearbook 1985/86, p. 6–33. International Federation of Landscape Architects, Versailles.

Keller, T. 1979. The possibilities of using plants to alleviate the effects of motor vehicles. TRRL Symposium Report 513 DOE/DT.

Kuchelmeister, G. 1991. Urban and peri-urban multipurpose forestry in development cooperation—experience, deficits and recommendations. Funded by the Commission of the European Communities, Illertissen, Germany. (Unpubl. final report)

Kuchelmeister, G. 1998. Urban forestry in the Asia-Pacific Region—status and prospects. Asia-Pacific Forestry Sector Outlook Study Working Paper Series No. 44. Rome,
FAO. (Also available at: <http://www.fao.org/forestry/FON/FONS/outlook/Asia/APF-SOS/44/Apfsos44.htm>)

Morales, D.J., Micha, F.R. & Weber, R.C. 1983. Two methods of evaluating trees on residential sites. Journal of Arboriculture, 9(1): 21–24.

NAA/ISA. 1991. The importance of large tree maintenance in mitigating global climate change. National Arborist Association, Amherst, USA.

Ninez, V. 1985. Working a half potential: constructure analysis of home garden programmes in the Lima slums with suggestions for an alternative approach. Food Nutr. Bull., 7(3): 8–14.

NUFU. 1998. Trees matter. The benefits of trees & woods in towns. National Urban Forest Unit, London.

Sanyal, B. 1985. Urban agriculture: who cultivates and why? A case study of Lusaka, Zambia. Food Nutr. Bull. 7(3): 15–24.

Skinner, G.W. 1981. Vegetable supply and marketing in Chinese cities. In D.L. Plucknett & H.L. Beemer, Jr, eds. Vegetable farming systems in China. Westview Press, Boulder, Colorado.

Streiffeler, F. 1987. Improving urban agriculture in Africa: a social perspective. Food Nutr. Bull. 9(2): 8–13.

Tyrvainen, L. 1999. Monetary valuation of urban forest amenities in Finland. Doctoral dissertation. Research Paper No. 739. Finnish Forest Research Institute, Vantaa, Finland.

Ulrich, R.S. 1984. View through a window may influence recovery from surgery. Science, 224: 420–421.

Ulrich, R.S. 1990. The role of trees in wellbeing and health. In P.D. Rodbell. ed. Proc. Fourth Urban Forestry Conference, St Louis, Missouri, 15–19 October 1990.

Yeung, Y. 1987. Examples of urban agriculture in Asia. Food Nutr. Bull., 9(2): 14–23.

Original Source

This article is excerpted from: Kuchelmeister, G. and S. Braatz. 1993. Urban Forestry Revisited. Unasylva 173, Vol. 44:13–18. FAO, Rome.
Web: http://www.fao.org/docrep/u9300e/u9300e03.htm.

Some material in "The Value of Urban Forests" was originally published in: Kuchelmeister, G. 2000. Trees for the urban millennium – urban forestry update, Unasylva 200, Vol. 51:49–55. FAO, Rome.
Web: http://www.fao.org/docrep/X3989E/x3989e09.htm

This excerpt was originally published as *The Overstory* #87.

Useful Species

"What should we plant?" may be the most commonly asked question in farming and reforestation. There is no need to be limited to a small handful of common plants. Consider the tremendous diversity of versatile and useful trees, bamboos, palms, mushrooms and vegetables.

Section Contents

Multipurpose Palms

Franklin W. Martin, Craig R. Elevitch, and Kim M. Wilkinson

Among the plants of the Tropics it is difficult to find a family of plants of more service to people than the palm family (Palmae, Arecaceae). In fact, this family has been called the most versatile of all due to its many uses.

Palms seldom receive the recognition they merit, perhaps because the family is almost entirely of the tropics, and almost completely absent in temperate zones where there are more writers of books and magazines as well as researchers. This article aims to stimulate readers to grow and use palms with the belief that these plants can be of much, much more service.

Records Involving Palms

Most versatile plant family in total uses	Palmae
Most versatile plant family in food uses	Palmae
World's longest woody vines	Rattan palms
World's longest leaves	Raffia palms (over 10 meters)
World's longest inflorescence	Talipot palm
World's largest seed	Double coconut (Coco-de-Mer)
World's hardest seed	Ivory palm
World's tallest palm	*Ceroxylon* (65 meters)
World's single best starch source	*Metroxylon*
Most versatile plant in the world	Coconut palm

The Uses of Palms Around the World

How are palms used around the world? It might take considerable study to find all the ways. More than 800 uses have been recorded for the date palm alone, for it is the very foundation of life for several cultures. One might divide the uses into three classes: for ecological purposes, for food, and for other uses.

Ecological Uses

Palms are seldom used purposely for ecological purposes, yet they play a great role in the ecology of the tropical forest, for they are, in size, from small and almost insignificant understory plants to large and dominating beauties of the forest. They are shelter for numerous birds and small animals. In the axils of the old leaves other plants such as ferns, orchids, and bromeliads grow, and their unique insects are many in number. Palms are principal sources of food for many birds and mammals, serving an important ecological function.

Food Uses

Almost all parts of the palm can be used as food in some cases, as shown below. The three most common food uses are of the sap, the accumulated starch, or the growing tip. The tapping of the inflorescence (flower cluster) or the apex of the palm yields sap, which can be made into a fresh drink, or fermented into toddy, or then distilled into a drink called arrack. The sap can also be boiled to yield palm sugar, or jaggery. The accumulated starch is harvested from the trunk of mature palms, and becomes not only a staple food but an industrial product as well. The third common use is of the growing tip hidden among the bases of the leaves. The tender tip, eaten raw or cooked, is frequently called millionaire's salad. Harvesting the tip destroys the trunk, and thus the best species for this purpose are those with multiple trunks. The above general uses are shared by many, many species of palms. In contrast, the edible qualities of the inflorescence, the flower, the pollen, the fruit pulp, and the nut inside vary with

Coconut is one of the most useful plants in the world. (photo: C. Elevitch)

each species and it is difficult to be sure of these uses without careful trial.

The Edible Uses of Palms

Sap	toddy, wine, vinegar, arrack, sugar, jaggery
Bud	palm cabbage
Flower cluster	cooked vegetable, candied flowers, pollen, bee nectar
Fruit pulp	fresh, cooked or candied, mixed in drinks, fermented for palm wine
Extraction of fruit	for cooking oil and medicine
Nut	fresh for drinking, raw or roasted, as drug or stimulant
Germinated seed	for edible root ball
Trunk	sago for starch
Roots	medicines

Other Uses of the Palms

The principal non-food uses of palms are summarized below. One very important use is for construction. Because the trunks and leaves may be long, they often contain tough fibers that are quite useful. The trunks, entire or cut into planks, and the petioles as well as the rib of the leaf are often used to support buildings, or as a framework, or even as floors. The leaves are woven in many ways to make useful mats and are often used in thatching of walls and roofs. Very thin trunks of vine-like palms are the sources of rattan used in furniture.

Useful wax is removed from some species, from the trunk, the mature leaves or even the young, unfolded leaves. This is an article of commerce such as carnauba wax. The fibers can be removed by hand after retting (partial rotting in water), or by hand techniques. Many woody parts of the plants are used for making charcoal. But, this is not all, for native peoples have found ways to use even the thorns of some species. Finally, some plant parts, especially the foliage, but also the trunks of some starchy palms are used for animal feed, especially during drought.

Other useful products of the palms

Trunks	As timbers, planks, fiber, rattan, charcoal, starch for pig feed
Fronds or leaves	For fences, thatching, weaving, arrow shafts, fiber, wax, fodder, to write on
Roots	Medicines
Thorns	Arrow tips
Fruit	Husks for fiber
Seeds	Ornaments
Nut shells	Utensils, or for charcoal
Oils	Soap making

Thus, the uses of palms are highly varied, and the cultures that depend on palms have discovered many uses for them.

Original Source

This article was excerpted from Multipurpose Palms You Can Grow: Twenty of the World's Best, by Dr. Franklin W. Martin, which can be viewed at: http://www.agroforester.com/articles/multi-palm.html

This chapter was originally published as *The Overstory #6*.

Further Reading

Johnson, D.V. 1997. Non-wood forest products: tropical palms. Non-Wood Forest Products Vol. 10, FAO, Bangkok. Covers the multiple uses of palms in great detail.

Mollison, B. The Palms. Permaculture International Journal, PO Box 6039, South Lismore, NSW 2480, Australia, Tel: +61 66 220020, Fax: +61 66 220579. Covers palms from a permaculture perspective.

Uhl, N., and J. Dransfield. 1987. Genera Palmarum, A classification of palms based on the work of Harold E. Moore Jr. International Palm Society and the L.H. Bailey Hortorium, Cornell University. This comprehensive treatment of all genera of palms includes ethnobotanical information. Order from the Palm Society: http://www.palms.org/pubs/palmarum.htm

Jones, D.L., and J. Dransfield. 1995. Palms Throughout the World. Smithsonian Institution Press. Comprehensive guide to world palms, including economic uses.

Romney, D.H. 1997. Growing Coconuts in South Florida, a comprehensive guide to growing the world's most useful palm. D. Romney, 26021 S.W. 199th Ave., Homestead, FL 33031, USA

Perennial Leaf Vegetables

Craig R. Elevitch and Kim M. Wilkinson

There are numerous tropical perennial trees and shrubs with highly nutritious edible leaves. Such plants can form the foundation of a very productive, low maintenance garden.

Most modern gardens have tended to focus on just a very few leafy edible species, the majority of which are short-lived annuals like lettuce, cabbage, and common spinach. Many of these are temperate species, which are poorly adapted to hot, humid conditions and require special tending and frequent replanting. Adding lesser-known tropical perennials to the garden contributes to diversity in the ecosystem and in the diet, while cutting down on the work to produce abundant quantities of nutritious leafy greens.

Apart from being ornamental and edible, many perennial vegetables can be grown on the edge of tree plantings, such as along paths. They can serve other functions around the house such as view screens, ground covers, and edge plants as a barrier to weeds. Many of these plants have medicinal as well as culinary utility.

Harvesting Perennial Vegetables

For most perennial vegetables, the best part to eat is the tender growing shoot or tip which includes the young leaves which have not yet matured and the soft growing stem. Shoots are favored for eating because they are sweeter and more tender than older growth. The mature leaves can often also be eaten, but require longer cooking times and can still be tough eating. The way to harvest shoots is to simply snap off the tender stem where it naturally breaks, leaving behind the more mature and fibrous stem and leaves. The plant then regrows more stems, and production of shoots is multiplied! If the plants receive sufficient water, growth of new shoots continues throughout the year in subtropical and tropical climates, and throughout the growing season in temperate climates.

Adding Perennial Vegetables to the Diet

Most plants have nutritive as well as non-nutritive effects on the body. In other words, eating too much of one thing can have toxic effects or upset digestion. The toxic effects can be moderated by including small amounts of a wide variety of leafy vegetables in the diet. For most plants, about ten shoots, a handful (1/2 cup cooked), is a good amount per person for one meal.

Some Cooking Usually Required

Plants from the tropics have evolved even more toxins as a defense against predators than those from temperate climates. For example, the leaves of Tahitian taro (and other taro species) contain calcium oxylate crystals that are highly irritating to mouth and throat. Cassava leaves often contain substances which can release highly toxic hydrocyanic acid. That is why many plants of sub-tropical or tropical origin require cooking in order to eat them. Cooking dispels or denatures the harmful toxins, and makes the remaining portion safe to eat. Because much of the nutrients and enzymes are destroyed in the cooking process, it is best to cook for the shortest time possible while still removing toxic effects. References such as Bailey (1992, see reference below) give recommendations for cooking times and methods for many popular subtropical/tropical perennial vegetables.

Knowledge of edibility of plants has been developed slowly over a long period of time. Experts in the edible plants recommend strongly against testing an unknown plant yourself for edibility. Such trials can be toxic to the system and/or fatal. There are some excellent reference books available (see list below).There are a surprising number of perennial vegetables available which have been selected for their vigorous growth, favorable taste, lower content of bad tasting or toxic substances, and beauty. Once es-

Subtropical and tropical perennial leaf vegetables (clockwise from top left): Okinawan spinach (Gynura crepioides), Pacific spinach (Abelmoschus esculentus), chaya (Cnidoscolus chayamansa), and Sissoo spinach (Alternanthera sissoo). (photos: C. Elevitch)

tablished, plantings of perennial vegetables can provide an abundance of leafy vegetables for years.

Some Examples of Promising Tropical Vegetable Species

katuk (*Sauropus androgynus*)	leaf tips
sweet potato (*Ipomoea batatas*)	leaf tips, tuber
cassava (*Manihot esculenta*)	leaves, root
Pacific spinach (*Abelmoschus esculentus*)	leaf tips
Tahitian taro (*Xanthosoma braziliense*)	leaves

Some Examples of Promising Tropical Vegetable Species

katuk (*Sauropus androgynus*)	leaf tips
chaya (*Cnidoscolus chayamansa*)	leaf tips
Okinawan spinach (*Gynura crepioides*)	leaf tips
Ceylon spinach (*Basella rubra*)	leaf tips
Sissoo spinach (*Alternanthera sissoo*)	leaf tips, leaves
moringa (*Moringa oleifera* or *M. stenopetala*)	leaf tips, leaves

References

Martin, F.W., R. Ruberté, and L. Meitzner. 1998. Edible Leaves of the Tropics, 3rd Edition. Available from ECHO, 17430 Durrance Rd., N. Ft. Myers, FL 33917, USA, Web: http://www.echonet.org

Facciola, S. 1990. Cornucopia: A Source Book of Edible Plant. Kampong Publications, Vista, California.

International Institute of Rural Reconstruction. 1993. The Bio-Intensive Approach to Small-Scale Household Food Production. IIRR, Room 1270, 475 Riverside Dr., New York, NY 10115

Martin, F.W. 1994. Plants for Use in Permaculture in the Tropics. Yankee Permaculture, P.O. Box 672, Dahlonega, GA 30533-0672

ADAP Project. 1994. Pacific Islands Farm Manual. ADAP Project, Tropical Energy House, University of Hawai'i, Honolulu, HI 96822

Bailey, John M. 1992. The Leaves We Eat, South Pacific Commission, B.P. D5, Noumea Cedex, New Caledonia

Original Source

This chapter was originally published as *The Overstory* #12.

Bamboos in Agroforestry

Craig R. Elevitch and Kim M. Wilkinson

Many of the most useful bamboo species can occupy much the same ecological niche as trees, and are well suited for agroforestry. Bamboo has many advantages over trees such as a relatively short time from planting to harvest, the ability to sustainably provide building materials and edible products for many years or even decades, and versatility of use which exceeds most tree species. For its ecological adaptability, and wide range of uses, bamboo can be an essential component of many agroforestry systems.

Bamboo is an extremely useful agroforestry component. (photo: C. Elevitch)

Bamboo belongs to the grass family (Gramineae), subfamily Bambusoideae. There are over 1500 bamboo species recorded, ranging in height from a few inches (cm) to over 100 ft. (30 m), with stem (culm) diameters of 1/8 inch (3 mm) to over 10 inches (25 cm). Bamboos are found in a very wide range of habitats from tropical to temperate, arid to humid and coastal to montane.

Along with the palm family (Palmae, see Multipurpose Palms, page 302) members of the bamboo family are some of the most useful and versatile plants on earth. Due to bamboo's desirable properties, materials harvested from bamboo lend themselves to low-technology processing for use as farm or community resources. Likewise, industrial manufactur-

ing techniques can produce a wide range of long lasting, strong and inexpensive goods from bamboo.

The many products of various bamboo species include:

- Durable materials for structural building, flooring, trim, and plybamboo (similar to plywood)
- Light and strong materials for crafts, handicrafts and furniture.
- Fiber for woven goods such as paneling and baskets
- Pulp for paper and other fiber products
- Raw materials for agricultural uses such as fencing, tools, rafts, trellises, water pipes, etc.
- Fodder for domestic animals such as cattle, sheep and goats
- Edible shoots for food
- Medicine
- Ornament in the landscape or as cut foliage

Examples of integrated agroforestry systems using bamboo:

- Erosion control
- Stream and pond bank stabilization
- Hedge, screen and windbreak
- Wastewater treatment
- Livestock fodder systems
- Wildlife habitat

There are two main categories of bamboo: clumping (sympodal) and running or open (monpodal). The clumping type of bamboos spread slowly at a rate of 1–4 feet (0.5 –1 meter) per year, and are easy to control. The running types can spread up to 100 feet (30 meters) in a single year, and readily spread into areas where they are unwanted. For most agricultural uses especially in tropical systems, clumping types of bamboo are recommended, and rarely, if ever, should spreading types be planted due to the severe rampancy problems, and extreme difficulty of removal.

Although the status of bamboo has been elevated to a luxury building and ornamental in many countries (such as the US and Australia), bamboo has received an undeserved negative reputation of "the poor man's wood" in so-called developing countries. As the many superior properties of bamboo are rediscovered and agroforestry systems are developed, there is no doubt of bamboo's potential value to people and healthy ecosystems.

Original Source

This chapter was originally published as *The Overstory #30*.

Further Reading

Farrelly, D. 1995. The Book of Bamboo. Sierra Book Clubs. An introduction to the biology, history and myriad use of bamboo.

Recht, C. 1992. Bamboos. Timber Press. A technical guide to growing bamboo, including descriptions of many tropical and temperate species.

Janssen, J.A. *et al*. 1995. Building With Bamboo—A Handbook. Intermediate Technologies. A rare resource for techniques of building with bamboo.

Cusack, V.1998. Bamboo Rediscovered. Chelsea Green Pub Co. Practical advise for selecting and using bamboo species on the small farm.

Bamboos

Soejatmi Dransfield and Elizabeth A. Widjaja

What Is a Bamboo?

Bamboos, commonly grown as woody bamboos, belong to the Gramineae, and form the tribe Bambuseae of the subfamily Bambusoideae. They often have a tree-like habit and can be characterized as having woody, usually hollow culms, complex rhizome and branch systems, petiolate leaf blades and prominent sheathing organs. Moreover, all members possess similar anatomical features in the leaf blades, i.e., fusoid cells and arm cells, which set the bamboos apart from grasses. In tropical Asia and America, several members of this tribe grow into giant bamboos, which are a familiar sight in rural South-East Asia.

Bamboo is frequently confused with rattan and its derived product cane. Bamboo furniture is often referred to as rattan or cane furniture, and vice versa. However, the products are very different. Bamboos, with very few exceptions, have hollow stems which cannot be bent easily unless split. Rattans and canes are always solid and flexible, and belong to the Palmae.

Origin and Geographic Distribution

Bamboos occur in the tropical, subtropical and temperate regions of all continents except Europe and western Asia, from lowlands up to 4000 m altitude. Most, however, occur at low to medium elevations in the tropics, growing wild, cultivated or naturalized in a great variety of habitats. Because bamboo classification is far from complete and most genera are still not well understood, it is therefore impossible to provide precise information on their origin. There has been some speculation, however, on possible centres of diversity of bamboos, such as tropical America, Madagascar, and the region including southern China and northern Myanmar (Burma), Thailand and Vietnam. The genera in tropical America (about 20, reasonably well defined) are not found outside the region (McClure, 1973; Soderstrom & Ellis, 1987), whereas all known native species in Madagascar are endemic. The geographical distribution of bamboo is greatly influenced by human activities (Holttum, 1958). Forest destruction,

e.g., by logging and building of new roads, has encouraged the spread of native bamboos, which subsequently become abundant and form mixed or pure bamboo forests.

Bambusa is the most widespread genus of bamboos in tropical and subtropical Asia. There are about 37 species in South-East Asia. Of these, 16 species grow wild, each with a limited distribution; 6 species are only found in cultivation (*B. balcooa* Roxb., *B. multiplex* (Lour.) Raeuschel ex J.A. & J.H. Schultes, *B. oldhamii* Munro, *B. tuldoides* Munro, *B. utilis* Lin and *B. vulgaris* Schrader ex Wendland). There are, however, two species with a wide distribution. *Bambusa vulgaris*, for example, is pantropical, planted or naturalized in all kinds of habitats, but particularly along river banks; its origin is not certain. The hedge bamboo *B. multiplex* is widely planted in the tropics, subtropics, and even outdoors in temperate regions as an ornamental or a hedge since it can withstand low temperatures.

Dendrocalamus and *Gigantochloa* are also native to tropical Asia. They comprise some species which are found solely in cultivation, and some which have limited distribution or are endemic to relatively small areas. There are about 29 species of *Dendrocalamus* growing in South-East Asia, mainly occurring in the lowlands from the Indian subcontinent to Indo-China and Peninsular Malaysia. *D. asper* (Schultes f.) Backer ex Heyne is planted throughout in the region, from the lowlands up to about 1500 m altitude; its origin is not known. *Gigantochloa*, with about 24 species, is mainly confined to the area from Myanmar, Indo-China to Peninsular Malaysia. It has been recorded that only one species of *Gigantochloa* in Java is native; the others are believed to have been introduced from the Asian mainland during the migration of people from the north.

Cephalostachyum, *Melocanna* and *Thyrsostachys* are mainly found on the mainland of Asia from the Indian subcontinent to Thailand, Vietnam and Laos.

Cephalostachyum is an interesting but poorly known genus of about 11 species, 5 of which occur from the Himalaya to northern Myanmar, whereas the others are found from Myanmar to Vietnam, mostly growing in the lowlands, and one species is found in Min-

Dendrocalamus giganteus has numerous construction uses including construction, scaffolding, and can be made into bamboo boards. (photo: C. Elevitch)

doro (the Philippines). *Melocanna* seems to have one species only, *M. baccifera* (Roxb.) Kurz, which is found in Bangladesh, Assam (India), Myanmar and Thailand. It has been introduced elsewhere in the tropics. *Thyrsostachys* is native to Thailand and Myanmar and consists of two species. *T. siamensis* Gamble is one of the most useful bamboos in Thailand. It has been introduced into other countries in South-East Asia.

Schizostachyum is distributed throughout South-East Asia, extending into the Pacific Islands, with its centre of distribution in Malaysia and western Indonesia. There are about 30 species, most of them having a limited distribution.

The genus *Phyllostachys* is native to China, comprising about 50 species. Some species have been introduced and cultivated in Japan, Europe, North America and the tropical highlands. *P. aurea* A. & C. Riviére has become naturalized in many parts of the tropics.

Dinochloa, comprising about 20 species, is found from the Andaman Islands and southern Thailand throughout Malaysia, western Indonesia and the Philippines. Species are found scattered in lowland and hill dipterocarp forest, but they become weeds in logged and disturbed areas.

Racemobambos is confined to Malesia including the Bismarck Archipelago and the Solomon Islands, but so far has not been found in Sumatra, Java or the Lesser Sunda Islands. It consists of about 16 species.

Nastus is found mainly in the southern hemisphere from Madagascar to the Solomon Islands, although it has been recorded in the northern hemisphere in Sumatra. It consists of about 15 species.

Uses

Bamboo is one of the natural resources of the tropics, and because of its wide distribution, availability, rapid growth, easy handling and desirable properties, has been used widely in the daily life of the local community as a sustainable resource. Bamboos are utilized intensively for a wide range of purposes. "No plant is known in the tropical zone which could supply to man so many technical advantages as the bamboo. The strength of the culms, their straightness, smoothness, lightness combined with hardness and greater hollowness; the facility and regularity with which they can be split; the different sizes, various lengths and thickness of their joints make them suitable for numerous purposes to serve which other material would require much labour and preparation" (Kurz, 1876). Even in this mechanical age, their usefulness continues and is likely to continue, because they are a necessity of life in South-East Asian communities (Holttum, 1958). In recent years bamboos have entered the highly competitive world market in the form of pulp for paper, parquet, plybamboo, and as a canned vegetable.

The most significant uses in South-East Asia are for building material, for making various types of baskets, and as a vegetable. Other important uses are as a source of raw material for making paper, for musical instruments and handicrafts.

Building material

Bamboo culms have many characteristics that make them suitable for numerous construction purposes

(Kurz, 1876; McClure, 1953). Some species are used only for building material (pillars, walls, roofs and floors). When used for pillars, bridges or scaffolding, culms should have a large diameter with thick walls and relatively short internodes. In South-East Asia species suitable for this purpose belong to *Bambusa* (e.g., *B. bambos* (L.) Voss, *B. blumeana* J.A. & J.H. Schultes, *B. tulda* Roxb. and *B. vulgaris*), *Dendrocalamus* (e.g., *D. asper*) and *Gigantochloa* (e.g., *G. apus* (JA. & J.H. Schultes) Kurz, *G. atter* (Hassk.) Kurz, *G. levis* (Blanco) Merrill, *G. pseudoarundinacea* (Steudel) Widjaja, *G. robusta* Kurz and *G. scortechinii* Gamble).

Species with culms of medium diameter and with relatively thin walls are suitable for the construction of walls, floors and roofs (e.g., *Schizostachyum brachycladum* Kurz, *S. zollingeri* Steudel, *Gigantochloa levis*). In South-East Asia there are several methods of preparation. The commonest and easiest way to make walls is to cut the culms to appropriate length, split them on one side only and then flatten them out; they are either used as such and joined together vertically, or they are woven into a large piece. In the most elaborate method, the culms are split into very thin long strips which are plaited into larger pieces with attractive motifs. This kind of plaited bamboo is also used for partitions and ceilings. In houses with floors raised above the ground, the floor is often made of split bamboo culms of about 5 cm wide, joined together and secured with strips of bamboo culms or other material. In roof construction the culms are split in two and laid in such a way that they resemble corrugated iron. In Bali, bamboo tiles, 30 cm x 5 cm, are used for roof construction. Locally, bamboo culms are used to reinforce cement/concrete structures in China, India, Japan, the Philippines and Indonesia.

Baskets

Bamboo species with culms of smaller diameter, relatively thick walls (e.g., *Gigantochloa apus*, *G. scortechinii*, *Schizostachyum zollingeri*), and which split easily are used for making various types of baskets (Widjaja, 1984; Wong, 1989). In many parts of East and South-East Asia, local people still prefer baskets made from split bamboo rather than from plastics for carrying vegetables and fruits, poultry or pigs, because braided bamboo "breathes." Although plastics are used ubiquitous, simple carrying baskets and boxes of bamboo are still being produced. In some parts of Indonesia, local people prefer to use thin-walled bamboos (such as *Bambusa atra* Lindley, *B.*

forbesii (Ridley) Holttum, *Schizostachyum brachycladum*) for making a fine basket, as this saves having to split the bamboo beforehand.

Vegetables

Bamboo shoots (*rebung*) are an important vegetable in East and South-East Asia. A shoot is the new growth of the rhizome apex into a young culm and consists of young internodes protected by sheaths. After removing these sheaths, the shoot is cut into small pieces or shredded and then cooked in boiling water.

The pieces are then used as a vegetable ingredient for various dishes such as pickles, fried meat or vegetables, meat or vegetables cooked in coconut milk. In general the shoots emerge during the rainy season and the desired shoot is the one which grows from the rhizome buried deep in the soil. In many parts of South-East Asia, shoots are consumed locally, but in Thailand a large-scale canned bamboo-shoot industry has developed.

In general, young shoots of many bamboo species are edible, but only a few bamboos produce superior shoots, i.e., *Dendrocalamus asper*, *Gigantochloa levis*, *G. albociliata* (Munzo) Kurz and *Thyrsostachys siamensis*. In China, superior bamboo shoots are produced by *Phyllostachys pubescens* Mazel ex H. de Leh., *Dendrocalamus latiflorus* Munro and *Bambusa oldhamii*.

Paper

For centuries the Chinese have used bamboo in paper making (e.g., *Phyllostachys pubescens*). In South-East Asia (e.g., Indonesia, the Philippines and Thailand) paper mills have been established using some bamboo species as raw material, such as *Bambusa bambos*, *B. blumeana* and *Dendrocalamus strictus* (Roxb. Nees). In India, the principal species used is *D. strictus*.

Musical instruments

Bamboo musical instruments have been developed by most tribes in South-East Asia. There are 3 types, i.e., idiophones (percussion or hammer instruments), aerophones (blown instruments) and chordophones (stringed instruments). Apparently, bamboo musical instruments have been known in South-East Asia for a long time, because flutes are known to every tribe. Filipinos, Indonesians and Thais have stringed instruments, although the number of strings varies. Species of the genus *Schizostachyum* are the most suitable for making aerophones (like "kan" or "sompotan"), because of small diameter culms, long internodes and thin walls. The main species used for making idiophones (e.g., "angklung") and chordophones are *Gigantochloa atroviolacea* Widjaja, *G. atter*, *G. levis*, *C. pseudoarundinacea* and *G. robusta*; sometimes *Dendrocalamus asper* and *Gigantochloa apus* are also used. The large-diameter culms of *G. atroviolacea* are used for making bass drums and bass horns.

Handicraft

Another important use of bamboo is in the handicraft industry. Table mats, handbags, hats and other woven bric-a-brac can be made of bamboo. The best developed bamboo handicraft industry is the weaving of bamboo splits. In weaving the bamboo splits, many different patterns have been created. However, there are some handicrafts made of unsplit bamboo. Usually this kind of handicraft consists of engravings on the outer part of the culm or the rhizome. The species employed in woven handicrafts are mostly species with long and flexible fibres such as *Bambusa atra*, *Gigantochloa apus*, *G. scortechinii*, and *Schizostachyum latifolium* Gamble. Species that are easily engraved are *Bambusa vulgaris*, *Dendrocalamus asper* and *Schizostachyum brachycladum*.

Furniture

People of South-East Asia living in bamboo-rich areas have long used bamboo culms to make their furniture. Recently, bamboo furniture has become popular, and elite bamboos are sought after. A number of species of *Bambusa*, *Dendrocalamus* and *Gigantochloa* are commonly used in the furniture industry (Widjaja, 1980). Two of the favoured species are *Gigantochloa atroviolacea* and *Dendrocalamus asper*, whose culms are straight and smooth.

Hedge, windbreak, ornamental

Some bamboos are used as a living hedge or windbreak when planted close together such as *Thyrsostachys siamensis* and *Bambusa multiplex*. Several species (e.g., *Bambusa multiplex*, *B. vulgaris*, *Schizostachyum brachycladum*) are planted as ornamental. The thorny bamboos (e.g., *Bambusa bambos*) are often planted around fruit orchards, vegetable fields, smallholdings or villages to protect them from intruders (e.g., wild animals).

Dendrocalamus giganteus shoots are creamy and tender when cooked. Pictured: I.G.P. Suryadarma. (photo: C. Elevitch)

Other uses

Culms of *Dendrocalamus asper*, for instance, are also used as containers for collecting water or palm juice, for pipes and troughs, etc. Unsplit internodes, e.g., of *Schizostachyum brachycladum*, are used as pots for cooking vegetables, meat, rice or glutinous rice. The internode is usually lined with banana leaf before being filled with uncooked food, and is placed over a fire. Glutinous rice with coconut milk cooked in a bamboo internode ("lemang") is a popular dish in South-East Asia.

Forest destruction has allowed some bamboo species to become abundant; they are a major source for native people to develop cottage industries of chopsticks, satay sticks and incense sticks (e.g., *Gigantochloa scortechinii*). Fish traps are made of split bamboo joined together with either rattan strips or bamboo strips. Bamboo rafts are usually made from culms with medium diameter and relatively thin walls.

Bamboo leaves are often used as fodder. Large and smooth leaf blades are used for wrapping food (e.g., Chinese "bak chang" made of glutinous rice). In Indonesia, large leaves are also used to make "tangerang" hats for working in rice fields or tea plantations. Bamboo culms are used for various poles, e.g., carrying poles, vegetable and fruit props, fishing rods, outriggers, boating poles, posts and fences.

Cultural Aspects

Since time immemorial, bamboos have exerted profound influence on the life and cultures of Asian people. For example, bamboos always figured in local paintings, legends, songs, folklore, etc. Since prehistoric time, bamboo has been used as one of the weapons for hunting and fighting. In Peninsular Malaysia, the Temiar and Semoi make their traditional hunting weapons such as blow-pipes from two internodes of bamboo. For both peoples, the blowpipe has both a symbolic and a practical value: the possession of a blowpipe is a sign that a man has reached adult status so that he is able to join hunting parties and become a full member of the community. In Irian Jaya, people make their arrowheads from small bamboo species of *Racemobambos* and of *Nastus*, and the arrow shafts from small, straight, thin bamboo culms of *Schizostachyum* species. Bamboo is also employed in traditional ceremonies; for example, in Bali the yellow variety of *Schizostachyum brachycla-dum* is used during the burial ceremony because yellow is considered the sacred colour of Hinduism. The roof of traditional houses and rice barns in Toraja, Sulawesi (Indonesia) is made from the green variety of the same species. "Garong" baskets are made of several internodes of another *Schizostachyum* species tied together with split bamboo or rattan; the baskets are filled with rice wine during the Gawai festival in Sarawak, Malaysia (Sandin, 1963).

References

Holttum, R.E., 1958. The bamboos of the Malay Peninsula. The Gardens" Bulletin, Singapore 16: 1–135.

Kurz, S., 1876. Bamboo and its use. The Indian Forester 1: 219–269, pl. I–II, 335–362, pl. III–IV.

McClure, F.A., 1953. Bamboo as a building material. United States Department of Agriculture, Foreign Agricultural Service, Washington, D.C. 52 pp.

McClure, F.A., 1973. Genera of bamboos native to the New World (Gramineae: Bambusoideae). Smithsonian Contributions to Botany 9: 1–148.

Sandin, B., 1963. "Garong" baskets. Sarawak Museum Journal 11(21–22):321–326.

Soderstrom, T.R. & Ellis, R.P., 1987. The position of bamboo genera and allies in a system of grass classification. In: Soderstrom, T.R. *et al* (Editors): Grass systematics and evolution. Proceedings of the international symposium on grass systematics and evolution, Washington, D.C., 27–31 July 1986. Smithsonian Institution Press, Washington, D.C. pp. 225–238.

Widjaja, E.A., 1984. Ethnobotanical notes on Gigantochloa in Indonesia with special reference to G. apus. The Journal of the American Bamboo Society 5(3–4): 57–68.

Wong, K.M., 1989. Current and potential uses of bamboo in Peninsular Malaysia. The Journal of the American Bamboo Society 7(1–2): 1–15.

Original Source

This excerpt was reprinted with the kind permission of the authors and publisher from:

Dransfield, S. & Widjaja, E. A. (Editors), 1995. Plant Resources of South-East Asia No 7. Bamboos. Backhuys Publishers, Leiden. 189 pp.

Publisher contact information: PROSEA Foundation http://www.proseanet.org and http://www.prosea.nl

To Order The Book

Developed countries: A hardcopy, luxury edition (blue cover) and a paperback, medium-price edition (green cover) of this book are available for purchase from Backhuys Publishers, P.O. Box 321, 2300 AH Leiden, the Netherlands.

Developing countries: A paperback, medium-price edition (green cover) and a low-price edition (green cover) are also available from the PROSEA Network Office, P.O. Box 332, Bogor 16122, Indonesia; Email: info@proseanet.org.

This excerpt was originally published as *The Overstory* #137.

Mushrooms in Agroforestry

Paul Stamets

Mushrooms are the fruiting bodies of certain types of fungi, many of which can play highly beneficial roles in forest ecosystems. Many of these fungi have unique abilities to break down wood, leaves, and other organic matter and recycle nutrients back into the system. Most plants depend on symbiotic relationships with certain types of fungi such as mycorrhizae (see page 66). Other types of fungi support plants indirectly by releasing enzymes into the environment, making nutrients available, and performing many other functions. Fungi can be a great asset to a farm system, both for their ecological services and for their valuable edible and medicinal products.

This chapter describes a number of important edible and medicinal mushrooms, and how they can be integrated into permaculture and agroforestry systems.

When edible and medicinal mushrooms are involved as key organisms in agriculture and forestry, the productivity of these agricultural systems can soar to extraordinary levels. Not only are mushrooms a protein-rich food source for humans but the byproducts of mushroom cultivation unlock nutrients for other members of the ecological community. The rapid return of nutrients to the ecosystem by mushrooms boosts the life cycles of plants, animals, insects (bees), and soil microflora.

What follows is a short list of some of the ways mushrooms can participate in permaculture and agroforestry systems:

1. Oyster Mushrooms

Oyster mushrooms can be grown indoors on pasteurized corn-stalks, on straw from wheat, rice, and rye, and on a wide range of other materials, including paper and pulp by-products. Soaking the bulk substrate in cold water creates a residual "tea" that is a nutritious fertilizer and potent insecticide. Submerging the bulk substrate in hot water produces a different brew that is a naturally potent herbicide.

Oyster mushrooms can also be grown on hardwood stumps and logs. Some strains of oyster mushrooms (*Pleurotus pulmonarius* for example) even grow on conifer wood. *Pleurotus* species thrive in complex compost piles, and are easy to grow outside with minimum care.

The water substrate from oyster mushroom production is useful as fodder for cows, chickens, and pigs. Since half of the mass of dry straw is liberated as gaseous carbon dioxide when it is used as substrate, pumping this CO_2 from mushroom growing rooms into greenhouses to enhance plant production makes good sense. (Cultivators filter the air stream from the mushroom growing rooms so spores are eliminated.)

Furthermore, the waste straw can be mulched into soils, not only to provide structure and nutrition but to reduce the populations of nematodes which are costly to gardeners and farmers

2. King Stropharia

The king stropharia (*Stropharia rugoso-annulata*) is an ideal player in the recycling of complex wood debris and garden wastes and it thrives in complex environments. While it will vigorously attack wood (sawdust, chips, twigs, branches), the king stropharia also grows in wood-free substrates, particularly soils supplemented with chopped straw. I have seen this mushroom flourish in gardens devoid of wood debris, benefiting the growth of neighboring plants. Acclimated to northern latitudes, this mushroom fruits when air temperatures range between 60–90°F (15–32°C) which usually translates to ground temperatures of 55–65°F (13–18°C).

For six weeks one summer our bees attacked a king stropharia bed, exposing the mycelium to the air, and suckled from the wounds the sugar-rich cytoplasm. From morning to evening, bees continuously flew from our beehives to the mushroom patch until the bed of king stropharia literally collapsed. When a report of this phenomenon was published in *Harrowsmith*, beekeepers wrote me to explain that they had long been mystified by bees' attraction to sawdust piles. Now it is clear the bees were seeking the underlying sweet mushroom mycelium.

King stropharia is an excellent edible mushroom when young, but its edibility quickly declines with maturity. Fly larvae proliferate inside the developing mushrooms. In raising silver salmon, I found that when I threw mature mushrooms into the fish-holding tank, they would float. Fly larvae soon emerged from the mushrooms, struggling for air.

Soon the fish were striking the large mushrooms to dislodge the swollen larvae into the water where they were eagerly consumed. After several days of feeding mushrooms to the fish, we I found the salmon would excitedly strike at the king stropharia as soon as they hit the water in anticipation of the succulent, squirming larvae. Inadvertently, I had discovered that king stropharia is a good base medium for generating fish food.

Growing king stropharia can have other beneficial applications in permaculture. The mushroom depends upon bacteria for growth. At our farm which included a small herd of Black Angus cows, I established two king stropharia beds at the heads of ravines which drained onto a saltwater beach where my neighbor commercially cultivates oysters and clams.

Prior to installing these mushroom beds, fecal coliform bacteria seriously threatened the water quality. Once the mycelium fully permeated the sawdust/chip beds, downstream fecal bacteria were largely eliminated. The mycelium in effect became a micro-filtration membrane.

I had discovered that by properly locating mushroom beds, greywater runoff could be cleaned of bacteria and nitrogen-rich effluent. Overall water quality improved. Massive mushrooms formed. After three to four years chunks of wood were totally reduced into a rich, peat-like soil. For nearly eight years I have continued to install king stropharia beds in depressions leading into sensitive watersheds.

Government agencies, typically slow to react to good ideas, have finally recognized the potential benefits of mycofiltration. Test plots are currently being implanted and monitored to more precisely determine the effects on water quality. If the testing is successful, I envision the widespread installation of king stropharia beds in basins leading into rivers, lakes and bodies of saltwater.

3. Shiitake/Nameko/Lion's Manes

Outdoors, inoculated logs can be partially buried or lined up in fence-like rows. Once the logs have stopped producing, the softened wood can be broken up, sterilized and re-inoculated. Indoors, these mushrooms can be grown on sterilized substrates or on logs using the methods described in *Growing Gourmet and Medicinal Mushrooms* (see Original Source).

Once the indoor substrates cease production, they can be recycled and re-inoculated with another mushroom, a process I call "species sequencing". Later, the expired production blocks can be buried in sawdust or soil to elicit bonus crops outdoors.

4. Maitake, Reishi, and Clustered Wood-lovers

Several species can be incorporated into the management of a sustainable multistage forest. The greatest opportunities for stump culture occur in regions of the world where hardwoods predominate. Few gourmet and medicinal mushrooms can make use of coniferous woods.

Nevertheless, enokitake (*Flammulina velutripes*), reishi (*Ganoderma lucidum*), clustered wood lovers (*Hypholoma capnoides*), chicken of the woods (*Laetiporus sulphureus*) and oyster mushrooms (*Pleurotus* spp.) are good candidates for conifer or hardwood stump decomposition.

5. Shaggy Manes

As cosmopolitan mushrooms, shaggy manes (*Coprinus comatus*) will grow in rich manured soils, disturbed habitats, in and around compost piles, and in grassy and gravel areas. Shaggy manes are extremely adaptive and tend to wander. Shaggy mane patches behave much like king stropharia and morels, travelling great distances from the place of inoculation in their search for fruiting niches.

6. Morels

Morels grow in a variety of habitats, from abandoned apple orchards and among diseased elms to gravelly roads and streambeds. However, the habitat that can be reproduced easily is the burn-site. Burn-sites, though increasingly restricted because of air pollution ordinances, are common out in the country where residents dispose of flammable trash.

If a burn-site is not possible, there are alternatives. The complex habitat of a garden compost pile also supports morel growth. When planting cottonwood trees you can introduce spawn around the root zones in hopes of creating a perennial morel patch. Cultivators should note that morels are fickle and elusive by nature, compared to more predictable species like king stropharia, oysters, and shiitake.

7. Mycorrhizal species

Mycorrhizal species can be introduced via several techniques. The age old, proven method of satellite planting is probably the simplest. By planting young

THE STAMETSIAN MODEL
FOR
Permaculture with a Mycological Twist!

1. Oyster Mushrooms
2. King Stropharia
3. Shiitake/Nameko/Lion's Manes
4. Maitake/Reishi/Clustered Woodlovers
5. Shaggy Manes
6. Morels
7. Mycorrhizal Species
8. The Sacred Psilocybes

seedlings around the base of trees naturally producing chanterelles, king boletes, matsutake, truffles, or other desirable species, you may establish satellite colonies by replanting the young trees elsewhere after several years of association.

8. The Sacred Psilocybes

In the Pacific Northwest of North America, the Psilocybes figure as some of the most frequently found fungi in landscaping bark and wood chips. These mushrooms share a strong affinity towards human activities—from chopping wood, the planting of ornamentals, landscaping around buildings, to the creation of refuse piles. Many spiritually inclined cultivators view the establishment of Sacred Psilocybe Mushroom Patches as another step towards living in harmony within their ecosystem.

Conclusion

These are but a few mushroom species that can be incorporated into systems which involve trees or other woody perennials. Clearly the integration of mushrooms enhances these systems to a level which is unattainable without them. I hope readers will develop these concepts further.

Original Source

The above was adapted from the original appearing (with photos and illustrations) as "Permaculture with a Mycological Twist" in Paul Stamets' book *Growing Gourmet and Medicinal Mushrooms*, ©1994 Paul Stamets. This book as well as other books, equipment, cultures, information and mycotechnology is available from Paul Stamets' company, Fungi Perfecti, P.O. Box 7634, Olympia, WA, 98507 USA; Web: http://www.fungi.com.

This excerpt was originally published as *The Overstory* #33.

Nitrogen Fixing Trees

Craig R. Elevitch and Kim M. Wilkinson

Nature has many ways of creating abundance under adverse conditions. Imagine plants that accumulate their own fertilizer, grow extremely quickly, tolerate harsh climatic conditions, and are prolific. Many nitrogen fixing plants fit this description, and have numerous uses in gardening, farming and forestry.

Although many nitrogen fixing plants lend themselves to agroforestry, nitrogen fixing trees (NFTs) have important uses in sustainable systems. The uses for NFTs include windbreak, shade, fodder, organic matter production, mulch, fuel, timber and food. Chances are that if you live in the tropics, there are several NFTs already growing as pioneers in your area.

Nitrogen fixing trees accumulate nitrogen from the air. Flower of *Calliandra calothyrsus*. (photo: C. Elevitch)

Nature has devised a unique path of nutrient cycling used by these trees. Air consists of approximately 80% nitrogen gas, which is normally unavailable to plants. NFTs utilize this atmospheric nitrogen. Through an association with Rhizobium, a bacteria which is hosted in the root system of NFTs, these plants biologically accumulate nitrogen, pulling this essential nutrient out of the air for their own use, and, if managed, making it available to other crops as well.

In addition to their ability to make use of atmospheric nitrogen, NFTs are often also deep rooted, which allows them to seek out nutrients in deep soil layers. This allows NFTs to fulfill many of their own needs in infertile, harsh conditions, and therefore have the ability to quickly "pioneer" bare or degraded lands. Pioneer plants are nature's first endeavor to establish vegetation wherever it is lacking. In addition, many NFT species can be pruned back frequently, and the nutrient-rich leaves used as a high-fertility mulch, or for animal fodder. In this way, NFTs support many other life forms on the farm.

The long list of useful characteristics of NFTs includes their ability to:

- establish readily
- grow rapidly
- tolerate poor soils
- tolerate drought
- thrive in full sun
- enhance overall fertility
- regrow easily from pruning

Selecting an NFT for a certain function can be tricky. As a start, a survey of your area will be helpful in determining the habit and vigor of some NFTs. You may notice some exemplary specimens which could be useful in a windbreak or for shade. Information may be available at the your local agricultural extension service, or you may contact one of many international organizations that have agroforestry programs.

If possible, use only NFTs which are already established in your area, or that have a history of not becoming weeds. For example, if an *Albizia* species is already naturalized on the site, it may be useful as a source of organic matter, fodder, shade and even a light weight timber.

There are also many NFTs which are not considered weedy and are extremely useful. The common pigeon pea (*Cajanus cajan*), a perennial edible "pea tree," has demonstrated little potential for becoming a weed in Hawai'i, and makes excellent fodder, quick windbreak, green manure, as well as many other uses.

Original Source

This chapter was originally published as *The Overstory* #4.

Further Reading

FAO. 1984. Legume Inoculants and Their Use. FAO of the United Nations. Rome, Italy. Excellent practical handbook for inoculation.

MacDicken, K.G. 1994. Selection and Management of Nitrogen-Fixing Trees. Winrock International Institute for Agricultural Development, Morrilton, Arkansas, USA. Comprehensive treatment of NFTs and their uses.

National Academy of Sciences. 1979. Tropical Legumes: Resources for the Future, National Academy Press, Washington, DC. A very useful reference at a reasonable cost.

Farm, Community and Tree Network (formerly Nitrogen Fixing Tree Association). 1989-1994. NFT Highlights. Nitrogen Fixing Tree Association, Morrilton, Arkansas, USA. Each highlight covers an NFT species in detail. (Available from FACT Net, listed below.)

Multipurpose Trees

Kim M. Wilkinson and Craig R. Elevitch

While all trees can be said to serve several purposes, such as habitat, shade, and soil protection, some trees really stand out in their usefulness. Such trees are called "multipurpose trees"—trees with the ability to provide numerous products and perform a variety of functions in farming or forestry. Multipurpose trees can be integrated with farming and forestry to improve yields, diversify products, increase economic resiliency, and improve farm viability and sustainability in the long-term.

Multipurpose trees are key players in supporting an overall farm system. When you plant a multipurpose tree, a number of needs and functions can be fulfilled at once.

Examples of multiple functions and products to look for in a tree:

- wind resistance (to use as a component in a windbreak)
- erosion control
- soil fertility improvement
- nitrogen fixation
- shade
- wildlife habitat
- mulch or green manure
- pest control
- animal fodder
- living fence
- fuel wood
- food (fruit/vegetables/root/shoot/oil)
- medicinal uses
- tannin/dyes/soaps/cosmetics
- bee forage for honey
- crafts, carving
- timber

Important multipurpose trees (left to right): breadfruit (*Artocarpus altilis*), citrus (*Citrus* sp.), and pandanus (*Pandanus* spp.). (photo: C. Elevitch)

When choosing a species for a particular purpose, consider the multiple uses and functions the species can provide. For example, while there may be many species that are wind-strong enough to suit your needs for windbreak, you may also ask, which species can I choose that are wind strong AND have other uses for this farm? Your windbreak may be able to serve as a long-term investment for timber, a short-term supplier of pole or firewood, a living fence, or possibly even a supply of fruit.

An added benefit of using multipurpose trees is that they can provide a certain amount of insurance in the event of a primary crop failure or market fluctuation. An emphasis on multipurpose trees in your planting creates resources that can allow the farm to be diversified and productive in the long-term, even if environmental or market conditions shift from the primary crops.

Examples of Some Outstanding Tropical Multipurpose Trees

Neem (*Azadirachta indica*) Powerful insecticidal and medicinal properties in seed, leaf, and bark; also food (leaves), timber, windbreak component.

Jackfruit (*Artocarpus heterophyllus*) Edible fruit, seeds, and young leaves; leaves used for animal fodder; bark used for dye; medicine; timber; windbreak component.

Ipil Ipil or giant haole koa (*Leucaena leucocephala*) Fixes nitrogen, provides mulch and organic matter, windbreak component, fodder, food, fuelwood, seeds used in jewelry and crafts.

Coconut (*Cocos nucifera*) One of the most useful palms for the nut, purified water (inside nut), timber, fuel, crafts (fronds, nut, husk and wood), housing thatch, wind protection, also used traditionally in the Pacific to shade cattle and taro.

Mango (*Mangifera indica*) fruit, medicine, leaves used as mulch, wood used as timber, windbreak component.

Peach palm (*Bactris gasipaes*) fruit, heart of palm, durable craft wood.

Tamarind (*Tamarindus indica*) Shade, fruit, light timber, medicinal uses.

Madre de Cacao (*Gliricidia sepium*) Nitrogen fixing, for shade, fodder, mulch, living fence.

Original Source

This chapter was originally published as *The Overstory* #16.

Fast Food (Part 1)

Craig R. Elevitch and Kim M. Wilkinson

This chapter is the first in a two-part series on creating food abundance quickly with perennial plants in the tropics. Unlike annuals, perennials are planted just once, and they will continue producing year after year, some for 10–20 years! By using perennials to provide a large portion of your food supply, you can save yourself the work of having to seed and establish large garden beds every few months. Once you have your perennials in place and producing, then you will have the time for annual crops to supplement your food.

Fast food is also fun food

Other chapters show how pioneering species (see Pioneering Difficult Sites (page 203)) can be used to quickly revegetate and how perennial leaf vegetables (see Perennial Leaf Vegetables (page 305)) can be the foundation for food abundance in a low-input, high production system. Here we look at those concepts and additional species for abundant and enduring food production. In this chapter, vining species which make use of horizontal space (ground covers) and vertical space (trellises) around dwellings or in orchards are the focus. The following chapter will cover abundant food-producing shrubs, bushes, and trees for hedges and living fences.

The purpose of gardening with perennials is to get the highest return from the least amount of effort. When choosing species to serve this purpose, use plants that:

- Are highly productive even in poor conditions
- Have multiple edible parts such as leaves, fruits, flowers and/or tubers
- Contribute important nutrients to diet
- Provide multiple functions in the landscape such as ground cover, hedge, animal fodder, etc.
- Are competitive with weeds

- Are pest and disease resistant
- Require minimal care
- Enhance other parts of the landscape
- Can make use of wasted, low-fertility, or unproductive spaces
- Can begin producing within 2–12 months
- Will continue producing for more than a year (perennial)
- Are easy to propagate and are widely adapted to a range of climates and soils.

There are a number of food-producing vines that fit the above description. Vines have the ability to root in one fertile place and spread horizontally or vertically to other, less favorable areas. This makes vines particularly useful for waste space in the garden and landscape, like rocky embankments or areas that are difficult to access regularly. Vines can also increase productivity in limited spaces because they can make use of vertical space, climbing up walls or trellis. Some vines can also take over large areas or climb over other plants—so be careful which species you use, and where you put them!

The example species below are appropriate for a range of tropical and subtropical conditions. As with any new plantings, consult with others who have experience in your area to help you select the best species and varieties for your area. There are thousands of edible and useful plants—these are just a selection to inspire you to seek out the best for your situation and tastes.

Some Perennial Vines for Fast Food

Vines for use of horizontal space (ground cover)

Tropical pumpkin (*Curcurbita moschata*) will form a cover over a very large area if you let it, and is an excellent choice for pioneering a newly cleared area. It produces large quantities of fruits and has little trouble with fruit flies or other pests. The stem tips and flowers are also edible.

Sweet potato (*Ipomoea batatas*) can be managed as a ground cover in which case it will be used for its delicious young leaves and stem tips, rather than for the tuber. While most varieties can be grown for ed-

Chayote (*Sechium edule*) is a fast growing vine that produces abundant edible parts in short order. (photo: C. Elevitch)

ible leaves, certain varieties may have been selected for leaf production. A patch of sweet potato managed for leaf production will also serve as a perennial source of propagative material for future tuber or leaf plantings.

Chayote (*Sechium edule*) is a vigorous vine that produces large quantities of fruits and stem tips, edible cooked or raw. It thrives especially well on embankments that are difficult to cultivate intensively.

Vines for use of vertical space (trellis)

Lablab bean (*Dolichos lablab*) Red lablab is a very vigorous nitrogen fixing vine which produces abundant edible pods that can be eaten young as a vegetable. Mature seeds can also be dried and stored for later use as a grain legume.

Perennial lima bean (*Phaseolus lunatus*) produces large quantities of lima beans that are eaten cooked at immature or mature stages.

Winged bean (*Psophocarpus tetragonolobus*) has almost all edible parts: pod, beans, tubers, young leaves, flowers and stem tips. Requires heat and good moisture to produce well. Once established, winged bean is extremely productive.

Passionfruit (*Passiflora* spp.) is a vigorous twining plant that can produce large amounts of fruit after a year. Many species of passion fruit can tolerate a large amount of neglect, while producing 2-3 crops per year. A beautiful addition to the landscape!

Malabar (Ceylon) spinach (*Basella rubra*) is grown for its leaves and stem tips, which are valued for their mucilaginous texture when cooked. Although this vine tends to die back annually, the plant persists well through self-seeding.

References

Martin, F.W. and R.M. Ruberté. 1978. Survival and Subsistence in the Tropics. Antillian College Press, Mayaquez, Puerto Rico.

Martin, F.W. 1994. Plants for Use in Permaculture in the Tropics, Yankee Permaculture, P.O. Box 672, Dahlonega, GA 30533-0672

Facciola, S. 1990. Cornucopia: A Source Book of Edible Plants, Kampong Publications, Vista, California.

Original Source

This chapter was originally published as *The Overstory #25*.

Fast Food (Part 2)

Craig R. Elevitch and Kim M. Wilkinson

Unlike an annual garden, perennials can be integrated in agroforestry systems to provide a relatively stable supply of nutritious food—usually with less work than establishing and maintaining a large garden of annuals.

"Fast Food" perennials can have a place in any agroforestry planting, but are especially valuable in the following situations:

- after a disaster (mud slide, hurricane, etc.) when conventional food supplies are diminished for months or years
- for people who have recently moved or relocated
- for people who do not have time or resources to maintain annual gardens, but want to grow a dependable supply of fresh, nutritious vegetables and fruits.

In the previous chapter, we looked at perennial vine crops that can be used to make use of horizontal space (ground cover) and vertical space (trellis). This chapter covers quick and abundant perennial shrubs and trees which can be used in hedges, living fences and shelter belts, or as part of a stacked system.

The example species below are appropriate for a range of tropical and subtropical conditions. As with any new plantings, consult with others who have experience in your area to help you select the best species and varieties. There are thousands of edible and useful plants—these are just a selection to inspire you to seek out the best for your situation and tastes.

Some Perennial Trees and Shrubs for Fast Food

Moringa (Moringa oleifera or M. stenopetala) is a tree which can be kept bushy by continual tipping of the new branches. The new leaves and tips are used in stir fries and soups. The African variety (*M. stenopetala*) has a wonderful nutty flavor. Both species are drought tolerant, and have many other uses, such as medicine, water purification, etc.

Chaya (Cnidoscolus chayamansa) is a very prolific plant that has highly nutritious leaves. Two or three of these plants will supply greens for a family 2-3 times a week. Tolerates drought very well, although requires regular watering for good leaf production. Spineless and high nutrient selections have been made. (Note: leaves must be cooked to deactivate toxins!)

Katuk (Sauropus androgynus) produces leaves with a wonderful nutty flavor. The branch tips are often steamed and eaten in stir fries or like asparagus. This plant is very prolific in hot and humid conditions.

Cassava, manioc, tapioca (Manihot esculenta) is very easy to grow from stem cuttings, and is a prolific source of carbohydrates from its edible tubers. The cooked leaves can be eaten as a nutritious green vegetable. All parts of this plant must be carefully cooked to remove toxins. This plant is very hardy and grows in a wide variety of conditions with little care.

Pacific spinach (Hibiscus manihot) is an okra relative, grown for its large tender leaves which are eaten throughout the tropics. This plant is very adaptable, but thrives in hot and humid conditions.

Pigeon pea, gandul, dhal (Cajanus cajan) is a remarkably useful and productive shrub or small tree. The young pods are used as a vegetable, and the mature seeds as a grain legume. Produces well even in dry conditions. Long-lived agroforestry selections have an upright form and high vegetative growth, and can be used for fodder and green manure banks, as well as hedges and quick windbreaks.

Sissoo spinach (Alternanthera sissoo) has edible leaves and stem tips and is a very productive creeping shrub which also does well as a ground cover. It holds its own well against weeds, and tolerates drought.

Papaya (Carica papaya) develops fruit rapidly, usually within a year if well mulched and watered. Fruits can be eaten green or ripe. Young leaves can also be used as a vegetable, and the plant has medicinal properties.

Banana (Musa spp.) is remarkably productive and useful, providing fruit, fodder and mulch material. Many varieties perform well in partial shade, and can be integrated into a stacked system.

Sugarcane (Saccharum officinarum) is an easily grown source of sweetener. Heritage cultivars are es-

Papaya (*Carica papaya*) can produce abundant fruit much earlier than most other fruits, often within 18 months of planting. (photo: C. Elevitch)

pecially easy to process or eat out-of-hand. The plants also make a good component in a living fence or wind break.

References

Martin, F.W. and R.M. Ruberté. 1978. Survival and Subsistence in the Tropics. Antillian College Press, Mayaquez, Puerto Rico.

International Institute of Rural Reconstruction (IIRR). 1993. The Bio-Intensive Approach to Small-Scale Household Food Production, IIRR, Room 1270, 475 Riverside Dr., New York, NY 10115

Martin, F.W., R. Ruberté, and L. Meitzner. 1998. Edible Leaves of the Tropics, 3rd Edition. Available from ECHO, 17430 Durrance Rd., N. Ft. Myers, FL 33917, USA, Web: http://www.echonet.org

Bailey, J.M. 1992. The Leaves We Eat. South Pacific Commission, B.P. D5, Noumea Cedex, New Caledonia

Facciola, S. 1990. Cornucopia: A Source Book of Edible Plants, Kampong Publications, Vista, California.

Original Source

This chapter was originally published as *The Overstory* #26.

Flowers of *Gliricidia sepium*. (photo: C. Elevitch)

A Great Start

Plato said, "The beginning is the most important part of the work." There are unrecognized forces already at work on the land; resources and processes present that may not have been noticed. Working with nature in the first few steps lays the foundation for sustainable systems.

Section Contents

Observation

Craig R. Elevitch and Kim M. Wilkinson

Sustainability is about working with nature, rather than against it. We can choose to impose our own agenda often at great expense to ourselves and to the local ecology, or we can appreciate the forces and processes that exist on the land, and work with them to benefit ourselves and the environment at the same time. The way to begin working with nature is to start by observing it, noticing and appreciating what nature is doing on a site. The observation process is a key tool that can mean the difference between results that are ecologically sound, and ones that are not. Observation is about letting nature teach us what works.

A well known permaculture teacher, Lea Harrison of Australia, recounts that as she was starting out, she was unable to work on her farm for an entire year as a result of a motorcycle accident. She was forced by her injury to sit back and watch her fallow land from the balcony of her house, and she couldn't *do* anything! While frustrating at first, in retrospect she realized that waiting that whole year to observe natural processes on her land enhanced her farm design tremendously, lowering her overall costs and resulting in higher yields and reduced maintenance.

Lea's situation forced her to observe, but for most if us it takes restraint and patience to practice the permaculture design principle: Prolonged and thoughtful observation rather than prolonged and thoughtless labor. The tendency is to see the land in terms of what we want it to be, what we can make of it, rather than take time to notice what is going on naturally, without any effort on our part.

Observation should be done before planning a project, or preparing the site and are essential for any kind of sustainable land use: farm or forestry plantings, situating buildings, installing water catchment, and so on. Even if a site is already partially or fully developed, observation is still a valuable exercise. There may be a lot going on that you don't know about!

Observing Nature

First of all, let go for the moment of your ideas and visions, and look around with no agenda but to experience what is going on around you. The most important thing is to notice *what is so*, setting aside temporarily thoughts of what *could be*.

The observation process begins with a walk around the perimeter of the site. Take a pad of paper and pen; a compass, site level and a camera are also useful. Make a sketch of the property as you walk, taking care to note every observation, and document visual observations with photos or a sketch. Allow all your senses to be active: see, hear, smell, touch, feel, sense the whole. It works best to let the mind flow with all details, rather than editing out what may seem to be inconsequential.

If the property is overgrown, walk, crawl and push through into all areas. This initial visit to an undisturbed site will reveal many secrets. (We once were lazy and avoided an overgrown corner of a farm site, only to discover later that the area was an old house site filled with valuable food plants, intricate terraces and rock walls!)

Important features to look for are land contour, the health and type of plants (noticing different plant assemblies, or variations in lushness in different areas), soils, visual and other pollutants, previous land use, signs of animals and birds, and special features. Evidence of surface erosion or other water patterns, past damage from high winds, and destructive grazing by cattle or goats are also important indicators to look for.

As the walk proceeds, make note of anything you perceive. All of your observations can have importance, no matter how insignificant they seem at first. Useful design features can be deduced out of apparently immaterial observations. Seemingly ordinary plants may have value, or close relatives might be desirable and will grow in the same niche. You may even discover that plants that at first appeared to you as weeds are identified as valuable medicinal plants; these days many weeds are fast becoming tomorrow's medicines. Perhaps previous cultivation or animal tracks have left clues of what might succeed in your area. It is also useful to note down the absence of something (such as, "no wind here").

After walking the perimeter of the site, you will have a good idea of contour, plant flora, access, and other

Soil sampling is just a small part of observation. Pictured: Kim Wilkinson. (photo: C. Elevitch)

general features. Now, explore the interior of the site. It will be well worth the effort to trek throughout the site coming into areas from various angles, all the while making notes on your observations. Ideally, make several visits to the site, during different seasons and weather conditions (when it is raining, when it is very windy, during drought, etc.). It is also valuable to observe what is going on in neighboring sites. As you make observations over several visits to a site, collect them on a large scale map for later reference.

Using Your Observations

Observations are lessons about natural processes. Keep notes of your observations. Over time, you will notice yourself beginning to use them as you make changes in your practices. For example, keeping an observation log enables you to:

- Take advantage of natural processes (variations in soil depth, accumulation of organic matter, especially wet or dry microclimates) as you develop your plantings or buildings.

- Plan for disasters like high winds, fires, or floods (because you were able to know the areas most affected by these in the past, and what survives)
- Monitor changes in your site over time

Working with nature will repay your observation efforts many times over!

Original Source

This chapter was originally published as *The Overstory #9*.

Further Reading

Mollison, B. 1990. Permaculture: A Practical Guide for a Sustainable Future, Island Press, Washington, DC. A comprehensive guide to permaculture in all climatic zone.

Mollison, B. and R. M. Slay. 1991. Introduction to Permaculture, Tagari Publications, Tyalgum, Australia. A very thorough introduction.

Fukuoka, M. 1978. The One Straw Revolution, Rodale Press, Manaus, PA. Documents rice cultivation based on observation of nature. This title is out-of-print, but is very much worth looking for in used bookstores.

Microenvironments (Part 1)

Robert Chambers

Agroforestry systems are often characterized by diversity and complexity. This includes a diversity of microenvironments (small-scale environments different from their surroundings, such as deep shade under a tree canopy).

Most agriculture creates or alters environments, through ploughing, irrigation, the effects of crop canopies, effects of grazing and browsing, and so on. A microenvironment (ME) is a distinct small-scale environment which differs from its surroundings, presenting sharp gradients or contrasts in physical conditions internally and/or externally. Microenvironments can be isolated, or contiguous and repetitive. They can be natural, or made by people or domestic animals.

Examples of Microenvironments (MEs)

Microenvironments include:

- clumps, groves or lines of trees or bushes
- sheltered corners or strips, protected by aspect of slope, configuration, etc.
- springs and patches of high groundwater and seepage strips, and pockets of impeded drainage
- home gardens (also known as household, kitchen, backyard or dooryard gardens)
- vegetable and horticultural patches (protected, with wells, etc.)
- river banks and riverine strips
- levees and natural terraces
- valley bottoms
- wet and dry watercourses: streams, dry river beds, drainage lines
- alluvial pans
- artificial terraces
- silt trap fields (depositional fields, gully fields, etc.)
- raised fields
- ditches or ponds (especially in wetlands)
- water harvesting in its many forms
- hedges and windbreaks
- pockets of fertile soil (old termite mounds, former livestock pens, etc.)
- plots protected from livestock
- flood recession zones
- small flood plains
- lake basins
- ponds, including fishponds
- animal wallows (e.g. for buffaloes or pigs)

Apart from personal observation, the main sources for this listing are Richards, 1985; Pacey with Cullis, 1986; Altieri, 1987; Harrison, 1987; Wilken, 1987; and IIED, 1989.

Properties of Microenvironments

There are a number of important properties and functions of MEs.

Specialisation Because MEs differ from their more uniform surroundings, their use also usually differs. An example is paddy grown in silt deposition fields in nallahs in semi-arid India. But specialisation, though general, is not universal. Some gully fields in Ethiopia are used to crow the same crop - sorghum - as in neighbouring more extensive fields though, it can be expected, with higher yields and lower risk.

Concentration Farmers' own soil and water "conservation" is often soil, water, and nutrient concentration. Soil concentration occurs when soil or silt is dug from common land and carted to build up fields and fertility. Erosion is exploited for the low cost transport it provides for silt which is then trapped by rocks, brushwood, trash lines, vegetative barriers or earth bunds. Water concentration occurs when it is channelled, captured and retained in water harvesting. Nutrient concentration occurs through silt deposition, farm yard manure in and near homesteads and in livestock pens, leaf litter under bushes and trees, and organic manures carted to the ME site. These forms of soil, water and nutrient concentration interact synergistically (see e.g. Kolarkar *et al* 1983).

Protection For domestic and wild animals, many MEs present attractive islands of green in dry expanses and they are therefore vulnerable to grazing and browsing. Protection is essential except where, as with some eucalypts, plants are unpalatable. Fences, hedges, and barriers are necessary and common. Difficulties in protection against animals can deter the creation or exploitation of MEs or determine what is grown in them. As for climate, many MEs are protected to create their own microclimates, often sheltered from excessive sun, wind and/or water.

Diversity and Complexity Diversity in species of plant and animal, and complexity in biological relationships between them, are common in MEs. Multiple canopies, agroforestry combinations, vining plants, variety of species, and plants at various stages of growth are common characteristics. The movement and arrangement of soil and stones often make the land surface less even and more varied. The untidiness of some MEs incorporates a large number of interactions.

Nutrition and Health Apart from the quantity and relative stability of the flows of food and income to households, MEs (especially home gardens) provide two other benefits: medicinal plants, and vegetables, fruits, and other foods for diversified diets which also include more vitamins. Findings of dramatic drops in child mortality with vitamin A supplementation (a 60% reduction in a study near Madurai in South India, and a 45% reduction in a study in Indonesia (pers. comm. Saroj Pachauri) point to the key poten-

tial of home gardens as a source of life-saving vitamins.

Reserves and Fallbacks MEs frequently provide reserves to meet contingencies, and for lean seasons and bad years. Trees to which people have clear rights increasingly serve as savings banks which can be cashed to meet seasonal or sudden needs (Chambers and Leach, 1989). A very poor family in Kakamega District in Kenya had in 1988 a line of Eucalyptus at the bottom of their half acre plot which they cut and sold in the lean times of February and March to buy food and soap. In Sudan, wadi cultivation is especially significant in bad years (pers. comm. Ian Scoones). In Zimbabwe, key resource habitat patches are important for cattle in bad years (Scoones, 1988). Leaf fodder from trees on private land was used by some farmers in Gujarat as their last fallback for feeding their livestock during the great drought of 1987-8. By accumulating reserves of value, and by providing output which lasts longer, MEs thus contribute to the sustainability of livelihoods.

Restraining Migration Following the analysis of Ester Boserup (1965), the technology used in agri-

Microenvironments present opportunities for specialized uses. (photo: C. Elevitch)

culture (in this case for MEs) is related to population pressure and labour availability. MEs will then be increasingly developed and exploited as population pressure increases. In some environments there may be a critical phase when more labour is needed to develop, protect, maintain, and exploit them. When paths diverge, either people migrate (seasonally or permanently) and leave an unsustainable and risky farming system; or, they stay and invest in mote sustainable intensification. One illustration is water harvesting near Yatenga on the Mossi Plateau in Burkina Faso where investment of labour in laying out rock bunds and digging pockets for crops has led to higher and more stable production and reportedly less outmigration. MEs greater productivity, stability, and spread of production period can thus locally support more livelihoods.

Innovation, Experiment and Adaptability MEs play a vital part in innovations, experimentation and adaptation. Some wild plants which are candidates for domestication are tried first in home gardens. Anil Gupta reports that a survey by women scientists in Bangladesh identified a large number of innovations in homegardens (Gupta, 1989). Calestous Juma notes that farmers place such plants first in environments similar to those where they were found, for example in moist ground near a stream (Juma, 1989) and gradually move them out into harsher environments. Paul Richards observes for West Africa that when farmers carry out experiments, they typically begin in the neglected run-off zone (Richards, 1985). Indeed, the past failure to observe farmers' experiments may partly stem from the failure to notice the MEs in which they are to be found. MEs thus contribute to the sustainability of livelihoods by providing locations for experiment, enhancing the adaptability of farmers and their ability to respond to changes and to exploit opportunities.

References

Altieri, M. A. 1989. Agroecology: the Scientific Basis of Alternative Agriculture, Westview Press. Boulder and IT Publications, London.

Boserup, E. 1965. The Conditions of Agricultural Growth: the Economics of Agrarian Change Under Population Pressure. George Allen and Unwin, London.

Chambers, R. and M. Leach. 1989. Trees to Meet Contingencies: savings and security for the rural poor. World Development 17 (3), 329-432.

Gupta, A. K. 1989. Scientists' views of farmers' practices in India: barriers to effective interaction. In Chambers, Pacey and Thrupp (eds). Farmer First, pp 24-31.

Harrison, P. 1987. The Greening of Africa: Breaking through in the Battle for Land and Food. Paladin Grafton Books, London.

IIED. 1989. Patchy Resources in African Drylands: a review of the literature and an agenda for future research and development. A proposal of the Drylands Programme, IIED, London.

Juma, C. 1987. Ecological complexity and agricultural innovation: the use of indigenous genetic resources in Bungoma, Kenya. Paper for the Workshop on Farmers and Agricultural Research: Complementary Methods, IDS 26-31 July, cited in Chambers, Pacey and Thrupp (eds). Farmer First, pp. 32-34.

Kolarkar, A.S., K.N.K. Murthy and N. Singh. 1983. Khadin - A method of harvesting water for agriculture in the Thar Desert, Journal of Arid Environments 6, pp. 59-66.

Pacey, A. and A. Cullis. 1986. Rainwater Harvesting: the Collection of Rainfall and Runoff in Rural Areas. Intermediate Technology Publications, London.

Richards, P. 1985. Indigenous Agricultural Revolution: Ecology and Food Production in West Africa. Hutchinson, London.

Scoones, I. 1988. Patch use by cattle in a dryland environment: farmer knowledge and ecological theory. Paper for the workshop of Socioeconomic Determinants of Livestock Production in Zimbabwe's Communal Areas, Mazvingo, Zimbabwe. Centre for Applied Social Science, University of Zimbabwe.

Wilken, G. C. 1987. Good Farmers: Mexico and Central America. University London. In: Traditional Agricultural Resource Management in Mexico and Central America. UC Press, Berkeley, CA.

Original Source

This chapter was excerpted from the original published as "Microclimates Unobserved" in the *Gatekeeper Series* (No. 22) by the International Institute for Environment and Development (IIED). For more information on the Gatekeeper Series or to purchase the original booklet, contact International Institute for Environment and Development (IIED), 3 Endsleigh Street, London WC1H ODD, United Kingdom; Tel: +44 (0)207 388 2117; or visit http://www.iied.org and go to the online book shop.

This excerpt was originally published as *The Overstory #72*.

Microenvironments (Part 2)

Robert Chambers

A microenvironment is small-scale environment which differs from its surroundings (such as shade under a tree canopy, a windbreak, or a distinct soil pocket). The previous chapter (page 332) discussed the importance of microenvironments to sustainable livelihoods. This chapter covers how producer-based, participatory research can legitimize and strengthen microenvironments for sustainable development.

The biases in both agricultural and social sciences combine to hide microenvironments (MEs) from sight, to understate or exclude them in statistics, and to undervalue their importance for livelihoods. In addition, there are other factors specific to the nature of MEs which conceal them from view or insulate them from attention. These can be understood by considering examples of MEs and reflecting on some of their characteristics.

Once recognized, microenvironments can be observed almost everywhere

There are many reasons why professionals have neglected MEs, including:

Smallness and dispersal. MEs are often half-hidden. They are usually small and dispersed, and many are low-lying. The small or intermediate scale of MEs combines with topography and with the way in which water and soil collect in low places to hide many of them in dips, depressions, valleys, gullies, and watercourses where they are easily overlooked by a casual visitor. Professional attention focuses on other scales. Gene Wilken has noted (1987) that "most research has been limited at the technical level to horizontal plant spacing and at the aggregate level to optimum farm size and economies of sale." Normal soils maps also miss much. In India their

scale is 1:500,000. In both Kenya and Zambia, it is said that because of their scale, soils maps have omitted the crucial MEs of riverine strips and areas of seasonal standing water and moisture (known as dambos in Zambia and Zimbabwe).

Research station conditions. Most research is conducted on research stations where undulations and irregularities tend to be eliminated and their ME potential ignored. Some ME types created by farmers may not be feasible or found at all on research stations—for example silt deposition fields. And where MEs are created on research stations, it is difficult to avoid creating special conditions quite different from those of farmers.

Sequential creation. Most professionals have shorter time horizons than most farmers. Soil and water conservation staff with targets seek to complete works within the financial year. But many farmers' MEs take years to develop. Some silt deposition fields in gullies are built up sequentially over years, with rock walls raised annually. Home gardens, and areas near homesteads, where farmyard manure and household organic wastes are used, gain in fertility over time. Runoff watercourse training may be developed gradually over many years, as may many forms of water harvesting which require physical works. Making raised fields and ditch ponds in wetlands in Indonesia leads to sequential cropping in which tree crops gradually come to dominate after 10 to 15 years (Watson, 1988).

Gender. Some MEs, especially home gardens, are mainly the concern of women, and women's concerns are normally neglected by male professionals who are still in the majority.

"Unimportant" crops. MEs often grow crops (vegetables, multipurpose trees, less common root crops) other than staple grains, root crops, and non-food cash crops which are the priorities of research and extension, which are marketed in bulk, and which are estimated and enumerated in official statistics. In Indonesia the products of home gardens are mostly consumed locally and rarely appear in the statistical record (Soemarwoto and Conway, 1989).

Misfit with normal research Normal research simplifies in order to measure. Due to apparent complexity, diversity, and untidiness, many MEs do not lend themselves to standard agronomic trials or measurement, or to mechanisation or high capital inputs. Many MEs use organic, not the preferred inorganic, fertilizers. Many are based on subsoil conditions and rooting patterns which would be costly and tedious to examine and observe. And many develop and exploit diverse complications such as linkages between earth shaping with soil and rocks, the channelling, harvesting and retention of water, a variety of crops and vegetables, livestock including fish, multiple canopies including bushes and trees, and mulches and manures.

Many illustrations of the above could be given. Paul Richards comments on the significance of the niche of run-off (seep-zone) agriculture, in parts of West Africa on fields which trap moisture and silt from higher up a valley profile, and notes its neglect by "formal sector" researchers (Richards, 1985). In an RRA in Ethiopia, only by walking a systematic transect was it revealed to outsiders that in a semi-arid environment farmers had, over the years, developed an intensive system for trapping and concentrating silt, water and nutrients in gullies, and growing high value crops including coffee, papaya and chat (a narcotic) in the MEs protected by the gully walls (ERCS, 1988). In India, RRAs undertaken in 1989 by MYRADA in Gulbarga District in Karnataka by Youth for Action in Mahbubnagar District in Andhra Pradesh and by the Aga Khan Rural Support Programme in Bharuch District in Gujarat have variously identified the creation of MEs to harvest water and soil as prevalent local technology significant economically but in no case recognized or supported by the official soil conservation programmes.

Home gardens are frequently overlooked or misinterpreted. In Bangladesh, Anil Gupta found (1989) that scientists believed that households used homestead space and other resources inefficiently, and that they planted most trees, bushes and vegetables randomly or just let them grow where they came up. But a survey by women scientists, and maps made of home gardens revealed great complexity and what appeared to be some order in what had been assumed to be disorder.

MEs are thus largely unobserved. Spatially they are hidden by their dispersal. Professionally they are hidden by their irregular untidiness and their misfit with the mainstream priorities of the major disciplines. And temporally they are hidden by their use in only certain seasons.

Yet in aggregate, they are at present of major significance to sustainable livelihoods. Because of their generally better moisture and fertility conditions than their surroundings, they provide the more reliable component of a farming household's food supply. Moreover, in many environments, MEs have been developed as a form of intensification linked with increasing population density. In the future, as rural populations in many places increase yet further, MEs will be developed even more, and will become even more significant for the livelihoods of poor farming households.

Whose Knowledge and Creativity Count?

MEs are a domain where villagers' knowledge, creativity and Research and Development (R & D) have advantages compared with the knowledge and R & D of scientists.

In terms of knowledge, scientists have an advantage in their knowledge of and access to information and genetic material from elsewhere; but their capacity for precise measurement is less useful faced with the complexity and diversity of ME conditions than with the simplicities and uniformities of industrial and Green Revolution agriculture. Villagers, on the other hand, know more about the complex and diverse detail of their livelihoods and of local ecology, and of how these mesh and are managed. Villagers also have advantages in local observations over time.

In terms of creativity and R & D, many MEs have been made and exploited by farmers over the ages without any formal scientific input. Home gardens, silt deposition fields, and terraces are examples. MEs proved support for the view that "...the farmers' role in technology development becomes more critical and increasingly cost-effective as the proposed technology becomes more multi-faceted and complex" (Sumberg and Okali, 1989). With most MEs scientists have serious disadvantages. Research station conditions are likely to be radically different from those of most MEs: wetland patches in dry areas, for example, cannot be replicated on research stations (IIED, 1989). With the possible exception of some basic research, on-station research concerning MEs is likely to mislead and generate recommendations that misfit rather than help.

In contrast, farmers have several comparative advantages. They are constrained neither by an inflexible experimental design nor by the simplifications demanded by reductionist statistical methods. They do not suffer from scientists' relatively short time horizons, but like the settlers in the wetlands of Java, can embark on processes which will take 10 to 15 years to mature. They can manage the complexities of simultaneous land shaping, concentration of soil, water and nutrients, and sequential changes as trees and other plants grow. They can adapt what they do to diverse and irregular topography, and climatic and social conditions. They can plant complicated mixtures of plants, and can place plants individually to exploit tiny pockets of fertility or protection. They can develop MEs sequentially, maintaining and modifying them as they observe and learn.

Not surprisingly, then, there is much evidence of farmers doing better than non-farming officials or scientists in developing MEs. In Singhbhum District in Bihar, it has been found that soil conservation staff are not as good at selecting water harvesting sites as villagers; those selected by the villagers capture more water (Sinha, 1989). In various parts of the world, government soil conservation programmes using contour earth bunds have actually contributed to erosion. As in Ethiopia, Mexico, and India silt deposition fields appear to be entirely a farmer's technology. In India, at least, they are far superior to the standard gully checks of official soil programmes. It is only reasonable to conclude that programmes for the creation, improvement and exploitation of MEs should be largely determined and implemented by farmers.

Action for the Future

The comparative advantage of farmers and disadvantage of scientists in the creation and use of MEs means that less has been lost from past neglect of MEs by non-farming professionals than might at first appear. All the same, the potential of MEs appears large, especially in the semi-arid tropics. And as populations in many countries continue to increase, the need to develop and exploit MEs will become greater. Already in water harvesting, soil conservation and agroforestry, considerable programmes have been mounted by governments and also NGOs, but with mixed results. The question is what non-farming professionals can do to enable the potential of MEs to be realised more rapidly, effectively and efficiently.

First, clear and secure rights and tenure are preconditions. Farmers who sense their tenure is insecure are deterred from taking a long view and from in-vesting labour in land shaping or planting trees. This has been the tragic situation in much of Ethiopia where the 1970s land reform perversely made farmers insecure. In parts of India, too, tree planting and protection by farmers is discouraged by restrictions on rights of harvest and transit (Chambers, Saxena, and Shah, 1989). In contrast, land consolidation and the provision of secure land titles to farmers in Kenya has had the opposite effect, supporting a soil conservation programme and also resulting in much tree planting and protection, with research showing the densities of planted trees to be higher the denser the population and the smaller the holdings (Bradley *et al* 1985; Peter Dewees, pers. comm.).

Second, observation and awareness by professionals are imperative. These can be achieved in many ways. The techniques of rapid and participatory rural appraisal (Khon Kaen University 1987; IIED, 1988-1990) and especially of agroecosystem analysis (Conway, 1986; McCracken *et al* 1988) have much to offer. These include walking transects, mapping village resources, mapping MEs, and the participatory use of aerial photographs to identify MEs and soil patches and zones. The simple act of mapping a homegarden or diagramming a transect can have a dramatic effect on personal awareness, sometimes provoking a "flip"—a professionally and intellectually exciting deeper change in what is seen and how it is seen.

Third, the appropriate paradigm is farmer first rather than Transfer of Technology (TOT). For non-farming agricultural professionals, farmer first entails changes and reversals:

- of location—from on-station to on-farm
- of learning—from learning from literature and from other non-farmers to learning from and with farmers;
- of role—from teacher who transfers technology to consultant who searches for technology and supports farmers' trials and experiments;
- of content—from the single simple package to the basket spread of diverse choices;
- of direction of transfer—from vertical to lateral with farmers' workshops and visits to each others' MEs;
- and of process—from simplifying and standardising to complicating and diversifying.

Farmers' participation throughout is of paramount importance.

To observe and learn about microenvironments, and to help farm families create and exploit them and improve and intensify their use, presents a challenge to the agricultural and social sciences. Microenvironments demand quiet professional revolutions. These will start not with the lecturer but with the farm family, not just in the classroom but in the field too, not on the research station but in the microenvironments themselves. They will entail not simplifying and standardising but enabling farm families to complicate and diversify. The future will show whether non-farming professionals can make that revolution and usefully meet that challenge, or whether it will be largely unassisted that farmers continue to experiment, innovate, develop and manage on their own.

References

Bradley, P.N., N. Chavangi and A. van Geldar. 1985. Development Research and Planning in Kenya. Ambio 14 (4-5), 228-236.

Chambers, R. 1983. Rural Development: Putting the Last First. Longman, Harlow, UK.

Chambers, R., N.C. Saxena and T. Shah. 1989. To the Hands of the Poor: Water and Trees. Oxford and IBH, New Delhi and IT Publications, London.

Conway, G.R. 1985. Agroecosystem analysis. Agric. Admin. 2, 31-55.

Dewees, P. 1989. Aerial photography and household studies in Kenya. RRA Notes 7, 9-12. TIED, London.

ERCS. 1988. Rapid Rural Appraisal: A Closer Look at Life in Wollo. Ethiopian Red Cross Society, Addis Ababa and IIED, London.

Gupta, A. K. 1989. Scientists' views of farmers' practices in India: barriers to effective interaction. In Chambers, Pacey and Thrupp (eds). Farmer First, pp 24-31.

IIED. 1989. Patchy Resources in African Drylands: a review of the literature and an agenda for future research and development. A proposal of the Drylands Programme, IIED, London.

Khon Kaen University. 1987. Proceedings of the 1985 International Conference on Rapid Rural Appraisal. Rural Systems Research and Farming Systems Research Projects, University of Khon Kaen, Khon Kaen, Thailand.

McCracken, J.A., J.N. Pretty and G. Conway. 1988. An Introduction to Rapid Rural Appraisal. LIED, London.

Sinha, A. 1989. Harvesting rain water in the tribal district of Singhbhum. Wastelands News 5, (2), November 1989—January 1990, 2-7. Society for Promotion of Wastelands Development, New Delhi.

Soemarwoto, O. and G. Conway. 1989. The Javanese Homegarden. Institute of Ecology, Padjadjaran University, Bandung, Indonesia.

Sumberg, J. and Okali, C. 1989. Farmers, on-farm research and new technology. In Chambers, Pacey and Thrupp (eds). Farmer First, pp 109-114.

Watson, G. 1988. Settlement in the Coastal Wetlands of Indonesia: an argument for the use of local models in agricultural development. Crosscurrents (Rutgers University) I 18-32, September.

Wilken, G.C. 1987. Good Farmers: Mexico and Central America. University of London. Traditional Agricultural Resource Management in Mexico and Central America. UC Press, Berkeley, CA.

Original Source

This article was excerpted from the original published as "Microclimates Unobserved" in the *Gatekeeper Series* (No. 22) by the International Institute for Environment and Development (IIED). For more information on the *Gatekeeper Series* or to purchase the original, contact International Institute for Environment and Development (IIED), 3 Endsleigh Street, London WC1H ODD, United Kingdom; Tel: +44 (0)207 388 2117; or visit http://www.iied.org and go to the online book shop.

This excerpt was originally published as *The Overstory* #74.

Patchiness: Living in the Real World

Peter Huxley

Agroforestry systems are characteristically diverse, containing a mosaic plants and animals within a broad range of natural land features, climates, and soils. This article discusses how spatial differences, or patches, are an important aspect of understanding and designing agroforestry systems.

Introduction

What Is "Patchiness?" We all live in very "patchy" environments, some more than others, and tropical agroforesters more than most! Patchiness is a form of variability in space. The term expresses diversity, a difference in the nature of something in degree or quality. Spatial differences can be gradual (a "cline"), or they can be more abrupt as in patchiness, where some area is distinguishable in some way from those around it. Patchiness often refers to the unlike nature of many adjacent small areas. Sometimes patchiness is used in a wider context to refer to any kind of dimensional variability, for example, changes throughout a three-dimensional soil profile. Change can occur over time, too, so that any particular pattern of patchiness can evolve into another.

Disadvantages and advantages

There are two ways of looking at patchiness. It can be seen is being a nuisance that we want to eliminate or avoid, or as something potentially useful that needs to be understood, explored and, perhaps, exploited. Locational variability encountered in the field when setting down an experiment falls into the first category. Researchers need to be aware of soil fertility changes across an experiment (without necessarily understanding them), so that they can design experiments to take account of, and effectively "remove" them from, the comparisons and contrasts between treatment effects. Farmers in a seasonally arid area may watch with horror as a rainstorm sweeps across their valley, wetting and resuscitating neighbours' droughted crops, but missing their own plots. Farmers who grow tea from seedlings will observe patches of higher and lower yielding bushes, an expression, in part, of their underlying genetic variability, in part of soil patchiness. These are a few examples of different ways in which environmental or biological patchiness is seen as non-beneficial or adverse.

There are many other examples, however, where patchiness is welcomed. An excellent example is the way home gardens have evolved. Here, through skill and shared knowledge and experience (trial-and-error, at first) farmers have optimised the numbers and kinds of plants grown, and have planted them in the best arrangements and in the most suitable environmental conditions so that they can all flourish together (Torquebiau, 1992). Such pragmatic designs also explore and exploit the vertical environment. Almost certainly many of them will have maximised environmental resource capture and, probably also, environmental resource use efficiency. They will also have optimised labour inputs and the flow of rewards in the form of various products and cash incomes.

Even farmers using relatively simple cropping practices still tend to manipulate them spatially so as to take advantage of particular areas that they know will suit different kinds of crops. Agroforestry, too, will be best served by such a practice, but more needs to be known about the specific environmental requirements of the trees. There is also competition to consider.

Of course, we remain quite unaware of a great deal of patchiness. However well-graded and carefully cultivated a plot may be, it is seldom that much is known about the different layers below ground and what effects it has on root systems. One of the most useful tools for agroforestry field experimenters is still a soil auger.

Agroforestry increases patchiness

Growing crops alone as monocultures will tend to diminish at least surface patchiness; the frequent cultivation will mix up the topsoil and make it more homogeneous. However, what can be expected from agroforestry? Mixtures of woody and non-woody plants will tend to increase existing patchiness over time. This will occur above ground as a consequence of the environmental changes brought about by the taller, woody species at the tree-crop interface

Monocultures are much less patchy than polycultures. Coffee monoculture (left) and coffee in a mixed system with avocados and timber trees (right). (photo: C. Elevitch)

(shade and temperature and humidity changes, shelter, rainfall redistribution, and so on). Below ground there will be soil changes brought about as a result of litterfall, mulching, fine root turnover, macropore formation, and so on. These "microsite" changes are an important, potentially beneficial aspect of trees on farmers' fields or in the wider landscape, but they will tend to be localised and form patches where trees do not form such a complete cover as they do in forests or commercial tree plantations. Indeed, tree-crop interfaces are the observed and measurable outcome of created patchiness, in part due to these immediate (short-term) effects of the plant components on one another and, as time goes by, as a consequence of changes (long-term) in the soil at this interface.

Questions of scale

The question of scale is all-important in exposing and defining patches. In dealing with environmental variability, for example, we expect things that are close together to be alike; but how close is "close"? For any level of change it often becomes possible to discriminate more and more patches as smaller and smaller areas are defined. Thus, choosing a scale level that will show the kinds of limits we want to observe is essential; too small a scale just increase the work without reward.

Patchiness can be observed at very small scales. Above ground the flutter of leaves and the creation of sunflecks through a canopy is one such example, reflecting changes in both space and time. This process is of some importance for shade-loving lower-

storey plants. Categorising the different within-canopy arrangements of cohorts of leaves or the ways fine roots of woody plants can be clustered are examples of relatively small-scale patchiness in agroforestry systems that could well be functionally important.

Very little land is absolutely flat. Soil surface topography changes over quite short distances, with effects that often are overlooked. For example, the puddles that form in hollows can bring about temporary waterlogging after heavy rainstorms; this can often be seen in cotton and groundnut crops. A reverse effect may occur in dry regions on sandy soils, such as in the Sahel, where millet will often germinate more rapidly in such spots. Microcatchments for water are a beneficial form of artificially created patchiness.

Below ground, a good example at the "micro" scale is the way fine roots explore the soil. Such roots branch and grow towards fertile patches of soil. They also die in places where soil conditions contain life-threatening elements: e.g., toxic levels of aluminum, extreme pH, and so on. Thus, at this scale, the root system is dynamically exploring the best of the soil it finds itself in. No wonder that soil analysis, where samples are commonly combined and variability is averaged out. may not always present conditions quite as the plant might see them. In agroforestry, there are additional implications for competition and complementarity if fine root clusters can occupy different microspaces, and so share the environmental resources to a certain degree, or if the trees and crops explore different macrospaces (i.e., if the trees root more deeply).

At this somewhat larger scale, the exploitation of nutrients and water in soil profiles by the root system as a whole certainly also encourages patchiness. Phosphorous uptake, for example, unlike that of soluble nutrients, is highly dependent on the level of fine root growth to soil beds where it is available. Again, in agroforestry the exploitation of soil water by a mixture of woody and non-woody plants can leave the soil water status in the profile extremely patchy, something that is less commonly found under agricultural crops.

Above ground, single trees offer an extraordinarily complex set of microclimatic patterns. Studying the single tree is not simple. Not only is distance from the trunk important, but also orientation. Shade patterns, and hence soil surface temperatures and ambient humidities above it, are dominated by the east-west passage of the sun. The rainfall shadow and leaf litter dispersal will be affected by prevailing winds, whatever their direction might be. Canopy throughfall will depend on the density of the canopy, and also on leaf size, which affects the size of droplets falling to the soil. It will also be supplemented from time to time by stemflow which, itself, projects another pattern around the trunk. In terms of biomass additions and nutrient recycling, working from what happens around an individual tree to the landscape level requires an understanding of the resource flows in the larger system, and the extent to which the individual trees contribute to this. The patchiness within such areas and the overall effect of scattered trees at a higher scale level have so far hardly been investigated (van Noordwijk and Ong, 1996).

Differences in tree behaviour (phenology) can present another form of observable patchiness. Natural vegetation or managed tree mixtures often contain species that at any one time are behaving differently. Indeed, herein lies a key to more effective environmental resource capture in agroforestry.

Conclusion

Patchiness is part of the world around us. Whether dealing with the "micro" level, the plot, farm or higher levels of scale, the spatial relationships involved need to be exposed and their interactions understood. Nowhere do we find forms of land use where this is more essential than in agroforestry.

References

Van Noordwijk, M. and C.K. Ong. 1996. Lateral resource flow and capture—the key to scaling up agroforestry results. In: Agroforestry Forum 7:29–31.

Torquebiau, E. 1992. Are tropical home gardens sustainable? In: Agriculture, Ecosystems and Environment, 41:189–209.

Original Source

This article is excerpted with the kind permission of the author and publisher from:

Huxley, P. 1999. Tropical Agroforestry. Blackwell Science, Oxford, UK, pp. 241–6.
URL: http://www.blackwell-science.com

Order this title from:

TROPAGR 01
Blackwell Science, c/o Marston Book Services
PO Box 269, Abingdon, Oxon OX14 4YN
Tel: +44 1235 465550; Fax: + 44 1235 465556;
Email: direct.order@marston.co.uk

This excerpt was originally published as *The Overstory* #84

Weeds as a Resource

Kim M. Wilkinson and Craig R. Elevitch

"There is nothing either good or bad, but thinking makes it so."—W. Shakespeare

A very useful design principle is: Turn constraints or problems into opportunities. Weeds are often seen as major problems, and much energy and resources are spent fighting them. But are weeds really the problem, or is our perception of them the problem? What follows is a short exploration of some ways that weeds can be a resource for farmers, foresters, and gardeners.

Beneficial Functions and Uses of Weeds

Weeds are vigorous improvers of land, constantly striving to create more diversity, organic matter, and abundance. Weeds on the land may be accomplishing what Nature knows needs doing there, better and faster than we are. For example:

Weeds support diverse soil microlife

Soil microlife feeds off plants. The diversity of plants on the surface is directly related to the diversity of microflora in the soil. Weeds can contribute greatly to that diversity. Removal of weeds to bare the soil reduces diversity. It is very likely that there is important soil life or function being supported by some family of weed that has yet to be documented. For example, several nitrogen fixing species used to be considered weeds, but are now valued and actively cultivated by many farmers.

Weeds control erosion and conserve water

Bare ground loses moisture to the air on sunny days, and soil to erosion when it rains. A healthy ground cover of living plants will conserve moisture and prevent erosion, and weeds can be part of that ground cover.

Weeds support insect and bird life, reduce risk insect pest problems

Butterflies, spiders, bees, dragonflies, praying mantis, ladybugs, and other insects need food and habitat to thrive. A variety of insects will also support birds. A healthy mix of insects encourages balance between predators and prey and reduces the chance of insect "problems."

Weeds are a source of food and medicine for people

Many plants that are sometimes considered weeds are prized as nutrient-rich vegetables or medicinals all over the tropics. A few examples in Hawai'i (all escaped introduced species) include amaranth, portulaca, bitter melon, chayote, Spanish needle and gotu kola. Many of these tolerate drought or other harsh conditions far better than cultivated vegetables, and can be quite delicious.

Commelina, Portulaca, and Amaranthus are weeds with edible and medicinal uses

Weeds are a source of food for animals

Animals can be integrated in the farm to do most of the weed resource management. For example, ducks are used for selective weed control, because they can often be trained as ducklings to develop a taste for some weeds, and will eat those plants first when allowed to range freely.

Weeds provide food for other plants

In the tropics, nutrients essential to crop plant health are primarily in the organic matter, not bound up in the soil. Organic matter needs to cycle through the soil for nutrients to get to plants. Cutting weeds back and mulching plantings with them is a common practice with tropical farmers, and increases crop plant health. It is important to cut the weeds before they seed to keep the seeds from sprouting right next to the crop.

For more about ways to work with weeds, including permaculture ways of handling very aggressive and competitive plants, please see the unabridged version of this article at: http://www.agroforester.com/articles/articles.html

Original Source

This chapter was originally published as *The Overstory #3*.

Further Reading

Pfeiffer, E.E. 1970. Weeds and What They Tell. Bio-Dynamic Farming and Gardening Association, Inc. P.O. Box 550, Kimberton, PA 19442 USA. This book focuses on what weeds reveal about their surroundings and how to use this information to improve our cultivation practices.

Facciola, S. 1990. Cornucopia: A Source Book of Edible Plants. Kampong Publications, 1870 Sunrise Drive, Vista, CA 92084 USA. Details many edible "weeds." A great resource on all sorts of edible plants and how to use them.

Scoones, I.,M. Melnyk, and J.N. Pretty. 1992. The Hidden Harvest—Wild Foods and Agricultural Systems. International Institute for Environment and Development, 3 Endsleigh Street, London WC1H 0DD, England. Comprehensive bibliography related to wild foods.

Weeds or a resource? Many so-called weeds have valuable uses—if we take the time to appreciate them. (photo: C. Elevitch)

Getting Started: Diversity of Species

Craig R. Elevitch and Kim M. Wilkinson

Natural forests are abundant systems–rich in diversity of species, stored nutrients, and yields. Much agricultural land has been degraded in tropical areas, typified by the loss of those characteristics which make forests so abundant–depleted soils, diminishing yields, lack of diversity. The problems of degraded lands are compounded by broadscale environmental influences such as erosion, watershed depletion, changing climate, and the presence of new diseases and insect pests.

Which species should be planted to help restore the natural abundance of a forest to degraded lands? Once a site has been degraded, it is often very difficult to predict which species will thrive there. The original forest species, if replanted, may not be able to cope in the changed conditions. It is usually unknown how other useful non-native species will behave in such circumstances. In other words, how a species will perform on a particular site is almost impossible to predict.

Whether you are seeking to plant a forest, orchard or garden, one promising step is to start with a diversity of species. By conducting small trials of many species, you allow nature to guide you in selecting plants that do well in your area. A trial may consist of growing 5–10 plants of each species you are considering, and watching them grow for a season or more. This beats picking a few species and forcing them to grow! Starting with a diversity of species in initial trials, you can allow for many of them to perhaps do poorly, while a good number will perform very well.

Depending on your goals (forestry, farming, etc.) and the size of your project, an initial trial planting may consist upwards of 100–300 species. Although you may have an idea of the species you want to focus on for commercial use, remember to also trial supporting species such as ground covers and fertility crops. The initial trial should include trees, shrubs, vines, ground covers, herbaceous plants, etc. It is a good idea to try at least ten plants from each species to get an idea of their performance on the site. Less than ten might not give a clear picture,

more than ten would become too costly during the trial period.

Keep in mind that within a single species there can also be tremendous variation in performance. For example, offspring from an *Acacia koa* tree that grows well on one site may perform poorly on another site, or it might be susceptible to certain pests and diseases. Therefore, for each species it is best to use several different selections from different sources when possible.

Within 1-2 years you will be able to narrow down your choice of species to those that are exemplary performers, with vigorous growth, resistance to disease and pests, and desirable behavior and products. At this point, a select group of species will become candidates for larger scale plantings. This follows the goal of starting small and expand on successes, as described in Start Small (page 351). Once you know which species thrive from small trials, you can expand successfully to a larger planting. Your trials will create a very valuable list of prime species that will make it easier and less costly to reestablish diverse and abundant plantings.

List of Plants to Use in First Trials

- Plants that appear to be thriving in surrounding areas with little or no care by people
- Plants that are known to tolerate harsh conditions such as wind, drought, and poor soils.
- Plants that are widely adapted to many different soil and climatic conditions, such as nitrogen fixing trees and other pioneers.
- Plants that have multiple uses to people, such as timber, food, medicine, etc.
- Plants that can be easily propagated from vegetative parts (cuttings, suckers, etc.)
- Native plants, especially those that are known to pioneer degraded sites in your area.
- Plants from many different plant families.
- Variety selections produced by farmers and university research programs.
- Old varieties used by indigenous farmers, that are no longer commonly used.

Avoid:
- Known weedy species, that produce large amounts of seed quickly
- Thorny and spiny species, especially those that are self-seeding
- Poisonous species
- Invasive, and rapidly spreading plants, such as certain running bamboo species.
- Illegal or offensive species

References

Mollison, B. 1991. Phases of Abundance, Permaculture International Journal #40.

Original Source

This chapter was originally published as *The Overstory* #14.

Sheet Mulch: Greater Plant and Soil Health with Less Work

Craig R. Elevitch and Kim M. Wilkinson

Introduction

Mulch is a layer of decaying organic matter on the ground. Mulch occurs naturally in forests; it is a nutrient rich, moisture absorbent bed of decaying forest leaves, twigs and branches, teeming with fungal, microbial and insect life. Natural mulch stores the nutrients contained in organic matter and slowly makes these nutrients available to plants. Mulch also protects soil from desiccation by the sun and wind, as well as from the erosive effects of rain and run-off.

Mulch forms a necessary link in nutrient cycling vital for our soils. When mulch is absent for whatever reason, the living soil is robbed of its natural nutrient stores, becomes leached and often desiccates. Natural terrestrial environments without a litter layer are usually deserts. Non-desert plants grown in bare soil require constant fertilization, nutrient additions, and water, not to mention the work required to keep the soil bare.

"Sheet mulch" is a four-layered mulch system for use around crops. The four layers (or "sheets") mimic the litter layer of a forest floor, and optimize the weed control and fertility benefits of mulch. The sheet mulch technique described here is for use with trees or in gardens. The techniques can also be adapted for landscaping and other agricultural uses. Sheet mulch is a simple and underutilized technique protecting soil, reducing weed competition, and restoring fertility.

Benefits of Sheet Mulch

- Improves nutrient and water retention in the soil
- Encourages favorable soil microbial activity and worms
- Suppresses weed growth and competition around crops
- Reduces labor and maintenance costs as compared to bare soil culture
- Provides crops with organic matter and nutrients
- Improves plants vigor and health, often leading to improved resistance to pests and diseases
- Enhances soil structure

Basic Techniques of Sheet Mulching

Once you get the hang of it, sheet mulching can be used almost anywhere. It may be used either in establishing a new garden or tree planting, or to enrich existing plantings. Below is described sheet mulching to cover an area such as a garden on a small scale, then, how to sheet mulch around a tree. In both cases, mulch is applied to bare soil or on top of cut weeds. New plantings are planted through the mulch, or a small area is left open to accommodate established plants and trees.

The benefits of mulching justify putting the energy into doing the job right, using ample materials. Collect all of the materials (as outlined below), and complete the mulching process in one session. A reduction in maintenance and increase in plant vigor will more than pay off the initial effort.

Sheet mulch is put down in four layers to mimic natural forest mulch: well decayed compost, weed barrier, partly decayed compost and raw organic matter, as described below.

Steps for Applying Sheet Mulch

Step 1: Prepare site

To prepare the site, knock down tall weeds and woody plants with a scythe, brush cutter, or by trampling the existing vegetation so that it lies flat. A poultry or pig tractor system is an excellent method of site preparation. There is no need to remove vegetation, unless it is woody or bulky. It fact the organic matter left now will decay and add nutrients to the soil. Once vegetation in the area is flattened proceed to lay down the sheet mulch.

Step 2: Add concentrated compost and mineral amendments (Layer #1)

Whether you are mulching bare soil or weeds, "jump start" microbial activity by adding high nutrient material which stimulates soil life. This material also accelerates the decay of weeds and grass under the mulch. Suitable materials are enriched compost,

Sheet mulching has many advantages in agriculture as well as landscaping. (photo: C. Elevitch)

poultry or stock manure, worm castings, feather meal or similar at the rate of about 2.2 kg/m2 (50 lbs/100 ft2). If the soil is overly acid, which is common in disturbed soils or those treated with conventional fertilizers, add lime. A soil analysis will indicate the need for adjustment of pH or mineral amendments. This is the appropriate time to add the recommended doses of minerals such as phosphorous and potassium.

Step 3: Water well

Now, soak the area well with water. This is essential as it starts the natural process of decomposition. Also it is much easier to soak the ground now, before the remaining layers of mulch are applied.

Step 4: Apply a weed barrier (Layer #2)

Most cultivated areas harbor untold numbers of weed seeds. There are also weed seeds blown by wind, animals and people. Soil borne seeds are lying dormant and waiting for sunlight, moisture and space to sprout. Simply pulling or killing growing weeds will not erase the weed problem: more seeds will sprout almost as soon as the soil is exposed to moisture and light. Therefore the next step in mulch-

ing is to put down an organic weed barrier. This barrier prevents the germination and eventual emergence of weeds through your mulch.

Underneath this weed barrier grasses and weeds die and quickly become food for earthworms. The worms turn and aerate the soil.

Of the four sheet mulch layers, the weed barrier has no natural counterpart on the forest floor. In the forest, weeds do not sprout because there is "no room for them," which simply means a lack of space above and below the ground, and a lack of light. By planting an area properly, there will eventually be no room for weeds. The weed barrier is needed only for establishment of the mulch, and disappears with time. If your area is planted appropriately, weeds will not emerge after the decomposition of the weed barrier.

Materials for the weed barrier that work well are: cardboard, 4–6 sheets of newspaper, burlap bags, old carpets of natural fiber, worn-out clothing, gypsum board, or any other similar biodegradable materials. Banana or other large leaves also work if laid down in several layers. Overlap the pieces of the material so as to completely cover the ground without any breaks, except where there are plants you want to save. Around these leave a generous opening for air circulation around the root crown. Care in laying down the weed barrier without gaps will save you the headache of emerging weeds later on.

Both water and good air circulation are necessary for healthy soil. Although the weed barrier forms a physical and light barrier, it is essential that is be permeable to water and air. Overlapped pieces of organic material as recommended above let water and air slowly permeate between and through them. If the weed barrier is applied too thickly, the soil can become anaerobic. Also, for the same reasons plastic mulches are not recommended for most situations.

Step 5: The Compost Layer (Layer #3)

This layer is on top of the weed barrier—it must be weed seed free. Well conditioned compost, grass clippings, seaweed or leaves are ideal materials to spread over the weed barrier. Any weed-free material mixture at the right moisture level for a good compost will do. This should form a fairly dense layer about 8 cm (3 inches) thick.

Step 6: The Top Layer (Layer #4)

The top dressing mimics the newly fallen organic matter of the forest. It also must be weed-seed free. Good materials for this layer include leaves, twigs and small branches, hay, straw, fern or palm fronds, coffee chaff, macadamia nut shells, chipped tree prunings, sawdust, bark, coir, bagasse, etc. The top layer will slowly decompose into lower layers, and therefore must be replaced periodically; it represents reserves of compost. This layer should be about 8–13 cm (3–5 inches) deep. Many materials suitable for the top layer often have a pleasant cosmetic appearance. For this reason, there should be no hesitation in using sheet mulch in all cultivation from landscaping to gardening to permanent orchard crops. In

fact, as you use mulch, bare soil will begin to seem ugly and undesirable.

When the soil is amended and sheet mulch applied properly, there will never be a need to turn the soil. Earthworms do the tilling. The only task left is to keep the soil covered by replenishing the mulch.

Sheet Mulch Around Trees

Planting trees with mulch assures optimal conditions for survival and early growth. The method is a specialized version of the steps above. Use locally available materials, and adapt this method to your situation. If you are unsure about the benefits of mulch, apply mulch to some trees and not to others planted at the same time. Usually the difference in growth and vigor is amazing.

1   Prepare the planting area and plant the tree the way you usually do.

2   Amend soil around tree out to a radius of 0.5–1 meter (1.5–3 feet) with a light layer of nitrogen fertilizer, such as chicken manure, and other mineral amendments if necessary. Water well. (If you are mulching an established tree, be sure to amend out to the edge of the crown of the tree, also called, "the drip line.")

3   Spread a permeable weed barrier around the tree in a ring shape, leaving a gap of 15 cm (6 inches) diameter around the trunk of the tree for air circulation. Make certain there are no gaps in the barrier through which weeds can emerge. If you are using loose materials such as paper that might blow away, water the weed barrier layer now.

4   Spread compost and/or mulch about 15 cm (6 inches) thick over the weed barrier, again making sure it is several centimeters away from the stem of the plant for good air circulation.

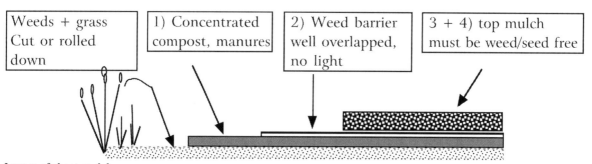

Weeds + grass Cut or rolled down

1) Concentrated compost, manures

2) Weed barrier well overlapped, no light

3 + 4) top mulch must be weed/seed free

Layers of sheet mulch.

Mulching around jackfruit trees (*Artocarpus heterophyllus*) to smother weeds, help retain soil moisture, and add organic matter to the soil. The mulch is supplied by fast growing nitrogen-fixing trees grown adjacent to the jackfruit trees. Pictured: Kim Wilkinson. (photo: C. Elevitch)

5   Leave a generous gap in the mulch around plants to allow for air circulation. Otherwise, the mulch can lead to rot on the plant stem.

Cautions/Considerations

In most cases (with exception of the last point below), the benefits of sheet mulching outweigh the costs. However, be sure to watch out for these potential problems and be prepared to handle them if they arise.

- Slugs and snails are particularly fond of mulch. Especially during the dry season, slugs will be attracted to mulch. This can be a threat to certain small tree seedlings and many garden plants.

- Poultry such as chickens, turkeys, Guinea fowl and more love to scratch in mulch. This may be a problem in certain situations, although usually not much more of a problem than without mulch.
- Rodents can find a cozy home in mulch. Certain rodents such as rats and voles can readily debark certain trees.
- Pigs love good, moist soils which harbor worms, and will grub out sheet mulch if they have access to it. Do not use sheet mulch if pigs have access to the area; they will be attracted to it and will destroy both your work and your plantings.

The Ongoing Process

Once a mulch is established, the soil is covered and weed-free. With time, the mulch materials will decay and begin disappearing into the soil from the bottom up. The rate decay will be fast during the hot and wet season, and slow during dry or cool periods. As in a natural forest, the mulch must be replaced or soon the mulch will disappear and the soil will once again see the sun and the weeds will take over. As long as organic materials are added to the surface of the mulch, there is no need to lay down the weed barrier layer after the first time. From time to time mineral amendments of phosphorous and calcium can be added to the mulch. However, for the most part maintaining sheet mulch requires only replenishing the top layer (Layer #4) with materials such as leaves, trimmings, husks, etc.

It is best to design a garden or orchard mulch system to produce its own top layer mulch in sufficient amounts. To make mulching as efficient and easy as possible, use mulch materials which are readily available. With good planning, mulching of gardens and orchards can become a regular part of maintenance—just mulch with handy materials such as grass clippings, plant prunings (roughly chopped), animal bedding, etc. Eventually, other tasks such as watering, fertilization and weeding will be reduced. The overall maintenance burden in mulched conditions, when efficiently using materials on hand, can be less than in conventional systems (which may use frequent tillage or applications of herbicide).

There are many ways to produce sufficient mulch at your site. Grass clippings, for example, represent nutrient rich mulch material. Deep rooted, vigorous growing plants that readily regrow after hard pruning can be cut 3–6 times per year to provide mulch. For example, several nitrogen fixing trees will produce copious amounts of green matter. Each should be evaluated for its appropriateness for a specific site before planting. Many other plants produce large amounts of organic matter including various trees and bunch grasses (e.g., vetiver or lemon grass). Also, many water plants such as water hyacinth and kelp are good mulch materials. Because fast growing, vigorous plants are desirable for mulch production, when selecting plants for this purpose extreme caution should be taken to avoid introducing weedy species.

Sheet mulching as described here seeks to recreate the organic mulch layer of the forest with a minimum of effort from people. Properly planned, a garden or orchard system will produce its own raw mulch in sufficient amounts and people are involved only in putting this material back onto the ground where it belongs.

References

Curry, M. 1996. Sheet Mulch Now! In: The Permaculture Activist, issue No. 34-A, August 1996.

Hemenway, T. 2001. Gaia's Garden: a guide to home-scale permaculture. Chelsea Green Publishing Company, White River Junction, Vermont, USA.

Mollison, B. 1990. Permaculture: A Practical Guide for a Sustainable Future, Island Press, Washington, DC.

Stout, R. 1998. Gardening without Work: For the Aging, the Busy, and the Indolent. Lyons Press.

Original Source

Elevitch, C.R. and K.M. Wilkinson. 1998. Sheet Mulching: Greater Plant and Soil Health for Less Work. Permanent Agriculture Resources, Holualoa, HI.

Web: http://www.agroforester.com/articles/Sheet_Mulching.html.

This excerpt was originally published as *The Overstory* #96.

Start Small...and Expand on Successes

Kim M. Wilkinson and Craig R. Elevitch

"First you make your habits; then, your habits make you." —Old saying

The first few months of a new planting form the foundation of the entire project. The more effort and attention that can be invested in doing things right in this crucial phase, the more smoothly things will go from there on. Even with large projects, the rule applies: Start small.

The "start small" guideline can be applied to all aspects of projects including home gardens, orchards, forestry plantings, animal systems, tree nurseries, and even community development projects. It can be applied to brand new plantings, as well as projects that are being diversified. Start small and do it as well as possible. When an area we started in feels like it is going well and no longer requires much attention, *then* we are ready to expand to a new area.

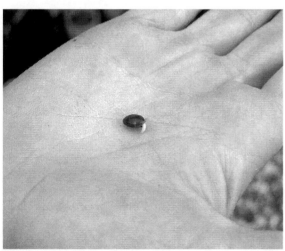

Start small and expand on success

Why does it work to start small? Starting small enables you to:

Do it right At the outset, you will have your hands full with planting, management of weeds, water, fertility, and much more... this is no time to be spread too thin! Once one area feels handled and isn't taking up all your time, then you are ready to move on to the next area.

Develop effective habits You will have to decide how and when to weed, water, fertilize, mulch, and more in the first month or two of the planting. On a small scale, you have the time and physical capability to handle everything appropriately, and learn by observation what is the most effective thing to do and when.

Innovate and improve You will gain great ideas and innovations from the experience of planting the first increment. If you installed the entire planting at once, how will you be able to benefit from what you have learned? Each increment will be better and easier if you started small.

Learn from mistakes It is a lot more fun to say, "Next time I'll know..." when there is going to *be* a next time. Mistakes are inevitable; on a small scale, they are also reparable. Even a huge mistake is not a big deal, if you started small. (For example, we once heard about a person who planted her first forestry trees upside-down. Luckily, she started small!)

Create a realistic time-line If you started small, you will have an idea what kind of time and resources it takes to nurse your plantings through the early stage, and so you'll know how big you can make your next increments. Maybe you can handle three times the work of your first increment; maybe only half. But at least you will know what is involved!

Trial species Some people do a giant planting of a new species they think has commercial value, only to discover that the species does not seem to thrive on their site. You can learn about this painlessly if you start small, which is much better than trying to struggle with poor growth and a poor investment for years! If you trial a number of species at the outset, you may also discover a unique niche for yourself and your property.

Know your limits You may reach a point when you realize that your resources are fully occupied maintaining what you have. For example, you may have planned to develop five hectares, but after developing three you realize that's all you can handle for now, time-wise, physically, or financially. Great! Leave the rest to nature, and manage what you have wisely.

As an example, when we started a tree nursery ten years ago, we got one small table tray, and started working with one species. Admittedly, we were tempted to do a lot more. We laugh now when we think how intensely and seriously we managed that tiny tray. But it was all new to us then, and things that are now routine were once skills and habits we had to teach ourselves back then. We held back until we were really comfortable with that one species and that tiny area. Then we added a few more tables, a few more species, and expanded in increments. We now have tens of thousands of plants going at once, and can grow over 100 different species. We likely would not have been successful had we started on that large scale.

Original Source

This chapter was originally published as *The Overstory* #5.

Further Reading

Mollison, B. 1990. Permaculture: A Practical Guide for a Sustainable Future, Island Press, Washington, DC. A comprehensive guide to permaculture in all climatic zones.

Mollison, B. and R. M. Slay. 1991. Introduction to Permaculture, Tagari Publications, Tyalgum, Australia. A very thorough introduction.

Mollison, B. 1991. Phases of Abundance, Permaculture International Journal #40.

Related Chapters

Getting Started in Farm Forestry

Australian Forest Growers

Farm forestry provides another means of diversifying your income base. If properly thought through—as part of a business or property management plan, for instance—it could increase your property's income.

As well as being another way to divide your eggs among different baskets, commercial tree crops can complement agriculture and protect your land, water and wildlife.

In this article, the terms "agroforestry" and "farm forestry" are used interchangeably to mean the commercially productive use of trees on farms as an integral part of the farming enterprise.

While many of the principles covered here apply to both planted and natural forest, the emphasis is on planting trees for profit on previously cleared agricultural land.

This article offers a very basic introduction to the principles and steps you need to consider before you put in your tree crop. After thorough consideration, you may decide that farm forestry is not for you. That may be the rational decision.

As part of the planning process, it would be wise to have a good understanding of the following issues and principles associated with designing a successful farm forestry enterprise:

- your own and your family's goals, aspirations and resources, and the importance of aiming to design a farm forestry operation most suitable to your circumstances;
- government laws, planning regulations, tax provisions and so on;
- likely tree crop products and their potential markets;
- selection of the best sites matched with the most suitable species;
- establishing healthy, vigorous commercial trees;
- ongoing management to optimise growth rates and the value of the final products;
- the challenge of harvesting, and the importance of joining forces when selling your wood;
- capturing other benefits beyond financial returns;
- some common options to guide you in your final design; and
- personal and family circumstances—age, health,

- where to get good information, advice and support for your endeavours.

Tree Crops Add a New Dimension to Farming

Trees form an essential part of a living landscape. By adding farm forestry or agroforestry to the equation, they can grow to become part of your property's annual cash flow. In suitable regions, commercial tree growing holds the potential to become at least as productive as cropping or grazing, dairying or horticulture.

Tree farming is a long term proposition, but then that's the nature of farming if you're serious about it. Many converts argue that the extended time frame involved in commercial tree growing offers flexibility, as there is less pressure to perform right on cue, compared with, say, harvesting a cereal crop.

Careful design and planning of farm forestry can enable you to capture not only the financial returns from commercial harvests, but also numerous indirect benefits although you may need to make compromises among your tree growing objectives. Planting upwards of 10% of your property to trees is a common rule of thumb for reaping the benefits that flow from providing shelter, shade and fodder, preventing erosion, lowering the water table to keep salinity at bay, and creating habitat that promotes a healthy diversity of plant, bird, animal and insect species.

You don't have to wait 40 years for a return from farm forestry. The sort of economic returns you make, and how quickly, depends to a large degree on your expectations and the type of farm forestry you undertake.

Your own goals will determine whether you grow trees for short, medium or long term returns. Whether you put in a small woodlot of mixed indigenous species, or a large plantation of single, fast growing highly commercial species, or a wide-spaced agroforest, or some other configuration, will be affected by such factors as:

family life cycle;

- the type of farm enterprise you have now, and its financial position—debt load, cash flows, overheads, disposable income, tax position, the need for quick returns;
- amount of land available, and its quality and suitability;
- availability of other resources—water, labour, equipment, skills, time, finance;
- individual and family values and aspirations;
- the need to make trade-offs between commercial returns and landcare and conservation benefits.

These factors will all have a bearing on the likely success of whatever farm forest you grow.

Your goals need not be mutually exclusive. You could aim for a mix of returns from short to long, from secure to speculative. Spreading risks is often recommended as the best long term growth strategy for all sorts of business endeavours.

Planning

No matter how small your intended start, make sure you get expert advice from someone in the know—whether it's a leading farmer in your area, a government extension officer or an agroforestry consultant. It wouldn't hurt to get advice from all three. It's better than finding out five years too late that you've put the wrong trees in the wrong place.

Select sites and layouts to suit your objectives

Beware consultants bearing "best bets" rolled up in their briefcase. There are no "magic pills." Each design drawn up ought to be unique to the situation.

Property management planning helps you identify the most suitable areas for tree farming so that it complements—rather than competes with—other productive uses for your land.

Careful planning over an extended period of time is an essential part of successful farm forestry. (photo: C. Elevitch)

Putting the right species in the right place is one of the most important lessons learnt by experienced forest farmers. To achieve optimum growth, you have to select the tree species to suit the climate, soil type and rainfall. Choosing poor quality sites can be okay, as long as you don't expect the best results. But sites with poor access are a waste of time if your objective is to make money.

Trees become very large and remain in the landscape for many years. If scenic views are important to you, drawing sketches from different perspectives will help you visualise the landscape when your tree crops have grown 20 metres tall, and also when they've just been harvested.

Set aside enough time, capital and land

Before getting started in farm forestry, consider how much time you're prepared to put in yourself. And if the answer is not much, then ask yourself how much money you're prepared to pay to ensure good management? Ensure you have enough time and finance so that you can do all the things that need to be done.

Where you have little cash, time or expertise, probably the best option is to find an industry or government investor and enter into a joint venture—if there is one operating in your region.

Those in the fortunate position to dedicate large areas to farm forestry can spread their risks with a mixture of different designs and tree crops. But small area landholders may have little choice other than aiming to produce high quality sawlogs or to put in a woodlot that meets their own needs for firewood, posts and poles.

Where you make only one or two hectares of trees available for harvesting, you may have difficulty finding a contractor willing to come and cut them, and then a processor prepared to take the time out to consider buying them. Look at it from their point of view: you could be too much trouble for too little return.

Too big an area planted out for high quality sawlog production could prove beyond the limits of a single landholder's resources to manage properly. Pruning, for instance, may start with secateurs, but it gets harder the higher you go.

Matching possible products with likely markets

Whether you want to manage your existing forest, or put in a woodlot as a retirement package, or a broad acre pulp plantation for fast returns, or a timberbelt for multiple benefits, ensure that you are aware of the prospects for selling your products—otherwise your expectations may not be realised.

The available markets within your region limit what is commercially feasible. Look at the final markets available for forest products in your region and then work out what you could grow to meet those markets. Study the market trends and product values, and consider whether the costs of establishment, management, harvest and transport for what you intend to do will enable you to take advantage of the market when you're ready to harvest.

Don't commit to any particular tree product until you have evaluated its prospects for future sale. Blind faith in the superiority of your product is not a substitute for market research on who the likely buyers are within your region and how you can go about obtaining a fair return for your effort and investment. Try to build in some flexibility, so you can have more control over when and to whom you sell.

Markets are dynamic, constantly shifting their patterns. It's unwise to make firm predictions about the future based on present markets.

The emergence and adoption of technologies such as finger-jointed beams, reconstituted wood, and laminated veneer lumber suggest that future markets could be quite different to those of today. A lot of attention is being given to such commercial applications for younger, smaller trees—a trend that improves the likelihood of earlier returns from farm forestry.

Possible products for the farm forester

Knowing the particular features—and therefore the target products—of your chosen species is a vital part of your market research. When analysing your options, remember to allow for losses and waste from defects, and from creating straight timber out of round logs. The percentage of useful timber sawn from a log is called the "recovery." Recovery from large defect-free eucalypts and softwoods can be about 60% and as low as 15% for furniture-grade timber from poorly shaped logs.

Growing timber for pulp or firewood offers a lower value-to-weight ratio (currently about $20–30/tonne) compared to sawlogs ($50–75/tonne). To compensate, you have to go for volume and commit at least 10ha of your land to a plantation monoculture.

Slower growth rates in lower rainfall areas may mean you have to think about other products to make farm forestry stand up commercially. Distilling essential oil from leaves, tannin from bark or brush for fencing are some non-timber options that have been pursued. In tropical and semi-tropical areas, research and growth of rainforest species for cabinet timbers is becoming increasingly popular.

Tree Establishment and Survival

Most farmers have the equipment and materials needed for tree establishment activities—for site preparation, weed control, planting, fertilising and fencing. Doing it yourself can be a lot cheaper than the fees sometimes charged by planting contractors, but you must know what you're doing, just as if you were growing macadamias, canola or carrots for the first time. You can't simply whack in a few rows of trees beside the boundary fence and expect them to perform commercially.

Once you've decided what to plant, find out where to get seed or seedlings of the highest and most suitable genetic quality, just as you would for livestock and conventional crops. Genetic variation is common in all species. Choosing selected provenances (seedlots) or genetically improved seed or clones with the traits you are seeking can lead to much higher productivity. Don't scrimp on seedling costs. Buy the best you can afford, and order six months ahead. Intensive site preparation can be expensive.

Intensive site preparation and fertilisation at planting are accepted as best practice in industrial plantations, because these steps can increase early growth rates and promote more uniform growth across the plantation. Deep ripping and mounding several months before planting is the common soil preparation technique. But the cost of these operations can be quite high, particularly for difficult sites or small areas. Some farm foresters accept slightly slower and less uniform early growth, then put the money saved into more intensive management that adds value to the final logs.

Incremental planting

Some of the most experienced forest farmers started out in their first year by planting a simply designed woodlot on unproductive land. Nothing wrong with that as long as you test the soil type, plant a species to suit, and know what to expect.

But that one simple woodlot can be just the start. Having a plan big enough to encompass annual increments of a couple of hectares allows you to spread investment costs over several years—similar to cumulative additions to a share portfolio or superannuation.

Each year's plantings could tie in with work needed around the farm. You could, for instance, arrange plantings to fit in with realigning fences as part of your property management plan. Or, when fencing out a gully for conservation reasons, you could add another four rows on either side as a future timber crop.

Keeping weeds and pests at bay

Control of weeds (especially grass) is the most important factor affecting survival and early tree growth. Weeds compete with young trees for moisture and light. Failure to remove this competition— with grazing, herbicides, mulch or cultivation—will result in very slow growth and even tree losses. Carry out weed control some months before planting then as necessary in the first full growing season so that the trees get a head start.

Livestock can wreck in two hours what took two years to grow. Failure to keep animals away from young trees could mean you're left with no trees at all. Protection from domestic livestock and browsing animals (such as goats, deer, rabbits, hares, wallabies and kangaroos) with fencing or tree guards is usually necessary until the young trees are about two metres high. Fencing is a major cost, but it doesn't need to be elephant-proof.

Young trees can also suffer extensive damage from insects and birds, and from climate and weather extremes such as wind, hail, and unseasonable frost. Some protection may be necessary.

How close do you plant your trees?

Tree crops are initially planted densely to provide mutual shelter, to force trees to grow tall reaching for light, and to minimise branching. Branches create knots, reducing a tree's strength and the appearance of the timber. This standard plantation design requires the removal of trees (termed "thinning") after several years, allowing those remaining to add valuable diameter growth more quickly.

In lower rainfall areas, a low density stocking rate for a tree crop will help counteract slower growth rates by optimising initial trunk growth. But you will need to set aside time for regular pruning of branch growth, a natural consequence of releasing the trees from the straitjacket of close competition.

- Where pulp is the target product, a high density stocking rate is generally utilised, consisting of 1,100 trees/ha planted out at 3 X 3m spacing.
- For wide-spaced agroforestry integrated with cropping or grazing, a low density stocking rate is generally utilised, consisting of 200 trees/ha planted out at 7 X 7m spacing.

Always Aim for Quality

Whether it's pulp or speciality sawlogs, quality sells. Quality is defined as fitness for purpose, conformity to industry requirements and specifications, and consistency of product. Quality is the one thing buyers remember long after they have forgotten the price or even problems with delivery. To accommodate future uncertainty, you should aim to produce a product that matches the highest quality requirements of the market, while also ensuring you produce enough of it to guarantee continuity of supply. A common mistake is to sacrifice quality for quantity, so don't plant more than you can handle—a sure way of letting quality slip.

Managing tree crops for quality outcomes

Whatever design and species you choose, you'll have to pay some attention to optimising growth and quality. Once a tree crop is established, it needs regular assessment for health and growth rate. This allows you to take timely action in case of nutrient deficiency or disease threat.

In general, you ought to know something about what you intend to produce or have the ability to buy in the necessary management skills and advice. Besides ensuring quality, learning the appropriate silvicultural practices will give you greater flexibility in the products you can offer timber buyers. Poorly managed, aging plantations may not even be good for wood chips—too many twisted trees and defects to suit the chipper's standards.

Striving for the best

For a significant number of forest farmers, consigning their tree crops to a low value per unit fate as pulpwood or firewood goes against the grain. As you gain experience and confidence, you may seek not only higher returns, but also a greater level of satisfaction by growing on for sawlogs. You can influence the form, diameter and wood quality of the trees by thinning and pruning—the two main silvicultural practices that add value to your tree crop. Both activities can fit into "quiet" times during the year.

Thinning helps good trees grow better and faster

By removing trees, thinning reduces competition for water, nutrients and light, allowing more rapid diameter growth of the trees remaining. Once a tree is felled and cut into lengths, it is the log diameter not the height of the original tree that influences log value.

While a number of different thinning regimes are available, the purpose of each is essentially the same—to increase the quality and diameter of the trees and the volume of wood at final harvest. Thinning can also shorten the time it takes for the stand to reach the target volume.

First thinnings are usually the smallest or worst-shaped trees, unlikely to find a use as anything but mulch or fuel. As tree canopies spread to crowd out their neighbours, a second thinning is called for in order to maintain the pace of growth. Posts, poles and rails produced from second thinnings can help reduce on-farm fencing and structural costs, or, if a market can be found, act as a welcome boost to cash flow.

- The timing of a first thinning depends on how fast the species grows, and therefore the length of the crop rotation (the time until harvesting). Any time from age 2 to age 10.
- To optimise growth, the spacing left between trees after a second thinning should be on average 25 times the diameter of the largest trees in the stand.

Pruning leads to valuable "clearwood"

Pruning branches and "double leaders" in the early years ("form pruning") helps shape the tree to grow straight and tall. Pruning the lower branches ("stem pruning") to a height of at least six metres optimises the length of log that is free of knots. To avoid removing too much leaf and retarding growth, stem pruning is usually done in three to four "lifts," two or three years apart.

Logs clear of defects offer greater strength and a cleaner appearance. Where branches are allowed to grow and form knots larger than 5–6cm, the resulting log will be downgraded, no matter how large its diameter.

Compared with unmanaged trees, good silvicultural practices will pay off by reducing the time your tree crop takes to reach maturity in your region by as much as half—and that rule of thumb holds whatever the species, from rainforest to eucalypt or pine.

Timely pruning and thinning greatly add value to a forest planting. Pictured: Kanoa Kimball. (photos: C. Elevitch)

Capturing Other Benefits Beyond Financial Returns

Although your main purpose in planting a commercial tree crop is to derive income in time from the sale of the trees, careful design and planning will enable you to capture other benefits, some of them after only a couple of years.

By protecting soil and water resources, improving the productivity of other farm enterprises, and enhancing the beauty and conservation value of the land, these extra benefits of trees can turn what might be only a marginally profitable sawlog operation into a very worthwhile investment. Be warned, though, that capturing multiple benefits can sometimes require more intensive management than a single purpose operation, and can also involve some compromise. So it's important not to lose sight of the main purpose of your farm forestry and your capacity to manage it.

Planting for multiple benefits

Trees can make conditions more favourable for the growth of plants and animals, and help keep farm ecosystems healthy. Many books and brochures describe in detail the benefits of trees on farms. Greening Australia is a good place to start for advice.

Many farmers are planting on fragile soils which are susceptible to erosion from wind and water. Tree crops can bind the soil, and belts of timber across a slope reduce soil erosion by dropping litter and slowing the flow of water. But remember that harvesting your trees can also cause erosion and remove nutrients.

Trees have deeper roots and use more water than crops and pastures. You could plant tree crops so their roots intercept groundwater movement and thus prevent waterlogging or salinity problems downslope. Plantations in recharge areas can reduce rising water tables. But optimum locations of trees for timber may not coincide with the best locations for salinity management. Upland recharge sites, for example, often have poor soils.

You could plant timber trees to protect stream banks, helping prevent their erosion and the silting of stream beds. Trees provide shade for river pools and reduce fluctuations in water temperature and oxygen levels.

Where appropriately designed, plantations make effective windbreaks for surrounding paddocks. Numerous studies have demonstrated that well-designed shelterbelts can increase yields by 20–30% over a distance of 10 to 12 times the height of the trees in the cropping and higher rainfall (over 600mm) areas of southern Australia.

Provision of adequate shelter for livestock in southern Australia can prevent the death from exposure of newborn lambs and newly shorn sheep. In hot areas, shade from trees can improve both crop and stock performance.

Some commercial tree species yield valuable livestock fodder, but browsing can adversely affect tree growth rates and form. You should prevent livestock access to pasture in young plantation paddocks until the trees are large enough to withstand possible damage. Don't forget that moderate to high tree densities will inhibit pasture production.

Restoring diversity

Your plantations could help restore the loss of habitat that often lies at the root of unhealthy agricultural land. Habitat includes the layers of ground cover and understorey shrubs as well as trees.

Providing a diverse range of habitat types on your property will meet the needs of a greater variety of native birds, animals and insects. For farm foresters, habitat diversity ensures natural predators are in place to limit the abundance of various pests, especially insect pests, and can reduce or eliminate the need for chemical pesticides. Diversity allows more scope for natural checks and balances to operate.

By planting tree crops adjacent to existing habitat, you could buffer it against extreme environmental conditions. Using tree crops to link isolated pockets of habitat remnants increases the chance for animals, birds and insects to move through the landscape.

But the requirements of fire management and uniform timber quality in plantations reduce their diversity, and therefore their habitat potential. Large block planting can also lower scenic quality, and may need creative silvicultural and harvesting solutions if you want to maintain scenic and conservation values without significantly reducing economic output.

Learning how your commercial trees interact with other habitat layers and with crops and pastures will help you choose species and layouts that optimise the balance between direct financial returns and the other benefits commercial trees can offer.

Original Source

This article was adapted with the kind permission of the publisher from:

Australian Forest Growers. 1998. *Getting Started in Farm Forestry*. Australian Forest Growers and the Commonwealth Government's Farm Forestry Program, Queensland, Australia.

Web: http://www.afg.asn.au/Site_files/publication s.html

Getting Started in Farm Forestry is funded by a grant under the Australian Government's Farm Forestry Program. Gib Wettenhall was responsible for the first drafts, for photography, and for managing the publication process. Alan Cummine contributed original and revised text, edited the final draft, and managed the project. The booklet has been reprinted twice, and more than 20,000 copies have been distributed around Australia. It is well-known among farm forestry extension organisations and personnel, and is still regarded as the definitive introductory document for farm forestry in Australia.

This excerpt was originally published as *The Overstory* #121.

Trunk and canopy of *Pometia pinnata*. (photo: C. Elevitch)

Seeds, Seedlings, and Tree Basics

Understanding the basics of seeds, seedlings, and trees can make all the difference in the success of a planting. Growing or obtaining the best quality plant materials will support the project's objectives. The endeavors of many future generations may depend on the diversity established today.

Section Contents

Selected Tree Seed

Kim M. Wilkinson and Craig R. Elevitch

For generations, people all over the world have un-wittingly been depleting the gene pool of many important trees by harvesting or removing trees with the best characteristics, and leaving behind the inferior ones. Hundreds of forestry and agroforestry tree species have also suffered from severe genetic loss due to indiscriminate deforestation.

It is crucial that reforestation, forestry and agroforestry projects make strides to improve the gene pool by propagating seed from carefully selected trees. By utilizing the highest quality selected seed and plant material available, you can begin to reverse the trends of genetic degradation while improving the productivity and health of your plantings.

The genetic quality of tree seed used in plantings is a major factor in the economic success and productivity of a project. Select seed will produce plants that are more productive, better adapted to local site conditions, and better suited to achieve the results planned for the project. The long-term ecological viability and future contribution of a planting is also at stake, as projects should contain enough diversity to reproduce healthy and productive offspring for future generations, while remaining resilient to environmental stresses. The short and long term impacts of genetic seed quality warrant careful consideration and planning when collecting or purchasing seeds.

Five Main Criteria for Selection

There are five main criteria in selecting tree seed for a particular species:

Characteristics of the tree products/services

Tree characteristics such as form, wood quality, or biochemical traits are likely to be passed on to the offspring of a tree. Select trees that are representative of the qualities that are desirable for your project.

Adaptation to site conditions such as soils, wind, elevation and rainfall.
Different populations of a species have varying tolerances to environmental conditions and stresses. Select from populations that are adapted to conditions similar to yours.

Tree growth rate Studies have shown that you can readily achieve a 20–100% increase in overall growth rate for a species by selecting seed from trees that are the best performers.

Resistance to pests and diseases Minimize collections from trees that are obviously prone to harmful pests and diseases.

Genetic diversity of the seed Diversity is an important factor. Create a local population with sufficient diversity and vigor in the gene pool to allow for viable populations and offspring into the future as well protect against loss to unforeseen biological and environmental stresses in the near term.

It pays to use the highest quality seed selections available

Three Tips for Collecting Select Seed

Here are three important standards to keep in mind when collecting seeds. If you're purchasing seeds collected by someone else, ask if they follow these standards too.

1) Collect from trees with the best form, vigor, and health—the offspring of such trees will tend to have

similar qualities. When you are out collecting, keep in mind that seed selection is definitely an area where "quality over quantity" has to be the standard. Distressed and stunted trees tend to produce the most abundant seed, and usually low to the ground where it is easier to access. AVOID collecting from such trees, as you will pass on their undesirable traits. Often the trees with the most desirable characteristics are also the most challenging to collect seed from because they are the tallest and most difficult to access. Rise to the challenge! The extra effort you make now will pay off many times over, for your purposes and for the future.

2) At a minimum, be sure to collect from at least 30 individual trees. To reduce the chance of collecting from closely related individuals, take seed from trees separated by 70 meters (200 feet) or more. If you can pick from more than 30 trees, do so. Pick from throughout the canopy of each tree to ensure that a range of pollinators is represented in the seeds. Pick similar quantities of seeds from each tree so that no one tree is over represented. This can help prevent inbreeding in future generations.

3) Collect from wild stands and within the native range wherever possible. Many plantings done by people have too narrow a genetic base to be a viable source of seed, and the offspring of such populations may be inbred. (Also, be sure to leave enough seed in the wild to allow that population to regenerate naturally.)

By collecting from a broad diversity of specimens selected for superior qualities, your will improve the productivity of your planting now, and its ecological viability into the future.

Original Source

This article was originally published as *The Overstory* #19.

Further Reading

Dawson, I. and J. Were, "Collecting germplasm from trees—some guidelines," Agroforestry Today, Vol 9, No 2, ICRAF House, United Nations Avenue, Gigiri, P.O. Box 30677, Nairobi, Kenya. Email: aftoday@cgnet.com, Web: http://www.cgiar.org/icraf

Simons, A.J. 1996. Delivery and improvement for agroforestry trees. In: Dieters MJ, *et al*, eds. 1009. Tree improvement for sustainable tropical forestry. QFRI-IUFRO conference, 27 October-1 November, Queensland, Australia. See Agroforestry Today issue referenced above.

The World Bank. 1992. Seed Collection Technical Bulletin Forests & Forestry. Asia Technical Department, Room F3055, 1818 H St. NW, Washington, DC 20433, USA.

Guidelines for Seed Production of Agroforestry Trees

Ian Dawson and James Were

The demand for tree seed of species and provenances that are particularly suited for specific agroforestry practices can be very high. Often demand outstrips supply. When this happens, farmers either do not plant trees, or use whatever seed is available, even if it is inferior. Once poor seed has been widely planted, it is very difficult to replace it with a better source. Ideally, therefore, it is important to anticipate future demand for seed through the early planting of seed multiplication stands. With foresight and planning, good quality seed is available when the demand arises.

This chapter suggests useful guidelines for producing quality tree seed. The guidelines are geared to extension organizations, researchers and others involved in spreading agroforestry techniques.

Getting the Seed You Need for Your Area

Find out the species and provenances (if known) best suited for your planting purpose and region. Look at local species or provenance trials. Ask for recommendations on what to plant from local or national forestry or agriculture services, from organizations involved in international trials such as the Oxford Forestry Institute, the Australian Commonwealth Scientific and Industrial Research Organisation and the International Centre for Research in Agroforestry—and from tree seed suppliers.

See if there is a need to establish seed multiplication stands to meet the demand for a chosen species/provenance by looking at the current sources of seed supply. For large-scale tree planting activities which have reached the dissemination phase, it is usually necessary to establish multiplication stands. Even if it's possible to buy smaller amounts of seed, it may still be worthwhile to establish multiplication stands because commercial suppliers often ask a high price for quality seed. For indigenous species, it may be possible to collect sufficient seed from wild sources, but collection sites are often distant and inaccessible it is often more convenient to establish local stands.

Get seed of the species/provenance you need from a well-reputed supplier, even if it costs more than getting it elsewhere. Adequate documentation on the origin of seed should be provided, because stands should only be established from material which has an identified source. Seed should be from a wide genetic base (that is, with high genetic variation) to give the most flexibility to changing user requirements and environmental conditions. If possible, multiplication stands should be established from seed initially collected from at least 30 mother trees.

Finally, seed must breed true. Hybrid seed should not be multiplied, as progeny will not be true-to-type. Farmers should not normally be encouraged to plant hybrid tree seed because these cannot then produce their own seed. Nationally, potential suppliers of seed are tree seed centres and forestry or agriculture services. Internationally, seed suppliers for more than 4000 tree species are listed by Kindt and others (1997), although information on particular provenances is not included and must be requested directly. If you collect seed yourself to establish a multiplication stand, follow the collection guidelines of Dawson and Were (1997). Also see Selected Tree Seed (page 362).

Choosing a Good Spot for a Seed Stand

Choose a site with suitable ecological conditions for seeding, or your efforts might be unsuccessful. Factors such as temperature (which is influenced by altitude), fluctuations in day length, annual rainfall and length of dry seasons, soil fertility and pollinator availability all determine whether a species will flower and fruit at a particular site. Generally, fertile well-drained soils, an abundance of appropriate pollinators (where relevant) and dry conditions after flowering all help seeding. You can gather information on the likelihood of good seeding of a particular species from observing locally planted trials or other

Seed pods of *Sesbania sesban*, one of the important species for which ICRAF has established seed multiplication stands of high-performance provenances in southern Africa. The seed from these stands is used for distribution to farmers for improved fallow establishment. (photo: I. Dawson, World Agroforestry Centre (ICRAF))

stands. Most species will seed under ecological conditions similar to their native environment. Salim and others (1998) list these conditions for a range of tree species. Occasionally, you can influence seed production for example, by introducing suitable pollinators if these are not normally available (such as using beehives for bee-pollinated species, see Bees and Agroforestry, page 100). Finally, a site close to base will be easier to manage and to collect seed from.

Stand Design

Before planting, plan the layout and management practices for the multiplication stand, considering the following:

Tree spacing and management Trees need to be widely spaced so that light can penetrate crowns to stimulate flowering, pollination and seed ripening. Wide spacing also allows easy access to trees for seed collection. Actual spacing will depend on the biology of the species (tree form, age before flowering and fruiting, and pollination mechanism). For legumes such as calliandra, gliricidia, leucaena and sesbania, which should flower within two years of planting, 4 x 4 m between trees should ensure satisfactory seeding. However, trees may be planted more closely to maximise initial seed production from a stand and then systematically thinned later as the canopy

closes. For some species, coppicing can increase crown density, leading to more flowering and fruiting sites, and if trees are smaller, it's easier to collect seed.

Number of trees Production stands should consist of sufficient trees to fulfil the predicted seed demand of users. Annual seed yield per tree can be roughly estimated for most species, and this will give an idea of how many trees are needed to produce a certain amount of seed. The extent of planting is also influenced by economic factors, such as the costs of stand maintenance and seed collection. To determine if sufficient resources are available for a project, costs should be budgeted before planting. To ensure a wide enough genetic base, a production stand should consist of at least 50 trees.

Isolation distance To ensure genetic purity, a multiplication stand should be isolated from any other stands it might cross with by at least 100 m. The actual distance might have to be greater if neighbouring stands are extensive or pollination can occur over long distances. In some cases, adjacent stands can be managed (for example, by coppicing) so that they do not flower while pollination is occurring in the multiplication stand.

Information on the design of stands for particular species may be available from the national and international institutions mentioned above.

Planting and Looking after Your Tree Seed Stand

Before they are planted out, nursery seedlings should be the right size for transplanting. Therefore, seed must be planted in the nursery at the correct time to coincide with planting out seedlings at the onset of the rainy season. Before planting, the chosen site should be well cultivated and marked out.

After planting, ensure the stand is properly managed, including protection from browsing animals and control of weeds. Weeding in the early stage of establishment prevents competition. Alternatively, a cover crop may be planted to choke weeds and reduce labour costs. A cover crop also reduces soil erosion and conserves soil moisture. Coppicing and other management practices need to be undertaken at the correct time. Coppicing should be done at the start of the rainy season, to minimize tree moisture stress and allow rapid regrowth.

Seed Harvesting

When multiplication stands reach maturity, ensure that seed of high physiological quality is harvested. The following should be considered:

Seed maturity Seed should be collected when mature, as immature seed has low viability and storage life. The interval between flowering and seed maturation varies for species and in different environments. For legumes such as calliandra, gliricidia, leucaena and sesbania, it is normally six to ten weeks. For most species, seed is mature when it can no longer be crushed between thumb and forefinger. Seed can be cut to check on the presence of a mature embryo and endosperm. Often, the colour of seed changes on maturation (for example, from green to brown or grey for many legumes). The same applies to fruit.

Seed harvesting method Seed can be harvested directly from trees by picking fruit, or collected from underneath trees. Harvesting directly from trees is better, because pest and disease attack (for example, mammals, insects, fungi and bacteria) is less likely. If seed is harvested from the ground, spreading a tarpaulin under the tree to catch the seed can reduce attack.

Seed harvesting interval Individual trees produce mature seed at different times in a season and, within trees, seed maturation varies through the crown. To get a good quantity, mature seed must be collected at several times in a stand. The interval chosen depends on the seed dispersal mechanism of the species, severity of pest and disease attack, and the labour cost of each round of collection. The interval should allow a reasonable quantity of seed to mature since the last collection, without excessive shedding. If a species sheds mature seed easily, more frequent collection will be required. The aim of harvesting is not necessarily to collect all seed from a stand, but to collect a reasonable proportion of the seed in a cost-efficient manner, while ensuring quality standards are met.

Seed harvesting conditions Collect fruit during dry weather. Dry seed is less susceptible to pest and disease attack during the time between collection and processing. Dry conditions reduce the time required to dry seed before storage. Before processing, store fruit in cloth bags that allow air to circulate freely, as this helps drying.

Ensure that seed of high genetic quality is harvested. Collected seed should be of the widest possible genetic base and should represent the initial seed used to establish the stand. Collect approximately the same quantity of fruit from individual trees and sample throughout the crown to ensure this. In practice, the quantity of seed produced by, or the ease of harvesting from, individual trees may vary greatly. It is important not to bias sampling by collecting substantially more seed from certain trees, especially in a small stand, because this narrows the genetic diversity of your collection. Finally, because of variation between trees in seed maturation, seed harvested from a stand at different collection intervals within a season should be mixed before being distributed to users.

Processing the Seed

After harvesting, process the seed carefully, using the following guidelines:

Seed extraction For most species, seed should be extracted from fruit as soon as possible. The method will depend on the species. For many legumes, pods can be dried in the sun for two days and then rubbed across a coarse wire mesh through which seed falls. The extraction method used should not damage seed so that a significant loss in viability occurs. During extraction, impurities (for example, diseased or partly eaten seed, contaminating seed, soil, chaff and insects) should be removed by winnowing or hand-sorting.

Seed drying After extraction, most seed should be dried further before storage. Generally, the lower the moisture of seed, the longer it can be stored. Normally, seed with a moisture content of 10% or less will maintain high viability for several years, if stored correctly. Sun drying seed for two to three days generally reduces moisture to an acceptable level, although more time is needed for large seed. Seed should be spread on raised beds to help air circulate and shaded from strong sunlight (move seed into the shade for about two hours at midday).

Seed testing During processing, the viability and purity of seed is normally tested. Viability is the percentage of germinating seed in a seedlot and is measured by germinating seed under conditions including any pretreatments (such as scarification or hot-water treatment) that would normally be applied during germination. This provides a reference level of germination for users. Purity is the percentage by weight of pure seed in a sample and is estimated by weighing a sample of seed before and after the removal of impurities. Particular impurities, such as contaminating seed, are recorded.

Seed documentation Seed must be properly label led during processing and storage. An unidentified seedlot is almost worthless. As a minimum, seed should be labeled with the species name, original collection source, production location, collection date, producer, viability and purity.

Seed storage Store seed under conditions that maintain viability. Normally, dried seed should be kept cool and dark in airtight containers (such as plastic or glass bottles with screw-tight lids). If possible, seed should be stored in a refrigerator.

Seed dispatch When dispatching seed, give users full documentation as above, plus information on any seed treatments required for a high and uniform level of germination.

References

AFSICH. 1993. Entrusting seed production to farmers. In: Agroforestry Seeds Circular, no.3. AFSICH, Department of Agronomy, U PLB, College, Laguna 4031, Philippines. 1–12.

Dawson, I., and J. Were. 1997. Collecting germplasm from trees: some guidelines. In: Agroforestry Today 9(2): 6–9

Dudley, N.S. 1995. Seed production guidelines for tropical tree legumes. Agroforestry for the Pacific Technologies, no. 14. Agroforestry Information Service, Winrock International, Rt. 3, Box 376, Morrilton AR 72110, USA.

Gutteridge, R.C., and W.W. Stur. 1994. Seed production of forage tree legumes. In: Gutteridge, R.C. and Shelton, H.M., (eds). Forage tree legumes in tropical agriculture. Wallingford OX10 8DE, UK: CAB Internat. 168–174.

Kindt, R., S. Muasya, J. Kimotho, and A. Waruhiu. 1997. Tree seed suppliers directory: sources of seed and microsymbionts. ICRAF, Nairobi, Kenya.

Roshetko, J. 1995. Community-based tree seed production with Desmodium rensonii and Flemingia macrophylla. Agroforestry for the Pacific Technologies, no. 13. Agroforestry Information Service [see Dudley citation for address].

Salim, A., A. Waruhiu, C. Orwa, C. Anyango, and A. Awiti. 1 998. Agroforestry tree database. ICRAF, Nairobi, Kenya.

Original Source

This article is excerpted from the original published as "Multiplication, that's the name of the game: Guidelines for seed production of agroforestry trees" in *Agroforestry Today*, Vol. 10 No. 4, October-December 1998. *Agroforestry Today* is a quarterly magazine that publishes practitioner-oriented reports from around the world on trees and crops on farms, and the people who plant them. Published by International Centre for Research in Agroforestry (ICRAF). Subscriptions: Agroforestry Today, PO Box 30677, Nairobi, Kenya, Fax: +254 2 521001, Email: aftoday@cgiar.org.

This excerpt was originally published as *The Overstory* #58.

Seed Source Establishment and Management

Mulawarman, James M. Roshetko, Singgih Mahari Sasongko and Djoko Iriantono

Farmers commonly plant trees on farms or community lands to grow products that satisfy household needs and market demands. Non-government organizations (NGOs) often support farmers' tree-planting efforts. Tree seed, a key input that determines the success of any tree planting activity, is often in short supply. As a result, farmers and NGOs use whatever seed is available, regardless of its quality. In most countries good quality tree seed is not readily available for a number of reasons, including:

- A lack of awareness concerning the importance of seed quality.
- Limited quantities of good quality seed are available; and government agencies, researchers and forest industry control access to this seed.
- Limited areas of forests and plantations exist that produce good quality seed (seed producing areas are called "seed sources").
- The genetic quality of forests is often degraded because the best quality trees have been harvested, leaving only poorer quality trees available for seed collection.
- Collectors, dealers and other workers in the tree seed sector have limited training and inadequate facilities to produce, handle and store seed properly.
- A lack of cooperation between governmental agencies at the community level to improve the availability and utilization of quality seed.
- No labeling or certification systems exist to provide adequate information (to the farmers and NGOs) concerning the origin and quality of the tree seed that is available.
- No premium is paid for better quality tree seed.

Definitions for Common Tree Seed Terms

It is appropriate to define some of the basic terms related to tree seed production and management. The definitions provided here are intended specifically for farmers and NGO field workers. They may differ from those used in the formal tree seed sector.

- Germplasm: Seed or vegetative material used for the purpose of plant propagation; most commonly germplasm refers to seed.
- Seed: Reproductive material of flowering plants.
- Seedling: Plants propagated from any form of germplasm.
- Seed source: Individual trees or stands, natural or planted, from which seed is collected. This manual addresses four types of seed sources: seed trees, seed stands, seed production areas and seed orchards.
- Seed trees: Trees from which seed is collected.
- Genotype: Genetic constituents of an individual tree which, in interaction with the environment, largely controls tree performance and is inheritable by its progeny. Generally, trees with good genotype produce good progeny.
- Phenotype: The observed characteristics of a tree, which result from the interaction of the genotype and environment.
- Plus trees (Selected trees): Superior phenotypic trees from which seed is collected.

Seed Quality

Another important term is seed quality. Seed quality has a direct impact on tree growth and the success of tree planting activities. Seed quality is comprised of three components.

- Physical quality: Quality related to physical characteristics, such as size, color, age, seed coat condition, occurrence of cracks, pest and disease attacks, or other damage.
- Physiological quality: Quality related to physiological characteristics, such as maturity, moisture content, or germination ability.
- Genetic quality: Quality related to characteristics inherited from the parent trees.

Seed quality helps determine:

- The quantity of seed that should be sown to produce the required number of seedlings;
- The number, health and vigor of the resulting seedlings; and

- The characteristics of the resulting seedlings and mature trees, such as growth rate, biomass production (wood, leaves, etc.), fruit and seed production, stem form (straightness, diameter, branchiness, merchantable length), general health and susceptibility to pests and diseases.

Establishment of Seed Trees on Farm

Most farmers generally own, or have access to, only small areas of land and do not have the time or financial resources required to invest in intensive seed source management. In most cases, it is not feasible for the farmers to establish seed orchards or seed production areas. The best option for most farmers is to integrate seed trees into their existing farming systems, which often include pre-existing trees of many species. To maximize the genetic base and productivity of on-farm tree sources, the following approach for establishing on-farm seed trees is recommended.

Site selection and tree planting

- First, environmental conditions of the site — rainfall, temperature, elevation, and soils — must be appropriate for the target species.
- To improve tree survival and growth thorough land preparation should precede seed tree establishment.
- Wider spacing between seed trees and other trees enhances seed production by exposing more of the seed tree's crown to sunlight and pollination. Appropriate spacing will differ by species and site. A general recommendation is that seed trees be planted at 2 x 4 or 3 x 3 m. After these trees become large, thinning should be conducted to achieve wider spacing and remove the poorer quality trees. Additionally, seed trees should not be planted closer than 4 m to pre-existing trees, unless the pre-existing trees can be removed once they begin to impede the growth of the seed trees.
- If improved germplasm is used to establish seed trees, the seed trees should be isolated from stands of unimproved trees of the same species to avoid pollen contamination and maintain the genetic superiority of the seed produced. Because landholdings are small and farmers can not control the land management practices of their neighbors, maintaining effective isolation distances is often impossible. Therefore, farmers should realize that the seed collected from on-farm trees results from both "improved quality mother trees pollinated by improved quality father trees" and "improved quality mother trees pollinated by average to below average quality father trees." To improve the pollen source from their own land, farmers should remove poor quality trees.

Seed trees management

- Active management of trees will improve on-farm seed production. Management options include: planting seed trees; weed control near seed trees; fertilizing seed trees; removing poor quality trees and trees that inhibit seed trees; pruning dead and non-productive branches from seed trees; maintaining a clean understory to facilitate seed collection (and reduce fire hazard); and implementing pest and disease protection measures. At the farm- and community-level these operations can be implemented in a cost-effective manner. However, labor is often a limiting factor for farmers. The potential positive impact of these management operations must be compared to the opportunity costs of individual farmers. The suitability of these operations will vary for each farm and situation.
- Seed tree planting on farms should be developed for multiple products and services, not solely for seed production. Seed trees can serve as living fences, border trees, hedgerows, and shade trees or to enhance soil and water conservation. Under multiple-purpose management seed trees and other trees may produce fodder, fuelwood, timber, fruit, seed and other products. Multipurpose management will increase the overall productivity of the stand, but decrease the productivity of each individual product. In other words, less seed but more products (and total value) for the farmer.

Establishment of a Small-Scale Seed Orchard

Although farm-level seed production is primarily based on seed tree management, in some cases it may be possible for farmers to establish seed orchards. As mentioned earlier, seed orchards are seed sources established for the specific purpose of seed production. They are usually established from families of improved genetic quality of either seedling or clonal origin. Seed orchards are planted at a regular spacing with a specific design. Seed orchards are not intended to produce multiple products or services.

Small-scale seed orchard on farm or community land (Wiyono 2002).

Their main objective is to maximize the production of quality seed to meet long-term needs. Because of this strong emphasis on seed production, seed orchards are usually managed intensively. Isolation distances of 200 m from unimproved stands or trees of the same species are recommended and selective thinning is conducted purposely to increase spacing as trees become larger and to remove poorer quality trees. Fertilization, pruning and intensive pest and disease monitoring are also recommended.

In most cases it is difficult for individual farmers to establish seed orchards. But farmer groups or NGOs may establish seed orchards by utilizing the lands of adjacent individual farmers or communal land. Because of the intensive design and management associated with seed orchards, it is recommended that farmer groups and NGOs seek assistance from technical experts when establishing seed orchards. The remainder of this chapter provides information on seed orchard establishment and management.

Site selection for seed orchards

Site selection is important and the first step in seed orchard establishment. Seed orchards are long-term investments. Appropriate sites should meet all of the following criteria:

- Environmental conditions—rainfall, temperatures, elevation, and soils—must be appropriate for the target species.
- Not vulnerable to natural disasters—floods, volcano, earthquake, landslide and frequent wildfires.

- Secure from wild and domestic animals.
- Isolated to avoid pollen contamination. The recommended isolation distance is 200m.
- Easy to access.
- Land tenure or land use rights are secure.

Germplasm selection for seed orchard

The seed used for seed orchard establishment should be collected from identified and improved seed sources. It may be seed from a large number of plus trees (30 or more) where the identity of the individual trees is recorded, or where the identity is not recorded (bulk seed). Seed from identified individual plus trees is good because the planting design can be developed to minimize inbreeding. However, if bulk seed is used seed orchard establishment and management is much simpler.

If the seed orchard design is intended to maintain the identity of individual mother trees, seed from each mother trees must be germinated separately in well-marked containers. The resulting seedlings must also be well marked in the nursery, during transportation and planting at the site. Before planting a detailed seed orchard map must be made that includes the identity of each tree. It is important that this map be followed during planting. If bulk seed is used to establish the seed orchard, seed can be germinated in any available and appropriate containers. The identification of individual seedlings is not necessary. The seed orchard map can be simple, showing the location of each tree, without specifying its identity.

Seed orchard size

As the area of the seed orchard increases it should be more attractive to pollinators. Even though individual farmers have limited areas of land, a farmer group approach can be used to establish a large-scale seed orchard at the community-level. With this approach individual farmer would establish small-scale seed orchard units of 0.1–0.25 ha on their own land. At the community-level, these small units scattered across different adjacent farms will form a large-scale seed orchard. One hectare is the minimum "target size" of a community-level seed orchard. This would require 4 to 10 farmers to establish small-scale seed orchard units of the size mentioned above. The more farmers involved, the larger and better the community-level seed orchard. An appropriate role for NGOs in this process is to develop linkages with technical specialists and document/monitor each small-scale seed orchard unit. Each small-scale unit should contain at least 30 families/trees. The more families included the broader the genetic base of the seed produced from the community-level seed orchard.

Seed Orchard Design

Tree spacing will depend on tree species, site conditions, and orchard design. If the orchard is established as a hedgerow, in-row space may be 10–50 cm with spacing between hedgerows 4–10 m. A hedgerow design is common for fast growing leguminous species, such as *Calliandra calothyrsus* (red calliandra), *Flemingia macrophylla* (flemingia), *Gliricidia sepium* (gliricidia) and *Leucaena* species (ipil ipil). Most other species will be established in a block design. Initial spacing may be 2 x 4 m, 3 x 3 m, or even wider. Narrow spacing such as 2 x 4 or 3 x 3 allows for intensive thinning, see details below under "Orchard spacing."

If the genetic identity of each tree is to be maintained, a detailed orchard design should be developed prior to establishment. The seed orchards should be arranged so that no individuals of the same family are planted close to each other. This precaution will minimize inbreeding. Farmers and NGOs should develop the orchard designs with assistance from a tree geneticist or tree improvement specialist who is familiar with seed orchard establishment. If the genetic identity of individual trees is not to be maintained, seed orchard establishment is easier, because there is no need to worry about the arrangement of individual trees or families. Trees can be planted in any arrangement. However, farmers and NGOs may still wish to seek assistance from a tree improvement specialist.

Seed Orchard Management

Pest and disease control

Because seed orchards contain many trees of the same species they are more susceptible to pest and disease problems than individual trees scattered across a farm or community. Orchards should be closely monitored for evidence of pest and disease problems. If problems occur assistance should be sought from agriculture and forestry plant protection specialists.

The importance of thinning and pruning

Wider tree spacing enhances seed production by exposing more of the tree crown to direct sunlight and pollination. If tree crowns are allowed to grow together sunlight exposure, flowering, pollination, and seed production will all decrease. As mentioned above, most seed orchards should be established at 2 x 4 or 3 x 3 m. As the trees grow, wider spacing is required. Wider tree spacing is achieved through 2–4 successive thinnings, each following an assessment of the orchard and ranking of the trees to identify inferior trees for removal. Poor quality trees may include those that are slow growing, attacked by pests or disease and produce low quantities of seed. Each thinning should remove no more then 30 to 40% of the trees. The subsequent thinning should occur when the crowns close and seed production declines. The recommended final density for a mature seed orchard of medium- to large-sized trees is 100 to 150 trees/ha (a tree spacing of approximately 8 x 8 to 10 x 10 m). Caution: Thinning should be conducted so as not to reduce the number of families below 30 per seed orchard. Pruning should be conducted periodically to remove lower branches that have grown large or no longer produce flowers. The pruning of some branches from the upper crown may be warranted to maintain full sunlight exposure to the branches that are retained.

Spacing management is different for hedgerow orchards. Hedgerows should be pruned to a 1 m height once or more per year. Every two m one tree should be retained unpruned to serve as a seed tree. After the canopies of the hedgerow seed trees begin to close, probably after 2–4 years, in-row spacing of seed trees should be increased to 4 m. In hedgerow orchards, spacing between seed trees greater than 4 m is probably not necessary. Once seed trees in the hedgerow become too large they can be cut down. Coppice growth from the seed tree, or other trees in the hedgerow, is then allowed to grow up and fill the place of the removed seed trees. To maintain high annual seed production, it is recommended that each year only a few large seed trees be removed. This will result in the hedgerow seed orchard containing seed trees of various sizes, with a relatively consistent annual seed production. The leaf and woody biomass harvested from hedgerows during pruning operations should be used as fodder, green manure or fuelwood.

Intercropping

Although seed orchards are intended for the sole purpose of seed production, it is possible to practices intercropping. Seed orchards can be intercropped with food crops—such as corn, upland rice, cassava, or vegetables—for 1 to 3 years after establishment. Intensive weed control and fertilizer application will benefit both the food crops and the orchard trees. Once the orchard trees become large shade-tolerant crops—such as ginger, turmeric or dwarf cardamom—may be cultivated in the understory. Cover crops may also be used to control weed growth and improve soil fertility. However, cover crops are often management intensive. Also, since cover crops do not provide a direct product, farmers and NGOs may prefer other crops.

A moderate amount of intercropping will not hinder seed orchard health and may enhance tree growth. However, intensive intercropping may damage trees and decrease seed production. All management practices should be implemented to favor the main objective of the orchard—seed production!

References

IFSP. 2000. Demo room poster. Indonesian Forest Seed Project (IFSP). Bandung, Indonesia.

IFSP. 2000. Visual presentation of extension material. Indonesia Forest Seed Project (IFSP). Bandung, Indonesia.

Chamberlain, J.R. 2000. Improving seed production in Calliandra calothyrsus a field manual for researchers and extension workers. Oxford University Press, Oxford, UK.

Dawson. I. and J. Were. 1997. Collecting germplasm from trees – some guidelines. Agroforestry Today 9: 6–9.

Schmidt, L. 2000. Guide to handling of tropical and subtropical forest seed. Danida Forest Seed Centre (DFSC). Humlebaek, Denmark.

Simons, A.J. 1997. Tree domestication – better trees for rural prosperity. Agroforestry Today 9: 4–6.

Stubsgaard, F. 1997. Tree climbing for seed collection. Technical Note. Danida Forest Seed Centre, Humlebaek, Denmark.

Willan, R.L. 1985. A guide to forest seed handling. FAO. Rome, Italy.

Yaacob, O. and S. Subhadrabandhu. 1995. The production of economic fruits in South-east Asia. Oxford University Press. Kuala Lumpur, Malaysia.

Original Source

Mulawarman, J.M. Roshetko, S.M. Sasongko, and D. Iriantono. 2003. Tree Seed Management: Seed Sources, Seed Collection and Seed Handling. Winrock International, Morrilton, Arkansas, USA, and International Centre for Research in Agroforestry (ICRAF), Bogor, Indonesia.

To order this title or download it in pdf format visit: http://www.worldagroforestrycentre.org/sea/products/publications/bookstore.asp

Publisher information:

Winrock International
38 Winrock Drive
Morrilton, Arkansas, 72110-9370 USA
Phone: 1-501-727-5435
Fax: 1-501-727-5417
Email: forestry@winrock.org

International Centre for Research in Agroforestry
Southeast Asia Regional Research Programme
PO Box 161, Bogor, 16001, Indonesia
Phone: 62 251 625-415
Fax: 62 251 625-416
Email: icraf-indonesia@cgiar.org

Indonesia Forest Seed Project (IFSP)

Taman Hutan Raya Ir. H. Juanda, Dago Pakar, Bandung, 40135, Indonesia
Tel/Fax: 62 22 251-5895
Email: ifsp@indo.net.id

This chapter was originally published as *The Overstory* #134.

Seed Sources

Lars Schmidt

Seed propagation is the principal mode of propagation for trees in temperate as well as in tropical regions. Seeds are unique in natural regeneration and propagation because:

1 Seeds constitute unique genetic compositions, resulting from mixing parental genetic material. The result is genetic variation of the offspring, which in turn enhances ecological adaptability.

2 Seeds are usually produced in large numbers and are readily available, each year or at longer intervals.

3 Seeds are (usually) small concentrated packages of plants-to-be, containing nutrients for the establishment of the plant and, except for recalcitrant (short-lived) seeds, usually resistant to damage and environmental stress.

4 Many seeds can be stored for long periods under cold dry conditions.

Considering that in a regenerational context only one successful seed (or two if the species is dioecious) is necessary to replace the parent tree(s), the production of seeds during the lifetime of a tree is exorbitant. A full grown *Eucalyptus camaldulensis* tree may produce a million or more seeds per year and may live and produce seeds for a century. Each year's production could afforest several hundred hectares. Although seed production is smaller in most other species, it is probably never a limiting factor in natural regeneration. Each seed contains the potential for becoming a full grown tree, but in nature most of the seed production will succumb to failed dispersal, predation, infestation, natural deterioration, germination failure, etc.

The objective of seed handling is to achieve a high survival and germination rate of the seed. Seed handling encompasses a series of procedures beginning with selection of the best quality seed source, collection, processing, storage, pretreatment, and germination. Each link of this chain implies a potential risk of losing seed, and any link in the process is of equal importance (though not necessarily equally sensitive). If a seed dies due to careless handling during collection or processing, even the best storage, pretreatment or germination conditions will not bring it

back to life. If a seed dies during a handling procedure, the whole preceding effort is wasted.

The whole process of seed handling begins with collection of good-quality seeds, both physiologically and genetically. The genetic quality of seed will affect a plantation for years ahead, and since the operational cost of seed handling is almost the same regardless of genetic history, expensive handling will pay better when applied to good quality seed. Referring to the genetic quality of seeds, the Australian Tree Seed Centre has adopted the slogan: "Good seed does not cost—it pays" (Midgley 1996), meaning that the small investment in obtaining the best seed source is minor compared to the potentially better growth of the offspring.

Genetic Quality of Seeds

The term "seed source" applies to the stand of trees where seed is collected. A seed source can be a number of single trees, a natural stand, a plantation, and a seed-production area or seed orchard. Seed trees are the individual trees from which the seeds are collected. Potential seed sources are identified in the planning phase; actual seed trees are often only selected during the seed collection. "Phenotype," simply put, is the tree as we observe it, and "genotype" is the genetic constitution of the tree.

A seed source should yield an appropriate quantity of seed with a high physiological and genetic quality which matches the plantation site and purpose. In general the seed trees should be of good phenotype, neither juvenile nor over-mature and good seed producers (Morandini 1962). For special planting purposes, for example conservation or provenance seed stands, special consideration on sampling for the capture of genetic diversity may be included. For plantations not intended for future seed production, genetic diversity is usually of less importance, but collection should avoid inbred seed and inferior parent trees, which may affect the performance of the plantation. If, however, the plantation is envisaged to become a seed source itself some time in the future, appropriate measures should be taken to assure reasonable genetic diversity.

The genetic constitution or inheritance carried by the seeds makes up the potential performance of the progeny: if the genetic potential is poor, the performance will remain poor regardless of environment and silvicultural efforts; if the genetic potential is good, this potential may be expressed by appropriate silvicultural measures. Genetic quality can only be proven by genetic tests (e.g., progeny tests) which are outside the scope of this article. Yet, in the selection of seed sources and seed trees of unknown genetic constitution a few measures and precautions can and should be taken in order to avoid genetic inferiority, *viz.*

Avoid Seeds from Related Individuals and Inbred Populations

A narrow genetic base implies a risk of inbreeding. In a population of few flowering individuals the risk of self-pollination is high, and unless the species has a strong inbreeding barrier, many seeds of a small breeding population may be inbred. Isolated trees or trees flowering out of phase with the majority of the population are more likely to self-pollinate and con-

sequently produce inbred seed. Therefore, such trees should be rejected as seed trees.

Neighbouring trees in natural stands are often half sibs or full sibs (Griffin 1990). Species with short-range pollination and dispersal are more likely to create groups of related individuals in the stand than species with long distance pollination and dispersal. This is especially to be considered in natural stands of a single dominant species, e.g., *Tectona grandis, Acacia senegal, Brachystegia* spp. and many pines and eucalypts. A distance of 100 meters between seed trees is usually considered a minimum in natural stands, but it depends on collection purpose (Gray 1990, Palmberg 1985). Genetic diversity is also assured by collecting from a large number of seed trees. Special sampling techniques are applied for special collections like trials or *ex situ* conservation (Eldridge *et al* 1992, Palmberg 1985).

The genetic history (e.g., the number of mother trees) of seed sources of planted material is important. Plantations raised from a narrow genetic base (i.e., few mother trees) should be rejected as seed sources. Obviously this is even worse in clonal plan-

Collect seeds from trees with superior form. Koa (*Acacia koa*) can have multiple, crooked stems (left) or a single, straight trunk (right). (photos: C. Elevitch)

tations, unless specifically designed for seed production.

Many exotic plantations are known to have originated from few mother trees during the first introduction. For example, mahoganies *(Swietenia* spp.) cultivated in many parts of Asia are believed to originate from a small number of seed trees in Honduras and Belize. Unless new material from a broader genetic base has been introduced later, plantations raised from seeds of such trees are likely to suffer from inbreeding depression. Other examples of exotic plantations based on a few mother trees are *Cupressus* in Kenya and *Gliricidia* in Sri Lanka.

Compared to natural stands, neighbouring trees in plantations are less likely to be related, provided the total genetic base is broad. This is because both seeds and plants are usually mixed during the establishment. Consequently, distance requirement for seed trees is less strict in plantations than in natural stands. However, as neighbouring trees are likely to be pollinated by the same pollen cloud, seeds collected from two adjacent trees may have a higher probability of being related on the paternal side than two distant trees.

Plantations raised from a broad genetic base and superior phenotypes are good seed sources. Since both seeds and plants have been mixed during establishment, the risk of neighbouring trees being related is not higher than for distant trees. Therefore distance requirement during sampling is less important.

Avoid Collecting from Trees that Appear Inferior

The phenotype (the tree as we see it) is a product of both genotype and environment. A poor phenotype can be caused by detrimental environment and the progeny may perform excellently when grown under favourable conditions in plantations. For example, Lake Albucutya provenance of *Eucalyptus camaldulensis* grows bent and crooked in its natural environment where it is heavily exposed to wind and sand flow. Grown in plantations (e.g., in Israel) the progeny grows fast and straight.

Yet, phenotypic selection does have a justification: if the phenotypic quality is good, then we know that the tree has the genetic potential for good performance; if the phenotype is poor, then we do not know the cause. Hence, in environments with moderate environmental stress a certain selection of seed trees is appropriate. Trees with exceptionally poor

phenotypes (multiple stems, forking, attack by diseases, etc.) should be avoided.

To avoid detrimental genetic effects in seed collection the following practical measures are recommended (For. Com. 1994):

1   Avoid seed collection from sites where seed crops are sparse or heavy crops restricted to isolated trees, i.e., give preference to stands with heavily fruiting trees in close proximity to each other.

2   Within the preferred stand, spread each collection over the largest possibly number of widely dispersed trees; collect from at least 15 trees which are preferably at least 100 m apart.

3   Collect from vigorous trees of good form; some defects due to physical damage (e.g., from fire or falling trees) can be ignored.

Species and Provenance

Within a species (or other taxonomic sub-unit) a large variation exists in terms of ecological adaptation and growth forms. In botanical ecology the term ecotype designates a special growth site (habitat), e.g., dry zone, humid zone or high altitude. In forestry the term provenance has come into common use as the place of origin of the planting material because it designates both the ecotype and the growth habit (e.g., fast growth, straightness of stem or other desired traits). For example, *Eucalyptus camaldulensis* grows over most of the Australian continent.

Despite its morphological similarity, various ecotypes occur according to different ecological conditions. Variations of growth habits have been revealed through provenance trials, i.e., trials of comparative performance of different seed sources grown under similar conditions. Provenance names such as Petford and Lake Albucutya are known sources of seeds of the species whose progeny has proven superior growth habit in many areas of the world with climate and soil similar to the original site.

The provenance name normally designates the distinct location of origin of the seed source, for example named from the nearest town, lake, river or hill. An ideal provenance is characterized by (after Barner 1975):

1   It is composed of a community of potentially interbreeding trees of similar genetic constitution (and significantly different from the genetic constitution of other provenances).

2 It is sufficiently large for the collection of reproductive material in quantities significant for forest practice.

3 It can be defined by means of boundaries that can
be identified in the field.

Although boundaries of gene flow (interbreeding)
may be difficult to define in areas with more or less
continuous population, the provenance concept is
practical in forestry and should be included in seed
documentation.

Holistic Planning

Planning of activities based on biological systems
must necessarily be flexible and adjustable since
these systems are often unpredictable or things can
change rapidly. A crop failure of one species or seed
source may be compensated for by a larger collection
of another species or seed source. A sudden abundant fruiting of a rarely fruiting species should be
taken advantage of by a large collection of that species. In some species, processing can be delayed
without detrimental consequences, e.g., for dry or-
thodox seeds; in other species lack of preparation or
shortage of capacity of the processing unit may ruin
an otherwise successful seed collection. In some
cases seed availability may influence the planting
programme, especially for those species where a
storage buffer is lacking, e.g., for recalcitrant seeds.
Hence, planning and management of seed collection
involves the whole seed-handling process.

References

Barner, H. 1975. Identification of sources for procurement
of reproductive materials. In: Report on FAG/DAN IDA
Training Course on Forest Seed Collection and Handling.
Vol. 2: 42–64, FAO Rome.

Eldridge, K., Davidson, J., Harwood, C. and Wyk, G. van.
1992. Eucalypt domestication and breeding. Oxford Science Publication.

For. Com. 1994. Seed manual. Procedures for seed collection, handling, storage, purchase and accounting. Forestry
Commission, Hobart, Tasmania.

Gray, R. 1990. Professional seed collection. In: Conference
Proceedings: Sowing the seeds, direct seeding and natural
regeneration conference. Greening Australia.

Griffin, A.R. 1990. Effects of inbreeding on growth of forest
trees and implications for management of seed supplies
for plantation programmes. In: Reproductive ecology of
tropical forest plants. (Bawa. KS. and Hadley, M., eds.).
Man and the Biosphere Series, Vol. 7. pp 355–374.

Midgley, S. 1996. Seed collection strategies in a changing
world. In: IUFRO: Innovations in tropical tree seed technology. Proceedings of the IUFRO Symposium of the
Project Group P.2.04.00, "Seed Problems", Arusha, Tanzania. 1995.

Morandini, R. 1962. Forest seed handling, equipment and
procedures, I: Seed production, collection and extraction.
Unasylva 15:4, 1–15.

Palmberg, C. 1985. Sampling in seed collection. In: Forest
tree improvement. FAO Forestry Paper No. 20: 41–45.
FAO Rome.

Original Source

This article was adapted with the kind permission of
the author and publisher from:

Schmidt, L. 2000. Guide to Handling of Tropical and
Subtropical Forest Seed. Danida Forest Seed Centre. Humlebaek, Denmark.

This exceptional guide covers forest tree seed handling from scientific, practical and administrative
perspectives. For further information about the
book and a wide range of other publications contact:

Danida Forest Seed Centre
Krogerupvej 21
DK-3050 Humlebaek, Denmark
Tel: +45-49 19 05 00; Fax: +45-49 16 02 58
Email: dfsc@dfsc.dk; Web: http://www.dfsc.dk

This excerpt was originally published as *The Overstory* #130.

Seed Collection

John K. Francis

A high degree of diversity is common in the Tropics, especially in the humid lowlands. In single-species operations, such as the extensive plantations of *Pinus* spp., natural diversity is irrelevant. But organizations that service a wide variety of users with diverse needs, and ecosystem restoration projects where nature dictates the species to plant, cannot ignore diversity. Poorly known species and species with difficult reproductive characteristics must be accommodated. With a good understanding of biology and ecology, innovative thinking, and a little luck, most of these new species can be collected and grown. In some cases research can provide answers, but for a few species, and for a variety of reasons, consistent collection and processing of viable seeds may be impossible. In a 14–year study of species suitable for revegetation of bauxite mine lands in Trombetas, Brazil, 600 species were evaluated and 160 were grown and outplanted; only 89 taxa demonstrated acceptable survival and growth during the first two years (Knowles and Parrotta 1995).

If diversity is a distinguishing feature of tropical forests, diversity also characterizes seed collection methods in the Tropics. Because the number of species collected is large and the objectives and budgets of seed collecting organizations are varied, a wide array of collection methods must be used. Redundancy is an important feature of high biodiversity; often several alternative species are available to fill any particular need. Seed collectors may not always be successful in harvesting seeds of all the species desired, but by using all the tools available, by taking advantage of seed opportunities as they arise, and by substituting species with similar properties, they can consistently offer an adequate range of seeds and seedlings to users.

This article reviews some of the challenges to seed collection and processing in the Tropics and the approaches to meeting these challenges.

Challenges

One of the most important differences between tropical and temperate forests is the high degree of species diversity in tropical forests. While a tract of temperate forest might contain 25 tree species, a tropical forest of similar size might easily support 10 times that number. Indeed, there are probably more than 50,000 arborescent species in the Tropics. As byproducts of this vast biological diversity and a broad range of climate, economic conditions, and political systems, tropical tree nurseries and seed-collecting organizations vary enormously in structure and in methods employed to collect and process seeds. These nurseries and organizations range from the most sophisticated and mechanized operations to tiny nurseries that use only hand labor and locally manufactured materials. All use valid and necessary means to solve the unique problems of each local situation.

Seed suppliers that produce seed for sale both within their own countries and for export are required to produce the highest quality product possible. It must contain little debris and be free of insects and weed seeds. Superior genotypes bring premium prices, but all lots must be forest-run (representing the average for wild trees) or collected from trees of selected phenotypes. There is constant pressure to offer as many species as possible, but costs tend to escalate with the number of species maintained in collections. These operations may employ one to many people, have varying degrees of mechanization, and be government affiliated or private.

The most common objective of seed collection in the Tropics is to support local tree nurseries. These nurseries are the principal source of tree seedlings for homeowners, cities, farmers, and conservation and forest management organizations who use the seedlings for ornamental, agricultural, agroforestry, conservation, and silvicultural purposes. They typically maintain a relatively large inventory of the few species that are in continual demand (all of which are reliable seed producers) and a group of other species that changes as seed collection opportunities present themselves. Seeds are usually collected by nursery employees or purchased from local seasonal collectors. Seeds are rarely stored for more than 1 year. Seed quality and handling are highly variable. Because wages are low in most of the Tropics and in some places the objective of providing employment supersedes that of producing seedlings, labor is often substituted for equipment or improvements requiring capital investment. Unfortunately, product quality and efficiency may decrease.

General Methods

It is important to remember that fruit characteristics evolved to facilitate a seed dispersal strategy. Often a seed collection, extraction, or germination technique has simply mimicked the natural process.

From the Ground

The mainstay of seed collection is and will remain the picking up of the fruits or their seeds from the ground after they fall. This method is especially convenient for species with large or conspicuous fruits or seeds such as *Melia azedarach* L., *Ormosia krugii* Urban, arid *Terminalia catappa* L. Protective pods enable collection of fruits of such species as *Crescentia cajute* L., *Hymenaea courbaril* L., *Pterocarpus macrocarpus* Kurz, and *Senna spectabilis* (DC.) Irwin and Barneby, weeks to months after fruit-fall. Even the seeds or fruits of relatively small-seeded species, such as *Bucida buceras* L. and *Petitia domingensis* Jacq., can be collected from the ground if it is bare or paved, or if a tarp is placed under the tree just before fruit-fall. In those circumstances, vacuuming or sweeping can sometimes speed the collection process.

Collecting seeds from the ground is usually the easiest and most rewarding method. Candle nut (*Aleurites moluccana*) seeds are usually readily available on the ground, with the added bonus of the thick husk removed by natural deterioration. (photo: C. Elevitch)

From the Tree

Another common means of collecting fruits and seeds is picking them from the trees. It is faster in many cases than collecting from the ground and it keeps the seeds cleaner. In addition, the seeds of many species are too small to pick up from the ground, and others are dispersed widely or consumed by animals and insects before they fall. Short trees may allow hand picking. Production can be accelerated by flailing into a basket attached to a picker's waist.

Picking must occur between physiological ripening (timed so the fruits will ripen in storage) and release by the tree or consumption by predators or dispersers. Ripeness is usually indicated by a color change of the fruit from some shade of green to an indicator color such as brown or red. In some cases, animal predation indicates ripeness. The sight of cockatoos feeding on the seeds indicates that *Agathis* seeds are ripe (Whitmore 1977). The seeds of many species, such as *Albizia lebbeck* (Kunth) Harms and *Melia azedarach* L., remain in their fruits on the trees for weeks or months, greatly facilitating collection. Many of the eucalypts carry large quantities of fruits for extended periods that open quickly after fires (Cremer and others 1978). These fruits will also open after the clipped twigs dry. Species with serotinous cones, such as *Pinus patula* Schiede & Deppe, produce cones that remain on the tree with viable seeds 1, 2, or more years after ripening (Wormald 1975).

Special Challenges

Tall Trees

Most species are too tall for hand picking. Pole pruners provide a convenient and inexpensive way to collect fruits from 2 m to about 9 m above the ground. Stepladders and easily portable, straight or extension ladders up to 7 m are also used. Fruits or seeds that shatter or detach easily, or seeds that are ejected from their fruits, can be collected by placing a tarp under the tree and flailing the tree with a long pole. In similar approaches, trees are shaken by hand (if small), by mechanical shaker, or by attaching a chain or rope to the trunk as high as convenient and to a vehicle or another tree, then jumping up and down on the chain or rope or pulling back and forth with a vehicle. A particular benefit of collecting seeds by shaking is that for species such as *Cordia alliodora* (Ruiz & Pavon) Oken, in which all the fruits or seeds do not mature at the same time, shaking releases the mature fruits while the immature fruits remain on the tree (Greaves and McCarter 1990).

When short-statured species, such as *Acacia farnesiana* (L.) Willd., *Hibiscus tiliaceus* L., and *Moringa oleifera* Lam., and precociously flowering species such as *Spathodea campanulata* Beauv., invade cleared areas, they are short enough to pick by hand or pole pruner. Trees planted in open-grown situations sometimes grow low enough for easy harvest. Open-grown *Swietenia* spp. will usually bear many of its fruits within 9 m of the ground but does not do so in closed forests. Many species will continue to bear fruits after pruning to a low crown. Fruit trees, including *Mangifera indica* L. and *Citrus* spp., are routinely managed this way. Crown-shaping trials with many tropical forest species should be conducted.

The seeds of timber trees in natural forests are often borne near the tops of very tall trees. Traditionally, these seeds are collected from trees felled by logging operations. The method is excellent, if available. However, felling can shatter seed clusters and produce enough slash to hinder fruit retrieval. In some areas, trees have been destructively felled to obtain the seeds (Britwum 1973). Generally considered unacceptable ecologically and economically, this method may be beneficial if the seed trees are scheduled for removal to improve the stand.

The challenge of collecting seed from tall trees has inspired a number of approaches. Arrows have been used to draw lines over limbs to cut down or shake down small quantities of seed. Traditionally, local climbers were hired to ascend the trees and pick the desired seed in quantity with little or no safety equipment. Any conscientious collector would now require the use of safety harnesses and belts, safety lines, and helmets. Tree-climbing spurs, tree bicycles, tethered sectional ladders, and other climbing aids can greatly accelerate an ascent up the tree bole. Once up the tree, a collector often uses a pruning pole to clip fruits on the ends of limbs or to saw off fruit-bearing limbs. Finally seed collectors with generous budgets use high-lift buckets on hard and nearly level ground to collect fruits from tall trees.

Widely Scattered Seed Trees

In tropical moist forests, seed trees of many species grow more than 1 km apart. Seed-producing adults of heavily exploited and rare species can often be very difficult to find. Random searches can be incredibly time consuming. Traditionally, seed collectors maintain a mental inventory of known seed trees or potential seed trees they have sighted during excursions through the forest over the years. Although it takes many years to accumulate this degree of experience, the system works well as long as these inventories are handed down to succeeding generations of collectors. The alternative is to maintain a written inventory of potential seed trees of at least the critical species along with maps of their locations. Modern technology can add efficiency and accuracy to this time-consuming process through the use of computer data bases and global positioning satellite (GPS) technology.

Genetic Impurity

A number of species hybridize freely with members of the same genus or varieties within the same species to produce undesirable or unpredictable offspring. The *Swietenia* species have hybridized freely in Puerto Rico and the seeds of *Eucalyptus robusta* Sm., obtained from Brazil many years ago, introduced many hybrids that were generally inferior to the pure species. The timber tree *Hibiscus elatus* Sw. has been reported to hybridize with the shrubby *Hibiscus pernambucensis* Arruda in Jamaica (Adams 1971). In the case of *Swietenia*, the hybrid seedlings can usually be separated from the parent species by leaf size. With *B. robusta*, sorting is impossible. The problem is solved by collecting from well-identified and isolated seed trees.

Unknown or Unpredictable Fruiting Seasons

In that portion of the Tropics with a strong wet-dry seasonal cycle, almost all species flower and fruit in certain well-defined seasons. Phenological studies can document these seasons and seed collection can be planned accordingly. However, in many species the flowering and fruiting dates may vary somewhat (Greaves 1978) and the level of fruiting may vary tremendously from year to year, depending on seasonal rainfall amounts and patterns, and other factors such as wind or insect damage. Seed years are theoretically predictable from climatic conditions and can be successfully predicted from flowering and fruit set for a few species, such as *Pinus caribaea* sensu Small, non Morelet, which flowers one year and bears seeds the next.

In those portions of the Tropics with a relatively even distribution of rainfall, many species, such as *Roystonea* spp., *Ficus citrifolia* P. Miller, and *Hibiscus elatus* Sw., flower and fruit irregularly throughout the year. Some species, such as *Leucaena leucocephala* (Lam.)

Special equipment and techniques are often required to collect seeds from large specimen trees. (photo: C. Elevitch)

de Wit, bear seed more or less continuously in moist habitats, but seasonally in habitats with a strong wet-dry cycle. *Vochysia hondurensis* Sprague in Costa Rica bears fruit twice per year (Nichols and Gonzalez 1992a, 1992b). Fruiting in some species is thoroughly unpredictable; individual trees fruit irregularly from year to year and by seasons and are not synchronized with others of their species. However, this can be an advantage. If seeds are unavailable on one tree, they may be present on the next tree; or if seeds are unavailable in one locality, they may be available a few kilometers away. *Byrsonima spicata* (Cay.) Kunth, *Cordia sulcata* DC., and *Buchenavia tetraphylla* (Aubl.) Howard illustrate this behavior. Although *Swietenia macrophylla* G. King is usually seasonally synchronized even outside its native range, a few unsynchronized individuals produce some seeds during most of the year. Continuous flowering and fruiting and discontinuous/irregular year-round fruiting is a natural strategy to avoid overloading the demand for pollinators and seed dispersers. Moreover, having a small percentage of the population out of synchrony helps avoid loss of regeneration to irregularities in normal rainfall pat-

terns. To solve the problem of collecting from species with this diverse behavior, phenology should be recorded and collection activities should be planned by species. Collectors should not become discouraged by a few failures.

Delayed and Rare Fruiting

Many species, such as *Bertholletia excelsa* Humb. & Bonpl., do not bear fruit until they become large canopy dominants, a process that may take 50 years or more. In plantations, the process can be shortened to 15 to 25 years and grafted stock will bear fruits in as little as 6 years (Ferraz 1991). Seed orchards exploit the tendency for open-grown trees to bear fruit more quickly and prolifically than forest trees. The abundance and ease of collection from open-grown trees has often led to excessive collection from phenotypically unproven trees in pastures and along streets. *Lagerstroemia specious* (L.) Pres. begin fruiting in as little as 3 years, but do not bear viable seeds until about 15 years (Food and Agriculture Organization 1957). Most species of *Bambusa* flower and fruit in regional synchrony only once every few decades, and

Corypha umbraculifera L., a palm, flowers once at the end of its long life and then dies.

The advantages to collecting seeds of species that can be stored during bumper crop years are numerous. The cost per unit of seed is lower; fewer seeds are damaged by insects; and the seed usually germinate at higher rates (Lamb 1993). A number of healthy exotic trees, such as *Araucaria heterophylla* (Salish.) Franco in Puerto Rico, do not produce seeds in their new habitats (Francis 1987), and seeds must be imported each season. Ringing, shallow girdling, stem strangulation, stem bending, root pruning, and water supply restriction has shown some promise in promoting seed production, although these methods ultimately injure the trees (Rudolf and others 1974).

Animal Predation

Rodents, monkeys, birds, bats, and grazing animals can quickly eliminate a seed crop in a limited area. Parrots in Central America can consume an entire seed crop of *Acacia aneura* F. Muell. before it ripens (Willan 1995). Although fences, screens, scarecrows, reflectors, and noise makers can successfully reduce or eliminate seed predation, they are usually practical only for seed orchards or concentrations of seed trees. Sometimes seeds can be harvested after they have become viable but before they or the fruits become attractive or accessible to animals. When forest species are scattered, collecting more widely and intensively appears to be the only way to obtain the needed seed stocks. In temperate areas, squirrel caches can be robbed; and in the Tropics, seeds are separated from the manure of predators that have been feeding on the fruit of the desired species.

Insect Infestation

Most species are attacked to some degree by seed insects. Occasionally, species such as *Prosopis juliflora* (Sw.) DC. and *Triplochiton scleroxylon* K. Schum. are so seriously attacked by insects that propagation is limited (Brookman-Amissah 1973, Marrero 1949). In some cases, insecticides can be used to prevent attack and assure good seed crops. *Zanthoxylum flavum* Vahl seeds in Puerto Rico are reduced to less than 5 percent viability by a seed weevil (Francis, personal communication 1994; Marrero 1949). A conservation organization was able to produce seeds free of insects and with good germination by spraying with insecticide (Rivera, personal communication). Many types of seeds should also be treated by fumigation, cold treatment, or insecticide application to eliminate insect damage during drying and storage.

Short Period of Availability

For various reasons, fruits or seeds of many species are ripe and available on trees for a very short time, often just a few days. The fruits of *Hyeronima oblonga* Muell. Arg. and *H. alchornioides* Allem. Diss. fall 3 to 4 days after maturity (Nichols and Gonzalez 1992a, 1992b). In the final stage of ripening, *Pinus caribaea* sensu Small, non Morelet cones change color from green to brown, the cones open, and the seeds are dispersed quickly (Greaves 1978). Frequent field checks are essential to best time seed collection. Because individual trees of a species are often not closely synchronized, collecting from tree to tree can extend the collection season. Often, the collector can lengthen the period of seed collection by moving up an elevational gradient or across a moisture gradient. Some species, such as *Maesopsis eminii* Engl. and *Pouteria* spp., picked up just before ripening, ripen in storage; thus the picking season is lengthened by a few days. The collector must know the species' traits, because some species, such as *Cordia alliodora* (Ruiz & Pavon) Oken, stop ripening as soon as they are detached from the tree (Greaves and McCarter 1990). The collector should also study how long seeds of critical species will remain viable on the ground after fruitfall. Collecting diptocarp seeds from the ground, for example, must be carefully timed because a delay of a few days can result in loss of viability (Domingo 1973).

Mature seeds of *Eucalyptus deglupta* are released from their capsules and disappear into the wind in just a day or two. (photo: C. Elevitch)

Conclusion

Collection and processing problems are species-driven. Hence, the greater the number of species handled, the greater the number of problems that must be solved. Unfortunately, some species are planted because their seed collection and management are easy, not because they are the best species available to meet the need. Many superb species are rarely or never planted because their seeds are difficult to collect or use. As experience in seed collection and management increases, many exciting species will be added to plantation inventories. Increasing the number of species we are able to successfully reproduce by seed will facilitate the difficult task of rehabilitating damaged ecosystems.

References

Adams, C.D. 1971. The blue mahoe and other bush: an introduction to the plant life of Jamaica. Singapore: McGraw-Hill Eastern Publishers (S) Ltd. 159 p.

Britwum, N.V.L. 1982. Seed problems of indigenous plantation species in Ghana. In: Seed problems. Paper 7. Stockholm, Sweden: International Union of Forest Research Organizations, Working Party S2.01.06. [not paged]. Vol 2.

Brookman-Amissah, J. 1973. Seed problems as they affect forestry practice in Ghana. In: Seed problems. Paper 32. Stockholm, Sweden: International Union of Forest Research Organizations. Working Party S2.01.06. [Not paged]. Vol 2.

Cremer, K.W., Cormer, R.N., Florence, R.G. 1978. Stand Establishment. In: Willis, W.E.; Brown, A.G., eds. Eucalypts for wood production. Adelaide, Australia: Commonwealth Scientific and Industrial Research Organization: 81–135.

Domingo, I.L. 1973. Seed problems in the regeneration of the Philippine diptocarp forests. In: Seed problems. Paper 32. Stockholm, Sweden: International Union of Forest Research Organizations. Working Party S2.01.06. [Not paged]. Vol 2.

Food and Agriculture Organization. 1957. Tree planting procedure in tropical Asia. Forestry Development Paper 11. Rome, Italy: Food and Agriculture Organization of the United Nations. 172 p.

Francis, J.K. 1987. Araucaria heterophylla Salisb. Franco Norfolk-Island-pine. Res. Note SO-ITF-SM-11. New Orleans: US Department of Agriculture, Forest Service, Southern Forest Experiment Station. 4 p.

Greaves, A. 1978. Description of seed sources and collections for provenances of Pinus caribaea. Tropical Forestry Paper 12. Oxford, UK: University of Oxford, Commonwealth Forestry Institute. 98 p.

Greaves, A.; McCarter, P.S. 1990. Cordia alliodora: a promising tree for tropical agroforestry. Tropical Forestry Paper 22. Oxford, UK: University of Oxford, Commonwealth Forestry Institute. 37 p.

Knowles, O.H.; Parrotta, J.A. 1997. Phenological observations and tree seed characteristics in an equatorial moist forest at Trombetas, Para State, Brazil. In: Lieth, H.; Schwartz, M.D., eds. Phenology in seasonal climates I. Leiden, The Netherlands: Backhuys Publishers: 67–86.

Lamb, A.F.A. 1993. Pinus caribaea. Fast growing timber trees of the lowland tropics 6. Oxford, UK: Oxford University, Department of Forestry, Commonwealth Forestry Institute. 254 p.

Marrero, J. 1949. Tree seed data for Puerto Rico. Caribbean Forester. 10: 11–30.

Nichols, D.; Gonzales, E. 1992a. Especies nativas y exoticas para la reforestacion en la zona sur de Costa Rica. San Jose, Costa Rica: Organizacion Par Estudios Tropicales and Direccion Tropical. 84 p.

Nichols, D.; Gonzales, E. 1992b. Especies nativas y exoticas para la reforestacion en la zona sur de Costa Rica. Memoria del II Encuentro sobre Especies Forestales. San Jose, Costa Rica: Cedicion Universidad Estatal a Distancia, Organizacion Par Estudios Tropicales and Direccion General Tropical. 73 p.

Rudolf, P.O., Dorman, K.W., Hitt, R.G., Plummer, A.P. 1974. Production of genetically improved seeds. In: Schopmeyer, C.S., ed. Seeds of woody plants in the United States. Agric. Handb. 450. Washington, DC: US Department of Agriculture: 53–74.

Whitmore, T.C. 1977. A first look at Agathis. Tropical Forestry Papers 11. Oxford, UK: University of Oxford, Commonwealth Forestry Institute. 54 p.

Willan, R.L. 1995. Problemas fitosanitarios en el abastecimento de semillas. Serie Materiales de Ensenanza 32. In: Jara, L.F., ed. Programas de abastecimiento de semillas forestales. Turrialba, Costa Rica: Danida Forest Seed Centre and Centro Agronomico Tropical de Investifacion y Ensenanza. [not paged].

Wormald, T.J. 1975. Pinus patula. Tropical Forestry Papers 7. Oxford, UK: University of Oxford, Commonwealth Forestry Institute. 212 p.

Original Source

This article was adapted with the kind permission of the author and publisher from:

Vozzo, J.A. (Ed). 2002. Tropical Tree Seed Manual. USDA Agriculture Handbook 721.

This excerpt was originally published as *The Overstory* #120.

Invasive Woody Plants

Pierre Binggeli, John B. Hall, and John R. Healey

Biological invasions are considered to be one of the major threats to the earth's biodiversity. Non-native woody species, introduced by humans, can spread into native forests, pastures, or cultivated areas. Such species are termed, "invasive." Many animals and plants are highly invasive and some species dramatically affect the structure and function of ecosystems.

Background

Nearly all introductions of woody plants which have become invasive, have been introduced intentionally by horticulturalists, botanists, foresters or gardeners. The bibliographic data showed that as early as last century a number of authors realised the regeneration potential and sometimes the invasive potential of introduced woody plants. Since these problems have been known for quite some time, it is important to investigate how aware practitioners of introductions were of the potential problems associated with species introductions.

Botanists, conservationists, foresters, agroforesters and horticulturalists have, and often still are, to varying degrees, responsible for the introduction and planting of woody species. While there was awareness of invasive potential and related environmental impact, it appears that often it has been considered that introduction of potentially invasive species would do more good than harm. A number of examples are given below to illustrate the problem. In our view, many more cases could also be documented.

- A number of species introduced to tropical botanical gardens have become invasive but there is no evidence to show that scientists responsible for their introductions were aware of the potential problems. The appearance of articles warning that tropical botanical gardens could be the source of invasive species is a very recent development (Sheil 1994). However, Miller & Lonsdale (1987) have shown that the weedy nature and associated problem of introduced species at the Darwin Botanic Gardens was recognised early this century, but the botanists still failed to foresee the implications for the vegetation of the Darwin region.

- During the 1980s it was realised that a number of introduced trees were spreading in the logged and natural forests of the East Usambaras in Tanzania (Binggeli & Hamilton 1990). Because the biological importance of the East Usambaras and the threat posed by logging, deforestation and invasive species an IUCN project was initiated to help in the sustainable management the mountains. One aspect of the programme consisted in rehabilitating or demarcating Forest Reserves to prevent forest encroachment. In order to make the demarcation noticeable exotics including species known to be invading the natural forest, such as *Cedrela odorata*, were planted.

- The original vegetation, rich in endemic species, of the isolated Atlantic island of St. Helena has almost entirely been destroyed. These changes have been induced by browsing, grazing, wood harvesting, forest clearance and plant introductions (Cronk 1989).

- Due to its prolific natural regeneration, *Leucaena leucocephala*, is generally considered to be a weed, yet it was planted, mainly as a fodder crop, in the Karnataka region of India in early 1980. Within ten years Patil & Kumar (1990) reported that the species had become a problematic weed in cultivated land, even today, new introductions of *Leucaena* germplasm are proceeding.

With respect to invasive species, little information from horticulture is readily available in the literature. Yet most invasive species have been introduced for ornamental purposes and this area necessitates much more attention. In many countries the introduction of species for ornamental purposes is subject to little regulations and is underreported.

Invasive Tendencies and Species Biology

Although most introduced species do not become invasive, it has been estimated that about 1% of introduced species do become invasive (e.g., Groves 1986). Until recently the problem of invasive woody plants has been publicized principally in relation to oceanic islands such as Hawai'i (e.g., Stone *et al*

In many parts of the dry tropics *Prosopis* spp have been introduced for re-afforestation and as a browse species. In many regions the taxa has spread rapidly to cover vast areas that were formerly mainly dominated by open vegetation to form dense stands, such as in the lower portions of the Awash Valley, northern part of the Rift Valley in Ethiopia. With the exception of the emergent *Acacia nilotica* tree (to left) the tall shrub vegetation consists of *Prosopis juliflora*. The impacts of the species on indigenous people are mixed but overall the species is generally viewed as deleterious to the environment. For more information on these issues, see Richardson *et al* 2004. (photo: P. Binggeli)

1992), Rodrigues (Strahm 1989), Réunion (Macdonald *et al* 1991) and Madagascar (Sussman & Rakotozafy 1994). In recent years a number of invasive species have been reported from Africa (Binggeli & Hamilton 1993, Sheil 1994), Australia (Swarbrick & Skarrett, 1994) and India (Saxena 1991). It has now been realised that biological invasions may become a serious and ever-increasing problem in some continental regions.

Below a number of reasons are given for tendencies for invasive species to become increasingly problematical. These reasons are mainly related to increasing direct and indirect human induced disturbance and to human ever-increasing use of nature.

- Large gaps created by logging operations appear to be more readily invaded by exotics than natural tree fall gaps. The shrub *Chromolaena odorata* is readily found in selectively logged forests of the Western Ghats (India) but absent from natural forest (Chandrashekara & Ramakrishnan 1994). The reason for this is probably due to the fact *C. odorata* seeds are usually locally wind-dispersed but can be readily transported by vehicles (see species account). In heavily exploited and degraded forests of lowland of southwestern Sri Lanka *Alstonia macrophylla* (Apocynaceae) is commonly found in large gaps but appear to be absent from unlogged forest. In Tanzania *Maesopsis eminii* becomes dominant in logged forest but is capable of regenerating in natural forests in large treefall gaps. In the same forests the shrub *Clidemia hirta* is also becoming quite common in natural forest gaps.

- Why do exotics matter in the general context of conservation of biodiversity? Increase in turnover rate has been observed (Phillips & Gentry 1994; Phillips *et al* 1994), potential rapid climatic change should result in increased intensity of disturbance, increased human pressure for firewood and forest products will all lead to conditions more favourable to known invasive woody species. Most of these species require a substantial amount of disturbance to spread extensively.

- If climate changes many areas of natural vegetation are isolated and species will fail to move to other islands.
- The conservation of biodiversity becomes increasingly significant in disturbed areas as areas of natural or semi-natural vegetation steadily decrease. In an overpopulated and resource hungry world secondary vegetation will become more and more important to the conservation of biodiversity. For instance in the British Isles motorway verges, railway embankments and abandoned quarries are now important assets to nature conservation.
- Susceptibility of natural areas to invasions is higher if a large seed source is available around it. The smaller the area of natural vegetation the more likely it is to be invaded.
- Data available from the tropics and subtropics on the incidence of invasions clearly show a higher reported number of cases in areas with more advanced economies and standards of living. This is probably not coincidental and rather reflects the large number of plants introduced and distributed in large numbers over wide geographical range for ornamental purposes. Assuming that the less developed world will increase its standards of living an ever increasing number of exotics species will be introduced to regions hitherto not widely affected by invasive species.

A combination of isolated natural areas surrounded by large tracts of potentially invasive species, higher human disturbance, higher natural disturbance, increased movement of exotic plants and potential impact of rapid climatic change (more important in areas without climatic gradients) will undoubtedly lead to an increased threat by introduced species.

Time lags

The populations of introduced species often remain small and localized for long periods of time before they exhibit very rapid expansion. Until very recently little evidence was available to support a number hypothetical explanations for these observed time lags or lag phases. The reasons for these time lags are threefold (Hobbs & Humphries 1995):

Leucaena leucocephala, noted for it's fast growth and productivity, has colonized thousands of acres throughout the tropics. (photo: C. Elevitch)

- genotypic adaptations
- cyclical disturbance or a combination of environmental conditions
- species, with exponential growth, not observed until the population reaches a critical size.

The time between the introduction of a species and its first record of spread and pest status in tropical invasive woody species varies, respectively, from 3 years to around 50 years and from 4 years to around 90 years (see table below). Most woody plant species were introduced between 1838 and 1937 with a peak in the late 19th century. No obvious differences are observed when the degree of invasiveness is taken into account. This data further supports the view that the existence as well as the duration of time lags is highly variable. A species may quickly become highly invasive even after it has already been present for a long time in a particular region.

In the tropics time lags appear to be much shorter (see table below) than those observed in temperate species. Kowarik (1995) reported that in the German Brandenburg province the average duration of the time lag between the introduction and the initiation of an invasion was 131 years and 170 years for, respectively, shrubs and trees.

Duration (in years) of known time lags between the introduction and first spread and pest status in tropical invasive woody plants.

Acacia nilotica	N. Australia, ca 1900	ca 57 yrs
Casuarina equisetifolia	Florida, ca 1900	ca 65 yrs
Cecropia peltata	Ivory Coast, 1910	69 yrs
Chromolaena odorata	Ivory Coast, ca 1955	ca 20 yrs
Cinchona succirubra	Galapagos, 1946	40 yrs
Lantana camara	Galapagos, 1938	40 yrs
Maesopsis eminii	East Africa, 1913	65 yrs
Miconia calvescens	Hawai'i, ca 1975	16 yrs
Mimosa pigra	N. Australia, ca 1880	ca 90 yrs
Pittosporum undulatum	Jamaica, 1883	105 yrs
Psidium guajava	Galapagos, 1858	90 yrs

Duration (in years) of known time lags between the introduction and first spread and pest status in tropical invasive woody plants.

Rubus sp.	Galapagos, 1983	4 yrs
Schinus terebinthifolius	Florida, 1898	75 yrs

In many cases the original introduction of a woody species was limited to one or a few individuals, but a number of subsequent introductions, usually consisting of many individuals, were made for a different purpose. For instance, in Hawai'i and Florida a few individuals of some tree species were planted as ornamentals but decades later the same species were either widely planted in forestry plantations or large quantities of seeds were aerially sown. Some of these species were observed to spread only following these secondary introductions.

The duration of the phase between the introduction of a species and its spread being so variable it is not possible to be certain that a species, although present for several decades, will not spread. For any particular region it is essential to understand the long-term disturbance regime as well as the specific ecology (inclusive of reproductive biology and regeneration requirements) of introduced species before any predictions can be made. Otherwise close monitoring of natural and semi/natural vegetation, particularly after exceptional disturbance events, is necessary for the early detection of new invasions.

Management Implications

Considering the difficulty in predicting the invasive potential of introduced species, it is therefore essential to look at the reasons and justifications for introducing plant species. Hughes (1994) has extensively discussed the pros and cons of species introductions and provided guidelines for the introduction or non-introduction of non native species. In case the introduction of a new species is the only means to satisfactorily fulfill a long-term need, Hughes (1994) suggested that it is then essential to make that its invasive potential will be as limited as possible. Procedures to reduce the risk of introducing a potentially invasive species should include extensive information searches prior to the proposed introduction and the establishment of limited trial plantings.

All introductions of non-indigenous plant species should be screened with great care in a process which considered the status in the native range and at other points of introduction. The following points require particular attention and should rapidly provide a clear indication to the introduced species invasive potential.

- Has the species or a related species has been reported as invasive elsewhere?
- How similar is the site of the proposed introduction to that of the species in its native and invaded regions? This includes comparisons of soil, climate, disturbance (both in terms of intensity and periodicity including that of fire, wind, flood) and human disturbance. Conditions favouring or limiting the species spread should be identified.
- Knowledge of the species reproductive biology is important and in particular that of seed production, seed longevity, and dispersal ability.
- Susceptibility of young individuals to grazing (e.g., whether the plant is thorny or not),
- Assessment of practical and effective methods of control in the case of weediness problems. The economics of control must be carefully considered.

If the above points indicate that the proposed species has no invasive potential an introduction may be considered. On the other hand if the proposed species exhibits invasive tendencies a strong justifications will have to be made for its introduction.

The following points are essential in detecting the early stages in an invasion:

1 awareness that the species is a problem in another region where climatic and environmental factors are similar,

2 first-hand knowledge in identifying and recognizing the species in the wild is essential, and

3 active governmental or voluntary organisation in the field of plant invasions is necessary to provide background response.

References

Binggeli, P. and Hamilton, A.C. 1990. Tree species invasions and sustainable forestry in the East Usambaras. In: Hedberg, I. & Persson, E. (Eds) Research for conservation of Tanzanian catchment forests, pp. 39–47. Uppsala Universitet Reprocentralen HSC, Uppsala.

Binggeli, P. & Hamilton, A.C. 1993. Biological invasion by Maesopsis eminii in the East Usambara forests, Tanzania. Opera Bot. 121, 229–235.

Chandrashekara, U.M. & Ramakrishnan, P.S. 1994. Successional patterns and gap phase dynamics of a humid tropical forest of the Western Ghats of Kerala, India: ground vegetation, biomass, productivity and nutrient cycling. Forest Ecol. Mgmt 70, 23–40.

Cronk, Q.C.B. 1989. The past and present vegetation of St Helena. In: J. Biogeogr. 16, 47–64.

Groves, R.H. 1986. Plant invasions of Australia: an overview. In Groves, R.H. & Burdon, J.J. (Eds) Ecology of biological invasions: an Australian perspective, pp. 137–149. Australian Academy of Science, Canberra.

Richardson D.M., P. Binggeli and G. Schroth. 2004. Plant invasions—problems and solutions in agroforestry. In: Schroth G., G. Fonseca, C.A. Harvey, C. Gascon, H. Vasconcelos and A.M. Izac (Eds) Agroforestry and biodiversity conservation in tropical landscapes, pp. 371-396. Island Press, Washington.

Hobbs, R.J. and Humphries, S.E. 1995. An integrated approach to the ecology and management of plant invasions. Conserv. Biol. 9, 761–770.

Hughes, C.E. 1994. Risks of species introductions in tropical forestry. In: Commonw. For. Rev. 73, 243–252.

Kowarik, I. 1995. Time lags in biological invasions with regard to the success and failure of alien species. In Pysek, P., Prach, K., Rejmánek, M. & Wade, P.M. (Eds) Plant invasions—general aspects and special problems, pp. 15–38. SPB Academic Publishing, Amsterdam.

Macdonald, I.A.W., Thébaud, C., Strahm, W. and Strasberg, D. 1991. Effects of alien plant invasions on native vegetation remnants on La Réunion (Mascarene Islands, Indian Ocean). Environ. Conserv. 18, 51–61.

Miller, I.L. and Lonsdale, W.M. 1987. Early records of Mimosa pigra in the Northern Territory. Pl. Prot. Quart. 2, 140–142.

Patil, M.S. and Kumar, H.D.M. 1990. Seed dispersion in subabul—a case study. Ind. Forester 116, 598–599.

Phillips, O.L. and Gentry, A.H. 1994. Increasing turnover through time in tropical forests. Science 263, 954–957.

Phillips, O.L., Hall, P., Gentry, A.H., Sawyer, S.A. and Vasquez, R. 1994. Dynamics and species richness of tropical rain forests. Proc. Natl. Acad. Sci. 91, 2805–2809.

Saxena, K.G. 1991. Biological invasions in the Indian subcontinent: review of invasion by plants. Ramakrishnan, P.S. (Ed.) Ecology of biological invasion in the tropics, pp. 53–73. International Scientific Publications, New Delhi.

Sheil, D. 1994. Invasive plants in tropical forests: warnings from the Amani Botanic Gardens, Tanzania. Bot. Gardens Conserv. News 2(3), 23–24.

Sussman, R.W. and Rakotozafy, A. 1994. Plant diversity and structural analysis of a tropical dry forest in southwestern Madagascar. Biotropica 26, 241–254.

Stone, C.P., Smith, C.W. and Tunison, J.T. (Eds) 1992. Alien plant invasions in native ecosystems of Hawai'i: management and research. University of Hawai'i Press, Honolulu.

Strahm, W. 1989. Plant red data book for Rodrigues. Koeltz Scientific Books, Konigstein.

Swarbrick, J.T. and Skarrett, D.B. 1994. The Bushweed 2 database of environmental weeds in Australia. The University of Queensland Gatton College.

Original Source

This article is excerpted with the kind permission of the authors from:

Binggeli, P., J.B. Hall, and J.R. Healey. 1998. An Overview of Invasive Woody Plants in the Tropics. School of Agricultural and Forest Sciences Publ. No. 13, University of Wales, Bangor. Web editions (August 2001):

http://www.safs.bangor.ac.uk/IWPT and http://members.tripod.co.uk/WoodyPlantEcology/

"This publication is an output from a research project funded by the United Kingdom Department for International Development (DFID) for the benefit of developing countries. R4742 Forestry Research Programme."

This excerpt was originally published as *The Overstory* #89

Tree Domestication

Roger R.B. Leakey

Throughout the tropics there are numerous perennial woody species that have provided indigenous peoples with many of their daily needs for millennia. Many of these people have now left the land for urban life, but they still demand traditional food, medicines, and other natural products. These traditionally important woody plants are virtually undomesticated.

These neglected "Cinderella" species have great genetic diversity and also play a key role in biological, chemical, and hydrological cycles, protecting soils and providing ecological niches. The food-producing species are also important for food security, especially in the dry season, as well as a source of vitamins and minerals critical for the health and nutrition of children and pregnant women.

There are four groups of wild trees, shrubs, and vines which could be rapidly domesticated for agroforestry and which can be viewed as potentially important sources of income for farmers. These trees produce:

1 The traditionally important wild foods, mostly fruits, nuts and leaves for vegetables;

2 The traditionally important fibers;

3 Locally and industrially important pharmaceuticals and other extractives such as gums and resins;

4 Commercially important quality timbers and woods.

The domestication of tree species is a dynamic process which develops from deciding which species to domesticate and proceeds through background socioeconomic studies, the collection of germplasm, genetic selection and improvement to the integration of domesticated species in land-use. Domestication is an ongoing process in which genetic and cultivation improvements are continuously refined. In genetic terms, domestication is accelerated and human-induced evolution. Domestication, however, is not only about selection. It integrates the four key processes of the identification, production, management, and adoption of tree resources.

Strategies for tree domestication will vary depending on the value of the products, the extent of genetic variation within a species, and many other factors.

For high-value species such as those producing marketable forest products the vegetative propagation of superior selections identified from within the existing wild populations will be appropriate. This is the approach generally followed in horticulture. Thus, an individual plant with superior yield, fruit flavor, stem form, or wood quality can be mass produced by vegetative propagation. In this way it is possible to select those clones likely to develop above-average characteristics in any given trait. By a series of ongoing selections and an ever-increasing intensity of selection, it is also possible to achieve rapid and substantial genetic improvements.

When identifying and selecting trees for cloning by vegetative propagation, there are two important criteria. It is important, 1) to ensure that those that are highly superior for the desired traits are chosen and, 2) to ensure that the selected individuals are unrelated and as genetically diverse in other traits as possible. This calls for strategy that allows intensive selection (e.g., 1 out of 100 to 10,000 trees) from among trees from different populations, ideally from throughout the range of the species. Furthermore, this should be an ongoing rolling program of multiple trait selection, in which more and more intensive selection is imposed through the addition of selection criteria for new traits while, at the same time, new sources of genetic stock are continually added as new genetic collections enter the program. These new collections should come from further exploration and from breeding programs and so continually broaden the genetic base of the planted trees. Molecular genetics techniques can be used to ensure that genetic diversity is maintained in the clones used for commercial production.

Selection procedures vary depending on the product and the situation. For example, for indigenous fruits, rapid progress will be made if indigenous knowledge can be used. Usually rural people know which are the best individual trees in their area for yield, fruit size, or flavor. Thus, as with temperate apples, pears, etc., people can be asked to report the existence of superior trees, so reducing the task of screening large numbers of trees. On the other hand, for medicinal trees, it is more likely that a chemical screening process will be required, but the magnitude of this task can probably be reduced by starting on a population basis, since it is likely that trees from certain environments will be richer in the required metabolites. Meanwhile, for timber trees, log size and straightness are the first selection criteria. Various forms of "plus-tree" (i.e., elite selection) provenance and progeny selection are well known. To these have recently been added some "predictive tests" which can be applied in the nursery as a procedure for mass screening from genetically diverse seedling populations. This involvement of farmers, however, has to be done for their ultimate benefit, in accordance with the Convention on Biological Diversity.

By capturing genetic diversity of a wide range of indigenous trees for growth in agroforestry systems, it is hoped the promises of agroforestry to alleviate poverty and to mitigate environmental degradation and the loss of biodiversity will be fulfilled.

Original Source

Reprinted with kind permission from the publisher. The original article "Agroforestry for Biodiversity in Farming Systems" in *Biodiversity in Agroecosystems*, W. W. Collins and C. O. Qualset (eds) ©CRC Press, Boca Raton, Florida. For order information on this title call (800) 272-7727 (in the US) or link to http://www.crcpress.com.

This excerpt was originally published as *The Overstory* #31.

Further Reading

Forest, Farm, and Community Tree Network (FACT Net). 1999. Domestication of Agroforestry Trees in Southeast Asia. Winrock International, 38 Winrock Drive, Morrilton, AR 72110-9370 USA Tel: 501-727-5435, Fax: 501-727-5417 Email: forestry@winrock.org, Web: http://www.winrock.org/forestry/factnet.htm

Diverse wild plants may become important food sources through selection and improvement. (photo: C. Elevitch)

Genetic Conservation of Tropical Trees

Gregory A. O'Neill, Ian Dawson, Carmen Sotelo-Montes, Luigi Guarino, and John C. Weber

Genetic erosion is the loss of genetic diversity within a species caused by human activities and environmental changes. Unsustainable forestry practices and high rates of land clearance for agriculture are causing genetic erosion of valuable tree species in the tropics. This process endangers the economic sustainability of rural communities and limits opportunities for the development of new timber and non-timber forest products. With a focus on local community involvement, this article covers potential utility and limitations of six low-input interventions to help forestall further tree genetic erosion.

Introduction

"The first rule of intelligent tinkering is to keep all the pieces."—Aldo Leopold

The tropics have the highest tree species diversity in the world (Gentry and Ortiz 1993). For example, over 200 tree species (>10 cm in diameter at breast height) per hectare have been recorded in parts of the upper Amazon (Gentry 1988). Tropical cultures are often heavily dependent on the many products and services these species provide: in a survey in the Peruvian Amazon, local farmers used more than 250 tree species and considered 155 of these as priorities for agroforestry (Sotelo-Montes and Weber 1997). In addition, numerous tropical tree species have promising national and international markets for fruit (Prance 1994; Villachica 1996), medicinal (Estrella 1995; Mejía and Rengifo 1995) and lumber products (Toledo and Rincon 1996). If appropriate cultivation techniques and markets were developed, these species could greatly assist in the economic development of some tropical regions (Anderson 1989; Castillo 1995; Leakey and Simons 1998).

Despite this, over-harvesting and other poor forestry practices in many areas of the tropics are reducing tree genetic diversity, thereby limiting the ability of both tropical and non-tropical societies to capitalize upon these valuable genetic resources. This note attempts to foster a dialogue regarding the potential utility and limitations of six interventions (agrofor-estry, domestication, woodlots, collection systems, seed zoning and in situ conservation areas) which aim to forestall further tree genetic erosion in the tropics—i.e., to "keep all the pieces," as Aldo Leopold has said. Where possible, attention has been placed on maximizing the role of farmers and other community members in interventions, so as to capitalize upon their knowledge and ensure their involvement.

Agroforestry

Expanding slash-and-burn agriculture by migration into forest areas is the primary cause of deforestation in many parts of the tropics (Brown and Pearce 1994). The increased, continuous and more diverse agricultural harvest associated with agroforestry (Denevan and Padoch 1987; Montagnini and Mendelsohn 1997) can increase farm productivity and profits, and thereby reduce subsistence land needs and forest encroachment by farmers (Portillo 1994; Scherr and Current 1997). For example, in Central America, farmers' profits were at least 10% greater in agroforestry systems relative to alternative land uses in 90% of cases examined.

Although the agronomic benefits of agroforestry systems have been demonstrated in many areas of the tropics, systems have often not been widely adopted (Scherr and Current 1997; Vosti et al 1997). Farmers' perceptions of food security risks, a lack of labour (Barton 1994), opportunity costs (Christoffersen 1989) and the potential lack of profitability (Current et al 1995) associated with agroforestry systems have been cited as factors inhibiting their adoption. In the Amazonian lowlands of Ecuador, lack of extension, credit, and product marketing have also been implicated (Follis and Nair 1994). In Central America, government regulation of tree harvesting and land tenure insecurity are disincentives for adoption (Current et al 1995). In order for the benefits of agroforestry to be realized, therefore, the causes of slow adoption will need to be addressed.

Genetic diversity and cone collection in the Amazon Basin of Peru. (photo: G. O'Neill)

Tree Domestication

By selecting and propagating the phenotypes that best suit their needs, farmers have been slowly domesticating trees for millennia. Modern domestication strategies can help meet the changing needs of farmers, resulting from increased land pressures and changing socio-economic conditions by increasing the productivity of tree plantings. Strategic approaches to domestication can help avoid the potential pitfalls of traditional methods, such as introducing narrow genetic bottlenecks, using maladapted materials or focusing on exotics (Weber *et al* 2001).

By conducting genetic trials on-farm, farmers may be more inclined to participate in them, particularly if the trials are designed in a way that they can be converted into seed production stands or produce other valuable products after the evaluation phase. Converting appropriately designed trials to seed production stands can also reduce the time required for improved germplasm to reach users, and stands can serve as ex situ genetic conservation sites.

The major limitation in using tree domestication to reduce genetic erosion may be the availability of sufficient quantities of high-quality planting stock (Si-

mons 1996). Few national government organizations and NGOs in the tropics are involved in tree domestication, and those efforts meet the needs of only a small fraction of tropical farmers. Larger-scale endeavours and the engagement of national organizations must be sought if tree domestication is to significantly reduce tree genetic erosion.

Woodlot Forestry

Selective extraction is the major form of logging practiced in much of the tropics. Logging of phenotypically superior individuals of commercial species removes the best genotypes from a population, leaving the poorest individuals of the least profitable species to produce seed for future generations.

Community- or farmer-based woodlot enterprises based on intensively managed tree plantations could supplant selective extraction as plantations are potentially more profitable. In addition, woodlot forestry may be more environmentally and economically sustainable than selective extraction or natural forest management (Bawa and Seidler 1998). Since most commercial tree species in the tropics are found at low-densities, woodlots, which have high marketable volume per hectare, could provide a timber supply with substantially lower extraction costs. In addition, management operations such as pruning, that add further value to timber, could be introduced. Investment costs could be reduced, and income and adoption rate increased, by locating woodlots on abandoned or degraded farms.

By promoting planting of well-known native timber species for the export market and developing markets for lesser-known native timber species, some of the logging pressures on the principal commercial species in wild stands may be deflected (Toledo and Rincon 1996). However, a number of issues remain to be addressed. First, if highly profitable, the promotion of woodlot forestry may actually increase deforestation if governments can not control activities on public land. Second, the long time required for most tree species to attain economic maturity may be a significant deterrent for poor farmers to adopt woodlot forestry. In order for woodlot forestry to reduce overall and selective extraction, therefore, several factors, including credit availability and land tenure, will need to be addressed (Current *et al* 1995).

Improved Seed Collection Systems

Seed collections for reforestation are frequently made from an insufficient number of trees, resulting in reduced genetic diversity. Moreover, seeds are often collected from trees that are the easiest to climb (i.e., the shortest and most crooked), which may result in slow-growing or poorly shaped progeny.

Seedlots collected from wild stands will continue to be of low quality unless regulation, training and monitoring programmes are established. National systems of tree seed registration should consider minimum standards for a) number of parent trees in each seedlot and seed bulking methods (Marshall and Brown 1975), b) separation distance between parent trees to minimize genetic relatedness (Dawson and Were 1997), c) yield and physiological quality of the harvested seed, d) health of the mother trees, and e) location data.

Strict standards for the documentation of collection localities will facilitate return to populations that perform well in particular environments, while populations that perform poorly can be avoided. Regulation of seed collection in this manner, however, will increase the cost of seed to consumers and re-

quires substantial investment in training and monitoring of collectors.

Cooperative seed collection is one approach to address the financial and logistical difficulties of implementing improved seed collection systems. For example, a cooperative invites farmers to collect seed from one or more of their "best" trees for a set of priority species. Collected seed is pooled by the cooperative and the genetically diverse pooled seedlots are then apportioned to contributors.

Demonstration plots that indicate the different performance of progeny collected from "good" or "bad" parental trees, or that illustrate the effect of genetic bottlenecks leading to inbreeding depression, can also be effective in illustrating to farmers and policymakers the value of good collection practices.

Seed Zones

When seed is planted away from its native environment, it may suffer from maladaptation, leading to pest attack, slow production or poor form, due to the new growing conditions. With the large investment in time and land area that tree planting demands, it is essential to ensure that planted germplasm is adapted to its planting environment.

Although the extent of maladaptation in most tropical plantations cannot be assessed because the original sources of seed are usually unknown, in some cases it is expected to be extensive. A seedlot registration system provides a simple method to minimize maladaptation by classifying administrative regions into ecologically similar "seed zones" and discouraging the transfer of seedlots across zones (Conkle 1997). In the absence of a well-defined ecological classification system, seed zones can be characterized based on climatic or elevation data.

Conservation Areas

Although natural forest areas are contracting, in situ reserves remain an important means of conserving intraspecific variation. Such reserves conserve ecosystem interactions, function as "workshops" for natural selection, and are sources of germplasm for recolonisation following catastrophic events. While establishment and management of *in situ* reserves has traditionally been the domain of formal national authorities, provincial and community delineated and managed reserves may significantly complement such schemes. A community approach may have particular value because indigenous resident managers may have an intimate knowledge of local biota and ecology (Pimbert and Pretty 1995) and recognise the value of conservation. Local knowledge may be applied in the identification of corridors between reserves or areas of high habitat value for target species. It may also be employed in designing management practices to produce conditions optimal for reproduction of target species.

Regardless of the mode of control of a reserve or reserve system, careful planning of the size, shape, location and composition of conservation areas can improve their integrity and viability (Harris 1984). Since many tropical forest trees, particularly in low-

Calycophyllum spruceanum **during a seed collection exercise in the Peruvian Amazon. It is an important timber species recognised as a high priority for research by farmers in the region in Peru. It is one of the species ICRAF has collected seed from, and an important focus of tree domestication and conservation activities. (photo: J. Weber © World Agroforestry Centre)**

land rainforests, occur at very low densities, their effective conservation in situ will require areas in the order of 2500 km² (Lawrence and Marshall 1997). Identification and management of areas of this size may require the support of national government and should be considered within the larger framework of integrated natural resource planning and economic and agricultural development policies.

The Challenge

Current land-use patterns and unsustainable forestry practices are eroding tree genetic resources in the tropics, reducing the economic options and food security of peoples in many developing nations. The interventions proposed in this article focus mainly on technical innovations to involve farmers and forest-dependent communities in conservation. However, social, political and economic factors (such as population growth, inequitable land and wealth distribution, and conflicting policies) may pose a greater threat to the conservation of genetic resources than do technical deficiencies (Ledig 1986). The challenge for the future, therefore, will be to engage all players—farmers, communities, governments and policy-makers—in approaches that protect these precious and often intangible genetic resources.

References

Anderson, A.B. (Editor). 1989. Alternatives to deforestation: steps toward sustainable use of the Amazon rain forest. Columbia University Press, New York.

Barton, D. 1994. Indigenous agroforestry in Latin America: a blueprint for sustainable agriculture. Natural Resources Institute, Chatham, U.K.

Bawa, K.S. and Seidler, R. 1998. Natural forest management and conservation of biodiversity in tropical forests. Conservation Biology 12: 46–55.

Brown, K., and Pearce, D.W. 1994. The Causes of Tropical Deforestation—The Economic and Statistical Analysis of Factors Giving Rise to the Los of the Tropical Forests. University of British Columbia Press, Vancouver BC, Canada.

Brush, S.B. 1991. A farmer-based approach to conserving crop germplasm. Econ. Bot. 45: 153–165.

Castillo, R.O. 1995. Plant genetic resources in the Andes: impact, conservation and management. Crop Science 35: 355–360.

Christoffersen, L.E. 1989. Agroforestry in Sub-Saharan Africa: a farmer's perspective. Environment Division, Technical Department, Africa Region, World Bank, Washington, DC, U.S.A.

Conkle, M.T. 1997. Zonificación de semillas en México. In Manejo de recursos genéticos forestales Edited by J.J.V. H., B.B. V., and F.T. Ledig. Colegio de Postgraduados, Montecillo, México y División de Ciencias Forestales, Universidad Autónoma Chapingo, Chapingo, México. pp. 67–88.

Cooper, D., Velleve, R., and Hobbelink, H. 1992. Growing diversity: genetic resources and local food security. Intermediate Technology Publications, London.

Current, D., Lutz, E., and Scherr, S.J. 1995. The costs and benefits of agroforestry to farmers. World Bank Research Observer 10: 151–180.

Dawson, I. and Were, J. 1997. Collecting germplasm from trees—some guidelines. Agroforestry Today 9: 6–9.

Denevan, W.M. and Padoch, C. 1987. Swidden-fallow agroforestry in the Peruvian Amazon. New York Botanical Gardens, New York, USA.

Estrella, E. 1995. Plantas medicinales amazónicas: realidad y perspectivas. Tratado de Cooperación Amazónica, Lima, Peru.

Follis, M.B. and Nair, P.K.R. 1994. Policy and institutional support for agroforestry: an analysis of two Ecuadorian case studies. Agroforestry Systems 27: 223–240.

Gentry, A.H. 1988. Tree species richness of upper Amazonian forests. Proc. U.S. Nat. Acad. Sci. 85: 156–159.

Gentry, A.H. and Ortiz, S.R. 1993. Patrones de composición florística en la Amazonia Peruana. In Amazonia Peruana –vegetación húmeda tropical en el llano subandino Edited by R. Kalliola, M. Puhakkaa, and W. Danjoy. Turku University Press, Turku, Finland. pp. 155–166.

Harris, L.D. 1984. The Fragmented Forest: Island Biogeography and the Preservation of Biotic Diversity. University of Chicago Press, Chicago, USA.

Lawrence, M.J. and Marshall, D.F. 1997. Plant population genetics. In Plant genetic conservation: the in situ approach Edited by N. Maxted, B.V. Ford-Lloyd, and J.G. Hawkes. Chapman and Hall, London, U.K. pp. 99–113.

Leakey, R.R.B. and Simons, A.J. 1998. The domestication and commercialization of indigenous trees in agroforestry for the alleviation of poverty. Agroforestry Systems 38: 165–176.

Ledig, F.T. 1986. Conservation strategies for forest gene resources. For. Ecol. Manag. 14: 77–90.

Marshall, D.R. and Brown, A.D.H. 1975. Optimum sampling strategies in genetic conservation. In Crop genetic resources for today and tomorrow. Edited by O.H. Frankl and J.G. Hawkes. Cambridge University Press, Cambridge. pp. 53–80.

Mejía, K. and Rengifo, E. 1995. Plantas Medicinales de Uso Popular en la Amazonia Peruana. Agencia Española de Cooperación Internacional and Instituto de Investigaciones de la Amazonía Peruana, Lima, Peru.

Montagnini, F. and Mendelsohn, R.O. 1997. Managing forest fallows: improving the economics of swidden agriculture. Ambio 26: 118–123.

Pimbert, M.P. and Pretty, J.N. 1995. Parks, people and professionals: putting "participation" into protected area management. Discussion paper No. 57. United Nations Research Institute for Social Development.

Portillo, Z. 1994. Sustainable farming in the Peruvian Amazon. IDRC Reports 22: 21–23.

Prance, G.T. 1994. Amazonian tree diversity and the potential for supply of non-timber forest products. In Tropical Trees: The Potential for Domestication and the Rebuilding of Forest Resources. Proceedings of a conference organized by the Edinburgh Centre for Tropical Forests. Edited by R.R.B. Leakey and A.C. Newton. HMSO, Edinburgh, U.K. pp. 7–15.

Scherr, S.J. and Current, D. 1997. What make agroforestry profitable for farmers? Evidence from Central America and the Caribbean. Agroforestry Today 9: 10–15.

Simons, A.J. 1996. Delivery of improvement for agroforestry trees. In Tree Improvement for Sustainable Tropical Forestry. Proceedings of a conference organized by the Queensland Forestry Research Institute. Edited by M.J. Dieters, C.A. Matheson, G.D. Nikles, C.E. Harwood, and S.M. Walker. pp. 391–400.

Sotelo-Montes, C. and Weber, J.C. 1997. Priorización de especies arbóreas para sistemas agroforestales en la selva baja del Perú. Agroforestería en las Américas 4: 12–17.

Toledo, E. and Rincon, C. 1996. Utilización Industrial de Nuevas Especies Forestales en el Perú. Cámara Nacional Forestal, Lima, Peru.

Weber, J.C., Sotelo Montes, C., Vidaurre, H., Dawson, I.K., and Simons, A.J. 2001. Participatory domestication of agroforestry trees: an example from the Peruvian Amazon. Development in Practice 11(4):425–433.

Villachica, H. 1996. Frutales y Hortalizas Promisorios de la Amazonía. Number 44. Secretaria Pro-Tempore, Tratado de Cooperacion Amazónica, FAO project GCP/RLA/118/NET.

Vosti, S.A., Witcover, J., Oliveira, S., and Faminow, M. 1997. Policy issues in agroforestry: technology adoption and regional integration in the western Brazilian Amazon. Agroforestry Systems 38: 195–222.

Yanchuk, A.D. and Lester, D.T. 1996. Setting priorities for conservation of the conifer genetic resources of British Columbia. Forestry Chronicle 72: 406–415.

Original Source

This article has been abridged from the original by the authors with the permission of Kluwer Academic Publishers (http://www.wkap.nl/):

O'Neill, G.A, I. Dawson, C. Sotelo-Montes, L. Guarino, and J.C. Weber. 2001. Strategies for genetic conservation of trees in the Peruvian Amazon. In: Biodiversity and Conservation 10: 837–850.

This excerpt was originally published as *The Overstory* #97.

Trees for Urban Planting:
Diversity, Uniformity, and Common Sense

Frank S. Santamour, Jr.

Our forefathers planted American elms throughout the towns and cities of eastern United States. Rather than being an unconsidered idea, our early horticulturists were taking advantage of the beauty and adaptability of a native tree that Thomas Jefferson called "Nature's noblest vegetable." The accidental introduction of Dutch elm disease and the consequent destruction of millions of city trees served not only to find replacements for American elm, but also to focus attention on urban forests.

We will not, and indeed should not, replace American elm with any single tree species in the quantities previously allotted to American elm. Instead, we need a diversity of trees in our urban forests, not only to guard against disasters like Dutch elm disease, but also to "put the right tree in the right place" as the evolution of our cities and suburbs creates new sites and settings for tree planting.

If we are to plant and sustain city forests that will delight and inspire the residents and visitors in our urban centers, we need both diversity and uniformity of plant material to reduce the costs of maintenance and reduce the use of potentially dangerous pesticides. We need to plant more of the superior trees developed through genetic research and utilize the practical experience of practitioners of urban forestry. We have to plan the planting of city trees, and understand the problems and potentials of our actions.

The Ten-percent Solution

In recent years, there has arisen a dictum that "Thou shalt not plant more than 10% of any species" in a particular area. Generally, that area is undefined, but for a municipal arborist or city forester it can be interpreted as being within the boundaries of his or her responsibility. I am not sure who first propounded the "10% rule", nor am I sure that anyone would want to take credit for it, but it is not a bad idea. However, in an example city of 100,000 trees, 10,000 trees each of 10 species still represents a large degree of uniformity.

The 10% rule is a reaction to the possibility that some major insect or disease pest could, at some point in time, virtually wipe out the trees in a city. In general, the rule is considered a safeguard against a new pest that might be introduced from a foreign country. The American experience with Dutch elm disease and chestnut blight is sufficient to explain our concern about such epidemics. More recently (although the jury is still out in regard to its origin), the continuing spread of dogwood anthracnose disease on our native *Cornus florida* has caused great alarm.

There are also many native insect and disease problems that we are well aware of and must consider as potential threats to the urban forest. While a complete listing of such pests is beyond the scope of this paper, a few examples may suffice: oak wilt and obscure scale on oaks, fire blight on trees of the rose family, borers in white and green ash, sycamore anthracnose on *Platanus* species and hybrids, and the elm leaf beetle on elms. Some of these pests can be lethal, but all pests may contribute to the suboptimal growth and appearance of host trees.

In addition, there are also many known pests, native and introduced, with such a broad host range that a diversity of species, or even genera, will not discourage them. Among these are the gypsy moth, "evergreen" bagworm, Japanese beetle, *Armillaria* root rot, *Verticillium* wilt, and various nematodes. Thus, while the 10% rule may serve as a target or goal to soothe the consciences of city councils and municipal arborists, it will not solve all potential pest problems nor guarantee the long-term stability and esthetics of the urban forest. The 10% rule alone, while reasonable, simply does not address the realities of host-pest relationships.

Monocultures, Clones, and Cultivars

To begin, let us deal with a few terms that must be properly understood if we are going to communicate our thoughts and results.

It is almost universally agreed that tree monocultures are bad, even though those who espouse this wisdom may not agree on what a monoculture really is. We can start with the premise that a monoculture consists of large numbers (hundreds, thousands, millions) of plants of the same species growing in a restricted area. From this perspective, we would have to conclude that monocultures are the fundamental basis of agriculture.

There are several reasons for agriculture's reliance on genetic uniformity. One of the principal reasons is that most crop plants grown on a large scale are the products of generations of genetic research to breed and select plants that are resistant to major pests and are adaptable to specific localities. The inherent superiority of these plants and the uniformity of reliability in sowing, culture, and harvesting suggests using monocultures. Also, most agricultural plants are annuals, and if pest problems do arise, an army of scientists is ready to battle the pest, usually successfully, with new genetic combinations, chemicals, or biocontrol agents.

The city forester is not as fortunate as the farmer. Few trees currently grown and sold as clones in the nursery trade have been purposely developed and thoroughly tested for pest resistance. The trees must endure for decades in frequently difficult situations where environmental and biotic stresses are continually changing. The development of a new "replacement" for a clone, with similar characteristics of growth and pest resistance may require decades of research.

Some of the clones (trees on their own roots) now available for city planting were originally selected for certain esthetic reasons, propagated by budding and grafting, and marketed as named cultivars. Clones may not be cultivars, and cultivars may not be clones: and the distinctions between clones and cultivars have been discussed in an earlier paper (Santamour, 1976). All it takes to make a clone a cultivar is the application of a name to that biological entity. All it takes to make a grafted cultivar a clone is to put it on its own roots.

A grafted cultivar is genetically uniform above ground, and it is likely that all trees of a given cultivar will possess the same degree of resistance or susceptibility to biotic or abiotic influences. However, the use of seedling understocks, whether of the same or a different species, introduces an element of diversity that might affect tree performance. Certainly, one of the major functions of a root system is the absorption and transport of water and mineral nutrients to the tree. Genetic variation among rootstocks must have profound effects on cultivar performance. Of course, those effects are seldom so drastic that the distinctive morphological characteristics for which the cultivar was originally selected are altered to the point that the cultivar is no longer recognizable.

In summary, tree monocultures may only pose major problems when the numbers of trees are large and the area occupied by the trees is restricted. Twenty to fifty trees of a single species, or even a single clone, planted along a few blocks of city streets do not constitute a "dangerous" monoculture. Genetic uniformity within a species is to be desired, especially when the clones, cultivars, or seedlings have proved to possess certain desirable characteristics. Genetic diversity is achieved by mixtures of uniformity, and will be discussed later.

Advantages of Cultivars

Cultivars are named selections. In landscape trees, a cultivar is generally propagated by budding or grafting scions from a single plant species. The above ground portion of all trees will be genetically identical, but there will be genetic variability among rootstocks.

The most obvious advantage of cultivars is their reliability, especially those cultivars that have been in the nursery trade for 20 years or more. They can be counted on to develop the form, color, and growth rate for which they were selected. Their longevity in the trade and their widespread planting has provided the testing necessary to determine both their good and bad characteristics. The urban tree planter knows what to expect of such trees.

One other characteristic of most cultivars, especially those that had been traditionally propagated by budding and grafting, is their genetic capacity for strong wound compartmentalization. Our studies (Santamour 1984, 1986) have shown that every cultivar tested, in a wide range of genera and species, were strong compartmentalizers. The conclusion was made that the grafting and budding process constituted an inadvertent screening and only strong compartmentalizing trees would be amenable to long - term commercial propagation by these techniques. Some of the cultivars formerly propagated by budding and grafting are now propagated on their own roots and have, of course, retained this important trait. On the other hand, cultivars of genera or species that had traditionally been propagated from cuttings (e.g., poplars, willows) were not subject to the "screening" process and may be either weak or strong compartmentalizers.

Interspecific and Intergeneric Diversity

If we are planting and managing the urban forest to minimize potential pest problems, we must look at host-pest relationships. Pests tend to follow the taxonomic categories of host plants at the species, section, series, genus, or family levels. Let us consider the genus as the major taxonomic category. The fact that we refer to many pests with host-generic names (Dutch elm disease, oak wilt, bronze birch borer, maple anthracnose) indicates that many species of the host genus are susceptible to those pests. Thus, the 10% (species) rule offers little protection against potential epidemics. Could we amend the 10% rule to include genera?

In a way, we have already done this. In many genera, only a single species in widely planted in urban landscapes: *Ginkgo biloba, Gleditsia triacanthos, Pyrus calleryana, Tilia cordata, Sophora japonica, Liriodendron tulipifera, Liquidambar styraciflua,* and *Zelkova serrata.* This is intergeneric diversity. There are relatively few tree genera in which there are several species with proven value as urban trees, most notably maples (*Acer* spp.) and oaks (*Quercus* spp.). The maples are divided by taxonomists into about 20 botanical sections, and the oaks into five subgenera. With few exceptions, hybridization between species belonging to these different categories does not occur; thus there may be important genetic differences among such species, The three most widely planted maples (red maple (*Acer rubrum*), sugar maple (*A. saccharum*), Norway maple (*A. platanoides*)) belong to three different sections, yet they are all susceptible in some degree to maple anthracnose disease. We know that red oaks (subgenus *Erythrobalanus*) may be more susceptible to oak wilt than the white oaks (subgenus *Lepidobalanus*) and that white oaks may be more susceptible to gypsy moth than red oaks. But there are notable and important exceptions to this generalization. Therefore, the quantity of trees planted in any particular genus must also be limited.

The next taxonomic category above the genus is the family. Generally, in urban America, trees of one ge-

nus of a particular family are planted in preference to others, e.g.: more *Quercus* than *Fagus* (beech) in the Fagaceae, more *Betula* (birch) than *Alnus* (alder) in the Betulaceae. There are, however, two large families that must be considered, the rose family (Rosaceae) and the legumes (Leguminosae or Fabaceae).

Leguminous trees include *Albizia, Cercis, Cladrastis, Gleditsia, Gymnocladus, Labumum, Maackia, Robinia,* and *Sophora.* Actually these genera can also be classified in three subfamilies or, indeed, into three separate families and there may be limited similarity among genera in host-pest relationships. Still, both *Gleditsia triacanthos* and *Albizia julibrissin* (mimosa) are highly susceptible to the so-called mimosa webworm.

Tree genera in the Rosaceae include *Amelanchier, Crataegus, Malus* (mostly crab apples in urban planting), *Prunus* (mostly cherries), *Pyrus* (mostly E. *calleryana*), and *Sorbus.* It would be extremely difficult to apply the "species" rule to the various cultivated *Crataegus, Malus,* and *Prunus* since "many (if not most) of the cultivars of these genera are really interspecific hybrids of unknown parentage. Of greater importance, however, is that trees of *Amelanchier, Crataegus, Malus,* and *Pyrus* are all potentially susceptible to the bacterial disease "fire blight". It is, therefore, likely that a "new" disease or insect pest may find a wide range of hosts in this family.

Thus, we can see that genetic diversity within a species is no safeguard against potential pest problems, generic diversity is most important, and family diversity must also be taken into account.

The 10–20–30 Formula

A broader diversity of trees is needed in our urban landscapes to guard against the possibility of large-scale devastation by both native and introduced insect and disease pests. Urban foresters and municipal arborists should use the following guidelines for tree diversity within their areas of jurisdiction. For maximum protection against the ravages of "new" pests or outbreaks of "old" pests the urban forest should contain:

1   No more than 10% of any single tree species.
2   No more than 20% of species in any tree genus.
3   No more than 30% of species in any tree family.

Strips or blocks of uniformity (species, cultivars, or clones of proven adaptability) should be scattered throughout the city to achieve spatial as well as biological diversity.

Common Sense

For uniformity, use clones and cultivars that have been in the nursery trade for a long time and that have proven their reliability. Use some of the newer introductions that have been developed through scientific research and that have been selected for survival traits such as pest resistance or salt tolerance. Use somewhat cautiously and on a trial basis some of the untested new cultivars of unfamiliar species or genera.

For uniformity, use seedlings of known geographic origin (or, in the case of exotics like *Tilia cordata*, from proven seed sources) so that the plants will be able to tolerate the general climatic conditions in your area.

For diversity, use the best clones, cultivars, and seedlings of many species and genera either as scattered strips or blocks of uniformity distributed throughout the city or as mixtures of individual trees along parkways and in parks.

For the education of The Next Generation, plant a wide variety of trees (e.g., catalpa, hickory, horsechestnut, sassafras, and even thorny honeylocust) in park areas that can and should be used to stimulate an interest in the diversity of Nature.

References

Santamour, F.S., Jr. 1976. Clone vs. cultivar: the root of the problem. Amer. Nurseryman, 144 (4): 20, 36.

Santamour, F.S., Jr. 1984. Wound compartmentalization in cultivars of Acer, Gleditsia, and other genera. J. Environ. Hort. 2:126–128.

Santamour, F.S., Jr. 1986. Wound compartmentalization in tree cultivars: addendum. J. Arboriculture, 12:227–232.

Santamour, F.S., Jr. 1988a. Graft compatibility in woody plants: an expanded perspective. J. Environ. Hort. 6:27–32.

Santamour, F.S., Jr. 1988b. Graft compatibility related to cambial peroxidase isozymes in Chinese chestnut. J. Environ. Hort. 6:33–39.

Santamour, F.S., Jr. 1988c. Cambial peroxidase enzymes related to graft compatibility in red oak. J. Environ. Hort. 6:87–93.

Santamour, F.S., Jr. 1989. Cambial peroxidase enzymes related to graft compatibility in red maple. J. Environ. Hort. 7:8–14.

Original Source

This article was adapted with the kind permission of the publisher and sponsoring organization (USDA-ARS, U.S. National Arboretum) from:

Santamour, Frank S., Jr. 1990. Trees for Urban Planting: Diversity, Uniformity, and Common Sense. Proc. 7th Conf. Metropolitan Tree Improvement Alliance (METRIA) 7:5765.

For more information about METRIA, visit http://www.ces.ncsu.edu/fletcher/programs/nursery/metria/

This excerpt was originally published as *The Overstory* #126.

Essentials of Good Planting Stock

Norman Jones

The extent of the world land base that is being reforested or afforested is significant and is growing still.
Unfortunately, several of these efforts are wasted in
planting poor quality trees. While some problems
are beyond the forester's control—inclement
weather, insect attacks, disease outbreaks, animal
browse, and the like—others fall within the forester's
influence. Two such areas are seed collection, and
planting stock preparation and selection. Measures
outlined here provide basic guidelines that will help
the forester ensure a cost-effective means of producing high quality seedlings.

A Measure of Quality

The basic goal of having quality seedlings is to
achieve the best growth possible and have the highest amount of desired outputs. Outputs can be timber, food, fuel, fodder or other uses such as site improvement. Seedling quality is gauged by two
factors: one, by the genetic make-up of the parent
stock and secondly by the physical growth, which is
influenced by the seedling's immediate environment
(i.e., nursery conditions and practices).

Selection for desirable genetic traits takes place in
the field at seed collection sites. When done properly, field selection will provide the best possible
seeds, containing the desired inherent traits seen in
the parent stock. Care in seed selection and collection will also reduce the amount of undesirable stock
coming from physically poor or damaged seed. Aside
from genetic traits, a seedling also displays physical
traits including sturdiness, good form, health and
vigor. Many of these traits, which are affected by
nursery practices, are within the forester's control.

Benefits Outweigh Extra Cost, Effort

Nursery-grown stock requires investment in infrastructure, staff training and skilled management.
The level of these costs relate to the type of nursery
stock produced, species growth responses and the
number of trees produced. But, the potential benefits of good nursery practices far outweigh their

costs. For instance, properly developed seedlings
stand a better chance of survival both in the nursery
and when replanted in the field.

In the long term, quality stock will also produce a
faster, higher return for the desired outputs. These
outputs may include products such as fuelwood,
building materials, industrial cellulose, animal fodder, erosion control, and soil and microclimate improvement. Given these benefits, seedling costs are a
small portion of the end-product value of plantations. Conversely, slackened efforts at ensuring stock
quality will result in lost opportunity throughout the
life of the plantation. Low-quality seedlings will experience slow growth after transplanting and add to
weeding and maintenance costs. In addition, the
trees will be less able to resist disease and insects and
will have smaller product yields.

Poor plant quality will result in uneven development
throughout the nursery and increase costs through
excessive culling needs. In addition, suboptimal
quality will increase the risk of losing the seedlings,
requiring a renewed effort or, at worse, cancel the
project due to lack of adequate seedlings.

Common Principles

Regardless of the size of the tree planting effort, several common techniques can be applied to ensure
the best planting stock quality possible. The techniques are applicable across a wide range of climate
and soil variations.

The application of good practices must begin when
the project, large or small, is planned and must continue through to outplanting in the field. In all cases,
everything that can be done, should be done, within
reasonable limits of time and capital constraints.

Seeking Optimum Growth

To ensure quality stock, a series of steps must be followed beginning with the planning stages and carrying through to outplanting in the field. Oftentimes
foresters or nursery managers focus their efforts on
only a few steps of the process. Under such circumstances, nursery stock may still grow. But the omis-

sion of any steps will slow the seedlings' progress and produce stock of suboptimal quality.

Such marginal results are unacceptable in light of the time and costs required to produce a forest crop. In fact, the best nursery managers take the trouble to visit field plantations and take pride in the way their plants have responded to the harshness of the real world. To ensure quality stock, a series of steps must be followed, beginning with the planning stages and carrying through to outplanting in the field.

Identifying Weaknesses

Lack of knowledge may be the greatest hindrance to producing consistent quality in growing stock. Indeed, due to the rapidly expanding planting programs, many foresters have never seen a truly high-quality seedling population. Small-scale projects that have minimal resources are particularly vulnerable to lack of proper information for nursery planning, management, operations, and problem solving. Such information voids may be further compounded by inexperienced labor or lack of supervisory skills. Again, because of the lengthy time frame involved between field planting and harvesting, there is little room for error or omission in nurseries.

Producing the Best Possible Plants

The forester must keep the primary objective in mind: to grow the best possible uniform seedlings, for the highest plantation outputs, for the least possible cost. Of course, cost and seedling quality must be carefully balanced. The best plants are derived from consistent nursery practices that produce uniform growth throughout the seedling crop. Such practices include all the elements involved in nursery operations—watering, soil mixes, root pruning, weeding, and the like. The demands of planting schedules alone leave little room for inconsistencies. For example, if seedling growth is not carefully monitored, so that abnormalities can be detected and corrected, seedling development may vary widely.

As a result, some stock may be underdeveloped when planting season arrives and the opportunity for using the stock will be lost. Moreover, it is a fallacy to believe increased watering or fertilization sched-

ules can correct the inadequacies of genetically poor stock that appears underdeveloped. A nursery manager can compound the problem if he keeps these underdeveloped seedlings for later use when "they are big enough." This is wrong. Never plant seedlings which have been held back for extra time.

What Does Good Planting Stock Look Like?

The prime targets are plant uniformity and health. Uniformity means there are few differences from plant to plant in height, stem thickness, the number and relative size of leaves. Health refers to both color and damage. Leaf and stem colors are often characteristic for a species and damage should be easily identified because parts may be eaten by insects or discolored by fungi.

Good planting stock can make the difference between success and failure. (photo: C. Elevitch)

Original Source

For the full version of this article, originally published by the World Bank (ASTAG), including more tips on nursery establishment and management, visit http://www.agroforester.com/articles/articles.html.

This excerpt was originally published as *The Overstory* #43.

Twelve Tree Myths

Alex L. Shigo

If we can understand more completely how trees function, then our work will be more enjoyable and profitable and our efforts to maintain healthy trees will be more effective.

Natural systems have more variables than any other system on earth. The responsibility of tree care professionals is to manage a large part of that system in ways that will benefit all members of the system. Not an easy task! Because there are so many parts of the natural systems that are beyond our regulation, we need every bit of clarity, exactness, and sound understanding of those parts we can regulate. Then, and only then, will we be able to manage tree systems, and environmental systems, in ways that ensure high quality survival for all the connected members.

Myth is used here to include misconceptions, misunderstandings, and half-truths

Many of the corrections to the myths listed here are known by many people. I believe the myths persist because many of the myths taken alone appear trivial or a matter of semantics. However, each myth is like a thread. When a hundred or more weak threads are used to make a fabric called a profession, the profession will only be as strong as the threads that form it.

Myth 1: Forests Are Groups of Trees.
Forests are highly ordered connections of many living communities with trees. The connections ensure survival of the trees and their associates.

Myth 2: Nature Is Balanced.
Balanced means the equalization of opposing forces. Natural systems survive because they are in continuing states of dynamic equilibrium. They vibrate. They adjust to a continuing feedback process for survival. Natural systems are not balanced in the sense of no motion or no change. They are not static.

Myth 3: Wood Is Dead.
In living trees there are more living cells in sapwood than dead cells. There are no living cells in heartwood, wetwood, discolored wood, and false heartwood. Wood is a highly ordered arrangement of living, dying, and dead cells. The cell walls are made up of cellulose, lignin, and hemicelluloses. Vessels and tracheids are very large compared to axial and radical parenchyma cells. Vessels, fibers, and tracheids live only a short time. Therefore, on a volume basis, sapwood is mostly dead, and on a number-of-cell basis, sapwood is mostly alive.

Myth 4: Photosynthesis Is Most Active During Bright, Hot Days over 100°F (38°C).
Photosynthesis decreases rapidly as temperatures begin to exceed 100°F (38°C). For photosynthesis to occur, guard cells must be open to receive carbon dioxide. When guard cells are open, moisture leaves the plant.

Myth 5: Water Causes Rot.
Microorganisms cause rot. Moisture at very precise amounts is a requirement for decay. Too much or too little moisture does not support decay. The high moisture content of wood in living trees is a protection feature against the spread of decay.

Myth 6: Roots Are the Most Important Part of a Tree.
Roots and the trunk with a crown of leaves are equally important; dynamic equilibrium. The roots (woody, nonwoody) and the crown (branches, leaves) act as a seesaw in motion. The seesaw functions only so long as it is going upward and downward. So it is with roots and crown. Each is dependent on the other, and the tree system survives

If we understand how trees function, working with trees will be more effective and rewarding. Pictured: Inocarpus fagifer. (photo: C. Elevitch)

because there is a continuing dynamic equilibrium between roots and crown. To say one portion is more important than the other indicates a complete lack of understanding of the way the tree system functions.

Myth 7: Ants Speed Up the Decay Process.
Ants keep their galleries very clean and in so doing they slow the decay process. Ants live in the tree and eat elsewhere. Termites "eat" in the tree and live elsewhere. (Some tropical termites live in nests on tree branches, but they still live outside the tree.)

Myth 8: All Insects and Fungi that Live on, in, and about Trees Are Harmful.
It is difficult to have an exact percentage, but roughly less then one percent of the insects and fungi and live on, in, and about trees are harmful. Insects are

highly beneficial for pollination. Thousands of fungus species are beneficial as symbiotes in mycorrhizae. Bacteria and actinomycetes form nodules that fix nitrogen. Decay fungi rot the base of dead branches and aid in shedding. The list goes on and on. The major point here is to make certain that we do not kill the ninety-nine percent while pursuing the one percent.

Myth 9: A Healthy Tree is a Tree Free of Infections.
A tree can be very healthy and still have thousands of infections. The infections will be walled off or compartmentalized. Isolations for microorganisms from the compartmentalized tissues usually yield bacteria and fungi. Health means the ability to resist strain. Strain means the irreversible point beyond stress. Stress means that reversible point where a system

begins to operate near the limits for which it was designed.

Myth 10: All Wood-product Problems Start after the Tree Is Cut.

Most wood-product problems start in the living tree. The problem here is that most studies on wood-product problems have started with the products, not with the living trees. The patterns of decay in products usually follow the patterns set in the living tree. But, if the living tree patterns are not understood first, then the products problems cannot be related to the tree. For example, wood altered only slightly in the living tree will be the wood first to absorb moisture in the product.

Myth 11: Fertilizer Is Tree Food.

This is a half truth were the wrong half has become the accepted part. Fertilizers provide elements that are essential for growth. Fertilizers do *not* provide an energy source for trees and other plants.

A food is any substance that provides the essentials for life; an adequate source of elements that are essential, but do not provide energy, and other types of elements that do provide energy (carbohydrates). Unlike animals, trees are able to trap the energy of the sun in a molecule called glucose. *This* is the essential energy source for the tree.

From the soil, trees obtain water and other elements that are essential for life. These do not provide an energy source for the tree.

Yes, soil elements in many chemical combinations can and do provide energy for bacteria and bacteria-like organisms. But trees do not work that way. Correct fertilization should consider the tree and its age and condition, the soil type and pH, the elements lacking in the soil, and the desires of the tree owner. The variables are almost endless.

The entire subject of fertilizers needs a thorough "clean up." Many people do not understand the numbers given to N, P, and K on bags of "plant food!" It is beyond the scope of this publication to try to clarify the subject here (see Shigo, 1991).

Myth 12: Anybody Can Plant a Tree Correctly!

The rush is on to plant trees. Kings, queens, presidents, governors, and many organizations worldwide are telling people to plant trees. The implication is that everybody knows how to plant a tree correctly. However, incorrect planting procedures, and planting the wrong tree in the wrong place, have caused a multitude of tree problems worldwide.

Yes, trees should be planted. They should be planted correctly.

If correct planting procedures are not known, then trees should be planted under the supervision of someone who understands how to plant correctly, and who also understands the concept of the right tree in the right place. And, after planting, a continuing health care schedule should be maintained.

Reference

Shigo, A.L. 1991. Modern Arboriculture: a systems approach to the care of trees and their associates. Shigo and Trees, Associates. Durham, New Hampshire 03824-3105, USA.

Original Source

This excerpt is adapted from *100 Tree Myths* with the kind permission of the author. The full text, including numerous photographs and figures can be ordered from Shigo and Trees, Associates, P.O. Box 769, Durham, NH 03824, USA. Tel: 603-868-7459; Fax: 603-868-1045.

This chapter was originally published as *The Overstory* #68.

Some Tree Basics

Alex L. Shigo

Understanding how to plant trees and planting the right tree in the right place are essential for tree planting success. Here are some key "tree basics."

Trees are plants that are:

- perennial—live for several to many years
- woody—have tough cell walls of wood
- shedding—use and shed woody and non-woody parts
- compartmented—made up of many compartments.
- usually have a single stem over three yards (meters) tall (shrubs usually have many stems less than three yards (meters) tall.)

Some champion trees:

- Giant sequoia (*Sequoiandendron giganteum*): Some over 2000 tons
- Swamp ash (*Eucalyptus regnans*): Some almost 300 feet (90 meters) tall
- Monkeypod (*Albizia saman*): Some trees with crown diameters of almost 200 feet (60 meters)
- Banyan (*Ficus benghalensis*): It takes 10 minutes to walk around the perimeter of the crown of a giant banyan tree in Calcutta
- Bristlecone pine (*Pinus longaeva*): Some are thought to be over 5000 years old

A Brief Overview of Some Unique Features of Trees

Trees are the tallest, most massive, longest-lived organisms ever to grow on earth.

Trees, like other plants, cannot move. However, trees, unlike other plants, are big, woody, and perennial, which means they are easy targets for constant wounding.

Trees are super survivors mainly because they grow in ways that give them defense systems that are highly effective against infections from wounds.

Trees have the capacity to adjust rapidly to changes that threaten their survival.

Animals move to get food, water, and shelter. They move to avoid destructive agents. When animals are injured and infected, processes of restoration and repair start. Animals heal after wounding.

When trees are injured and infected, processes of boundary formation start. Trees do not restore or repair wood that is injured and infected. In this sense, trees do not heal. Instead, trees compartmentalize wound infections.

Understanding trees is essential for tree planting success. (photo: C. Elevitch)

Compartmentalization is the tree's best defense process after injuries where boundaries form that resist the spread of infections. The boundaries also protect systems involving water, air, energy storage, and mechanical support. In a sense, the boundaries are like an inside bark.

To support their massive systems for long periods, trees require high amounts of energy. Trees trap more of the sun's energy than any other groups of organisms. In a sense, trees are like big batteries, the biggest on earth.

Trees use energy very efficiently with almost no waste. They pass energy on to many associates, and the associates provide many benefits in return to the trees. Trees help soils to remain healthy.

Trees, as big batteries, store energy as insoluble starch and oils in living cells in the wood of branches, trunks, and other woody roots. The wood itself is a form of stored energy for other organisms because cellulose is made of long twisting chains of glucose—sugar.

In animals, a process of programmed cell death regularly takes place. Dead cells are broken down and eliminated. Other processes form new living cells in the same positions of those that died. Animals are regenerating systems. Regenerating means new cells form in old places.

Trees are generating systems. Generating means new cells form in new places. In trees, the woody framework consists of highly ordered connections of living and dead cells. Some dead cells function for liquid transport. Other dead cells maintain mechanical support, and hold water. Unlike animals that are constantly replacing dead cells, trees incorporate dead cells into their framework.

Trees regulate their growth within the limits of available energy, water, elements, and space. Trees do not grow beyond their means. Trees use and shed leaves and needles, reproductive parts, nonwoody rots, and dead twigs, branches, and woody roots.

Trees in nature are connected with each other and with many communities of other organisms in ways that ensure long-term survival for the trees and their associates. This system is called a natural forest.

Some Correct Planting Procedures for Trees

1. Select healthy trees Money is wasted when you buy or plant trees that have roots crowded or crushed in bags or containers. Check roots before you buy or plant. If only a few roots are crushed, remove them with a sharp cut.

2. Plant the right tree in the right place *Do   not* plant large-maturing trees near buildings or power lines. Money is wasted when trees are topped or mutilated later. If a tree must be planted near power lines, plant only dwarf or low, compact species or varieties. Talk to knowledgeable people about the many choices you have for trees that have mature shapes and sizes that will fit your planting site.

3. Plant properly

DO:
- Plant at the depth where roots spread from the trunk.
- Prepare a planting site, not just a hole in the ground.
- Loosen the soil far beyond the drip line of the tree.
- Brace the tree only if it will not remain upright in a moderate wind.
- If necessary, brace only with broad, belt-like materials that won't injure the bark.
- Mulch away from the trunk with composted material (mulch should not touch trunk).
- Keep soil moist, not water-logged, to the depth of the roots.
- Remove dead and dying branches.
- Wait until the second growing season to begin training cuts for shaping and to begin fertilizing.

DO NOT:
- Do not plant to deep.
- Do not bury roots in small deep holes.
- Do not wrap trees.
- Do not amend the soil, unless the soil is very poor.
- Do not brace the tree so tightly that the tree cannot sway.
- Do not brace with wire in a hose.
- Do not fertilize at planting time.
- Do not plant grass or flowers near the tree.
- Do not remove branches to balance crown with roots.

Original Source

This excerpt is adapted from *Tree Basics* and *5 Minute Tree Care* with the kind permission of the author. The full text, including numerous photographs and figures can be ordered from Shigo and Trees, Associates, P.O. Box 769, Durham, NH 03824, USA; Tel: 603-868-7459; Fax: 603-868-1045.

This excerpt was originally published as *The Overstory* #69.

How Trees Survive

Alex Shigo

Trees are the tallest, most massive, longest-living organisms ever to grow on earth.

Trees, like other plants, cannot move. However, trees, unlike other plants are big, woody and perennial, which means they are easy targets for living and nonliving agents that could cause injuries. Trees cannot move away from potentially destructive conditions. Wounding agents and destructive conditions do destroy trees, but somehow, trees have grown in ways that give them super survival powers.

The big question is, how do trees do it?

The answer lies in concepts of biology and mechanical engineering.

This article examines the question of tree survival power more from the concepts of biology, but also to be aware of concepts of mechanical engineering. Details on all subjects given here are in my books.

Because different disciplines often use similar terms that have different meanings for their work, it is important to start with some definitions of terms I will use. You may not accept my definitions, but you will know what I mean when I use a term. I believe if a person cannot define a term in 25 words or less, they should not use it because they probably do not understand it.

Keyword Definitions of Terms

Capacity What you have as a result of your genetic code; a potential source for some future action or product.

Ability What you are doing with what you have; a dynamic or kinetic process.

System A highly ordered connection of parts and processes that have a predetermined end point - product, service.

Stress A condition where a system, or its parts, begins to operate near the limits for what it was designed.

Strain Disorder and disruption of a system due to operation beyond the limits of stress.

Vigor The capacity to resist strain; a genetic factor, a potential force against any threats to survival.

Vitality The ability to grow under the conditions present; dynamic action.

Health The ability to resist strain.

Disease A process that decreases the order and energy of a living system to the point of strain.

Survival The ability to remain alive or functional under conditions that have the potential to cause strain.

Generating system New parts and processes form in new spatial positions; plants.

Regenerating system New parts and processes form in old, or preoccupy, spatial positions; animals.

Wood A highly ordered connection of living, dying and dead cells that have walls of cellulose, hemicellulose and lignin.

Symplast The highly ordered connection of living axial and radial parenchyma in wood and bark.

Apoplast The highly ordered connection of dead cells and cell parts that make up the framework that holds the symplast.

Quality The characteristics that define a product, service or performance; quality can be low or high.

Hypothesis for Survival

Because trees cannot move away from potentially destructive agents and conditions, they have grown in ways that give them the capacity to adjust rapidly after being threatened by agents or conditions that could cause strain or death.

The capacity to adjust is a genetic feature called vigor. The program of vigor of an organism is defined by the limits of factors essential for survival. For example, one tree may have broad limits for water utilization. When drought occurs, it will still survive. Another tree may have very narrow limits for water utilization. Even the slightest disruption in availability of water would lead to strain or even death.

A vigor code then determines the limits for such essential factors as space, water, elements, temperature and soil pH.

The vigor of an organism cannot be measured until a life threatening stimulus contacts the organism.

When any potentially destructive stimulus occurs, the ability of the tree to adjust will be due not only to its vigor, or genetic code, but to its vitality. A tree that is very vigorous by nature of its genetic code may be growing on a rock. It would not be very vital. What this means is that for survival, both the vigor and vitality of a tree must be optimized.

Forest Tree, City Tree

Trees became tall, massive and long-living plants as they grew in groups. Trees not only connect with other trees by way of root grafts but also by way of the fungi that are associated with non-woody roots; the organs are called mycorrhizae. Trees also connected with many other organisms, very large to very small, in ways that benefited the trees and their associates. Synergistic associations are important parts of the tree system.

A forest is a system where trees and many associates are connected in ways that ensure survival of all members.

It is important to remember that the genetic codes for survival, or vigor, came from trees growing in forests.

When the forest-coded tree is brought into the city, the factors that affect vitality become extremely important. The architecture of most city trees as they grow as individuals is different from most of their relatives in the forest where trees grow in groups. Forest trees have group protection and group defense. The individual tree has neither.

The good news is that most of our city trees have strong vigor codes that have made them super survivors for hundreds of millions of years.

The bad news is that many human actions and mistreatments affect vitality and undo all the benefits of wondrous vigor code. It is only because most trees have such strong vigor codes that they still survive in cities.

There is no doubt in my mind that the greatest threat to survival faced by city trees are mistreatments by humans. Many trees tolerate mistreatments. Too often their tolerance is perceived as justifications for the mistreatments. I have heard it said many times that the tree did not die, so therefore the treatments must have been correct.

This ʻohiʻa lehua tree (*Metrosideros polymorpha*), native to Hawaiʻi, is estimated to be 400–600 years old. (photo: C. Elevitch)

How Do Trees Adjust?

Reaction zones and barrier zones

After injuries, boundaries form that resist spread of infections. By resisting spread of infections, the boundaries protect and preserve the water, air and mechanical support systems of the tree. Two types of boundaries form: reaction zones and barrier zones. The reaction zone is a chemically altered boundary that forms within the wood present at the time of wounding. The barrier zone is an anatomical and chemical boundary that forms after wounding. The barrier zone separates the infected wood from the new healthy wood that continues to form in new spatial positions. The tree is a generating system. The tree has no mechanism to form new, healthy cells in the same positions as those that are infected. Regenerating systems in animals do restore, repair, replace and regenerate parts in the same spatial positions. Animals have a process call apoptosis, which means programmed cell death followed by lysis, and new cells forming again in the same positions of those that died, lysed, and were eliminated. This normal process of apoptosis accelerates after animals are injured and infected. This accelerated restoration process is then called healing. In this sense, trees have no healing process.

Trees are highly compartmented, woody, shedding, perennial plants. Trees are generating systems. Every growth period, trees form new compartments over older ones. Trees grow as their apical and vascular meristems produce cells that differentiate to form all parts of the tree. The important part to remember is that trees grow as new parts form in new spatial positions.

Trees cannot "go back" to restore, repair, replace or regenerate parts. You do not restore a church by building a new one next to it. All words in English that start with "re" mean that new parts will go back in previously occupied positions or back to an original state. These words have no meaning for trees. These words have been the basis for great amounts of confusion. A tree cannot function in the same ways as animals do after injuries or threats to their survival. The continuing use of such meaningless words for trees is a strong indication why tree basics should be understood by people who work with trees.

Reaction Wood and Wound Wood

Now for the second adjustment feature of trees. After wounds or threats to their survival, trees also grow in ways that will maintain their mechanical structures. Now we come to the mix of biology and mechanical engineering.

There are two basic ways trees adjust to maintain and strengthen their structural stability: reaction wood and woundwood.

Reaction wood can be of two types. Compression wood forms on the down side of leaning trunks and tension wood forms on the upper sides. Compression wood is common in conifers and can be seen on a transverse dissection as dark bands in the wood, usually resin soaked. Or the growth increments could be larger in width and still be dark and resin soaked.

It is not possible to see tension wood because the changes take place in the cell walls. A gelatinous layer forms in the cell walls, and this layer can only be seen when properly stained and viewed under a microscope. The important part here is to know that these altered cell forms occur and that they occur after a stimulus that threatens survival mainly because of a lean in the stem that could lead to a fracture.

Woundwood is altered wood that forms about the margins of wounds. When wounds release the pressure of the bark, some of the still living parenchyma in the symplast begin to divide and produce new cells in new positions. These new cells no longer are held in place by the pressures of the bark or of the apoplast. The new cells become rounded and have a thin, primary cell wall. The cells exercise their ability (now) to divide and divide and divide. Because they are thin-walled, dividing cells, and because they contain the genetic codes for forming all parts of the tree, some of the cells begin to differentiate to form sprouts, prop roots, roots or flowers. This capacity for division and differentiation is called meristematic.

Callus is the name given to the thin walled, mostly round, meristematic cells that first form after wounding about the edges of the wound. Callus has very little lignin, the tough "natural cement" that gives cell walls great strength.

Within a few weeks to a few months after wounding during the growth period, callus formation begins to diminish and woundwood formation begins.

Woundwood has fewer vessels than "normal" wood. The cell walls are usually thicker than normal and usually contain more lignin. The woundwood cells cease to be meristematic. A new vascular cambium forms and continues to form woundwood. These woundwood tissues are seen as ribs about the margins of wounds. The woundwood ribs also add new strength to the weakened side of a stem, branch or woody root.

When woundwood closes wounds, then normal wood continues to form. The internal boundary-forming processes of compartmentalization are separate from the processes of callus and woundwood formation.

What Can Go Wrong?

It appears that trees could live forever. Of course, that is not so because the tree system, like all systems, must obey natural laws. And, again, the laws bring together biology and mechanical engineering.

Because a tree is a generating system, it is bound by its genetic codes to increase constantly in mass. The second law of energy flow begins to take its toll. The second law states that no system can remain in an orderly condition without a continuous supply of energy. As the tree system begins to increase in mass, the demands for energy to maintain order in the system begin to increase at exponential rates.

The tree still has ways of living within the limits of this law. The tree is a shedding organism. It uses and sheds non-woody and woody parts as they die. Decayed wood that develops within boundaries is even a form of shedding. Also, as trees age, the percentage of the entire tree that is symplast begins to change. The ratio of apoplast to symplast increases. So, the tree has both dynamic mass—symplast—and apoplast.

As the inner cells in the symplast die, the inner apoplast that now has all dead cells is called protection wood.

Protection is a static feature. Defense is a dynamic action. Protection wood is more protective than the sapwood because protection wood often contains substances called extractives that resist decay. Protection wood may also be so altered that its water, pH and available elements may not support growth of microorganisms.

Sapwood has a symplast. When sapwood is injured and infected, dynamic processes take place. There are two types of sapwood: sapwood that conducts free water, and sapwood that has its vessels plugged and does not conduct free water.

When protection wood is injured and infected, the intrinsic characteristics of the wood resist spread of infections. There are four types of protection wood: heartwood, false heartwood, discolored wood in early stages and wetwood.

The Biology of Fractures

Trees, like all organisms, die in three basic ways: depletion, dysfunction and disruption.

Depletion means that energy decreases to the point where disorder increases and the survival of the system is threatened. Examples are infections and starvation.

Silver oak (*Grevillea robusta*) with severe fracture in main trunk (left) and a China berry (*Melia azedarach*) that split in two where the main trunk was cracked (right). (photos: C. Elevitch)

Dysfunction means that highly ordered parts and processes begin to become disordered to the point where survival is threatened. Some examples are genetic problems and toxins.

Disruption means that the highly ordered structure of a system is disordered to the point where survival is threatened. Some examples are storm injuries and wounds inflicted by large machines.

Limits for Survival

There are no absolutes. There are no perpetual motion machines. Every system has its limits for survival. The tree system also has its limits for survival. As it increases in mass and gets older, the likelihood for injuries increases. A mature, healthy tree may have thousands of compartmentalized infections. Yet, there comes a time when even the limits of a super survivor begin to be approached. There are no absolutes.

When trees are young, depletion and dysfunction are the major causes of death. As trees get older and have survived thousands of injuries and infections, disruption becomes the greatest threat for high-quality survival. When a branch fractures and falls, it dies. When a trunk splits and falls to the ground, it dies. And, as larger and larger wounds result from such fractures, the likelihood of more fractures increases greatly.

When the pattern of fractures begins in city trees, not only are the trees in potential trouble, but so is the property near the trees. Also, people who go near the trees could have problems if trees or their parts fracture and fall.

Summary

Trees are living systems. They are unique living systems because they have the capacity to add strength to their structure at exactly the most effective places. This capacity is built into their genetic code. As generating systems, they are always building in front of themselves. When any part of the structural framework is weakened to the point where survival is threatened, the new parts that form in new positions form in ways that add strength to the weakened place.

Having the capacity to respond effectively to survive is dependent on having the energy, conditions and other ingredients necessary to turn the capacity into an ability

Both capacity as a vigor ingredient and ability as a vitality ingredient are necessary for long-term, high-quality survival. Vigor without vitality, or vitality without vigor will not support long-term, high quality survival.

The vigor codes for trees have met the test of time in forests. Many trees in many cities of the world are having great difficulties in expressing their vigor codes because human activities and treatments have affected their vitality.

There are no absolutes. No system, or its parts, will survive when stress goes to strain.

It is time to reexamine the tree system.

It is time to start basing tree treatments on tree biology.

It is time for modem arboriculture!

References

Shigo, A.L. 1994. Tree Anatomy. Shigo and Tree Associates, Durham, New Hampshire, USA.

Original Source

This excerpt was reprinted with the kind permission of the author from:

Shigo, A.L. 1996. "How Trees Survive". In: Tree Care Industry, Volume VII, Number 2.

The full text of this article including many excellent full color images can be viewed at: http://www.chesco.com/~treeman/SHIGO/SUR-VIVE.html, or purchased as part of a compilation of articles entitled *Shigo on Trees* from Shigo and Trees, Associates, P.O. Box 769, Durham, NH 03824, USA. Tel: 603-868-7459; Fax: 603-868-1045.

This excerpt was originally published as *The Overstory* #132.

Trees and Their Energy Transactions

Bill Mollison
© Bill Mollison 1988, 2001

This article deals with the complex interactions between trees and the incoming energies of radiation, precipitation, and the winds or gaseous envelope of earth. The energy transactions between trees and their physical environment defy precise measurement as they vary from hour to hour, and according to the composition and age of forests, but we can study the broad effects.

The planting of trees can assuredly increase local precipitation, and can help reverse the effects of dryland soil salting. There is evidence everywhere, in literature and in the field, that the great body of the forest is in very active energy transaction with the whole environment. To even begin to understand, we must deal with themes within themes, and try to follow a single rainstorm or airstream through its interaction with the forest.

A young forest or tree doesn't behave like the same entity in age; it may be more or less frost-hardy, wind-fast, salt-tolerant, drought-resistant or shade tolerant at different ages and seasons. But let us at least try to see just how the forest works, by taking one theme at a time. While this segmented approach leads to further understanding, we must keep in mind that everything is connected, and any one factor affects all other parts of the system. I can never see the forest as an assembly of plant and animal species, but rather as a single body with differing cells, organs, and functions. Can the orchid exist without the tree that supports it, or the wasp that fertilises it? Can the forest extend its borders and occupy grasslands without the pigeon that carries its berries away to germinate elsewhere?

Trees are, for the earth, the ultimate translators and moderators of incoming energy. At the crown of the forest, and within its canopy, the vast energies of sunlight, wind, and precipitation are being modified for life and growth. Trees not only build but conserve the soils, shielding them from the impact of raindrops and the desiccation of wind and sun. If we could only understand what a tree does for us, how beneficial it is to life on earth, we would (as many tribes have done) revere all trees as brothers and sisters.

In this article, I hope to show that the little we do know has this ultimate meaning: without trees, we cannot inhabit the earth. Without trees we rapidly create deserts and drought, and the evidence for this is before our eyes. Without trees, the atmosphere will alter its composition, and life support systems will fail.

The Biomass of the Tree

A tree is, broadly speaking, many biomass zones. These are the stem and crown (the visible tree), the detritus and humus (the tree at the soil surface boundary) and the roots and root associates (the underground tree).

Like all living things, a tree has shed its weight many times over to earth and air, and has built much of the soil it stands in. Not only the crown, but also the roots, die and shed their wastes to earth. The living tree stands in a zone of decomposition, much of it transferred, reborn, transported, or reincarnated into grasses, bacteria, fungus, insect life, birds, and mammals.

Many of these tree-lives "belong with" the tree, and still function as part of it. When a blue jay, currawong, or squirrel buries an acorn (and usually recovers only 80% as a result of divine forgetfulness), it acts as the agent of the oak. When the squirrel or wallaby digs up the columella of the fungal tree root associates, guided to these by a garlic-like smell, they swallow the spores, activate them enzymatically, and deposit them again to invest the roots of another tree or sapling with its energy translator.

The root fungi intercede with water, soil, and atmosphere to manufacture cell nutrients for the tree, while myriad insects carry out summer pruning, decompose the surplus leaves, and activate essential soil bacteria for the tree to use for nutrient flow. The rain of insect faeces may be crucial to forest and prairie health.

What part of this assembly is the tree? Which is the body or entity of the system, and which the part? An Australian Aborigine might give them all the same "skin name," so that a certain shrub, the fire that germinates the shrub, and the wallaby that feeds off it are all called *waru*, although each part also has its name. The Hawaiians name each part of the taro plant differently, from its child or shoot, to its nodes and "umbilicus."

It is a clever person indeed who can separate the total body of the tree into mineral, plant, animal, detritus, and life! This separation is for simple minds; the tree can be understood only as its total entity which, like ours, reaches out into all things. Animals are the messengers of the tree, and trees the gardens of animals. Life depends upon life. All forces, all elements, all life forms are the biomass of the tree.

Wind Effects

Apart from moisture, the wind may carry heavy loads of ice, dust, or sand. Strand trees (palms, pines, and Casuarinas) have tough stems or thick bark to withstand wind particle blast. Even tussock grasses slow the wind and cause dust loads to settle out. In the edges of forests and behind beaches, tree lines may accumulate a mound of driven particles just within their canopy. The forest removes very fine dusts and industrial aerosols from the airstream within a few hundred metres.

Forests provide a nutrient net for materials blown by wind, or gathered by birds that forage from its edges. Migrating salmon in rivers die in the headwaters after spawning, and many thousands of tons of fish remains are deposited by birds and other predators in the forests surrounding these rivers. In addition to these nutrient sources, trees actively mine the base rock and soils for minerals.

Temperature Effects

Evaporation causes heat loss locally and condensation causes heat gain locally. Both effects may be used to heat or cool air or surfaces. The USDA's Yearbook of Agriculture on Trees (1949) has this to say about the evaporative effects of trees: "An ordinary elm, of medium size, will get rid of 15,000 pounds of water on a clear dry hot day" and "Evapotranspiration (in a 40 inch rainfall) is generally not less than 15 inches per year."

Thus, the evaporation by day off trees cools air in hot weather, while the night condensation of atmospheric water warms the surrounding air. Moisture will not condense unless it finds a surface to condense on. Leaves provide this surface, as well as contact cooling. Leaf surfaces are likely to be cooler than other objects at evening due to the evaporation from leaf stomata by day. As air is also rising over trees, some vertical lift cooling occurs, the two combining to condense moisture on the forest. We find that leaves are 86% water, thus having twice the specific heat of soil, remaining cooler than the soil by day and warmer at night. Plants generally may be 15°C or so warmer than the surrounding air temperature.

Small open water storages or tree clumps upwind of a house have a pleasant moderating effect. Air passing over open water is cooled in summer. It is warmed and has moisture added even in winter. Only water captured by trees, however, has a dehumidifying effect in hot and humid tropical areas, as trees are capable of reducing humidity by direct absorption except in the most extreme conditions.

Trees and Precipitation

Trees have helped to create both our soils and atmosphere. The first by mechanical (root pressure) and chemical (humic acid) breakdown of rock, adding life processes as humus and myriad decomposers. The second by gaseous exchange, establishing and maintaining an oxygenated atmosphere and an active water-vapour cycle essential to life.

The composition of the atmosphere is the result of reactive processes, and forests may be doing about 80% of the work, with the rest due to oceanic or aquatic exchange. Many cities, and most deforested areas such as Greece, no longer produce the oxygen they use.

The basic effects of trees on water vapour and windstreams are:

- Compression of streamlines, and induced turbulence in air flows;
- Condensation phenomena, especially at night;
- Rehumidification by the cycling of water to air;
- Snow and meltwater effects; and
- Provision of nuclei for rain.

We can deal with each of these in turn (realizing that they also interact).

Compression and Turbulence Effects

Windstreams flow across a forest. The streamlines that impinge on the forest edge are partly deflected over the forest (almost 60% of the air) and partly absorbed into the trees (about 40% of the air). Within 1000 m (3,300 feet) the air entering the forest, with

Hawaiians considered trees to be "the hair of the earth" and protected them in part due to their intimate connection to the water cycle. (photo: C. Elevitch)

its tonnages of water and dust, is brought to a stand-still. The forest has swallowed these great energies, and the result is an almost imperceptible warming of the air within the forest, a generally increased humidity in the trees (averaging 15–18% higher than the ambient air), and air in which no dust is detectable.

Under the forest canopy, negative ions produced by life processes cause dust particles (+ +) to clump or adhere each to the other, and a fall-out of dispersed dust results. At the forest edge, thick-stemmed and specially wind-adapted trees buffer the front-line attack of the wind. If we cut a windward forest edge, and remove these defences, windburn by salt, dust abrasion, or just plain wind force may well kill or throw down the inner forest of weaker stems and less resistant species. This is a commonly observed phenomenon, which I have called "edge break." Con-

versely, we can set up a forest by planting tough, resistant trees as windbreak, and so protect subsequent downwind plantings. Forest edges are therefore to be regarded as essential and permanent protection and should never be cut or removed.

Condensation Phenomena

On the sea-facing coasts of islands and continents, the relatively warmer land surface creates quiet inshore airflows towards evening, and in many areas cooler water-laden air flows inland. Where this humid air flows over the rapidly cooling surfaces of glass, metal, rocks, or the thin laminae of leaves, condensation occurs, and droplets of water form. On leaves, this may be greatly aided by the colonies of bacteria (*Pseudomonas*) which also serve as nuclei for frost crystals to settle on leaves.

These saturated airstreams produce seaward-facing mosses and lichens on the rocks of fresh basalt flows, but more importantly condense in trees to create a copious soft condensation which, in such conditions, may far exceed the precipitation caused by rainfall. Condensation drip can be as high as 80–86% of total precipitation of the upland slopes of islands or sea coasts, and eventually produces the dense rainforests of Tasmania, Chile, Hawaii, Washington/Oregon, and Scandinavia. It produced the redwood forests of California and the giant laurel forests of pre-conquest Canary Islands (now an arid area due to almost complete deforestation by the Spanish).

The effects of condensation of trees can be quickly destroyed. Felling of the forests causes rivers to dry up, swamps to evaporate, shallow water to dry out, and drought to grip the land. All this can occur in the lifetime of a person.

Rehumidification of Airstreams

If it rains again, and again, the clouds that move inland carry water mostly evaporated from forests, and less and less water evaporated from the sea. Forests are cloud-makers both from water vapour evaporated from the leaves by day, and water transpired as part of life processes. On high islands, standing clouds cap the forested peaks, but disappear if the forests are cut. The great bridging cloud that reached from the forests of Maui to the island of Kaho'olawe, remembered by the fathers of the present Hawaiian settlers, has disappeared as cutting and cattle destroyed the upper forests on Maui and so lifted the cloud cap from Kaho'olawe, leaving this lower island naked to the sun.

It is a wonder to me that we have any water available after we cut the forests, or any soil. There are dozens of case histories in modern and ancient times of such desiccation as we find on the Canary Islands following deforestation, where rivers once ran and springs flowed. Design strategies are obvious and urgent—save all forest that remains, and plant trees for increased condensation on the hills that face the sea.

Effects on Snow and Meltwater

Although trees intercept some snow, the effect of shrubs and trees is to entrap snow at the edges of clumps, and hold 75–95% of snowfall in shade. Melting is delayed for 210 days compared with bare ground, so that release of snow melt is a more gradual process. Of the trapped snow within trees, most is melted, while on open ground snow may sublime directly to air. Thus, the beneficial effects of trees on high slopes is not confined to humid coasts. On high cold uplands such as we find in the continental interiors of the U.S.A. or Turkey near Mt. Ararat, the thin skeins of winter snow either blow off the bald uplands, to disappear in warmer air, or else they sublime directly to water vapour in the bright sun of winter. In neither case does the snow melt to groundwater, but is gone without productive effect, and no streams result on the lower slopes.

Provision of Nuclei for Rain

The upward spirals of humid air coming up from the forest carry insects, pollen, and bacteria aloft. This is best seen as flights of gulls, swifts and ibis spiralling up with the warm air and actively catching insects lifted from the forest; their gastric pellets consist of insect remains. It is these organic aerial particles (pollen, leaf dust, and bacteria mainly) that create the nuclei for rain.

Summary

All of these factors are clear enough for any person to understand. To doubt the connection between forests and the water cycle is to doubt that milk flows from the breast of the mother, which is just the analogy given to water by tribal peoples. Trees were "the hair of the earth" which caught the mists and made the rivers flow. Such metaphors are clear allegorical guides to sensible conduct, and caused the Hawaiians (who had themselves brought on earlier environmental catastrophes) to "tabu" forest cutting or even to make tracks on high slopes, and to place mountain trees in a sacred or protected category. Now that we begin to understand the reasons for these beliefs, we could ourselves look on trees as our essential companions, giving us all the needs of life, and deserving of our care and respect.

It is our strategies on-site that make water a scarce or plentiful resource. To start with, we must examine ways to increase local precipitation. Unless there is absolutely no free water in the air and earth about us (and there always is some), we can usually increase it on-site.

Here are some basic strategies of water capture from air:

• We can cool the air by shade or by providing cold surfaces for it to flow over, using trees and shrubs, or metals, including glass.

- We can cool air by forcing it to higher altitudes, by providing windbreaks, or providing updraughts from heated or bare surfaces (large concreted areas), or by mechanical means (big industrial fans).
- We can provide condensation nuclei for raindrops to form on, from pollen, bacteria, and organic particles.
- We can compress air to make water more plentiful per unit volume of air, by forcing streamlines to converge over trees and objects, or forcing turbulent flow in airstreams (Ekman spirals).

If by any strategy we can cool air, and provide suitable condensation surfaces or nuclei, we can increase precipitation locally. Trees, especially crosswind belts of tall trees, meet all of these criteria in one integrated system. They also store water for local climatic modification. Thus we can clearly see trees as a strategy for creating more water for local use.

In summary, we do not need to accept "rainfall" as having everything to do with total local precipitation, especially if we live within 30–100 km of coasts (as much of the world does), and we do not need to accept that total precipitation cannot be changed (in either direction) by our action and designs on site.

References

Chang, Jenhu, Climate and Agriculture, Aldine Pub. Co., Chicago, 1968.

Daubenmire, Rexford F., Plants and Environment: a textbook of plant autecology, Wiley & Sons, N. Y., 1974.

Geiger, Rudolf, The Climate Near the Ground, Harvard University Press, 1975.

Odum, Eugene, Fundamentals of Ecology, W. B. Saunders, London, 1974.

Plate, E. J., The Aerodynamics of Shelterbelts, Agricultural Meteorology 8, 1970.

U. S. Department of Agriculture, Trees, USDA Yearbook of Agriculture, 1949.

Vogel, Stephen, Life in Moving Fluids, Willard Grant Press, Boston, 1981

Original Source

This edition of The Overstory is excerpted with the kind permission of the author and publisher from:

Mollison, B. 1988. PERMACULTURE: A Designer's Manual. Tagari Publications, Tasmania, Australia. ©Bill Mollison

TAGARI PUBLICATIONS Tagari Publications — Permaculture Institute 31 Rulla Road Sisters Creek Tasmania 7325 Australia; Tel: 61 (0)3 6445 0945; Fax: 61 (0)3 6445 0944; Email: tagariadmin@southcom.com.au

This excerpt was originally published as The Overstory #92.

Tree Defences

Peter Thomas

It's a tough world. Trees face a constant battle in competing for light, water and minerals with surrounding plants. As if that were not enough, they also have to fend off the attention of living things, which view trees as good to eat and places to live. Insects chew away on all parts of a tree and are quite capable of completely defoliating it. Larger leaf-eating animals (which are usually on the ground since a belly full of compost heap is a heavy thing to carry around; leaf eating monkeys are an exception) chew away at the lower parts of the tree, although giraffes can reach up around 5.5 m. Whole armies of animals that can climb and fly will feed on the more nutritious flowers, fruits and the sugar-filled inner bark. The grey squirrel, introduced to Britain from North America in the 1880s, is a prime example. This rodent does extensive damage to hardwoods by stripping bark in spring to get at the sweet sap. It seems that dense stands of self-sown hardwoods have little sap and are largely immune (which may be why it does not cause problems in its native home) but well-tended planted trees have thin bark and a high sap content and are mercilessly attacked. So big is the problem that ash, lime and wild cherry may become more common in Britain because of their relatively low palatability to squirrels at the expense of palatable beech and sycamore.

Other animals are not adverse to making their homes from or in trees. Many birds, including various eagles, have been seen tearing off sizeable branches for nest making. Others live completely off the tree. Gall wasp larvae stimulate their host plant to grow galls on whichever part each species specialises in (leaves, flowers, fruits and stems). The nutritious tissues swell up around the grub and give it a home and food supply. Witches' brooms, the mass of densely branched small twigs that resemble a besom lodged in the canopy, are grown in the same way, induced by a range of different organisms: sometimes by fungi (e.g., *Taphrina betulina* in birches), mites, or even in N America by dwarf mistletoes (such as the *Arceuthobium* species). To this list of parasites you can add a number that normally live off the tree's roots and are only seen when they flower, such as the broomrapes (*Orabanche* spp.) and toothwort (*Lath-*

raea squamaria) of Europe. European mistletoe (*Viscum album*), in contrast, is only partly parasitic; it just takes water from the tree's plumbing and grows its own sugars by using its green leaves.

Epiphytic plants such as lichens and ivy merely use the tree as a place to grow up near the sun. In theory they take nothing from the tree. However, there is some evidence that tropical epiphytes, including a range of bromeliads and orchids, may intercept nutrients washed from the tree's leaves and branches by rain which would otherwise eventually reach the tree's roots. This "nutritional piracy" may be significant to tree health in the tropics and explains "canopy roots."

As if all this was not enough, diseases also take their toll. Fungal diseases, especially of the roots and stems, are particularly important in tree health. Bacteria and possibly viruses also play a role. For example, "wetwood" is a bacterial rot creating pockets of moist rot with plenty of methane.

Being firmly rooted in the ground, a tree cannot move to escape harsh conditions or the unwanted attentions of animals and diseases (seeds are the only parts with an option for movement). And there are no two ways about it, because trees are so long-lived they face a tremendous number of problems over their lives. They have therefore developed an impressive array of defences to protect themselves where they stand. The living skin of a tree is normally no older than two or three decades, and the leaves, flowers and fruits are usually even shorter-lived. Consequently, the defences of these parts are similar to those in non-woody plants. The real specialisation of defence comes in maintaining the woody skeleton which may persist for centuries or even millennia. We'll consider these defences in turn.

First-line Defences: Stopping Damage

Physical defences: spines, thorns and prickles

Large herbivores are capable of eating copious quantities of leaves along with the odd twig. Indeed the low nutritional value of leaves requires large volumes to be eaten. The chief defences against these large herbivores are spines, thorns and prickles. Spines and thorns (which botanically are the same thing) are modifications of a leaf, part of a leaf, or a whole stem. In *Berberis* species (as in cacti) it is the leaf that is turned into a spine; this leaves the branch with no green leaves so new ones are produced from the bud in the leaf axil growing out this year rather than next as is normal. Holly (*Ilex aquifolium*) could be regarded as a half-way house with just the margin growing spines. In false acacia (*Robinia pseudoacacia*) it is just the stipules (outgrowths of the leaf base) that are modified into persistent thorns. Hawthorns (*Crataegus* spp.) and firethorns (*Pyracantha* spp.) have thorns above the leaf, showing that the thorn is a modified branch, grown out from the bud. Growth next year can still take place because these trees cunningly grow extra buds beside the thorns. Again there are half-way houses; some brooms (*Cytisus* spp.), blackthorn (*Prunus spinosa*) and other *Prunus* species produce thorns at the ends of normal branches.

As with many palms, *Pigafetta filaris* protects itself with a carpet of sharp spines. (photo: C. Elevitch)

Spines and thorns are expensive things to produce and will only be grown where they are needed. Since most leaf-eaters stand on the ground to eat, simply because they are too heavy to climb or fly, it is perhaps not surprising that trees like holly produce leaf spines mostly on the lower 2 m of the canopy. But why do thorns appear in some trees but not others? Peter Grubb of Cambridge University proposes a solution to what appears to be a haphazard distribution. First of all, physical defences are found in habitats where nutritious growth is scarce. This explains

why thorny plants are found in deserts and heathlands (e.g., gorse). But it also explains why thorns are found on plants that invade gaps in forests, e.g., hawthorns, apples, honey-locust (*Gleditsia triacanthos*), and false acacia (*Robinia pseudoacacia*): food is scarce because other vegetation is out of the reach of large herbivores. The same principle applies to European holly, which, being an evergreen in a background of deciduous trees, provided scarce fodder in the winter. (Indeed around the southern Pennines in England, shepherds would cut the upper branches of holly (no prickles!) as fodder, particularly in spring when other foods were not available.) Finally the spines common around the growing points of palms and tree ferns are well worth the investment because they have only one growing point which, if damaged, means death to the plant.

Other physical defences

Trees have not been slow in evolving other physical defences. Hairs help deter insects attracted to young vulnerable growth. In some cases this is a physical barrier (like us having to chew through a pillow to get food), in others the hairs contain chemical deterrents (as in the nettle-like hairs of the Australian rainforest stinging trees, *Dendrocnide* spp.).

Other physical defences can be quite subtle. For example, because of the arrangement of their mouths, caterpillars have to eat a leaf from the edge; so holly has evolved a thickened margin to prevent the caterpillars getting a start. So why haven't more trees evolved a similar mechanism? Probably because the cost is only worthwhile in long-lived evergreen leaves and these are usually protected by chemicals instead. Physical defence can be yet more subtle. One example of many is the subterfuge indulged in by passion flower vines (*Passiflora* spp.), which are eaten by the caterpillars of heliconid butterflies. The butterflies rarely lay their yellow eggs where there are already plenty (this would be pointless competition for food amongst the caterpillars) so the vine grows imitation yellow eggs on its leaves!

Ants and other beasties

Around the world, there are many examples of tropical trees that use ants as their main defence. The ants run around the tree preventing birds and animals from nesting, dissuading herbivores, cutting away epiphytes and lianas, and in some cases killing anything growing within a 10 m radius of their tree. These ants usually have vicious stings as is rapidly found out if you lean against their tree! In return the tree provides food and often a home as well. For example, the "ant acacias" of the New and Old World have swollen thorns in which ants hollow out nests. Nectar is delivered from leaf stalks ("extrafloral nectaries", i.e., nectaries not in flowers) and protein from bright orange bodies produced at the tips of the leaflets. Ant acacia leaves are less bitter than in other acacias: presumably the cost of looking after ants is cheaper than producing internal deterrent chemicals.

Employing guards can work on a much smaller scale. It is common to find little tufts of hair at the junctions where veins join together on the underside of leaves. A study on the European evergreen shrub *Viburnum tinus* found 10 species of mite—mostly predators and microbivores (i.e., eating microbes)—living in the crevices (or "domatia") between these hairs. In other words, the plant is providing homes for mites that help keep other harmful organisms at bay.

Chemical defences

Woody plants produce a great variety of chemical compounds to provide protection against other plants, diseases and herbivores big and small. These include alkaloids, terpenes, phenolics (e.g., caffeine, morphine, tannins and resins), steroids and cyanide producers (cyanogenic glycosides). These chemicals can be found in just about any part of the plant (for example, the waxy surface of apple leaves contains toxins to repel certain aphids). They can also be emitted into the air in considerable quantities which explains why pine woods smell so nice and the eucalypt-dominated bushlands of Australia have a blue haze. These chemicals seep out through the bark or the holes in a leaf (the stomata) or ooze out of special glands, often on teeth around the leaf edge (as found in pines, alder, willows, hornbeam, maples, ashes, elms and viburnums) usually when the leaf is young but sometimes (as in crack willow) even late in life. Are these emissions of expensive chemicals just inadvertent leaks or do they have a purpose? Certainly in oaks it allows the trees to communicate with each other: just how is revealed below.

Chemical defences work in several ways. Some are highly toxic and will kill attackers in small doses (referred to as "qualitative" defences since they work by being what they are rather than how much is there). These include the alkaloids in rhododendron (honey from its flowers is poisonous to humans but is so bitter it's uneatable), and cyanide (hydrocyanic acid)

produced, for example, by crushing leaves of cherry laurel (*Prunus laurocerasus*) and consequently used to effect in an insect-killing bottle. Other chemicals work by building up in the herbivore (called "quantitative" defences since they become more effective the more there is). Classic examples are phenolic resins in creosote bushes and tannins found in a number of plants. Tannin is a "protein precipitant" which makes food less digestible so herbivores end up starving and stunted. These often have the effect of causing the herbivore to move elsewhere. Incidentally, it is possible that the endangered British red squirrel is declining not through competition with the introduced N American grey squirrel but because of acorns. Acorns contain digestion inhibitors that greys can disarm but reds can't. Red squirrels do well in conifer plantations feeding on the more nutritious pine seeds and where there are no oaks to give the greys a competitive edge.

Plants are not immune to the effects of chemical defences. Spanish moss (*Tillandsia usneoides*) that festoons trees in southern USA and South America (and is not a moss but a sophisticated relative of the pineapple) never grows on pines, presumably because of the resins. Perhaps the best known example of anti-plant chemical defences was first reported by Pliny the Elder in the first century AD, who wrote that "The shadow of walnut trees is poison to all plants within its compass". Walnuts (and all trees in the genus *Juglans*) contain the chemical juglone, which, seeping from the roots, reduces the germination of competitors, stunts their growth and even kills nearby plants, resulting in open-canopied walnuts having very little growing under them. Tomatoes, apples, rhododendrons and roses are very susceptible but many grasses, vegetables and Virginia creeper (*Parthenocissus* spp.) will happily live under walnuts.

Defensive chemicals are costly to produce and store (many are toxic to the plant producing them). Oaks may put up to 15% of their energy production into chemical defences (which explains why stressed trees are most prone to attack: they have less energy available to produce defences). Thus, although there may be large pools of defences swilling around (preformed) where attacks are common and ferocious, it makes evolutionary sense in lesser situations to produce the chemicals in earnest only when they are needed (induced). Oaks (and a number of other trees) will tick along with low concentrations of tannins in their leaves but once part of the canopy is attacked, the tree will produce tannins in large quantity. More than that, the tannins released into the air are detected by surrounding oaks and they in turn will produce more tannins in preparation for the onslaught. In a similar way, willows in Alaska browsed by snowshoe hares produce shoots with lower nutritional concentration and higher levels of lignin and deterrent phenols, thus rendering them less palatable. These "induced" defences may have an effect for some time; birches can remain unpalatable for up to three years after being browsed.

Defending The Woody Skeleton

At first sight it may seem that wood does not need much defending: it's pretty inedible stuff. The large quantities of cellulose (40–55%), hemicellulose (25–40%) and lignin (18–35%) are all tough carbohydrates that are quite hard to decompose. Moreover, wood is incredibly poor in protein and hence nitrogen (typically 0.03–0.1% nitrogen by mass compared with the 1–5% found in green foliage). Just how poor wood is as a food is illustrated by the goat moth, whose caterpillars burrow through wood and take up to four years to grow to maturity, and yet they can mature in just a few months if fed on a good rich diet. Despite the starvation diet that wood offers, there are many insects, fungi and bacteria that are capable of living off wood.

Keeping Things Out: Resins, Gums And Latex

These fluids have a primary role in rapidly sealing over wounds (whether created by insects or by physical accidents) and in deterring animals from forcing their way in. Any animal rash enough to burrow is physically swamped and trapped, and may be overcome by chemical toxicity (though bark beetles are seen swimming through resin apparently unharmed, if a little hindered).

Resins

If you have leant against an old pine or handled a cone you will be well aware of the ability of conifers to produce copious quantities of resin. The typical "pine" smell of conifer foliage comes from the resin. Yews (*Taxus* spp.) do not contain resin and consequently do not smell.

In most conifers, including pines, Douglas fir (*Pseudotsuga menziesii*), larches and spruces, the resin is contained in ducts that run through the bark and wood, tapering off into the roots and needles. Others such as the hemlocks, true cedars and true firs, have resin restricted more or less to the bark, although, like other conifers, they are capable of producing "traumatic resin canals" in the wood after injury or infection. In the true firs (*Abies*) the resin is contained in raised blisters. Cells along the ducts or blisters secrete resin, creating a slight positive pressure, so if the tree is damaged the resin oozes out. Once in the air, the lighter oils evaporate, leaving a solidified scab of resin over the wound.

Gums

Fulfilling a similar function, a wide range of woody plants produce gums. The family of Anacardiaceae is notable for gum-producing trees including the varnish tree (*Rhus verniciflua*), a native of China, whose gum is used as the basis of lacquer. Gums are also found oozing from wounds in a variety of temperate trees such as those in the genus *Prunus* (the cherries, plums, etc.). These gums are carried in ducts, which, as in the conifers, are in the bark and often the wood where they follow the rays and grain. Traumatic canals can be formed in the wood of some hardwoods, for example, sweet gum (*Liquidambar styraciflua*) and cherries.

Latex

Latex (a milky mixture of such things as resins, oils, gums and proteins) is found in different plants from fungi to dandelions to trees. Many types of trees and shrubs have had their latex collected for making rubber (including the "rubber tree", *Ficus elastica*, now grown commonly as a house plant). Around one third of rainforest trees have latex. The best commercial supply comes from *Hevea brasiliensis* in the spurge family (Euphorbiaceae) native to the Amazon and Orinoco river valleys of South America. The rich latex of this tree is about 33–75% water and 20–60% rubber. Latex is found in special ducts (lactifers) running through the bark in concentric circles. As with resin in conifers, the latex is under slight pressure, ensuring that any wound is sealed by coagulating latex (including those made deliberately to collect the latex, and which are treated with an anticoagulant to ensure a good collection).

Callus growth

The production of resins, gums and latex is often insufficient to seal over large wounds such as the breakage of large branches and the removal of areas

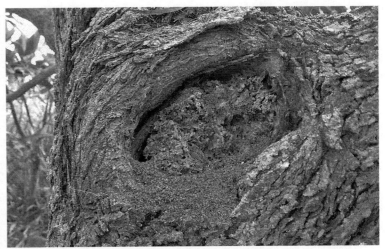

Wounds in the process of healing over where branches have been pruned off *Toona australis* (left) and a wound which has not healed over before rotting and insect attack have compromised the interior wood of *Acacia koa* (right). (photos: C. Elevitch)

of bark by, for example, squirrels. If the wound is kept artificially moist (by covering with plastic, lanolin or other non-toxic substance) so that the living cells of the rays do not dry out, a new bark will regenerate in the same season in many species. (Note, though, that in pruning off branches it is only the younger parenchyma cells of the sapwood around the edge of the stump that are capable of doing this, leaving a hole in the centre.) But if the newly exposed parenchyma cells are killed by toxic materials in paint or allowed to desiccate, then the wound can only be covered by the slow growth of callus tissue from the living cambium and rays around the edge. As the callus grows, it starts off uniformly around the wound but the sides tend to grow more rapidly resulting in a circular wound ending up as a spindle-shaped scar. Once the sides of the callus meet, the cambium joins so new complete cylinders of wood are again laid down underneath the scarred bark.

Healing wounds

Unlike animals, trees cannot heal wounds; they can only cover them up. Once wood starts to rot it cannot be repaired. New wood can be grown over the top and look healthy but the rotting wood underneath is still there. Hence the wise saying quoted by William Pontey in The Forest Pruner (1810), "An old oak is like a merchant, you never know his real worth till he be dead".

References

Bernays, E.A., Driver, CC. and Bilgener, M. (1989). Herbivores and plant tannins. Advances in Ecological Research, 19, 263–302.

Bond, W.J. and Midgley, J.J. (1995). Kill thy neighbour: an individualistic argument for the evolution of flammability. Oikos, 73, 79–85.

Bonsen, K.J.M. and Walter, M. (1993). Wetwood and its implications. Arboricultural Journal, 17, 61–7.

Bryant, J.P., Provenza, F.D., Pastor, J., Reichardt, PB, Clausen, T.P. and du Toit, J.T. (1991). Interactions between woody plants and browsing mammals mediated by secondary metabolites. Annual Review of Ecology and Systematics, 22, 431–46.

Coutts, M.P. and Grace, J. (1995). Wind and Trees. Cambridge University Press.

de la Fuente, MAS. and Marquis, R.J. (1999). The role of ant-tended extrafloral nectaries in the protection and benefit of a Neotropical rainforest tree. Oecologia, 118, 192–202.

Gasson, PE. and Cutler, D.F. (1990). Tree root plate morphology. Arboricultural Journal, 14, 193–264.

George, M.F., Hong, S.G. and Burke, M.J. (1977). Cold hardiness and deep supercooling of hardwoods: its occurrence in provenance collections of red oak, yellow birch, black walnut and black cherry. Ecology, 58, 674–80.

Grace, S.L. and Plait, W.J. (1995). Effects of adult tree density and fire on the demography of pregrass stage juvenile longleaf pine (Pinus palustris Mill.). Journal of Ecology, 83, 75–86.

Grostal, P. and O'Dowd, D.J. (1994). Plants, mites and mutualism: leaf domatia and the abundance and reproduction of mites on Viburnum tinus (Caprifoliaceae). Oecologia, 97, 308–15.

Klein, R.M. and Perkins, T.D. (1988). Primary and secondary causes and consequences of contemporary forest decline. Botanical Review, 54, 1–43.

Loehle, C. (1988). Tree life history strategies: the role of defenses. Canadian Journal of Botany, 18, 209–22.

Lundqvist, L. and Valinger, E. (1996). Stem diameter growth of scots pine trees after increased mechanical load in the crown during dormancy and (or) growth. Annals of Botany, 77, 59–62.

Mattheck, C. and Breloer, H. (1994). The Body Language of Trees: a Handbook of Failure Analysis. Research for Amenity Trees, No. 4, HMSO, London.

Mountford, E.P. (1997). A decade of grey squirrel bark-stripping to beech in Lady Park Wood, UK. Forestry, 70, 17–29.

Philips, D.H. and Burdekin, DA. (1982). Diseases of Forest and Ornamental Trees. Macmillan, London.

Radley, J. (1961). Holly as winter feed. The Agricultural History Review, 9, 89–92.

Rank, N.E. (1994). Host-plant effects on larval survival of a salicin-using leaf beetle Chrysomela aeneicollis Schaeffer (Coleoptera: Chrysomelidae). Oecologia, 97, 342–53.

Roy, AK., Sharma, A. and Talukder, G. (1988). Some aspects of aluminum toxicity in plants. Botanical Review, 54, 145–78.

Shigo, AL. (1984). Compartmentalization: a conceptual framework for understanding how trees grow and defend themselves. Annual Review of Phytopathology, 22, 189–214.

Smirnoff, N. (1996). The function and metabolism of abscorbic acid in plants. Annals of Botany, 78, 661–9.

Stapley, L. (1998). The interaction of thorns and symbiotic ants as an effective defence mechanism of swollen-thorn acacias. Oecologia, 115, 401–5.

Stephenson, N.L. and Demetry, A. (1995). Estimating ages of giant sequoias. Canadian Journal of Forest Research, 25, 223–33.

Strobel, GA. and Lanier, G.N. (1981). Dutch elm disease. Scientific American, 245, 56–66.

Welch, H. and Haddow, G. (1993). The World Checklist of Conifers. The World Conifer Data Pool. Landsman's Bookshop, Hertfordshire.

White, J. (1998). Estimating the age of large and veteran trees in Britain. Forestry Commission, Information Note 12, HMSO, London.

White, J.E.J. (1989). Ivy—boon or bane? Arboricultural Research Note 81–89.

Original Source

This excerpt was reprinted with the kind permission of the author and publisher from:

Thomas, P.A. 2000. Trees: Their Natural History. ©Cambridge University Press.

To Order The Book:

This book provides a comprehensive introduction to the natural history of trees, presenting information on all aspects of tree biology and ecology in an easy-to-read and concise text. Fascinating insights into the workings of these everyday plants are uncovered throughout the book, with questions such as how trees are designed, how they grow and reproduce, and why they eventually die, tackled in an illuminating way.

The book can be purchased here:
http://titles.cambridge.org/catalogue.asp?isbn=0521453518

This chapter was originally published in *The Overstory* #138.

Designing with Nature

Fighting with nature is ultimately too costly. Basic
principles and practices enable people to work with
nature for healthy and abundant systems.

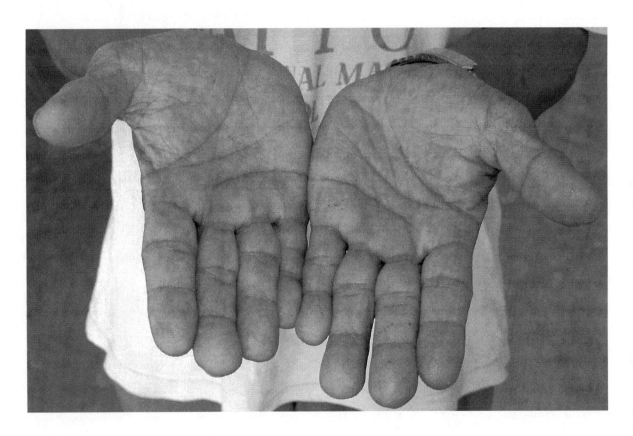

Section Contents

Integrated Systems Approach

Kim M. Wilkinson and Craig R. Elevitch

An integrated approach to farm systems comes from the perspective that whatever we are growing now, it was originally part of an ecosystem, its native environment, where for thousands of years it interacted with many kinds of other living things, from soil organisms to animals, insects, and plants. It was "plugged in" to natural processes, and grew without any human help. The integrated approach is about recreating and integrating into the farm some of the beneficial connections and natural processes that support productivity.

Chicken and Egg Example

A classic example for thinking about the integrated systems approach is called the "Chicken and Egg Example," from Bill Mollison, the author of Permaculture. This example consists of two illustrations, one of a production approach that is not integrated, and another of a system that is integrated.

Picture on one hand an industrial chicken factory, with chickens in cages. Here the chicken is isolated from its natural environment, and virtually all that is needed to sustain it is provided by humans. A huge infrastructure is needed to grow food for the chicken, and to transport the food to the chicken. Because this is a stressful environment for the chicken, it tends to lead to disease so there is also a large pharmaceutical industry to provide medicines and hormones to keep the chicken alive. Every step in the process in energy-intensive, including the disposal of the chicken's waste products and manure, which usually have to be treated as a pollutant. And the end product, and egg in this case, tends to be of questionable quality in the eyes of consumers.

Picture now another scenario: an orchard designed to have chickens run through it to scratch and feed, then return to their roost at night. Here, the animals in more of a natural environment, can feed and mostly medicate themselves from the environment. Their products like manure are used in the system, and rather than being a pollutant, contribute to the productivity of the trees. And the end product, in this case an egg again, may be of higher value in the eyes of consumers. Free range eggs at our local gro-

cery store sell for about 60% more than conventional eggs.

The two examples above represent two extremes, a system that is not integrated (chickens isolated in a factory), and an integrated system (chickens integrated with orchard crops).

The Continuum

All our farms are somewhere on a continuum between the two extremes illustrated above: between high-input, highly controlled systems on one end, and more integrated systems on the other.

More importantly, our farms are also changing and evolving over time, and as they do they move more toward one end or the other on this continuum. It is important to ask ourselves in our daily activities: Are we heading towards integrating natural processes, or are we setting it up to have to fight them?

On one end of the continuum is a petri dish, a sterile container that is used in laboratories, usually to culture one kind of organism. It is a very controlled system that requires high inputs to set up and maintain. Interactions of any kind are discouraged, and in fact outside influences such as normal air can ruin the culture.

On the opposite end of the continuum are natural ecosystems, like a tropical forest. In contrast to the petri dish, these systems are very diverse, with uncountable interactions between the elements in them, such as plants, insects, and soil life. There is very little human intervention, and they are not stable but instead are very dynamic.

The chicken factory example belongs toward the petri dish end of the continuum, as it is a very controlled, high input system. The integrated animals in an orchard setting belongs more toward the ecosystem end.

All our farms fall somewhere in this continuum now, and the things we do every day are moving them more toward one end or the other.

Here are some common production systems and where they would fall on this continuum:

Hydroponics: very controlled, high input.

Monocultures: large single-species plantings

Petri dish   hydroponics   monocultures   agroforestry   wild harvest   natural ecosystems

Agroforestry: more diverse

Wild harvest: reliant on natural processes

On this continuum, "organic" can go somewhere in the middle (between monocultures and agroforestry), although the term doesn't have a whole lot of meaning from the integrated systems perspective. Organic can mean simply substituting one kind of fertilizer for another, and may still be high-input. However, many organic growers are very integrated, and would belong on the ecosystem side of the continuum.

As systems move toward the natural ecosystem end of the continuum, they become more integrated: more diverse, with more beneficial connections formed between the diverse elements. Generally, less inputs (such as fertilizers) are needed off-farm as the natural connections that support productivity are utilized.

Examples of Integrated Systems Using Trees

Agroforestry systems are integrated systems using trees. Three examples include:

Silvopasture Silvopasture systems integrate livestock, forage pasture, and trees. In this system, the livestock keep down the grass, reducing or eliminating the need to mow, slash, or herbicide. Their manure contributes fertility to the trees, reducing the need to throw fertilizer. And, they produce a steady economic income. The trees in this system provide shade for the livestock, which is important in the tropics where heat affects the productivity of livestock. The shade may also benefit the forage component. Also, the trees provide a diversified and long-term economic product.

Orchard Alley Cropping Orchard alley cropping systems integrate orchard crops with nitrogen-fixing trees. Nitrogen-fixing trees provide the major source of fertility in natural ecosystems, and this natural source is reestablished in the farm by planting rows of nitrogen-fixing trees in the orchard. The orchard crops are grown in the middle of the "alleys" formed by the nitrogen fixing trees. The nitrogen fixing trees are cut back and applied as mulch to the orchard crops, fertility. The mulch also conserves moisture,

suppresses weeds, and encourages beneficial soil microorganisms.

Mixed Coffee Agroforest Coffee agroforest such as those found in Central America include coffee trees, nitrogen-fixing trees, and long-term timber trees. In this system, the nitrogen-fixing trees provide mulch and fertility to the coffee crops, as well as a managed shade system. The timber component provides diversified products and can make the total yield of the system over time higher than if coffee were grown alone. Also, some ecologists have determined that these systems provide excellent wildlife habitat for birds and other wildlife, which contributes to the pest/predator balance and can also help with market positioning for eco-friendly products.

The above systems have in common that they are more diverse than monocultures, and beneficial connections between the diverse elements are encouraged. Human inputs can be reduced as natural functions such as the cycling of organic matter, the grazing of livestock, or the balance of pests and predators come into play to support productivity.

Conclusion

The integrated approach to farm systems is about learning to work with and take advantage of natural processes that support productivity. It is not an approach that farmers make out of the goodness of their hearts; instead, this approach can help reduce inputs from off-farm, contribute to ecological balance, and provide diversified economic products. Essential to the approach is a long-term view of the direction the farm is moving on the continuum towards becoming an integrated system.

References

Mollison, B. 1990. Permaculture: A Practical Guide for a Sustainable Future, Island Press, Washington, DC.

McHarg, Ian. 1969. Design with Nature, Doubleday/Natural History Press, Garden City, NJ.

Original Source

This chapter was originally published as *The Overstory #44*.

Designing Resource Systems

Kim M. Wilkinson and Craig R. Elevitch

"The significant problems we face cannot be solved at the same level of thinking we were at when we created them." —Albert Einstein

Paradigm Shift

Up until a few decades ago, modern agriculture and resource management focused on manipulating, mining, and harvesting the vast bounty of nature, using resources that had built up naturally over thousands of years. Our task now is to do more than to stop the degradation. We have got to actually reverse the damage, restore natural processes, and manage in a way that resources are not only conserved and but built up over time. To accomplish this will require a fundamental shift in the way we think and work with nature and agriculture. It is a shift from exploiting resources to actively designing and re-creating resource systems that can mimic nature in form and function.

This shift is affecting people working with agriculture and resource management worldwide, from small growers to massive public works projects. For example, slash-and-burn or shifting subsistence farmers used to be able to count on natural processes to restore fertility to their farms over time. Now they must find ways to maintain and even improve fertility using their own management practices. On the other extreme, soil conservation experts and engineers now recognize that we'll never have enough resources to control flooding with expensive earthworks, and that instead we must conserve and re-create forest watersheds to prevent flood disasters at their source. In both cases, the conclusion is the same: resource systems must be actively re-created.

We are entering a new era in agriculture and resource management, one in which we actively design and create agro-ecosystems, forests, and watersheds, instead of depleting them. In the process of learning how to design, create and manage these new resource systems, we learn more and more about how to work with nature rather than against it.

Project Design

"I always wanted to be somebody, but I should have been more specific."—Lily Tomlin

In times of exploitative resource management, most land managers primarily reacted to what nature dished out—harvesting when there was abundance and moving on when resources became low. Decisions were also made reactively, and the vision was focused on short-term gains. Today, we become partners with nature, considering the system as a whole, asking what we can contribute to natural processes while still providing for our own needs. We take a long view focused on adding to the health, diversity, and abundance of the system. In essence, we become designers of ecosystems. The design process is essential in creating viable resource systems that are in harmony with nature.

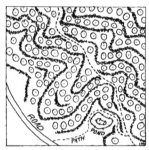

Integrated resource planning involves all farm elements.

For example, designing an agroforestry system is more than simply adding trees. The key is to maximize the number of beneficial connections formed between trees and other elements. As an example, alley cropping is an agroforestry technique that integrates trees with crops to provide fertilizer and mulch. With careful design, this technique can also provide erosion control, windbreak, and animal fodder. In other words, a systems approach enables the trees to work together with other elements to provide many more benefits than the elements could provide independently.

A good design with a systems approach enables growers to maximize connections between elements, increasing stability, diversity and total yield of a planting. The initial investment in the planning process will also pay off by making the most efficient use of resources and work with nature to create a true resource system, where many elements interact to benefit all life.

Original Source

This chapter was originally published as *The Overstory* #18.

Further Reading

Mollison, B. 1990. Permaculture: A Practical Guide for a Sustainable Future, Island Press, Washington, DC. An excellent guide to designing resource systems in harmony with natural processes.

McHarg, Ian. 1969. Design with Nature, Doubleday/Natural History Press, Garden City, NJ. Describe an ecologically sound approach to the planning and design of communities.

Elevitch, C.R. and K.M. Wilkinson. 2000. Information Resources for Pacific Island Agroforestry. Permanent Agriculture Resources, Holualoa, HI. Provides an introduction to agroforestry, followed by descriptions and contact information for books, guides, periodicals, organizations, and web sites useful to practitioners of agroforestry in Pacific Islands: http://agroforestry.net/afg/book.html

Observe and Interact

David Holmgren

In hunter-gatherer and low-density agricultural societies, the natural environment provided all material needs, with human effort mainly required for harvesting. In preindustrial societies with high population densities, agricultural productivity depended on large and continuous input of human labour. Industrial society depends on large and continuous inputs of fossil fuel energy to provide its food and other goods and services. Permaculture designers use careful observation and thoughtful interaction to reduce the need for both repetitive manual labour and for non-renewable energy and high technology. Thus, traditional agriculture was labour intensive, industrial agriculture is energy intensive, and permaculture-designed systems are information and design intensive.

In a world where the quantity of secondary (mediated) observation and interpretation threatens to drown us, the imperative to renew and expand our observation skills in all forms is at least as important as the need to sift and make sense of the flood of mediated information. Improved skills of observation and thoughtful interaction are also more likely sources of creative solutions than brave conquests in new fields of specialised knowledge by the armies of science and technology.

The proverb "beauty is in the eye of the beholder" reminds us that the process of observing influences reality and that we must always be circumspect about absolute truths and values. Good design depends on a free and harmonious relationship to nature and people, in which careful observation and thoughtful interaction provide the design inspiration, repertoire and patterns. It is not something that is generated in isolation, but through continuous and reciprocal interaction with the subject.

Observe, Recognise Patterns and Appreciate Details

A process of continuous observation in order to recognise patterns and appreciate details is the foundation of all understanding. Those observed patterns and details are the source for art, science and design. The natural and especially the biological world provides by far the greatest diversity of patterns and details observable without the aid of complex or expensive technology. Those patterns and details provide us with a great repertoire of models and possibilities for the design of low energy human support systems.

While good observation is the source of new insight and creativity, it is also the foundation for renewing the most basic abilities that we appear to be losing as fast as technology finds substitutes. For example, observation of a baby's pattern of bowel movements and early action to hold them over the potty at the right time can lead to easy and early toilet training, saving endless work, water and energy. Computerised Geographical Information Systems, while very useful, often substitute for, or cover up, a deficit in simple skills of reading the landscape.

Interact with Care, Creativity and Efficiency

There is little value in continuous observation and interpretation unless we interact with the subject of our observations. Interaction reveals new and dynamic aspects of our subject and draws attention to our own beliefs and behaviour as instrumental to understanding. The interplay between observer and subject can be thought of as the precursor to design. The accumulation of the experiences of observation and interaction build the skill and the wisdom needed both to intervene sensitively in existing systems and to creatively design new ones.

The Thinking and Design Revolution

Everyone knows about the breathtaking emergence of the information economy. The information and knowledge systems that direct and organise the physical economy of goods now have the greatest value and power. Computers are the most obvious feature of the information economy, but changes in the way we think, especially the emergence of design thinking, are more fundamental to the information economy than the hardware and software we use. Permaculture itself is part of this thinking revolution.

Peter Harper of Centre for Alternative Technology Wales, examining cabbages for hoverfly parasitism of aphids. (photo: D. Holmgren)

A large part of the thinking revolution involves the emergence of design as a universal skill alongside those of literacy and numeracy. It is not so much that we are just beginning to design; rather, we are becoming more conscious of the power of our individual and collective design processes and how to improve them. Design is fundamental to humanity and nature, and yet it is so difficult to define.

Victor Papanek defines design as "the conscious and intuitive effort to impose meaningful order." This emphasises that design is not simply the result of rational, analytical and reductionist thinking, but also depends on our intuitive and integrative capabilities.

To design requires that we are familiar with models generated by nature and humanity (past and current solutions and options) as well as having an ability to visualise some new adaption, variation or possibility. The capacity to imagine other possibilities is another important aspect of design thinking. The most creative design involves the promiscuous hybridisation of possibilities from apparently disconnected, or even discordant sources to create a new harmony.

From a systems ecology perspective, "design by nature" is not simply a metaphor but a result of the forces of self-organisation which can be observed everywhere in the living and wider universe. This imposition of meaningful order is a counter-flow to the prevailing entropic forces of disorder within nature and the wider universe. Self-organisation occurs wherever energy flows are sufficient to generate storages. *Designing is as natural as breathing and, like breathing, most of us can learn to do it better.*

Observation and interaction involve a two-way process between subject and object: the designer and the system. The maxim "everything works both ways" is a useful general reminder that finds expression in many diverse examples. The following more specific maxims provide the concrete guidelines and reminders which can help us as designers.

Design Thinking Guidelines

All observations are relative

Observation can be a reflection of an internal state rather than objective fact. Even the concept of objective fact in science is now acknowledged as flawed; scientists know that observation, directly and indirectly, influences reality.

Given the limits to objectivity, it is better to be clear and articulate about our assumptions, preconceptions and values, and to acknowledge how these influence and structure how we see. Ethics and ideology act as filters that determine what and how we see. These filters are unavoidable—in fact, essential—but the rush to judgment of right and wrong frequently clouds our observation and prevents understanding. This commonly occurs in our attitude to pest plants and animals.

Top-down thinking, bottom-up action

In considering any subject it is always useful to step back and look for the connections and contexts which can reveal our subject as part of large-scale systems. This assists us to identify important inputs to the system that are outside system control or feedback effects and also to see outputs and losses that larger-scale systems are absorbing.

This "top-down" systems thinking is a useful balance to "bottom-up" reductionist perspectives that seek to understand a subject by looking for its fundamental parts. On the other hand, bottom-up action focuses on the leverage points that are available for small-scale elements or individuals to influence large-scale systems in which they participate. This is especially important when we are trying to manage rangelands, forests and other wild landscapes where our "management" options are a small part of the larger system. Similarly, in trying to foster appropriate community change in a context of more powerful forces, recognising leverage points where we can make a difference is essential. Perhaps the current prevailing mode of action could be characterised as "top-down" (dominant) action typified by governmental and corporate management. Instead what is needed is more bottom-up (participatory) action at all levels in natural and human systems.

The landscape is the textbook

The natural world provides such a vast diversity of subject material for the observer and designer that we can characterise the landscape as the textbook to follow. All the knowledge we need to create and manage low energy human support systems can come from working with nature.

By observation we usually mean using our eyes, but this just reflects how visually dominated modern people are, raised in a literate and now graphical world. All of our senses have great potential to provide valuable information. For example, smelling or tasting soil can reveal otherwise invisible aspects of its biological, physical and chemical balance. An experienced bird-watcher often learns more from songs and calls than from glimpses of birds that may be elusive.

The development of good observation skills takes time and a quiet-centred condition. This in itself requires a change from a lifestyle that is indoor, semi-nocturnal and media-dominated to one that is outdoor, mainly daytime, and nature-focused. At our office we balance indoor desk work with observation and physical work in the garden that supplies most of our food. As well as feeding us, working with nature provides the inspiration for, and testing of, the more abstract ideas expressed here.

I have found that skills in "reading landscape" to be the most important a designer can develop to be useful in advising others on the potentials, limitations, land use history and successional processes of any particular parcel of land.

Failure is useful so long as we learn

Planning and design processes (like life in general) often involve incremental adjustment in response to experience. No matter how little knowledge we have, we can proceed from a very narrow perspective to a broader and more wholistic one by incremental adjustment.

Although this is an excellent and simple process, when working with complex natural systems we need to remember that we don't understand, let alone control, all the factors; and that cause and effect are often a loop or a web, rather than a linear chain. When you try some action, don't assume you were the reason for any success. Conduct small trials and think about other possible causes for success or failure.

Elegant solutions are simple, even invisible

In science the simplest answer that explains all the facts is regarded as having more validity than a complex answer. Similarly in design, enormous complexity often indicates poor design. A really effective design solution may be remarkably simple. This simplicity may be inherent, or it may arise because self-organising (living) complexity that works without us understanding or controlling it is doing most of the job.

Effective systems may work so well that we don't even notice them. This is common with free environmental services, such as purification of air and water or soil rehabilitation and good design solutions that go unnoticed until they fail from abuse. The saying "we don't know what we've got till it's gone" is relevant here. Careful observation and a respect for humble life forms and processes is a partial antidote for this perennial problem.

Make the smallest intervention necessary

In attempting to adjust systems to fix problems, we need to be careful that we don't damage or disrupt other processes that are working perfectly. Because much effective design is invisible, large-scale interventions are likely to do more harm than good, and they require large amounts of energy and resources to implement. Japanese natural farmer and philosopher Masanobu Fukuoka has written eloquently about the value of doing nothing and the damage from large-scale intervention in nature. The Bradley method of bush regeneration, based on the careful observation and minimal interventions of the Bradley sisters, has been acknowledged as highly effective in conserving bushland from spread of environmental weeds. Its focus on minimal disturbance to remove weeds from the most intact areas of native vegetation runs counter to the prevailing approach, which is to attack the weeds head-on with herbicide and other high-impact methods.

Avoid too much of a good thing

When we experience a positive result from an action, there is almost always a powerful temptation to repeat the action, working on the often misguided idea that if some is good, more must be better. In sustainable societies and nature, limited resources often acted as a natural constraint on such actions, but in the modern world these temptations are everywhere. One of the universal effects of affluence is the change in diet towards consuming more sugar, fat and protein. Foods with these concentrated energy sources have always been desirable, but in the past natural limits protected us from the adverse effects of overindulgence.

Any gardener or farmer who has a great harvest following use of a fertiliser knows the temptation to use more next time. The slowing in growth of world food yields, despite increases in fertiliser use, shows the problem is widespread. As in the case of overindulgence in sugar, fat and protein, overuse of any fertilisers creates imbalances that reduce long-term yields and plant health.

Many of these statements that caution us against bold and impulsive action reflect a general observation: that success or function in any system may represent failure in connected systems that are larger or smaller in scale.

The problem is the solution

This slogan expresses the idea that things are not always as they seem; the things we view negatively may have a positive aspect that is more important than, or at least compensates for, the predominant negative perception.

The most common examples of this idea relate to weeds or other life forms which we regard as pests. Weeds or pests may be:

- environmental indicators of need for management change
- agents repairing damaged soil, etc.
- resources which, for economic or cultural reasons, we fail to value.

An open, inquiring attitude to problems is almost always more fruitful than an urgent demand for solutions. The latter is often driven by fear and an unquestioned consensus about the nature of the problem.

Another aspect of this maxim is that the best solutions to problems can be found in places and cultures where the problem is extreme. In these situations co-evolution over time will develop the best responses. In places where the design problem is less severe, people often ignore it or come up with solutions that use more effort or resources to overcome the problem. For example, in my brief time on the precipitous Amalfi coast in southern Italy, I became aware of several creative solutions to the problems and limitations of very steep land, some traditional and others modern and imported. Conversely, while travelling in the Mediterranean I was surprised by the poor development of rainwater tanks and small earth dams compared with Australia. Despite the dry summers, the prevalence of permanent streams, springs and good quality groundwater in the Mediterranean has reduced the stimulus to harvest rainwater.

Recognise and break out of design cul-de-sacs

When we recognise the potential to turn problems into solutions, we often encounter the inertia of fundamental beliefs, system architecture and power structures that stand to lose by the innovation. Although modern culture appears to encourage innovation (within narrow limits), we need to be aware why conservatism—resistance to radical change—is an important characteristic of both natural and human systems.

In nature and in human behaviour, proven solutions tend to become entrenched, while recent innovations are easily swept away by unfavourable conditions. In the history of life, mutations in the basic chemistry of cellular life almost never manage to get past early embryo stage because evolution over hundreds of millions of years has perfected these processes and any variations are usually lethal. More recent evolutionary patterns have rarely been vested with fundamental functions, so occasional mutations survive, at least initially. For example, variation in the number of nipples, and even of digits, is common in mammals. Stress and competition tend to suppress such variations through low success in reproduction.

In families, most parents deliberately or unconsciously teach their children the lessons (good and bad) that they learnt in childhood from their parents, in preference to their own insights as adults. The more stressed parents are, the more this becomes true. The cycle of battered child to battering parent is now well recognised. Similarly in human culture, patterns of proven behaviour or knowledge become entrenched through tradition and institutions. Over long periods of relative stability, institutions rather than individuals are the critical keepers of culture. What is needed in these situations is the capacity to think laterally, readiness to abandon the proven and take risks.

Broad experience and observation of the world outside the particular situation or system can allow recognition of the patterns of design cul-de-sacs and the general nature of transformative solutions. In most cases these solutions will challenge and undermine existing structures of power and wealth in society and are therefore strongly resisted.

The Importance of Interaction

These and other insights, drawn from the interpretation of traditional systems of knowledge and for the great thinkers of the modern world, provide a wealth of ideas that can help us make sense of observation and experience. But unless we get out there, and open our eyes and use our hands and our hearts, all the ideas in the world will not save us.

Thus the thinking and design revolution, of which permaculture is a part, only makes sense when it reconnects us to the wonder and mystery of life through practical interaction.

Original Source

This article is excerpted with the kind permission of the author from:

Holmgren, D. 2002. Permaculture: principles and pathways beyond sustainability. Holmgren Design Services, Hepburn, Australia.

To order this or other publications by David Holmgren, contact:

Holmgren Design Services
Melliodora (Hepburn Permaculture Gardens)
16 Fourteenth St.
Hepburn
Victoria 3461
Australia
Tel/Fax: +61 (0)353483636
Email: info@holmgren.com.au
Web: http://www.holmgren.com.au

This excerpt was originally published as *The Overstory* #116.

Revegetation Planning for Farm Forestry

David Holmgren

Revegetation is defined here as, "the planting of trees and shrubs, the encouragement of natural regeneration and the use of deep rooted and/or perennial crops and pastures" (Oates 1987).

Introduction

Whole farm planning provides a framework within which revegetation can be integrated with farming. Whole farm planning considers the natural resource base, the physical improvements of the farm, land management practices, and the financial basis of the farm.

Landholders interested in revegetation tend to be planners by nature and are often recognised in a district as "good farmers." This reinforces the thesis that planning is fundamental to sustainable land use. The next step for these farmers is to become more conscious of the planning process to develop more integrated farm plans.

There is a role for input from a large range of professionals including landscape designers, but it is the landholder who must become the lead planner. Only the landholder can consider and balance all the strategic, technical and practical elements which make a whole farm and develop a plan which can grow and change over time.

General Eisenhower once said "plans are useless but planning is essential." In other words, planning is a process rather than bits of paper, or put another way, strategic planning rather than master planning.

Master planning (where detailed plans are implemented producing a final fixed state which represent exactly what is on paper) has been discredited in the planning profession due to its failure to deal with complex evolving systems such as cities. Many attempts at farm planning by consultants, including soil conservation officers and landscape architects, have tended to be master plans which encourage the notion of a final state for the landscape and farm. It might be noted that the final state for everything is death.

Strategic planning emphasizes on-going processes of development which respond to changing circumstances. It recognises that complex systems can never be completely described, predicted or controlled but that forces can be identified and worked with to develop a more balanced and productive system. Most important, strategy planning can help pinpoint the initial step to initiate the desired processes without later having to undo what has already been done.

The planning process can be considered as a sequence of five steps:

Inventory: the collection of relevant data.

Evaluation: organising the data into comprehensible patterns.

Strategy: the general direction and framework for development.

Design: the particular forms which express the strategy.

Management: processes of implementation and operation.

Feedback at every stage is essential. Without feedback, planning becomes a rigid ritual of no particular use. In fact, all steps occur to some extent simultaneously. For example, we usually have some notion of the strategy and even the management before all the data is in. Thus the planning process in practice involves the ordinary skills of responding effectively to the unpredictable and chaotic nature of reality.

The natural environment, seasonal conditions and our imperfect knowledge will determine what gets done and what succeeds. Capital and labour availability will limit what can be attempted, and the heritage of past decisions and developments, good and bad, must be accepted to some degree.

Whole Farm Planning

The following methodology for whole farm planning was originally applied to small farms where a shift from pastoral farming to more intensive tree based land uses often requires radical changes to layout and substantial capital investment. However it is also applicable to broadacre farms where diversification and revegetation demand good planning.

The planning process can be applied to four interwoven "development streams" which together constitute a whole farm.

i. Landscape

This is the natural foundation upon which any farm is built. The land systems approach most effectively integrates all the data about the natural environment. Sustainable land use focuses the natural forces towards providing for human needs while continuing to perform the landscape's essential functions.

ii. Infrastructure

This is a planning term to describe the improvements which form the framework of any farming system. Infrastructure includes fencing, water supply, access, maintenance facilities, power supply and even shelterbelts. A method used in planning complex systems is analysis in terms of networks and nodes, zones and sectors and can be useful in looking at farm infrastructure.

In sustainable systems, infrastructure development reflects and reinforces the natural landscape. For example fence lines along soil boundaries make varying management possible and provide a permanent indication of differences which would otherwise be hidden. A contour belt of trees along a break of slope may mark sites susceptible to saline discharge while depressing the water table and reducing the risk, or it could delineate lower slopes suitable for cropping and upper slopes suitable for grazing only.

iii. Domestic environment

Most farms are homes. Traditionally (and in any sustainable system) the home is an important sub-system in the farm economy. Well planned and managed, it can:

- provide some family needs more effectively than the money economy;
- be a refuge during environmental or economic catastrophe from which farming can re-establish;
- provide a testing ground for new ideas, processes and species before they are applied on a broad scale.

In revegetation, the domestic environment should be an arboretum and nursery for species which may have potential for stabilising the landscape, shelter, or commercial crops. In the agribusiness approach to farming, the domestic scene is ignored as irrelevant and tends to become an incongruous island of suburban consumerism in a sea of agricultural production. That such farms are alienating, unbalanced and increasingly uneconomic is becoming more widely accepted after less than a generation of obsession with domestic escape from rural reality. The domestic environment is really a microcosm of the farm and planning its development or redevelopment can be a first step towards whole farm planning.

iv. Enterprise

This is the engine, linked to regional and world economics, which makes or breaks the whole farm. Husbandry and management have traditionally been seen as the key factors in making a living from farming. Today it requires increasing consideration of design at one end of the business (especially where trees add a third dimension) and marketing and finance at the other.

Past strategies of maximising production and specialization have contributed to over-investment in capital equipment, vulnerability to market collapse, high production costs, land degradation and product contamination. Post-industrial economic forces demand more emphasis on input cost minimisation, diversification and recognition of the value of "information" as an essential and continuing input. The imperative of sustainable resource use requires the same changes. Thus farms will increasingly involve several enterprises integrated in ways which complement and support each other.

In the four-point approach outlined above, it is important to note the increasing complexity of planning and management as we move from landscape to enterprise. However, the landscape always remains the foundation and reference point for farming. If we fail to work within its parameters then success at other levels will be superficial and short lived.

Planning Practicalities

Documentation of a whole farm plan could include written material, time lines and budgets as well as plans and overlays. Since landholders are generally unfamiliar with the use of plans, some brief notes on the practicalities of using plans may be useful.

Ideally each farm would have a comprehensive base map at an appropriate scale (1:5000 for broadacre farms) with one meter contour intervals. This accurately describes landform and slopes but is very costly to have prepared for a single farm. A practical alternative is to use an aerial photograph (preferably colour) as a base for a farm plan.

Clear plastic overlays can then be prepared showing the existing features of the land, improvements, and farming enterprise. It is best to document these as three separate overlays which relate to the development streams mentioned previously.

The landscape overlay might show drainage lines and swamp topography (contours transferred from a topographic map) soil features, rock outcrops, natural vegetation, specific land degradation and "problem" areas.

The infrastructure (improvements) overlay would show fencing, water systems including dams, lanes, buildings, power lines and plantings and include the main features of the homestead. The homestead (domestic) systems should be recorded on another larger scale plan (1:250 or 1:500) using the same series of overlays which apply to the whole farm.

The enterprise overlay would show paddock names, sizes, characteristics and land use history. Most of the documentation for the farm enterprises would consist of more conventional records and budgets.

Plan Development

By various combinations of overlays and base photos, different aspects of the farm can be highlighted and draft overlays of proposed changes prepared. A number of different options can be developed reflecting different development strategies and external factors including markets. By developing drafts of the Enterprise plan, the implications for infrastructure and landscape systems can be explored and vice versa.

Even the landscape overlay can evolve over time. It may develop into a land systems map showing components derived from slope class and soil types. As revegetation proceeds, new drafts can be used to map all the woody vegetation systems on the farm.

More definite plans of proposed changes can be prepared covering a specific time period (e.g., 5 yrs) with associated time lines, specifications and budgets. Annual reviews can adjust the plans in the light of new information or changed circumstances.

Government Assistance

Increasingly government assistance for land degradation control is being tied to landholders having a whole farm plan. While these sorts of controls may result in less than adequate planning, they do indicate the importance of better planning within farms. The general crisis of farm financing and the relatively unregulated nature of agricultural land use (compared with forestry for example) may lead to whole farm plans being increasingly seen as a precondition for bank finance and planning permits for new land uses.

Strategic Issues

- A portion of the annual budget of any farm (or public land management) should be allocated to revegetation. Areas of annual expenditure might include research, planning and design, site preparation and pest control, fencing, planting and seeding, follow up maintenance and general management and harvesting.
- In general, some planting should be done each year to spread the risks of bad seasons and develop a regular demand from nurseries (commercial or on-farm).
- Reliable sources of proven species and provenances should be established to assure continuity in programs while unproven species can be trialled in small plantings to continually expand and improve planting stock.
- On arable land, planting and direct sowing can be combined with a cropping phase using the same treatments to prepare ground for crop and trees and allow a period without stock before fences must be in place.
- Fostering or responding to natural regeneration must be more opportunistic since favourable conditions, such as following bushfires or droughts, tend to be episodic. Response to changing markets can also provide unpredicted opportunities, (e.g., decline in wool prices gives an opportunity to destock marginal wool country and allow regeneration).
- Fencing technologies are critical for broad acre revegetation since protection from stock is the greatest cost in any program. Management neglect or fence failure is the greatest cause of tree loss. Heavy conventional fencing is inappropriate in almost all situations for the following reasons: 1) lightweight electric fencing systems are now well proven for all livestock and are less than half the cast of conventional fencing; and 2) land form fencing with frequent changes in direction can be affordable if light weight systems are used.
- Pruning and thinning are the key management tasks which follow from any successful broad acre revegetation program and can provide useful yields of firewood and fodder within 5 years. Failure to perform these tasks will generally reduce the long term values and yields from revegetation.

Practical Issues

i   Trees are long term elements in the landscape with the following implications:

- successful establishment involves planning and action over several years.
- planted along badly located fence lines or other farm improvements, they can lock the farmer into maintaining that position for a generation or more.

ii   Changes in land use and management need to be considered. For example:

- a shift to cropping and wide cultivators may make scattered paddock trees a distinct disadvantage
- stubble burning and herbicides can have detrimental effects on trees
- diversification into goats can increase the relative attraction of tree fodder, require more elaborate fencing to protect trees and change noxious species such as gorse and blackberries into valuable fodder species.

iii   Vehicle movement and mustering can be restricted on otherwise accessible land by inappropriately located trees and fencing.

iv   Trees are tall and add a third dimension to an otherwise two dimensional landscape, having a huge impact on wind, frost, sun, fire, views and visibility. Good planning and design maximises the benefits and minimises the problems created by this third dimension.

v   Tree harvesting is an inevitable consequence of successful revegetation and involves large weights and volumes. Designs should take this into account and allow for the use of appropriate machinery.

Conclusion

The role of revegetation should not be confined to landscape stabilization. Perennial crops and pastures (included in wider definitions of revegetation) are now widely recognized as an essential aspect of sustainable pastoral farming while tree crops are providing opportunities for enterprise diversification.

Development of low cost establishment techniques and the application of basic selection and breeding techniques will greatly improve the economic viability of new tree and shrub based enterprises while major advances with conventional crops will increasingly depend on centralized and specialized genetic engineering with all its environmental and social hazards. The progressive development of sustainable land use will be characterised by increasing use of perennial vegetation systems. This is a fundamental premise of the Permaculture concept proposed in the 1970's by the author and Bill Mollison.

References

Mollison, B, and D. Holmgren. 1978, Permaculture One. Corgi, Melbourne, Australia.

Oates, N. and B. Clarke. 1987. Trees for the Back Paddock. Goddard & Dobson, Australia.

Victorian Govt. 1987. SALT ACTION Draft Strategy. Victoria, Australia.

Original Source

This article is excerpted with the kind permission of the author from:

Holmgren, D. 1994. Trees on the Treeless Plains: Revegetation manual for the volcanic landscapes of Central Victoria. Holmgren Design Services, Hepburn, Australia.

Trees On The Treeless Plains is no longer in print. A more detailed and updated coverage of the article subject is provided in Article 9, "Whole Farm and Landscape Planning" included in *David Holmgren: Collected Writings 1978-2000* published by Holmgren Design Services.

To order this or other publications by David Holmgren, contact Holmgren Design Services at Holmgren Design Services, Melliodora (Hepburn Permaculture Gardens), 16 Fourteenth St, Hepburn, 3461, Australia; Tel: +61 (0)353483636; Email: info@holmgren.com.au; Web: http://www.holmgren.com.au.

This excerpt was originally published as *The Overstory #88*

Permaculture

Steve Diver

A personal note from Bill Mollison

I have been vitally concerned about the environment for over thirty years, first as a scientist and naturalist, later as a vigorous campaigner against environmental exploitation.

As a child I lived in a sort of dream, and I didn't really awaken until I was about twenty-eight years old. I spent most of my early working life in the bush or on the sea. I fished and hunted for my livelihood. It wasn't until the 1950s that I noticed large parts of the system in which I lived were disappearing. First fish stocks became extinct. Then I noticed the seaweed around the shorelines had gone. Large patches of forest began to die. I hadn't realised until those things were gone that I'd become very fond of them; that I was in love with my country.

This discovery shifted the emphasis of my work in the late 1960s. This lead to the development of the "Permaculture Concept," a strategy which focuses on sustainable design for urban and rural properties. Permaculture, or PERMAnent CULTURE, is the conscious design of agriculturally-productive ecosystems and energy conserving settlements which have the resilience, dynamic stability and diversity of natural systems, like forests or grasslands. Such systems provide for their own needs, do not pollute or exploit, and are therefore sustainable in the long term.

Permaculture design is taught in a 72 hour, two-week intensive course, as a series of strategies which draw on traditional knowledge and modern technology. Graduates of these courses can then teach others, or can design for themselves or others. Permaculture information has thus been freely and quickly disseminated. There are approximately 250,000 Permaculture graduates worldwide, and many thousands more who use Permaculture texts and information. There are very few countries which do not have a Permaculture group, association and indigenous teachers teaching in their own languages.

All of this has been achieved entirely independent of government and institutional support. There are no expensive showcase sites; rather the sum total of many people working in their backyards, farms, schools, community gardens, projects and villages.

The impetus for all the work I do has been the desire to leave our children gardens, not deserts. I see the great challenge of sustainable agriculture is to produce the food and fibre needed while sustaining fertile soils; maintaining supplies of clean water, and protecting and enhancing biological diversity and the health of ecosystems. Societies can meet this challenge by supporting vital ecosystems, farmers in their roles as producers and stewards and urban conservation groups.

Introduction To Permaculture by Steve Diver

The word "permaculture" was coined in 1978 by Bill Mollison, an Australian ecologist, and one of his students, David Holmgren. It is a contraction of "permanent agriculture" or "permanent culture."

Permaculture is about designing ecological human habitats and food production systems. It is a land use and community building movement which strives for the harmonious integration of human dwellings, microclimate, annual and perennial plants, animals, soils, and water into stable, productive communities. The focus is not on these elements themselves, but rather on the relationships created among them by the way we place them in the landscape. This synergy is further enhanced by mimicking patterns found in nature.

A central theme in permaculture is the design of ecological landscapes that produce food. Emphasis is placed on multi-use plants, cultural practices such as sheet mulching and trellising, and the integration of animals to recycle nutrients and graze weeds.

However, permaculture entails much more than just food production. Energy efficient buildings, waste water treatment, recycling, and land stewardship in general are other important components of permaculture. More recently, permaculture has expanded its purview to include economic and social structures that support the evolution and development of more permanent communities, such as co-housing projects and ecovillages. As such, permaculture design concepts are applicable to urban as well as rural settings, and are appropriate for single households as well as whole farms and villages.

"Integrated farming" and "ecological engineering" are terms sometimes used to describe permaculture, with "cultivated ecology" perhaps coming the closest. Though helpful, these terms alone do not capture the holistic nature of permaculture; thus, the following definitions are included here to provide additional insight.

Permaculture Defined

Bill Mollison

Permaculture is a design system for creating sustainable human environments.

The Permaculture Drylands Institute (The Permaculture Activist, Autumn 1989)

Permaculture: the use of ecology as the basis for designing integrated systems of food production, housing, appropriate technology, and community development. Permaculture is built upon an ethic of caring for the earth and interacting with the environment in mutually beneficial ways.

Lee Barnes (former editor of Katuah Journal and Permaculture Connections)

Permaculture (PERMAnent agriCULTURE or PERMAnent CULTURE) is a sustainable design system stressing the harmonious interrelationship of humans, plants, animals and the Earth.

To paraphrase the founder of permaculture, designer Bill Mollison:

Permaculture principles focus on thoughtful designs for small-scale intensive systems which are labor efficient and which use biological resources instead of fossil fuels. Designs stress ecological connections and closed energy and material loops. The core of permaculture is design and the working relationships and connections between all things. Each component in a system performs multiple functions, and each function is supported by many elements. Key to efficient design is observation and replication of natural ecosystems, where designers maximize diversity with polycultures, stress efficient energy planning for houses and settlement, using and accelerating natural plant succession, and increasing the highly productive "edge-zones" within the system.

Permaculture adopts techniques and principles from ecology, appropriate technology, sustainable agriculture, and the wisdom of indigenous peoples. The ethical basis of permaculture rests upon care of the earth—maintaining a system in which all life can thrive. This includes human access to resources and provisions, but not the accumulation of wealth, power, or land beyond their needs.

Characteristics of Permaculture

- Permaculture is one of the most holistic, integrated systems analysis and design methodologies found in the world.
- Permaculture can be applied to create productive ecosystems from the human-use standpoint or to help degraded ecosystems recover health and wildness. Permaculture can be applied in any ecosystem, no matter how degraded.
- Permaculture values and validates traditional knowledge and experience. Permaculture incorporates sustainable agriculture practices and land management techniques and strategies from around the world. Permaculture is a bridge between traditional cultures and emergent earth-tuned cultures.
- Permaculture promotes organic agriculture which does not use pesticides to pollute the environment.
- Permaculture aims to maximize symbiotic and synergistic relationships between site components.
- Permaculture is urban planning as well as rural land design.
- Permaculture design is site specific, client specific, and culture specific.

The Practical Application of Permaculture

Permaculture is not limited to plant and animal agriculture, but also includes community planning and development, use of appropriate technologies (coupled with an adjustment of lifestyle), and adoption of concepts and philosophies that are both earth-based and people-centered, such as bioregionalism.

Many of the appropriate technologies advocated by permaculturists are well known. Among these are solar and wind power, composting toilets, solar greenhouses, energy efficient housing, and solar food cooking and drying.

Due to the inherent sustainability of perennial cropping systems, permaculture places a heavy emphasis on tree crops. Systems that integrate annual and perennial crops—such as alley cropping and agroforestry—take advantage of "the edge effect," increase biological diversity, and offer other characteristics missing in monocultural systems. Thus, multicropping systems that blend woody perennials and annuals hold promise as viable techniques for large-scale farming. Ecological methods of production for any specific crop or farming system (e.g., soil building practices, biological pest control, composting) are central to permaculture as well as to sustainable agriculture in general.

Since permaculture is not a production system, per se, but rather a land use and community planning philosophy, it is not limited to a specific method of production. Furthermore, as permaculture principles may be adapted to farms or villages worldwide, it is not site specific and therefore amenable to locally adapted techniques of production.

As an example, standard organic farming and gardening techniques utilizing cover crops, green manures, crop rotation, and mulches are emphasized in permacultural systems. However, there are many other options and technologies available to sustainable farmers working within a permacultural framework (e.g., chisel plows, no-till implements, spading implements, compost turners, rotational grazing). The decision as to which "system" is employed is site-specific and management dependent.

Farming systems and techniques commonly associated with permaculture include agroforestry, swales, contour plantings, Keyline agriculture (soil and water management), hedgerows and windbreaks, and integrated farming systems such as pond-dike aquaculture, aquaponics, intercropping, and polyculture.

Gardening and recycling methods common to permaculture include edible landscaping, keyhole gardening, companion planting, trellising, sheet mulching, chicken tractors, solar greenhouses, spiral herb gardens, swales, and vermicomposting.

Water collection, management, and re-use systems like Keyline, greywater, rain catchment, constructed wetlands, aquaponics (the integration of hydroponics with recirculating aquaculture), and solar aquatic ponds (also known as "living machines") play an important role in permaculture designs.

Traditional agricultural systems such as this one in Bali can serve as models for sustainable resource systems. (photo: C. Elevitch)

Human settlements can be designed with site-specific goals according to permaculture design principles. Crystal Waters, Queensland, Australia. (photo: C. Elevitch)

The Ethics of Permaculture

Permaculture is unique among alternative farming systems (e.g., organic, sustainable, eco-agriculture, biodynamic) in that it works with a set of ethics that suggest we think and act responsibly in relation to each other and the earth.

The ethics of permaculture provide a sense of place in the larger scheme of things, and serve as a guidepost to right livelihood in concert with the global community and the environment, rather than individualism and indifference.

1. Care of the Earth

…includes all living and non-living things—plants, animals, land, water and air

2. Care of People

…promotes self-reliance and community responsibility—access to resources necessary for existence

3. Setting Limits to Population & Consumption

…gives away surplus—contribution of surplus time, labor, money, information, and energy to achieve the aims of earth and people care.

Permaculture also acknowledges a basic life ethic, which recognizes the intrinsic worth of every living thing. A tree has value in itself, even if it presents no commercial value to humans. That the tree is alive and functioning is worthwhile. It is doing its part in nature: recycling litter, producing oxygen, sequestering carbon dioxide, sheltering animals, building soils, and so on.

The Principles of Permaculture Design

Whereas permaculture ethics are more akin to broad moral values or codes of behavior, the principles of permaculture provide a set of universally applicable guidelines which can be used in designing sustainable habitats. Distilled from multiple disciplines—ecology, energy conservation, landscape design, and environmental science—these principles are inherent in any permaculture design, in any climate, and at any scale.

1 Relative location
2 Each element performs multiple functions
3 Each function is supported by many elements

4   Energy efficient planning
5   Using biological resources
6   Energy cycling
7   Small-scale intensive systems
8   Natural plant succession and stacking
9   Polyculture and diversity of species
10 Increasing "edge" within a system
11 Observe and replicate natural patterns
12 Pay attention to scale
13 Attitude

Permaculture Resources

Four ways to learn about permaculture include: the permaculture design course, the permaculture literature, the Internet, and permaculture workshops.

The Permaculture Design Course is the primary vehicle for transfer of permaculture expertise. The standard course is 72 hours in length and lasts two weeks. Graduates are issued a permaculture design certificate and are entitled to use the term "Permaculture" in the pursuit of livelihood and for educational purposes. Graduates are eligible to continue studies and become certified permaculture consultants.

The permaculture literature is a rich source of information on a wide range of topics dealing with land

In permaculture, resources are used efficiently and then recycled. Here run-off from a tree nursery (in background) flows downslope through a reed bed (on left side, behind water) for filtration and then into a holding pond for agricultural use. (photo: C. Elevitch)

use, plant and animal agriculture, water management, appropriate technology, energy-efficient and toxic-free housing, and community design.

Since 1995, the Internet (e.g., World Wide Web and email) has become an important resource and networking tool in the dissemination of permaculture information. A selection of web sites is listed below.

Permaculture workshops are commonly held as one to three day events to provide training on technologies such as vermicomposting, solar greenhouses, straw bale construction, sheet mulching, and organic gardening.

Periodicals and Organizations

The Permaculture Activist
P.O. Box 1209
Black Mountain, NC 28711 USA
Tel: 828-669-6336; Fax: 828-669-5068
Email: pcactiv@metalab.unc.edu
http://www.permacultureactivist.net

The Permaculture Activist is the leading periodical for North American permaculture. It publishes articles on permaculture, edible landscaping, bioregionalism, aquaculture, etc., and provides a current listing of upcoming permaculture design courses. It serves as an important networking tool in the U.S., Canada, and Central America. Back issues are available.

Permaculture Drylands Journal
Permaculture Drylands Institute
P.O. Box 156 Santa Fe, NM 87504-0156 USA
Tel: 505-983-0663; Fax: 505-986-0339
Email: Pdrylands@aol.com
Web: http://www.permaculture.net/PDI%20Web/PDI.html

Permaculture Drylands Journal (formerly *Sustainable Living in Drylands*) is published in April, August, and December by the Permaculture Drylands Education and Research Institute. It focuses on permaculture concepts and designs for arid lands, with a heavy focus on New Mexico and Arizona. PDJ has published articles on straw bale buildings, solar box cookers, dryland farming, and many other topics of interest; back issues are available. PDI offers a regular series of Permaculture Design Courses.

Permaculture International Journal
Permaculture International Ltd.
P.O. Box 6039 South Lismore, NSW 2480 Australia
Email: pgould@mullum.com.au

Web: http://www.nor.com.au/environment/perma/index.html

Permaculture International Journal was the leading permaculture magazine for two decades, yet ceased publication in mid-2000. Permaculture International Ltd. continues its activities online, with a web page that features a newsletter, a global directory, an email discussion list, educational resources, and permaculture events in Australia. Back issues of PIJ, found in a few libraries here and there, is a gold mine of valuable information.

Tagari Publications—Permaculture Institute
31 Rulla Road
Sisters Creek Tasmania 7325 Australia
Tel: + 61 (0)3 6445 0945; Fax: + 61 (0)3 6445 0944
Email: tagariadmin@southcom.com.au

The International Permaculture Institute serves as the international coordinating organization for permaculture activities such as permaculture design accreditation.

Books on Permaculture

Introduction to Permaculture by Bill Mollison and Reny Mia Slay. 1991. Tagari Publishers, Tyalgum, Australia. 198 p.

Permaculture: A Designer's Manual by Bill Mollison. 1988. Tagari Publications, Tyalgum, Australia. 576 p.

Gaia's Garden: A Guide to Home-Scale Permaculture by Toby Hemenway. 2001. Chelsea Green Publishing Co., White River Junction, Vermont, USA. 222 p.

Earth User's Guide to Permaculture by Rosemary Morrow and Rob Allsop. 2000. Simon & Schuster Intl.

On-Line Articles, Fact Sheets, & Proceedings on Permaculture

Permaculture: Design For Living by Bill Mollison. Originally published in IN CONTEXT #28, Spring 1991: http://www.context.org/ICLIB/IC28/Mollison.htm

"Building A Bamboo Farm: Using Permaculture Principles in Bamboo Agroforestry" by Simon Henderson. One of several on-line articles at Permaculture the Earth: http://www.permaearth.org/bamboo.html

On-line articles on Permaculture the Earth: http://www.permaearth.org/writings.html

Original Source

This edition of *The Overstory* is excerpted with the kind permission of Steve Diver from the full version:

Introduction to Permaculture: Concepts and Resources posted at http://www.attra.org/attra-pub/perma.html.

Appropriate Technology Transfer for Rural Areas (ATTRA) P.O. Box 3657 Fayetteville, AR 72702

Phone: 1-800-346-9140; Fax: 1-501-442-9842; Web: http://www.attra.org

"Characteristics of Permaculture" is from: Pilarski, M. (ed.) 1994. Restoration Forestry. Kivaki Press, Durango, CO. p. 450.

This excerpt was originally published as *The Overstory* #94.

Agroecology: principles and strategies

Miguel A. Altieri

Sustainable agriculture is a relatively recent response to the decline in the quality of the natural resource base associated with modern agriculture (McIsaac and Edwards 1994). Discussion of agricultural production has evolved from a purely technical one to a more complex one characterized by social, cultural, political and economic dimensions. The concept of sustainability is controversial and diffuse due to existing conflicting definitions and interpretations of its meaning. However, it is a useful concept as it addresses concerns about agriculture which are the result of the co-evolution of socioeconomic and natural systems (Reijntjes et al 1992). A wider understanding of the agricultural context requires the study of agriculture, the global environment and social systems given that agricultural development results from the complex interaction of a multitude of factors. It is through this deeper understanding of the ecology of agricultural systems that doors will open to new management options more in tune with the objectives of a truly sustainable agriculture.

The sustainability concept has prompted much discussion and has promoted the need to propose major adjustments in conventional agriculture. Several possible solutions to the environmental problems created by capital and technology intensive farming systems have been proposed and research is currently in progress to evaluate alternative systems (Gliessman 1998). The main focus is the reduction or elimination of agrochemical inputs to assure adequate plant nutrition and plant protection through organic nutrient sources and integrated pest management.

Although hundreds of environmentally oriented research projects and technological development attempts have taken place, the thrust is still highly technological, emphasizing the suppression of limiting factors or the symptoms of disease. The prevalent philosophy is that pests, nutrient deficiencies or other factors are the cause of low productivity, as opposed to the view that pests or nutrients only become limiting if conditions in the agroecosystem are not in equilibrium (Carrol et al 1990). For this reason, there still prevails a narrow view that specific causes affect productivity, and overcoming the limiting factor via

new technologies continues to be the main goal. This view has diverted agriculturists from realizing that limiting factors only represent symptoms of a systemic disease inherent to unbalances within the agroecosystem. By ignoring the context and complexity of agroecological processes the root causes of agricultural limitations are not fully appreciated (Altieri et al 1993).

The science of agroecology, which is defined as the application of ecological concepts and principles to the design and management of sustainable agroecosystems, provides a framework to assess the complexity of agroecosystems (Altieri 1995). Agroecology goes beyond the use of alternative practices to develop agroecosystems with minimal dependence on high agrochemical and energy inputs. It emphasizes complex agricultural systems in which ecological interactions and synergism between biological components provide the mechanisms for the systems for their own soil fertility, productivity and crop protection (Altieri and Rosset 1995).

Principles of Agroecology

Scientists and developers have disregarded a key point in the development of a more self-sufficient and sustaining agriculture: a deep understanding of the nature of agroecosystems and the principles by which they function. Given this limitation, agroecology has emerged as a discipline that provides basic ecological principles for how to study, design and manage agroecosystems that are both productive and conserve natural resources, while remaining culturally sensitive, socially just and economically viable (Altieri 1995).

Agroecology goes beyond a one-dimensional view of agroecosystems—their genetics, agronomy, edaphology, and so on—to embrace an understanding of ecological and social levels of co-evolution, structure and function. Instead of focusing on one particular component of the agroecosystem, agroecology emphasizes the interrelationship of all agroecosystem components and the complex dynamics of ecological processes (Vandermeer 1995).

Agroecosystems are communities of plants and animals interacting with their physical and chemical environments that have been modified by people to produce food, fiber, fuel and other products for human consumption and processing. Agroecology is the holistic study of agroecosystems, including all environmental and human elements. It focuses on the form, dynamics and functions of their interrelationships and the processes in which they are involved. An area used for agricultural production, e.g., a field, is seen as a complex system in which ecological processes found under natural conditions also occur, e.g., nutrient cycling, predator/prey interactions, competition, symbiosis and successional changes. By understanding these ecological relationships and processes, agroecosystems can be manipulated to improve production and to produce more sustainably, with fewer negative environmental or social impacts and fewer external inputs (Altieri 1995).

The design of such systems is based on the application of the following ecological principles (Reinjntjes *et al* 1992) (see also Table 1 at end):

1 Enhance recycling of biomass and optimizing nutrient availability and balancing nutrient flow.

2 Secure favorable soil conditions for plant growth, particularly by managing organic matter and enhancing soil biotic activity.

3 Microclimate management, water harvesting and soil management through increased soil cover.

4 Species and genetic diversification of the agroecosystem in time and space.

5 Enhance beneficial biological interactions and synergism among agrobiodiversity components resulting in the promotion of key ecological processes and services.

These principles can be applied by way of various techniques and strategies. Each of these will have different effects on productivity, stability and resiliency within the farm system, depending on the local opportunities, resource constraints and, in most cases, on the market. The ultimate goal of agroecological design is to integrate components so that overall biological efficiency is improved, biodiversity is preserved, and the agroecosystem productivity is self-sustaining (capacity is maintained). The goal is to design a quilt of agroecosystems within a landscape unit, each mimicking the structure and function of natural ecosystems.

Biodiversification of Agroecosystems

From a management perspective, the agroecological objective is to provide a balanced environment, sustained yields, biologically mediated soil fertility and natural pest regulation through the design of diversified agroecosystems and the use of low-input technologies (Gleissman 1998). Agroecologists are now recognizing that intercropping, agroforestry and other diversification methods mimic natural ecological processes, and that the sustainability of complex agroecosystems lies in the ecological models they follow. By designing farming systems that mimic nature, optimal use can be made of sunlight, soil nutrients and rainfall (Pretty 1994).

Agroecological management must lead to optimal recycling of nutrients and organic matter turnover, closed energy flows, water and soil conservation and balance pest-natural enemy populations. The strategy exploits the synergism that results from the various combinations of crops, tree and animals in spatial and temporal arrangements (Altieri 1994).

In essence, the optimal behavior of agroecosystems depends on the level of interactions between the various biotic and abiotic components. By assembling a diversity of functional components it is possible to initiate synergism which subsidize agroecosystem processes by providing ecological services such as the activation of soil biology, the recycling of nutrients, the enhancement of beneficial arthropods and antagonists, and so on (Altieri and Nicholls 1999). Today there is a diverse selection of practices and technologies available. Key practices are those of a preventative nature and which act by reinforcing the "immunity" of the agroecosystem through a series of mechanisms (Table 2 at end).

Various strategies to restore agricultural diversity in time and space include:

1 Crop Rotations. Temporal diversity incorporated into cropping systems, providing crop nutrients and breaking the life cycles of several insect pests, diseases, and weed life cycles (Sumner 1982).

2 Polycultures. Complex cropping systems in which two or more crop species are planted within sufficient spatial proximity to result in competition or complementation, thus enhancing yields (Francis 1986, Vandermeer 1989).

3   Agroforestry Systems. An agricultural system where trees are grown together with annual crops and/or animals, resulting in enhanced complementary relations between components increasing multiple use of the agroecosystem (Nair 1982).

4   Cover Crops. The use of pure or mixed stands of legumes or other annual plant species under fruit trees for the purpose of improving soil fertility, enhancing biological control of pests, and modifying the orchard microclimate (Finch and Sharp 1976).

5   Crop/Livestock Mixtures. Animal integration in agroecosystems aids in achieving high biomass output and optimal recycling (Pearson and Ison 1987).

All of the above diversified forms of agroecosystems share in common the following features (Altieri and Rosset 1995):

• Maintain vegetative cover as an effective soil and water conserving measure, met through the use of no-till practices, mulch farming, and use of cover crops and other appropriate methods.

• Provide a regular supply of organic matter through the addition of organic matter (manure, compost, and promotion of soil biotic activity).

• Enhance nutrient recycling mechanisms through the use of livestock systems based on legumes, etc.

• Promote pest regulation through enhanced activity of biological control agents achieved by introducing and/or conserving natural enemies and antagonists.

Research on diversified cropping systems underscores the great importance of diversity in an agricultural setting (Francis 1986, Vandermeer 1989, Altieri 1995). Diversity is of value in agroecosystems for a variety of reasons (Altieri 1994, Gliessman 1998):

• As diversity increases, so do opportunities for coexistence and beneficial interactions between species that can enhance agroecosystem sustainability.

• Greater diversity often allows better resource-use efficiency in an agroecosystem. There is better system-level adaptation to habitat heterogeneity, leading to complementarity in crop species needs, diversification of niches, overlap of species niches, and partitioning of resources.

• Ecosystems in which plant species are intermingled possess an associated resistance to herbivores as in diverse systems there is a greater abundance and diversity of natural enemies of pest insects keeping in check the populations of individual herbivore species.

• A diverse crop assemblage can create many microclimates within a cropping system that can be occupied by a range of non-crop organisms—including beneficial predators, parasites, pollinators, soil fauna and antagonists—that are of importance for the entire system.

• Diversity in the agricultural landscape can contribute to the conservation of biodiversity in surrounding natural ecosystems.

• Diversity in the soil performs a variety of ecological services such as nutrient recycling and detoxification of noxious chemicals and regulation of plant growth.

• Diversity reduces risk for farmers, especially in marginal areas with more unpredictable environmental conditions. If one crop does not do well, income from others can compensate.

Agroecology and the Design of Sustainable Agroecosystems

Most people involved in the promotion of sustainable agriculture aim at creating a form of agriculture that maintains productivity in the long term by (Pretty 1994, Vandermeer 1995):

• optimizing the use of locally available resources by combining the different components of the farm system, i.e., plants, animals, soil, water, climate and people, so that they complement each other and have the greatest possible synergetic effects;

• reducing the use of off-farm, external and non-renewable inputs with the greatest potential to damage the environment or harm the health of farmers and consumers, and a more targeted use of the remaining inputs used with a view to minimizing variable costs;

• relying mainly on resources within the agroecosystem by replacing external inputs with nutrient cycling, better conservation, and an expanded use of local resources;

• improving the match between cropping patterns and environmental constraints of climate and landscape to ensure long-term sustainability of current production levels;

• working to value and conserve biological diversity, both in the wild and in domesticated landscapes, and making optimal use of the biological and genetic potential of plant and animal species; and

- taking full advantage of local knowledge and practices, including innovative approaches not yet fully understood by scientists although widely adopted by farmers.

Agroecology provides the knowledge and methodology necessary for developing an agriculture that is on the one hand environmentally sound and on the other hand highly productive, socially equitable and economically viable. Through the application of agroecological principles, the basic challenge for sustainable agriculture to make better use of internal resources can be easily achieved by minimizing the external inputs used, and preferably by regenerating internal resources more effectively through diversification strategies that enhance synergism among key components of the agroecosystem.

The ultimate goal of agroecological design is to integrate components so that overall biological efficiency is improved, biodiversity is preserved, and the agroecosystem productivity and its self-regulating capacity is maintained. This aim is achieved by designing an agroecosystem that mimics the structure and function of local natural ecosystems; that is, a system with high species diversity and a biologically active soil, one that promotes natural pest control, nutrient recycling and high soil cover to prevent resource losses.

Conclusion and Tables

Agroecology provides guidelines to develop diversified agroecosystems that take advantage of the effects of the integration of plant and animal biodiversity. Such integration enhances complex interactions and synergism and optimizes ecosystem functions and processes, such as biotic regulation of harmful organisms, nutrient recycling, and biomass production and accumulation. The end result of agroecological design is improved economic and ecological sustainability of the agroecosystem, with the proposed management systems specifically in tune with the local resource base and operational framework of existing environmental and socioeconomic conditions. Management components highlight the conservation and enhancement of local agricultural resources (germplasm, soil, beneficial fauna, plant biodiversity, etc.) by emphasizing a development methodology that encourage farmer participation, use of traditional knowledge, and adaptation of farm enterprises that fit local needs and socioeconomic and biophysical conditions.

Table 1. Ecological processes to optimize in agroecosystems

- Strengthen the immune system (proper functioning of natural pest control)
- Decrease toxicity through elimination of agrochemicals
- Optimize metabolic function (organic matter decomposition and nutrient cycling)
- Balance regulatory systems (nutrient cycles, water balance, energy flow, population regulation, etc.)
- Enhance conservation and regeneration of soil-water resources and biodiversity
- Increase and sustain long-term productivity

Table 2. Mechanisms to improve agroecosystem immunity

- Increase of plant species and genetic diversity in time and space.
- Enhancement of functional biodiversity (natural enemies, antagonists etc.)
- Enhancement of soil organic matter and biological activity
- Increase of soil cover and crop competitive ability
- Elimination of toxic inputs and residues

References

Altieri, M.A. 1987. Agroecology: the scientific basis of alternative agriculture. Boulder: Westview Press.

Altieri, M.A. 1994. Biodiversity and pest management in agroecosystems. Hayworth Press, New York.

Altieri, M.A. and C.I. Nicholls. 1999. Biodiversity, ecosystem function and insect pest management in agricultural systems. In W.W. Collins and C.O. Qualset (eds.) Biodiversity in Agroecosystems. CRC Press, Boca Raton, FL.

Altieri, M.A., D.K. Letourneaour and J.R. Davis. 1983. Developing sustainable agroecosystems. BioScience 33: 45–49.

Andow, D.A. 1991. Vegetational diversity and arthropod population response. Annual Review of Entomology 36: 561–586.

Carrol, C. R., J.H. Vandermeer and P.M. Rosset. 1990. Agroecology. McGraw Hill Publishing Company, New York.

Finch, C.V. and C.W. Sharp. 1976 Cover Crops in California Orchards and Vineyards. USDA Soil Conservation Service, Washington, DC.

Gliessman, S.R. 1998. Agroecology: ecological processes in sustainable agriculture. Ann Arbor Press, Michigan.

Hendrix, P.H., D.A.Jr. Crossley and D.C. Coleman. 1990. Soil biota as components of sustainable agroecosystems. In C.A. Edwards, Lal, Rattan, P. Madden, R. Miller, H. House, Gar (eds.) Sustainable Agricultural Systems. Soil and Water Conservation Society, IA.

Liebman, M. and T. Ohno. 1998. Crop rotation and legume residue effects on weed emergence and growth: implications for weed management. In J.L. Hotfield and B.A. Stwerrt (eds.). Integrated weed and soil management. Ann Arbor Press, MI

Magdoff, F.R. 1992. Building soils for better crops: organic matter management. University of Nebraska Press, NE.

Nair, P.K.R. 1982. Soil Productivity Aspects of Agroforestry. ICRAF, Nairobi. Pearson, C.J. and R.L. Ison. 1987. Agronomy of grassland systems. Cambridge University Press, Cambridge.

Pretty, J.N. 1994. Regenerating Agriculture. Earthscan Publications Ltd., London. Reijntjes, C.B., Haverkort and A. Waters-Bayer. 1992. Farming for the future. MacMillan Press Ltd., London.

Sumner, D.R. 1982. Crop rotation and plant productivity. In M. Recheigl, (ed). CRC Handbook of Agricultural Productivity, Vol. I CRC Press, Florida.

Thies, C. and T. Tscharntke. 1999. Landscape structure, and biological control in agroecosystems. Science 285: 893–895.

Vandermeer, J. 1989. The ecology of intercropping. Cambridge University Press, Cambridge.

Vandermeer, J. 1995. The ecological basis of alternative agriculture. Annual Review of Ecological Systems 26: 201–224.

Original Source

This edition of *The Overstory* is excerpted with kind permission of the author from:

Altieri, M.A. 2000. Agroecology: principles and strategies for designing sustainable farming systems. Web edition: http://www.cnr.berkeley.edu/~agroeco3/principles_and_strategies.html

This excerpt was originally published as *The Overstory #95*.

Improving Income

Whether cultivating fruits, vegetables, timber or nontimber products, improving income does not have to mean pushing the land to be more produc- tive. Innovation, creativity, and good marketing can increase returns sustainably.

Section Contents

Value-Added Products

Kim M. Wilkinson and Craig R. Elevitch

Selling agricultural products at their lowest market value is not sustainable, as it can force growers to push the land and themselves past a healthy threshold just to survive economically. Sustainable agriculture has to be about more than just how we treat the planet—it has to create a day to day economic and personal reality that the grower can sustain healthfully.

"Value-added" is simply anything you can do to raise the value of your product in the market, anything you can add to it that enables you to increase your profit margin. Value-added practices often mean the difference between a farm that is economically viable and personally fulfilling, or one that ultimately cannot be sustained financially or personally. Value-added practices are key to the future of sustainable farming, because they enable growers to advance economically without having to "pump up" the production of raw materials from the land.

Value-added agricultural products range from very intricately processed and packaged, to simple additions or processes that can add to the worth. Let's look at a Kona, Hawai'i coffee farm for an example of how value-added works. In the world commodity market the farmer's price for generic coffee is about $0.15/lb. If you were growing coffee in Kona, you wouldn't have to sell in the world commodity market, but can sell your coffee cherry to a Hawai'i Island processor at premium prices up to $1.10/lb. If instead you processed your own coffee during the off-season, roasted and packaged it, you could then sell it to retailers at about $8/lb. Finally, by setting up a outlet on your farm, coffee connoisseurs would then pay you directly upwards of $20/lb. You increased your gross income 10–15 times by processing and selling rather than just selling the coffee berries. You may be interested to know that at least 100 Kona farmers are processing their own coffee and selling it as a high-value product. And nobody sells Kona coffee at its lowest value on the world market.

Another example comes from the town of Esperance, Western Australia, a coastal desert town that once had a failing fishing economy. The fishing economy was based on the fishermen selling large tuna fish to a local cannery. Large fish were hard to find,

though, and small fish were not accepted by the cannery. However, by doing research and taste-tests, some fishermen discovered that their small "worthless" fish qualified as Grade A sashimi in Japanese and restaurant markets. Suddenly a resource they had in abundance- smaller fish- could be sold for about 6 times more money than they ever made selling the hard-to-catch big fish to the cannery. Esperance is now rather famous for quality sashimi, as well as some spin-off value-added operations including smoked fish.

Even products such as fruits and vegetables sold in a "raw", fresh state can be more profitable if marketed well.

On-farm value added strategies can improve profits sustainably

Ways to Add Market Value to Agricultural Products

- Grow organically (many people happily pay 30–60% more for better taste and health)
- Sell something unusual or hard to find (exotic fruits, medicinal herbs, etc.) Have a special farm or estate label, or a recognizable brand
- Assemble produce in special ways (stir-fry bundle, prewashed salad mix, mixed fruit baskets)
- Sell direct and deliver to high-end consumers such as restaurants, who put a premium on freshness
- Focus on produce which is of special quality from your land or climatic niche (sweeter papayas, special varieties of onions, etc.)

Perhaps you already are familiar with some of these practices, but are reluctant to try to charge more than your competitors even though you know your product is worth more. If this is you, remember: it is something of a myth that buyers always want to get the cheapest thing. Most buyers really are looking for the best value for their money, and they know that the cheapest is not always the best. If your product is more expensive than they can get it elsewhere, make sure they understand why. Is it higher quality? Better tasting? A superior variety? Sustainably or organically grown? Crafted by an artist? As long as the value is there, people are glad to get it, and may even choose a higher priced product if they are convinced it is worth it. Building a personal relationship with buyers is also very useful in this process, as is having a recognizable, known farm or estate name.

Value-adding to your products can improve your economic situation, as well as add value to your life. Value-adding to your products gives you room to express yourself more fully, be more creative, to create a personal presence in your products. Marketing more like an entrepreneur than a wholesaler is also a good feeling, as you'll start to feel more in control of your financial life and less at the mercy of the market prices.

References

Lee, A. 1993. Backyard Market Gardening: The Entrepreneur's Guide to Selling What You Grow. Good Earth Publications, Box 4352, Burlington, VT 05406-4352.

Sirolli, E. 1995. Ripples in the Zambezi: Passion, Unpredictablility and Economic Development. Institute for Science and Technology Policy, Murdock University, Murdock, WA 6150, Australia.

Schumacher, E.F. 1989. Small is Beautiful: Economics as if People Mattered. Harper & Row, New York, NY.

Original Source

This article was originally published as *The Overstory* #13.

The Full Extent of Value Adding: It Starts with Forest Management

K.R. Matthews

The true extent of value-adding is a way of thinking... a process, not just processing.

Every aspect of private forest management should be seen as an opportunity to add value. Often it is suggested that additional returns may be possible through the use of portable sawmills and other processing technologies. For private forestry, adding value should take place long before post-harvest processing—it starts with forest management.

The timber industry has traditionally seen only post-harvest timber processing as constituting value-adding. The sawmilling industry's primary concern has been to access the best of the resource and concentrate on adding value to this raw product through sawing/processing. Instead of inheriting this limited definition of value-adding from the timber industry, private forestry needs to adapt the concept to its area of greatest potential returns and expertise, that is, growing quality timber.

After considering all constraints, there may indeed be an opportunity to increase profit or sales from processing in any forestry business. However, this is only a small part of the potential value-adding for private forestry. Essentially, maximising timber quality and saleability are the critical issues for production-driven private forestry. The long-term nature of forestry necessitates looking for the opportunities that exist in every aspect of forest planning, establishment, management, harvesting and processing. These opportunities will have the greatest impact upon future value and represent the full extent of value-adding.

What Is "*Value*-adding"?

As with any business, value-adding (increase in profitability) is achieved when any financial saving, increase in expenditure, or other management action, leads to an increased *net* profit. The increase in profit may also be derived through greater accessibility to the market as a consequence of improved volumes or timber quality.

There are many values that have been identified as a result of integrating the management of trees on private land. The benefits that can complement forestry include aesthetics, amelioration of land degradation, crop protection, enhancement and protection of biodiversity, etc. These values are vitally important for the sustainability of any project. Perhaps these values are more than sufficient for those who have ventured into private forestry as a "Life Style Choice" or for multiple benefit/outcomes.

For private foresters who have planned and established their forestry ventures for the purpose of financial gain, the term "value" needs to take on far greater significance. There are always opportunities for complementary benefits even from purely investment/production type forestry. However, if the farm forester is serious about forestry as a financially rewarding, environmentally sustainable venture then net profitability is the important measure of value.

A wood product may increase in sale price after processing, but this doesn't necessarily translate into a higher profit margin. An increase in sale price may in fact return a lower net profit if the input costs incurred in achieving the higher price are disproportionately increased. Sometimes access to the market may only be possible by going through the additional process, even though it seems that the profit margin is less due to the extra costs involved. In this case, the "value" comes from simply being able to access the market. For example, meeting a quality specification may be necessary in order to access the market. This should be regarded as value-adding (after taking into account costs) if the market is dictating a standard that unless is met, will render the timber unsalable.

Seeing Through the "Value-adding" Hype

Frequently, well-publicised financial opportunities associated with various types of forestry are promoted at unrealistic levels. Rather than focus on wood quality, there are terms used that apply to wood products. Some examples of potentially misleading terms include:

"Cabinet Species" or "Cabinet Wood Plantation"

A sawlog is a product of a forest and "Cabinet Wood" is a product of a sawlog (i.e., wood of a quality suitable for use in the fabrication of furniture). It is neither a species type nor a plantation type. Regardless of the species being grown, whether it is *Eucalyptus*, *Pinus*, *Toona* or any other, the end use of the tree can range from firewood through to kitchen cabinets. "Cabinet Species" gives the impression of some higher order in the series of plantation regimes and is more hype than an indication of future value or management style.

Thinning is one of the greatest value adding tasks available to forestry. (photo: anonymous)

"Niche Markets"

A "niche market" is simply a market that is undersupplied or has a finite capacity, and so the price of the product reflects its limited availability. In most cases when the niche is filled the market becomes the same as any other. This is a simple example of how price is a function of both supply and demand.

"High Value Sawlog"

The "High Value Sawlog" is often used without definition. A sawlog's value is dependent upon variables such as:

- Species
- Durability
- Diameter
- Defect
- Colour
- Figure
- Potential recovery
- Market demand
- Processing costs
- Distance from the market, etc.

When private foresters state they are growing high value sawlogs, they are really aiming to grow quality trees with the intention of achieving as high a return as the market permits in 25–40 years time. The future value in fact may be quite low if the timber properties are not appropriate or production costs are excessive.

The above three terms focus on wood products rather than *wood properties*. The perception that value can only be achieved by venturing into processing trivializes the critical need for quality and cost-effective forest management. Wood properties that are inherent in commercial native forest timbers have to be managed for in plantations if the wood is to meet the required market specifications.

Planned forest management can influence the following attributes and qualities:

- Density
- Strength
- Durability
- Colour
- Figure
- Bole Length
- Taper
- Diameter
- Stability/growth stress
- Percentage of defect

Forestry would be extremely simple, if it only required planting a certain number of trees per hectare and then waiting 25 years to achieve these properties and attributes. This is not the case—forest management for timber production requires planned intervention and active management. Some examples of the types of intervention that can be applied to add value include:

- Selecting species and provenance for the required colour, durability, figure, strength and density.
- Manipulation and achievement of bole length by form pruning and provenance selection.
- Addressing timber stability, diameter and taper by applying appropriate thinning regimes.
- Managing the incidence of defect by appropriate thinning, form pruning and stand protection during thinning and harvesting.

Increasing the Value

Many private foresters are not fully realising the numerous opportunities that exist to increase the value of their standing trees. The most simple management tasks can have an increasing value-adding effect if appropriately applied. An obvious example is the value of business and operational planning. To maximise the positive impacts on profitability of each forest management task, it is essential to consider what elements have the greatest cost effective impact. Using a farm forestry financial planning spreadsheet or financial model to explore profit sensitivity to key management variables is a most worthwhile exercise.

The Four Essentials

In order to achieve more value from your forestry enterprise, each task you undertake in your forest should be viewed as an opportunity to add value. If something is not going to add value, why would you bother? To assist in obtaining maximum value results from each **task** you undertake, pay careful attention to **tools** you are using, the **timing** of the task and the **technique** that is being applied.

Task Define each activity in your management plan. Common forestry tasks include planning, design, species and provenance selection, planting, weed control, pruning, thinning, fire preparation and maintenance, etc.

Tools What equipment will be required to undertake each activity. Depending on the task, these could include air photos, tractor, grubber, species information, pruning shears, chainsaw, chemicals, etc. You may consider the use of your own labour, contractors and consultants as "Tools." What are the costs of all these items?

Timing When are you going to do the task? Is the time of the year right? How long will the operation take? Have you enough time, money, and energy? Is the stand at its optimum time for the operation? Is the timing appropriate to the technique?

Technique Is the technique appropriate for the task, tools and timing? Do you have the appropriate skill to perform the task well or to ensure it is well performed by others? Do you need to purchase skills (training) or services you cannot provide your self?

Examples

Example 1
Task: Planning

Tools: Budgets, soil test, mapping, air photo, assessments, schedule of operations, etc.

Timing: Before, during and after all operational activities

Technique: Taking into account efficiencies of scale, assessment of available resources, time, financial, labour input, development of a schedule of operations

Added value: Knowing what you are aiming to achieve and how you will get there. By planning at the scale that is appropriate to your circumstances and constraints, you are able to choose options that will yield the best outcomes.

Example 2
Task: Product identification

Tools: Diameter tape, clinometer, height sticks, specifications, etc.

Timing: At planning, before harvest, at harvest, after harvest, etc.

Technique: Height of tree, merchantable log length, allowable defect, allowable sweep, calculation of volume, minimum dimensions, understanding of specifications and hierarchy of values.

Added value: Being able to identify products is important in knowing what you are aiming to produce. As the stand matures it is possible to manage for a range of products by manipulating the stocking, pruning and timing of operations. Prior to harvesting, an assessment of products is needed to enable estimation of the merchantable volume within each product class. During harvest the ability to recognise products aids in ensuring optimal utilisation. The

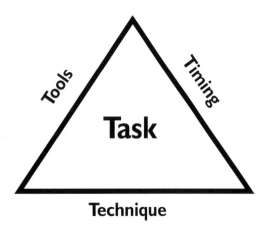

ability to identify timber products is crucial throughout the management of a plantation or native forest.

Example 3

Task: Thinning

Tools: Chemical, tree injector, axe, chainsaw, machinery, combinations, etc.

Timing: When values of green crown ratio or basal area reach critical thresholds. Before a stand becomes locked up and growth increment has stalled, etc.

Technique: removal of a specified number of stems, removal of suppressed and poor formed stems, protection of retained stems, etc. Often private foresters perceive they are loosing potential future product value by thinning. In reality if the stems that require removing are retained, the value of the whole stand is compromised. Thinning needs to be seen as an essential value-adding exercise for sawlog and pole production.

Added value: There is no such thing as a non-commercial thinning. All thinning has a commercial impact. The real value of removing stems is the perceived future value of the stems removed is transferred onto the stems retained. Increases in growth rates, improved timber quality, enhanced forest health and vigour, larger diameter logs—all translate into added value, economic viability and sustainability. Returns from sales of culled timber are a bonus.

Conclusion

"The simplest, and in the end, most effective value-adding is to ensure that the timber stand is in a healthy, vigorous state with optimum stocking and few defective trees." (Ryan 2001).

Every aspect of private forest management should be seen as an opportunity to add value. However, each opportunity needs careful evaluation to ensure that it will indeed be efficient and in time, profitable.

The emphasis for private forest growers should not be on processing, but on growing quality timber efficiently with a good understanding of market requirements. To achieve this end, a higher degree of cost/benefit analysis needs to be employed throughout our forest planning, establishment, management, harvesting and marketing. Forest owners need to ensure that, by good stand management, there is a range of future product options.

After achieving maximum value of a forest stand by managing for quality, the private forester can con-

sider adding value through successive stations of timber processing—felling, log-making, debarking, sawing, docking, grading, seasoning, kiln drying, machining, etc. At each additional stage along the value line the levels of financial and physical risk are compounded. Additional knowledge, time and skills are required, and each investment of extra effort should be evaluated for profitability.

The true extent of value-adding is a way of thinking…a process, not just processing.

References

Clark, M., Neitzel, K., Borschmann, G. 2002. "Tropical hardwoods hold the key to the promised land". Australian Forest Grower, 25 (1): 25–26.

CSIRO, 2002. "New Leader for Value Added Wood". CSIRO, Media Release, April.

Ede, E. 2001. "New directions in secondary wood products research". CSIRO, OnWood, 33.

Hanson, I., Stewart, M. 1997. Processing Trees on farms. Rural Industries Research and Development Corporation, Research paper 97/20.

Picot, A. 2000. "The Need For Revisionist Destructionist Propaganda" Email communication.

Ryan, S. 2002. On Farm Value Adding of Mixed Hardwood Forest Products in S.E.Q. Mary Valley Sunshine Coast Farm Forestry Association and Queensland Forestry Research Institute, Case Study 3.

Stephen, P. 2001. Pete's Story. The Farmers Forest, 2001: 121–131.

Van Herk, P. 2001. The pursuit of profits along the value adding chain. Australian Forest Grower, 24 (2): 10–11.

Wilson, G. 1992. Farm sawmills: a new money maker. Australian Farm Journal, January: 54–56.

Original Source

This article was adapted with the kind permission of the author from:

Matthews K.R (2002). The Full Extent of Value Adding. Proceedings of Australian Forest Growers 2002 National Conference, Albany, Australia. October 2002.

The author gratefully acknowledges the valued contributions of the following people:

Geoff Borchamann, Greening Australia Queensland Justin Black, Private Forestry Southern Queensland Laurie Capill, Private Forestry Southern Queensland Sean Ryan, Mary Valley Sunshine Coast Farm Forestry Project

This excerpt was originally published as The Overstory #122.

Value-Added Enterprises for Small-Scale Farmers

Sylvia Kantor

Economic viability is an important aspect of the success of agroforestry projects. This chapter addresses the subject of value-added enterprises using farm food products to illustrate value-added strategies.

Introduction

Small farmers are under tremendous pressure to develop innovative business strategies to stay afloat. Value-adding is one such strategy that is also a logical extension of many farm businesses and can exploit underutilized farm resources for increased returns. Value-adding offers farmers the potential to capture a larger share of the consumer dollars.

What is value-adding? Value-adding is any step taken to increase the value of a raw product anytime between harvesting and sales of the final product. Typical value-adding includes processing in some way such as cleaning, cutting, packaging, smoking, drying, freezing, extracting, or preserving.

What are the benefits of value-adding? Value-added products offer a higher return, open new markets, create brand recognition and add variety to a farm operation. Adding value means consumers are willing to pay more than they would for a raw product.

Developing Value-Added Product Ideas

Valued-added enterprises can be very rewarding. Benefits accrue from matching underutilized farm, labor, and management resources with potential markets.

- Talk with nonfarming friends, Cooperative Extension agents and specialists, lenders, coworkers, and people in both urban and rural areas for their input.
- Ask current buyers if they have any unfulfilled demands.
- Visit specialty grocery stores and gift shops.
- Look at mail order catalogs.
- Read agriculture magazines, food magazines, and trade journals.
- Read the food section of your daily newspaper.

- Talk to other farmers about what they have heard other farmers are doing.
- Keep your eyes, ears, and mind open to new, innovative ways to process farm products and to make use of existing resources.

Three Keys to Success

Value-adding offers no guarantee of profitability. Though more money may be coming in, more time and resources are also going out. Careful planning and management are necessary to promote profitability. Three factors key to the success of value-added enterprises are: quality products, good marketing, and sufficient capital.

Quality product

- Do some test marketing at various venues like farmers' markets, county fairs, and festivals.
- Get assistance with product development from local resources like chefs, classes, culinary colleges, freelance product developers, independent food technology labs, and university extension, and friends and relatives who offer feedback.
- Consider whether your product is unique enough to survive in market competition.
- Be consistent in quality, supply, delivery, and service and you will foster a loyal customer base.

Good marketing

- Do market research to see if there is a market for your product.
- Keep your market research simple and cost effective; make it objective (beyond friends and family); monitor repeat sales. An example is to put out samples or sell small quantities of a product for customers to try.
- Look into possibilities for distributing your product in the market. Options include selling direct (on farm or off), selling wholesale, mail order, roadside stands, internet, specialty retailers.
- Consider working with brokers or distributors once your business has expanded beyond the territory it can service.

- Also consider wholesalers. A growing number of specialty food wholesalers deal with smaller quantities.
- Think about collaborating with other small-scale processors to help promote each other's products.
- Packaging is critical! Label and packaging designs represent your business, so make sure they have appeal.
- Seek out advertising and promotion opportunities that will fit within your budget. Examples include sending out samples, offering tasting opportunities, handing out sales literature, or merchandising at point-of-sales purchase locations.

Sufficient capital

- Start small. Invest ingenuity first, labor second, and money third.
- Keep your day job. You will need an independent source of income to cover your costs for at least the first three to five years.
- Research regulations at the beginning because they may add costs.
- Reduce capital costs by borrowing equipment, buying used equipment, sharing resources with other small-scale enterprises, or using community processing facilities.
- Save on initial labor costs by seeking help from family and friends, and consider hiring outside labor later on.
- Develop a business plan that includes outside financing for future expansion of your business.

Other qualities of success for value-added enterprises as described by successful processors are:

- A unique product.
- An enthusiastic promoter of the product.
- The right kind of labeling and packaging.
- Aggressive marketing.
- A full-time presence on the farm.
- Strong agricultural or livestock knowledge.
- Ability to cater to customers.
- Assistance from agencies and universities.
- A strong relationship with the local community.
- Having vision, taking risk, and believing in yourself.

Food Safety and Liability

Safe food handling is crucial to effectively marketing a product and maintaining a trustworthy reputation. Food safety regulations are in place not only to protect consumers' health but to prevent businesses from being destroyed by a consumer getting ill from their product.

Regulations are complex and can frustrate processors. All small businesses must comply with federal, state, and local laws and regulations.

Product liability insurance is necessary because most value-added products are not covered under general farm policy programs. Be sure to have this protection from the beginning, even if you are just handing out samples. Contact an insurance agent for advice.

A Few Value-Added Product Ideas

cut flowers and ornamental greens	recipe "kits" (e.g., ingredients for salsa)
dried flowers	mixed salad greens
dried fruit	organically grown products
dried gourds	pastured lamb, beef, pork, and poultry
dried mushrooms	pickles/relishes
dried whole or processed herbs	pie filling
dry mixes	preserves
essential oils	sauces, pesto, chutney, etc.
fermented and cultured foods	vinegars
free range eggs	wreaths
herbal products (soaps, lotions, oils, etc.)	

Conclusion

If you have identified some underutilized physical or by-product resources, untapped management and labor resources, promising market opportunities, and significant financial resources, you are in an excellent position to start a new enterprise.

Farmers can work together with small-scale processing enterprises to create new markets for higher value farm products. Often, small-scale processors look to their community for local ingredients, staff, and markets. Value-adding can serve to showcase the uniqueness of communities.

References

Markley, K., and D. Hilchey. 1998. Adding Value for Sustainability: A Guidebook for Cooperative Extension Agents and Other Agricultural Professionals. Pennsylvania Association for Sustainable Agriculture (PASA). Milheim, PA, USA.

Northeast Regional Agricultural Engineering Service (NRAES). 1991. Farming Alternatives: A Guide to Evaluating the Feasibility of New Farm-Based Enterprises. NRAES. Cornell University. Ithaca, NY, USA.

Original Source

This article was adapted with permission from the original, *Value-Added Enterprises for Small-Scale Farmers*, Agriculture and Natural Resources Fact Sheet #518 by Sylvia Kantor. The original can be downloaded from http://king.wsu.edu/Ag/agpubindex.htm. It was published by: Washington State University Cooperative Extension (WSUCE), King County, 500 SW 7th St, Ste A200, Renton, WA 98055-2983, USA; Tel: 206-205-3100; Web: http://king.wsu.edu.

This excerpt was originally published as *The Overstory* #63.

Further Reading

Lee, A. 1993. Backyard Market Gardening: The Entrepreneur's Guide to Selling What You Grow. Good Earth Publications, Box 4352, Burlington, VT 05406-4352. Addresses virtually every aspect of the business, from planning crops to running a farm stand and a mail-order operation.

Sirolli, E. 1995. Ripples in the Zambezi: Passion, Unpredictablility and Economic Development. Institute for Science and Technology Policy, Murdock University, Murdock, WA 6150, Australia. An inspiring look at breathing new life into a rural economy through value-added processing.

Sigmund Rehm, S., and G. Espig. 1991. The Cultivated Plants of the Tropics and Subtropics. Verlag Josef Margraf, Weikersheim, Germany. Covers cultivation, economic value, processing, and utilization of over 1,000 plants.

Marketing Principles

Richard Finlay-Jones

Economic viability is an important aspect of agroforestry development. Whether selling timber, fruit, tree seed, or other products, agroforesters will benefit from understanding some principles of marketing. This chapter provides a brief introduction to professional marketing.

Seven Secrets of Successful Selling

The seven secrets of successful selling can be summarized as follows:

- Know your customer
- Know your product
- Know the process of production, manufacture and distribution
- Know your costs
- Know your competitive edge
- Know the communication process
- Know yourself

Simply put, the process of successful marketing stems from sound knowledge, good products, innovative distribution channels and successful communication processes.

Very often potential customers may be grouped together to form market sectors or segments. It is important for the marketer to be able to identify how different sectors of the market vary from each other, and how the different requirements of each sector may be targeted using specific selling techniques.

1. Know Your Customer The customer may be an end user, a processor or a manufacturer. The marketer must have an understanding of the requirements of each end user, processor, and manufacturer and in terms of:

- product quality specifications
- product volume
- product appearance and finish
- product supply consistency

Understanding the needs of the customer requires the marketer to develop empathy and trust for the customers business and/or personal requirements. This has been recently termed, "relationship marketing." A marketer with a similar product and an established relationship with the customer has a distinct competitive advantage.

Understanding marketing helps grow money from trees

2. Know Your Product In order to successfully market a product or service, the seller must be able to define the benefits of the products over those of the opposition's products. Benefits are different to advantages in that benefits relate to the specific needs of the individual customer, rather than the strengths of one product over another. The seller should also have a comprehensive knowledge of the disadvantages of their products in particular processing or utilisation situations (for example, the use of untreated pine products in exposed situations as opposed to treated products). The better the marketer knows and understands the product and its idiosyncrasies, the greater the level of service afforded to the customer, and the more trust created between the parties. Remember to always underpromise and overdeliver!

3. Know The Process Getting the product to the customer can be one of the more trying exercises for the marketer. The marketer of farm forestry products should possess some knowledge of the species, site, silvicultural processes, harvesting techniques, processing, transportation and distribution required for the product to get into the hands of the customer. The more information that the marketer has to assist the customer in the decision making process, the greater the chance of the sale.

4. Know Your Costs Without understanding the fixed and variable costs of production, it is difficult to successfully plan for profitability and sustainability of production. Consequently the marketer must place a sufficient margin on the product to cover the costs of all processes and labour, whilst remaining competitive in the marketplace. Understanding the costs and desired profitability level will also allow some flexibility in the marketplace, should a situation of price warring occur.

5. Know Your Competitive Edge The greater the understanding of the marketing chain and the product, the more likely the relative strengths may be ascertained. The strengths or competitive advantages commonly relate to price, product, positioning, perception and process. In the traditionally conservative timber industry, competitive strengths are achieved through proximity to the resource, ease of harvesting and processing and proximity to marketplace. Note that competing on price alone destroys the market's perception of quality!

6. Know the Communication Process Some customers enjoy regular contact from marketers, whereas other customers prefer to be in control of the event. It is important for the marketer to understand the preferences of the customer, to know how often the customer prefers to receive information and through which media (see 1.). For example, using current technology, it is possible to sell products using photographs and text on a web site. However, this may only attract business from a certain sector of the market.

7. Know Yourself It is extremely difficult to sell products and services that one doesn't believe in or doesn't understand. It is also difficult to sell products if one does not believe in oneself! To be a successful marketer, appraise your own strengths and weaknesses in order to present the selling opportunity to your customer in a way that works for you. This will usually occur in a situation where all parties are comfortable and relaxed, able to understand and relate to each other's situations and requirements. It's fun, enjoy it.

Conclusion

The seven secrets to successful marketing are no secret at all! Common sense and courtesy, with a respectful attitude to customers, the product and the processes will afford you the opportunity to market your products and services. Securing the order requires the trust and respect of your potential customers through honesty and integrity.

Further Reading

Kotler, P. 1991. Marketing Management Analysis, Planning Implementation and Control. Prentice-Hall International.
Romano, F. 1995. Sold! On Life. Turning Point Corporation. National Library of Australia.

Original Source

This article is adapted from *Agroforestry News*, Volume 8, Issue 4 with the kind permission of the author and publisher. *Agroforestry News* features practical and timely information for farm foresters growing timber with many examples from Australia. Address: Agroforestry News Editor, NRE Port Phillip Region, Locked Bag 3000, Box Hill, 3128 Victoria, Australia; Fax: +61-3-9296-4722; Email: wendy.davies@nre.vic.gov.au.

This excerpt was originally published as *The Overstory* #62.

Niche Markets

U.S. Department of Agriculture Cooperative State Research, Education, and Extension Service

Growing fruits, vegetables, and other farm products—particularly specialty items preferred by ethnic populations, unusual minor crops grown on a limited scale, or certified organic produce—offers profitable niche markets for small farmers.

Many unique crops do not easily adapt to large-scale production—so corporate farm enterprises, which control so much of the world's food business, do not produce them. Small farmers can capitalize on growing this specialty produce.

Today's customers want high-quality, interesting, attractive, tasty, nutritious, and convenient foods. Many want to know who grows their food and under what cultivation practices.

Increasingly, successful small fruit and vegetable growers need to know as much about business and marketing as horticulture.

To maximize profit, small growers need to sell a diversity of farm-raised products directly to consumers through various marketing methods. Small farmers are better suited to do relationship marketing than are larger firms, whose sheer size requires selling food in an impersonal marketing system.

As agriculture increasingly moves to a global market, what crops can you specialize in and market better than anyone in the world? What regional or environmental quality or cultivation practices can you capitalize on to promote your produce?

Crop Selection

Choose a crop mix compatible with your climate and soils for which there is unmet market demand. Some issues to consider in selecting your niche market crops:

Cultivation techniques Each crop has special requirements in planting, pruning, fertilizing, etc. University libraries offer local or international publications that may help with information that would be costly and time consuming to learn through experience.

Regulations Certain crops or value-added products may be regulated by law, such as processed foods,

medicinal herbs, or on-farm activities for the public. Check with government agricultural and health agencies to see if your product line may be subject to regulations, permit approval, etc.

Risk management. As with all new crops, there is added risk involved for crop or market failure. Limit risk by starting with a small investment, and expanding on success; by spreading risk over 2–3 crops; and by selecting crops with multiple products and benefits. Consider selling to several markets in case one does not perform as expected.

Value-added Food processing and packaging can add greatly to the value of a crop. Also, increasing the perceived value of products by offering an enhanced user experience (freshness, desirable varieties, etc.) add value to products.

Food safety Clean, fresh, and pesticide free, products can bring higher prices.

Resources Check your industry or local fruit and vegetable associations for workshops, conferences, technical assistance, and other information.

Some ways to direct-market fruits and vegetables

Farmer cooperatives Small growers can spread risks by forming a cooperative to gain market power through joint supply purchasing, bargaining, processing, and marketing.

Farmers markets These are usually no more than an hour's drive from large populations, and draw many customers to one selling location.

The Internet Web site advertising exposes a business to a markets in a wider local community and worldwide.

Roadside stands Location on a high-traffic road is essential. Clear directional signs, adequate parking, and attractive displays of fresh, clean, and quality products draw repeat customers. Stand setups can be simple or elaborate. Understand your customer base to know what produce they seek and what times your stand should be staffed.

Community-supported agriculture (CSA) At the beginning of the growing season, a CSA farmer forms a direct relationship with a customer base before planting. CSA members invest in a harvest share by giving the farmer money up front for farm operations. Members receive weekly in-season produce deliveries. Customers sign a CSA agreement stating that they assume risks and bounty of farming.

Subscription farming Customers do not pay for a year's harvest share at one time but weekly, monthly, or quarterly. Customers expect a weekly share, which usually must be made up if the crop fails.

U-pick farms Customers come on farms to pick fruits and vegetables, eliminating the farmer's harvest and delivery costs to buyers. Some pre-picked produce may be offered. Local advertising, clear road signs, parking, a clean bathroom, shady rest area, refreshments, picking containers, weigh site with cash register, and friendly sales people are key. Let customers know clearly what produce is available and hours of operation (and when the operation will unexpectedly be closed).

Food circles A food circle is an informal network of small farmers who sell food to a targeted group like neighbors. Farmers pay a small membership fee to be able to be listed in a directory describing their farm-raised products. A coordinator handles customer inquiries and event publicity like festivals. Food circles offer farmers a steady customer base. Customers know who grows their food and by what agricultural practices. Farmer-to customer relationships help each other better understand rural-suburban-urban cultures.

Agri-tourism Agri-tourism includes entertaining attractions or educational on-farm events to draw customers. School and tourist tours, farm specialty gift shops, on-farm restaurants, bed and breakfast accommodations, nature photography, or sports events, offer customers opportunities to stay longer and spend more money on produce and value-added products. Festivals and other attractions can benefit whole communities.

Other marketing outlets Investigate local eatery establishments to target local shops and finer restaurants willing to invest in superior quality produce. Offer crop varieties unavailable through regular suppliers. You may also sell a portion of your crop through a contract to small cooperative stores specializing in quality organic produce, food chains that buy direct from farmers or farmer cooperatives, schools, nursing homes, the military, prisons, hospitals, caterers, produce company suppliers or airlines.

Tips for success

- Identify your customer base and target your market early in the season.
- Know your customers, including ethnic groups wanting specialty produce and marketing methods that fit their culture.
- Visit nearby shops and study what fruits and vegetables are carried, product display techniques, and people traffic flows. Do stores buy produce locally or import? Consider producing fruits and vegetables not carried there.
- Know customers' buying habits and regional growing seasons' windows of opportunity.
- Every region has its own mix of crops that can be successful—find your niche.
- Market your region's and farm's identity in a unique way through a logo and quality products.
- Choose marketing plans that are adaptable to your family, operation, lifestyle, and personality.
- Diversify crops and have complementary marketing outlets to keep income flow steady.
- Plan years ahead for your operation's growth.
- Successful growers know how much cost they have in their operation and where they are losing money. Focus labor and expenditures on high-profit crops.
- Farms should look tidy and produce should be clean.
- Be dependable with produce availability and hours of operation.
- Market fruits and vegetables by telling what sets your produce apart—such as growing practices, varieties, etc.
- Consider turning your fruits and vegetables into a value-added retail consumer item through processing and packaging.
- Take time to talk with customers.
- If you don't like dealing directly with the public, assign that job to another family member or hire someone with strong people skills.
- Cultivate community presence by forming a connection to your local community.

Original Source

This article is adapted from "Fruits and Vegetables: A Niche Market for Small Farmers," which originally appeared in Small Farm Digest 4(2), Winter

2001, 1–4, published by the Cooperative State Research, Education, and Extension Service, U.S. Department of Agriculture, Mail Stop 2220, 1400 Independence Ave., S.W., Washington, DC 20250-2220. Download the original in pdf format at: http://www.reeusda.gov/agsys/smallfarm/sfd/index.htm.

For more information about the newsletter of the Small Farm Program, Small Farm Digest, contact the editor Stephanie Olson at CSREES, USDA, Mail Stop 2220, Washington, DC 20250-2220; Tel: 202-401-6544; Fax: 202-401-1602; Email: solson@reeusda.gov. Or visit http://www.reeusda.gov/smallfarm.

This excerpt was originally published as *The Overstory* #83.

Further Reading

Lee, Andrew. 1993. Backyard Market Gardening: The Entrepreneur's Guide to Selling What You Grow. Good Earth Publications, Box 4352, Burlington, VT 05406-4352.

Salatin, Joel. 1998. You Can Farm: The Entrepreneur's Guide to Start & Succeed in a Farming Enterprise. Polyface Inc.

Sirolli, Ernesto. 1995. Ripples in the Zambezi: Passion, Unpredictablility and Economic Development. Institute for Science and Technology Policy, Murdock University, Murdock, WA 6150, Australia.

Direct Marketing

Appropriate Technology Transfer for Rural Areas (ATTRA)

Many growers, especially new ones, are inclined to start production without giving a second thought to the business of marketing. Good marketing is an absolute must for a successful agricultural enterprise. Some would even argue that it ranks higher in importance than production itself—especially for farmers planning to diversify. After all, what good is a product if one cannot sell it consistently for a profit?

Diversification out of commodity crops may mean becoming familiar with, or even creating, new marketing systems. Existing marketing channels very often do not accommodate the new producer well—especially the small producer.

Some farmers may use direct marketing for particular products while simultaneously participating in traditional markets. No two growers are the same, and the reader will have to determine through trial and error what works best.

Sustainable farming, has given impetus to diversified, decentralized systems in which farmers take greater control of marketing by bypassing traditional channels and marketing directly to consumers at the local and regional level. Foods that do not require much processing before consumption—like fruits, vegetables and meat—are ideal for one-on-one marketing. Direct marketing is often quite unorthodox and may take the form of roadside stands, pick-your-own operations, farmers' markets, and sales to restaurants, upscale retail or specialty stores—even supermarkets and institutional food service. Prospects for direct farmer-consumer interaction are particularly promising at the rural-urban fringe, where producers can take advantage of specialty market niches and the demand for local and ethnic food and non-traditional products, while promoting agricultural tourism and education.

Direct marketing can give the farmer a larger share of the retail sales price and possibly a higher return on each unit sold, offset to some extent by loss of economies of scale. For some farmers, adding value or marketing some minimally processed farm products directly to the consumer is a way of enhancing financial viability. Farmers who are unable to compete in, or are locked out of, distant markets can build a thriving local business. However, finding the right niche and marketing directly to the public is a hard and labor-intensive job requiring time and effort, creativity, ingenuity, sales expertise, and the ability to deal with people in a pleasant and positive manner.

Importance of Marketing

For too long, farmers have thought of marketing simply as how to dispose of their products. Locked into producing a very small number of major crops and insulated from the market, they have not been required to have a clear understanding of ever-changing consumer wants and needs. Producers have traditionally taken whatever price they could get while wholesale and retail distribution networks undertook the business of marketing.

Marketing does not begin after production, but well before the first seed is planted. For farmers working outside the conventional system, the importance of marketing cannot be over-emphasized. Consumer-focused marketing is the single most important factor that determines the success of an enterprise. Marketing is not just about selling. It requires a clear and astute understanding of what consumers want and the ability to deliver it to them through the most appropriate channels for a profit. It includes the planning, pricing, promotion and distribution of products and services for consumers, both present and potential.

The qualities of a successful marketer (Hils 1989)
- Not afraid to take risks
- Takes pride in the product and is not shy about saying so
- Willing to plan, research and experiment
- Flexible
- Independent
- Creative
- Thrifty

Enterprise Evaluation

A good marketing strategy begins with making sure the enterprise is right for you and is feasible. This will require a review and evaluation of your present situation, goals, possible enterprises, physical, financial and marketing resources, and market potential. The evaluation should help you answer some key questions, chiefly: Is this really what you want to do? Is there a market for the product? Do you have the necessary skills to do it? Are you going to develop the market? Or will you raise a crop for which there is a pre-existing market? Will it be profitable? Can you expand in the foreseeable future?

- Start by listing your business and personal goals. Prioritize them.
- Is this going to be a full-time enterprise?
- Is your family involved and supportive?
- Inventory physical resources like land, soil, machinery, water, buildings, livestock etc.

Define constraints:

- Is family and/or off-farm labor available?
- Is your spouse involved in the planning? A spouse's knowledge of medicinal herbs or cooking for example, could spin off into an additional on-farm enterprise.
- Do you have access to financial resources in the form of savings, credit or investment by family or friends?
- What are some of the crops that will grow well in your area and will fetch the price you need?
- What are the marketing resources in your region? Check out the farmers' markets and the retail stores. Is a roadside stand feasible? Talk to others who have one. Are there restaurants, grocery stores and supermarkets willing to buy locally raised produce or meat?
- Who are your potential customers? Would they like to buy direct-marketed products or do they prefer buying at mass retail outlets where price is the main consideration? Is there scope in your business plan for consumer education? Have you considered the potential for entertainment farming and tourism?
- What information and resources do you need to help you along the way? How can you best access such resources?

Market Research

Following the enterprise evaluation, begin to identify and define your product. Get all the information you can about sources, marketing, production, processing, packaging and sales. This will require a good bit of systematic research. Check the libraries in your area. Read all the extension publications you can lay your hands on as well as trade journals and periodicals, books on market gardening and seed catalogs.

Talk to your extension agent, visit the local stores (gourmet and otherwise) and supermarkets to see what is selling, and why one product appears more appealing than another. Talk to customers, local stores, food clubs, specialty distributors, ethnic stores, restaurants and other prospective outlets in your region. What do they want? Is there an unfilled niche? With your production, labor and marketing resources, will you be able to fill this niche?

Find out what your prospective competitors are doing. Look for ways to improve upon what they are offering.

You can either start small and grow bit by bit, or you can start in a big way from the very beginning. Either way, you must be prepared to do your homework and get to know your markets to be successful. One way to identify potential markets that exist in your area is by using the "30-mile market technique" (Rocky Mountain Inst. 1987). Most customers of direct marketers are believed to live within 30 miles of the point of sale. Market research within this radius will unearth useful information about production possibilities and the presence of competitors. Detailed market analysis and research is imperative before you promote and sell your product. Not only does it reduce business risk by providing credible information, it can help identify problems in the market as well as little-known opportunities for profit. By knowing the size and makeup of your market, its geographic location, demographic and behavioral characteristics, it will be easier to create the appropriate marketing strategy and you will avoid wasting time and money marketing to the wrong people.

Marketing Plan

Marketing is an essential element of a small agricultural enterprise. The marketing environment will ultimately exert a strong influence on the nature of the business. The crop grown will be determined less by the farmer's personal tastes than by what the market will absorb at a price the farmer is willing to take. A good market plan broadly aims to define the consumer, the products or services they want, and the most effective promotion and advertising strategies

Direct marketing and community supported agriculture are options for reaching target markets such as for organic produce. School-operated market in Kuta, Bali. (photo: C. Elevitch)

for reaching those consumers (Bjergo 1986). It clarifies objectives, appropriate actions, projected income, pricing structures, costs and potential profitability.

A market plan alone does not guarantee success, but it does indicate that many of the factors that affect the profitability and continued survival of the operation have been given consideration. A market plan is usually part of a larger business plan that includes production, financial, staffing and management plans. The process of writing a business plan is not within the scope of this paper but listed at the end of this section are resources to help you find more information on the subject.

Elements of a marketing plan are (J.E. 1997):

- Marketing situation—a summary of your present situation, what you are currently selling and how, who your customers are, what their needs are, your competition, your own strengths and weaknesses, how you are promoting your product, what the current food and marketing trends are, etc.

- Marketing objectives—a summary of your short and long term goals, product diversification, additional market segments (alternative outlets) to tap. Objectives should be realistic and measurable—e.g., you would like to increase sales by 10% within the next year.

- Marketing strategies—ways to achieve your goals, what you will produce, how you will promote and advertise the new product, the channels of sale, how you plan to beat your competition.

- Budgets—include estimated costs and return based on sales, and strategies for monitoring and curtailing costs.

- Action plan—immediate steps (e.g., look in the yellow pages for graphic artists to design logo, shortlist names of newspapers for a press release, assign person to deliver products to market, etc.)
- Evaluation—a summary of progress on marketing objectives. The frequency of evaluation depends on the plan and could be each month, every six months or annually.

Objectives and strategies are a dynamic part of the planning process and change depending on the market situation and competition.

Pricing and Profitability

Setting a price is one of the more challenging tasks faced by the direct marketer. How does one know how much a pound of tomatoes or a head of lettuce is worth? On what information are these pricing decisions based?

In general, prices are set by production and marketing costs at the lower end, while the upper limit is set by what your customers are willing to pay, how much competition you have, and your own desired profits. It pays to figure your costs and set your prices accordingly, rather than just going by what others are charging; steady, consistent prices encourage steady, consistent customers.

Clearly marked prices are a must to let customers know exactly how much a grower is charging.

Finally, this advice from growers:

- Don't sell your goods for a lower rate at the end of the day
- Compete fairly on quality and service, never undercut
- Don't badmouth other growers
- Raise a good product and ask for a good price

Direct Marketing Alternatives

Ordinarily, retail markets command the highest price per pound of product, while wholesale markets move more of the product than retail markets but at lower prices. Farm sales and farmers' markets, you-pick, mail-order are typically low-volume markets. Restaurants, retail stores, cafeterias, health food stores, and caterers constitute mid-volume markets, where prices are better than wholesale but on the lower end of retail. Smaller farmers may find that selling to low- and mid-volume markets works best for them. Mid-volume markets, especially, offer the advantage of small to medium crop production as well as medium to better prices (Warr 1993).

Organizing and selling at farmers' markets

Farmers' markets seem to work best for growers who offer a wide variety of produce of the type desired by customers. Consumers want markets to be easily accessible with good parking facilities. A little related entertainment never seems to hurt—seasonal festivals, street musicians, tastings, demonstrations, etc. Sales help must be pleasant and courteous, willing to answer questions. Farmers interested in this marketing method can find opportunities for creative selling and fresh ideas through participating in the local farmers' market association and direct marketing meetings.

Community Supported Agriculture (CSA)

Community Supported Agriculture (CSA) plans operate in several different ways. One involves a single farmer selling "subscriptions" or "shares" at the beginning of the season and then delivering, on a regular schedule, baskets of whatever is produced. Another method involves consumers who band together to rent land and hire a farmer to raise food for them.

On-farm sales and agri-tourism

On-farm sales include pick-your-own (PYO) and roadside stands or farm markets. Pick-your-own began in response to the 1974 energy crisis, appealing to customers (mainly families) who had the time and the necessary expertise to process their own foods in quantity. More recently, PYO enterprises have been integrated into the growing "farm entertainment" sector. Marketing strategies may include educational tours, an on-farm market with opportunities to buy fresh produce or value-added products, ready-to-eat food, festivals, classes, seasonal events such as a personalized pumpkin patch, or agricultural mazes. A buffalo ranch, besides selling hides and meat, charges admission to view the animals.

Such enterprises work best when farms are within thirty miles of a major population center, preferably on or near a good road. Pick-your-own is most adapted to crops which require stoop labor to harvest.

Selling to restaurants and stores

High quality is a prime requisite for sales to such restaurants. Specialty crops such as herbs, garlic, mushrooms, salad greens, cut flowers, and edible flowers for restaurants may be grown on very small parcels of land. One of the main requirements for selling to an upscale restaurant seems to be developing a good relationship with the chef. In some instances sales by local farmers to local institutions may be arranged.

Mail order and home delivery

Mail order sales generally involve value-added products or fresh fruits. Value-added products are often decorative, rather than culinary. Home delivery of fresh farm products was much more common in the U.S. sixty years ago than it is today. The sight of a horse-drawn farm wagon loaded with bushels of apples, squash, potatoes, and live chickens making its way slowly through a residential neighborhood while the farmer (or his children) knocked on doors was not unusual. But it is still possible for farmers to meet consumers at the doorstep and deliver quality food. This method is currently most used by dairy and meat producers. Transactions are more likely to take place in offices than in residential neighborhoods. Nowadays arrangements are made in advance by telephone or email and meats are usually frozen.

Marketing on the Internet

Farms can do business on the internet either by maintaining their own individual web sites, or participating in a directory listing. Research providers and costs; look at bartering to get a web site designed. Look at internet marketing as an opportunity to attract a new clientele, but first determine whether existing customers are on the internet. Do they have email? Be aware of certain barriers to internet buying:

- pricing (include shipping costs)
- potential return hassles
- credit card concerns of customers
- privacy issues
- navigating the site

Do everything possible to show you are honest and reputable. Do not sell or lease email addresses. Have a privacy statement that you won't sell customer information.

Customers like a web site that is easy to use, quick to download, and updated frequently. Be cautious about graphics that take a long time to come up on screen. At least give customers the option to bypass graphics.

Promotion and Publicity

Promotions help to increase sales per customer and the number of clients, and enhance the image and visibility of the farm, company and/or product. Promotions come in different shapes and sizes but they all have some common characteristics.

- They draw attention and communicate information
- They provide an incentive or premium to the consumer
- They invite the consumer to buy

Word-of-mouth advertising by satisfied customers is priceless and cannot be purchased or engineered except by providing good service and a good product. Because an estimated 80% of business comes from return buyers, the focus is on rewarding loyal customers by offering discounts, gift certificates or a free service.

Coverage by the local newspaper or radio/television station can bring in more sales than any paid advertisement. Events on the farm—festivals for children, availability of a new and unusual food item, a tasting contest—may lure reporters in search of human-interest or weekend-event stories. Invite the local newspaper's food editor over for a dinner of grass-fed beef, or pastured chicken so she or he can taste the difference from supermarket fare. While writing up a press release, look for the news peg that makes the story—an accomplishment, an award, anything that seems interesting or valuable to the community. Give the press plenty of notice, good photo opportunities, and always return phone calls.

Paid advertising is the non-personal promotion of an idea, product or service directed at a mass audience. Its aim is to generate an increase in sales, induce brand recognition and reinforce the "unique selling point," inform potential customers about the availability of a product, and create demand for that product. An advertisement should emphasize benefits, not objects. What will people get from your product or from a visit to your farm? High-quality, fresh, delicious produce or meat? Family fun? Friendly service? You can either advertise continuously through the season to maintain your presence in the marketplace, or you can advertise just before a product is available.

Attractive road signs are another effective form of advertising. Signs that are legible to the speeding motorist are a way to induce people to stop and visit the roadside market or farm-stand. Signs should have a logo and should reflect the kind of goods being sold—more upscale if they are high-priced and a "no-frills" sign if otherwise. Signs that advertise an unusual or out-of-the ordinary product will draw the curious to the farm. The first sign should be placed a good distance (at least 2500 feet) before the market to give the motorist time to decide whether or not to stop. Keep signs neat and well-maintained.

Direct mail is advertising with a personal touch and requires an up-to-date and extensive mailing list. Postcards with pictures of your farm, a logo and a promotional message may be sent just before a farm festival or when produce is available. Direct mailing is only as effective as its mailing list (i.e., its targeting of people who will buy your product). Mailing lists should be revised each year. Target groups of people likely to buy your product (e.g., members of a health food store or co-op). A mailing list can be developed by asking people to sign up for mailings. Also, ask them where they heard about your product or farm. This information will help you plan future advertising.

The catalog is marketing tool that serves many purposes. Common elements of a catalog are:

- It should tell a story which differentiates your business from others by explaining why and how you are different.
- It should work like a reference, providing detailed information about the product, service and business.
- In addition to providing information, it must promote your product, service and business.
- It should create a good first impression.

Business cards have a way of sticking around in people's wallets long after they have been distributed. Print and hand out business cards with your name, phone number, farm location and product.

The internet offers a whole new world of marketing opportunities. Its key features are 24-hour accessibility by anyone with internet capabilities and greatly expanded reach without the costs and limitations of direct mail. Customers may be to able to place an order on line, but the chief value is the publicity an attractive web site can bring to a producer. Another advantage is making your on-line catalog available to internet users.

A lively and regular newsletter, written in the first person, discussing upcoming produce, recipes, farm events and life on the farm, makes the reader feel more involved and connected. Ideas for content may come from customers or from employees.

When creating a newsletter, consider the following (Frederick 1996):

- What items do you want to promote?
- What should you say to induce readers to buy?
- Are readers made to feel included and important?
- Have necessary details such as farm hours, phone number, deadlines, etc. been included?
- Is the newsletter uncluttered and visually pleasing?

Including a map of how to get to the farm is always helpful. Newsletters may also be sent to the news media or published as an insert in the regional newspapers.

Single event promotions like harvest festivals, and other holiday events can be combined with ongoing promotions like school tours or Friday happy hours or open house. Publicize the promotions well ahead to ensure a good turnout.

Conclusion

Finally, some parting advice to people considering direct marketing or processing of farm products. First of all, do something you love and enjoy doing. Success will follow. Invest time and, if necessary, money in research. Have a well-considered plan before proceeding but don't be rigid. Learn as you go. Start small and keep your costs and debt as low as possible. Provide a reliable supply of high quality products and build a good relationship with your customers. Take time to listen to their wants, identify market possibilities, and find a unique market niche for your product. Be adaptable to shifting market opportunities. Ensure diverse markets, so that if one fails, you can fall back on the others. Set a fair price and avoid competing directly with big business, especially on price.

References

Bjergo, Alan. 1986. Marketing: Why Have a Marketing Plan? University of Montana Coop Extension Service, Missoula, Montana.

Frederick, Peggy. 1996. "Newsletters to encourage customer loyalty." In: Proceedings 1996 North American Farmers' Direct Marketing Conference. February 22–24, 1996. Saratoga Springs, New York.

Hils, R.J. 1989. Market What You Grow. The Chicot Press, Atlanta, Georgia.

J.E. 1997. Marketing ideas for small farmers. Maine Organic Farmer & Gardener.

Rocky Mountain Institute (ed.) 1987. "Marketing" How To Survive As A Small Farmer. RMI, Snowmass, Colorado.

Warr, A.M. 1993. Basil, Chives, Parsley...Idea Sheet: Farming and Farm–Related Business Ideas. Skylands Small Business Development Center at Warren County Community College.

Original Source

This article was excerpted with the kind permission of the authors from:

Appropriate Technology Transfer for Rural Areas (ATTRA). 1999. Direct Marketing., Fayetteville, Arkansas.

Web: http://www.attra.org/attra-pub/direct-mkt.html

The PDF version of this document is available at: http://www.attra.org/attra-pub/PDF/direct-mkt.pdf

This excerpt was originally published as *The Overstory* #108.

Human Connections

Environmental health is the foundation for human health. At the same time, healthy people are needed to carry on the work of restoring healthy forests and land use systems. Connections between people, farms, and ecosystems are cultivated for the good of all.

Section Contents

Native Intelligence

Jon Young

Connection to and understanding of nature is the foundation of appropriate resource management. But too often for resource managers and planners, the idea of "site observation" consists of clomping around with a clipboard making notes. Other times we may turn to indigenous or local people to help us understand the environment better. Within each of us, is there a way we can we begin to cultivate a sense of place and depth of understanding parallel to that of a native? This article by consummate naturalist, tracker and author Jon Young introduces some keys to native intelligence. At the end is a basic exercise that can set anyone on the path to seeing with native eyes.

Native or native?

We observe the following conventions with respect to our use of the words Native and native. "Native" refers to a person or persons from a specific indigenous cultural background, and is most often prefixed to a description or place, such as in Native American or Native Australian. The uncapitalized "native" refers to refers to a person of any cultural or ethnic background who is on a first-name basis with the natural world, a person who has the knowledge, a spiritual feeling for and therefore the mind set of being a part of the land, not separate from it.

Where has Native Intelligence Gone?

There are many studies indicating that the indigenous people from many natural areas around the world are capable of identifying, harvesting and using for medicine, food and craft, hundreds of species of wild plants over all four seasons. The knowledge possessed by these people, common average citizens of their societies, includes similar information about trees and their uses, bird and animal language and its significance, weather patterns indicated by clouds, and animal behavior indicated by track and sign.

If we were to walk in the Kalahari with a native of the land, and we asked them to identify the most common plants, animals, tracks, and trees we encoun-

tered, they would do so with 100% accuracy, men, women, and most of the children alike.

If I were to take you, a resident of Metropolis, USA, on that same walk in the Kalahari and ask you the same questions, you would not do so well, I'm afraid. "Of course," you would say. "I'm not from around here! I live in Metropolis."

But what if I asked you the same questions about your own area? When I give people a test about plants and animals in their own region, they fail as badly as if they were walking in a foreign land. What does this mean?

Are We Aliens in our Own World?

If a "native" is in harmony with his or her environment and the natural world, what can we call the rest of us who are unable to pass even the simplest identification test? There is only one word that fits—we are "aliens" in our own world. This condition and feeling of alienation from our own world, I refer to as the dread disease of "Alienitis." Its symptoms are a lack of knowledge about our world, and with that, a lack of appreciation, understanding and concern. For many so afflicted, the natural world consists of grass—something that is a pain to mow every week, but must be greener than their neighbors'—and the neighbor's dog who uses our patch of green as a waste recycling station.

In advanced stages of Alienitis, many people do not recognize that the natural world even exists. They move from back-support mattress to drip-grind breakfast to heated garage, then on to a bumper to bumper commute on a cement-smooth roadway, into another heated garage, and up to the 32nd floor in an inertial-damped elevator. After staring at a computer screen and manipulating numbers for several hours, they dash down to the ground floor where they hurriedly throw down a few mouthfuls of pale lettuce and imitation texturized meat, held together by two pieces of white bread, which was made from wheat that had been sprayed with chemicals, harvested by machine, bleached, baked and denuded, then labeled as "enriched." Is it surprising that many of us have succumbed to Alienitis?

It is not only our life-style that makes Alienitis such a virulent disease. The only kind of education that the average citizen receives about the environment is a frightening digestion of the issues concerning its destruction, misuse, or degradation. Little or no opportunity exists to learn about the positive side of our natural world or to learn to appreciate its gifts to life. Is it any wonder there is such a sense of hopelessness among our young people today, or that we have so many overwhelming problems involving the environment?

Who Are the "natives"?

The ability of native and indigenous people to read the ground through tracks and sign left by humans and animals is astounding. Tracking, as an art, is unknown to most people in the modern world, yet indigenous trackers are quite capable of seeing and interpreting incredible information from what appear to be random marks on the ground.

So what does all this add up to? These people are perfectly at home in the natural world. They understand everything about their surroundings that they need, not only to survive, but to live in cooperation and harmony with the other elements of nature.

Does this mean that only people who sleep on the ground, dress in skins and eat food that they themselves have caught or gathered can be called natives? Does it mean that only hunting and gathering people who were born and raised in a particular location, whose parents, grandparents, and ancestors, back to the beginning of recorded time, have lived in that same location, can be called "natives" of that place?

Observing nature on a regular basis creates a bond with and abiding love for the natural world. Pictured: Kim Wilkinson. (photo: C. Elevitch)

One of the most important parts of being in harmony with the natural world is a deep understanding and appreciation of nature, and that promotes the ability to solve current problems and to prevent future problems by care-taking the environment on behalf of the future generations. This comes quite naturally to people who are personally knowledgeable and spiritually bonded with the natural world, and who consider the other elements of Creation to be their honored relatives.

It is not place of origin, nor skin color, nor family tree that makes a native—it is bonding with and having a deep and abiding love for the natural world. It is an understanding between the natural world and ourselves that goes so deep as to approach the realm of the spiritual. It is an attitude of thankfulness, and actions taken with consideration for their effects on the future generations. And most of all, it is the willingness to set aside our own preconceived notions about reality, our technologically oriented patterns of thinking, and to see the Earth as it really is—a natural system, a whole, with all the elements interdependent upon each other.

A Key Routine: Sit Spot

Good field and research skills are inherent qualities of people in indigenous cultures. These qualities are cultivated by a number of routines, including a simple but essential routine called "Sit Spot" (or sometimes "Secret Spot"). The Sit Spot is a place to observe and interact with nature on a regular basis. It can be practiced by anyone, from very young children to adults. Sit Spot consists of going to one place (under a favorite tree, for example), and being quiet and still. The Sit Spot practice has these essential elements (after Moon, 2000):

- choose one place (a spot that speaks to you or has some special significance)
- make sure the location is convenient
- visit frequently (ideally, daily)
- visit at varied times of day
- go by yourself
- sit for at least 20 minutes

Being quiet and still at the Sit Spot is key, staying open to the senses and observing. Extend your awareness as far as you can. Eventually, questions will come up naturally: what kind of tree am I sitting under? Is that herb edible? What kind of spider is that? What is that bird doing now, what do those noises mean? Which way is North? These questions will be answered through observation and through further research, which will lead to more questions. It's also very important to record observations and feelings in a journal. Journal writing gives structure and meaning to the questioning, to act as a mentor to the whole process. Before you know it, you will have a deeper understanding of place, and be on the path of a naturalist.

References

Young, Jon. 2001. Kamana One: Exploring Natural Mystery. Owlink, San Gregorio, CA, <http://www.owlinkmedia.com>

Young, Jon. 2001. Kamana Two: Path of the Naturalist. Owlink, San Gregorio, CA, <http://www.owlinkmedia.com>

Moon, Warren. 2000. "Building the Secret Spot Routine." FoxPrint News, Wilderness Awareness School, Duvall, WA, <http://www.wildernessawareness.org/>

Original Source

This article was excerpted with the kind permission of the author from:

Young, Jon. 1996. Songline: Introduction to Wilderness Awareness School's Natural Training Programs, Third Edition. Owlink, San Gregorio, CA, http://www.owlinkmedia.com.

For training programs in awareness of the natural world (including the excellent home-study Kamana Naturalist Training Program) or to order this or other publications contact:

Wilderness Awareness School P.O. Box 5000, PMB 137 Duvall, WA 98019 USA Tel: 425-788-1301; Email: wasnet@wildernessawareness.org; Web: http://www.natureoutlet.com/

This excerpt was originally published as *The Overstory* #118.

Human Health and Agroecosystems

D.G. Peden

During the past century, both the agricultural and health sciences have become compartmentalized, making great technical advances in relatively specialized technologies. These advances generated significant increases in food production and reductions in human diseases. Although the primary purpose of agriculture is to maintain human health and human health depends on agriculture, there have been few efforts to integrate the two.

At a time when both health and agricultural workers are questioning the sustainability of their achievements, the concept is emerging that effective agroecosystem management may provide a cost-effective strategy to improve human health.

Human health and ecosystem health are intimately linked

Agriculture now faces the tasks of enhancing food production while simultaneously reversing soil degradation, replenishing soil capital and overcoming the harmful effects of agricultural chemicals. Degraded agricultural ecosystems (agroecosystems) are less resilient to stresses caused by global variation and climatic changes. Agricultural ecosystems are the focus of growing concern about how degraded agroecosystems are related to the projected increase in risks to human health.

Human health is directly linked to and dependent on the state of health of the ecosystems that support them. Because people are an integral component of agroecosystems, a range of socio-economic and bio-physical factors affect their health. A few examples illustrate this point.

In subsistence agricultural systems, nutrition is a primary factor. Without food security, human health inevitably suffers. Although increased food production in terms of quantity has largely kept pace with the demands of a growing population, the quality of food available may be declining. Maintaining the high rate of production may be difficult.

Food shortages affect about 800 million people, but more than two billion people suffer from malnutrition. Although in some cases, nutrient deficiencies are simply characteristic of otherwise stable agroecosystems, land degradation aggravates the harmful effects that some factors in agroecosystems have on human nutrition. For example, iron deficiency alone affects 40 to 50% of women worldwide. Two hundred and fifty million children suffer from severe or moderate vitamin A deficiency with up to 500–1000 pre-schoolers becoming blind annually. There is a growing evidence that even in developed countries, deficiencies in fiber, folic acid, etc., threaten human health.

Apart from nutrition, naturally occurring heavy metals, vector-borne and non-vector-borne diseases, naturally occurring toxins, agricultural chemicals as well as imports and exports associated with a cash economy, contribute to the health risks faced by people within the context of their agroecosystem. In recent years, mercury contamination of fish in the Amazon basin and the consequent rise in toxicity symptoms in people who depend on fish has focused attention on the perceived negative impact of gold mining. However, new evidence suggests that gold mining is not the only source of this heavy metal. Rather, forest clearance followed by cultivation resulted in the leaching of mercury from exposed soil into adjacent aquatic ecosystems where it entered the food chain.

The introduction of agriculture initiated a process of soil degradation that directly threatened human health. With this knowledge, local people are in a position to modify their diets by shifting from the consumption of carnivorous to herbivorous fish, to establish vegetative buffer zones between the exposed soils and the rivers and to consider other community efforts to better manage vegetative cover of their crop lands. The solution to this health problem lies in the better management of the aquatic and terrestrial agricultural ecosystems.

Adoption of new or innovative agricultural technologies and policies often leads to unexpected or counterintuitive impacts. Understanding and responding to these often requires an agroecosystems perspective. Transformation from a subsistence to cash economy can generate a number of adverse health consequences. The move to cash economies can also result in new health risks. For example, chemical fertilizers, pesticides, herbicides and fungicides applied to food crops can be leached into ground water supplies, thus contaminating downstream and underground water.

Land degradation can adversely affect human health by changing the ecology of pathogenic and harmful organisms. One consequence of soil degradation is reduced water holding capacity and greater likelihood of drought-stressed crops. Peanuts subjected to drought develop high concentrations of pre-harvest aflatoxin. Aflatoxin is believed by many to cause acute liver damage and cancer. Although this connection has not been conclusively demonstrated in humans, the fear of its carcinogenic effect motivates a number of governments to regulate trade in potentially-contaminated food crops.

Not only do the condition and management of agroecosystems affect the health of people that depend on it for sustenance, human health also directly influences the ability of people to manage the system itself. For example, Acquired Immunodeficiency Syndrome (AIDS) causes major labor shortages and the diversion of family income to cover increased health care costs. Beyond AIDS, other aspects of poor health make effective management of agroecosystems more difficult.

The working hypothesis is that better management of agroecosystems is a cost-effective strategy to improve human health. This implies that agriculture must be viewed as ecosystem management, and that the principles of natural resource management are applied to it.

Original Source

This excerpt originates from the 1999 publication *Agroecosystem Management for Improved Human Health: Applying the Principles of Integrated Pest Management* published by the International Institute of Rural Reconstruction. To order this book and for more information contact:

IIRR Bookstore, Publications Unit International Institute of Rural Reconstruction Y. C. James Yen Center Silang, Cavite 4118, Philippines; Tel (63-46) 414 2417, Fax (63-46) 414 2420; Email: pubiirr@cav.pworld.net.ph; Web: http://www.iirr.org

The original article can also be viewed in its entirety at: http://www.crdi.ca/ecohealth/Agro/peden.html

This excerpt was originally published as *The Overstory* #46.

Sustaining Physical Health

Kim M. Wilkinson and Craig R. Elevitch

Just as we tend the land for the long-term, we must learn to sustain our own physical health for the long-term. Ultimately, it is not sustainable to create abundance on the land by depleting our own health. While this book focuses on concepts and strategies for creating and improving agroforestry systems, we wanted to share with you some suggestions for maintaining or improving your health as you do your work. We hope this information will encourage you to learn more about ways to use your body in the most healthful manner, giving yourself and your community the gift of your sustained energy and vitality.

"Our bodies are our gardens...our wills our gardeners."
—William Shakespeare

Far from being a luxury to be indulged in by the affluent, physical health and fitness is the right of every person—especially those who do physical work. Most farmers have a lot of physical activity integrated into their day. However, healthful exercise and hard work are not always accomplishing the same thing. By gaining an understanding of your body and integrating some simple principles into your day, it is possible to make farming activities something your body will be able to sustain for your entire lifetime, with minimal injury, stress, and exhaustion.

There are a number of links and resources in this chapter where you can learn more, and we hope you will take some time to look at them. Space only allows us to touch on the subjects by way of introduction.

Condition Your Body for Endurance

Whether activities benefit health and fitness over a lifetime, or whether they wear the body down, leaving a person exhausted and prone to injury, depends not so much on *what* is done, as *how* it is done. As a farmer, you can maintain and even improve your fitness while you work. One key is the difference between aerobic and anaerobic exercise.

Aerobic means "with oxygen," and applies to moderate levels of activity that can be sustained over a long period of time, fueled by oxygenated blood that is moved through the body by the heart, lungs, blood vessels. Anaerobic, on the other hand, means "without oxygen," and refers generally to the short bursts of high-powered energy that are fueled by your body's glycogen, or, if that runs short, fueled by depleting your body's blood sugar.

While small amounts of anaerobic activity have their place in any fitness program or regular work day, generally speaking it is stressful on the system and cannot be sustained for very long. If you feel exhausted and famished after you work, or if you experience a lot of strained muscles and injuries, chances are you have been using your body in an anaerobic way. If you or someone you know (and envy) can sustain the same kinds of work while feeling only pleasantly tired at the end of the day, chances are that their system functions aerobically when they work. Regardless of your current situation, you can train your system to function more aerobically.

Activating your aerobic system is very beneficial to your long-term health and energy level. Some types of farming are suited for getting the right level of exercise from the work itself. If your work schedule is irregular, or you find that the nature of your work forces your body into anaerobic activity, you may really benefit from building up an aerobic base with some moderate exercise. The optimal way to train your system to function aerobically is to take a walk (or a bike ride) at the proper pace 3–5 times a week for about 20–30 minutes (not including warm-up).

Ways to activate your aerobic system while you work or exercise:

Warm up Most traditional farmers started the day with a walk to the fields or forest. Nowadays, many farmers expect to leap out of a truck and start full-speed on their work. This is very stressful on the system, immediately throwing your body into an anaerobic state, shunting blood and oxygen from vital organs to fuel the muscles. Warming up with a *slow* and leisurely walk for about 10–15 minutes before your start in on working will gradually distribute the blood to your muscles, activating your aerobic capacity. This will vastly improve your energy level throughout the day.

Pace yourself properly Once you have warmed up and are ready to start in on your work, be aware of your breath. If you are aerobic, your breath will be steady, your work will be pleasurable but tiring, and you should be able to speak if necessary. If you are too winded to speak and your breath is labored, you are probably anaerobic. The most accurate way to learn about your aerobic capacity is to monitor your heart rate.

Breathe and keep your stress down Keep   in mind that stress can raise your heart rate above the aerobic zone, even if your body is working at a proper pace. Watching some of the most productive workers or laborers in your area, you may notice they tend to seem relaxed when they work, and focus on the job at hand. This is important for keeping the blood and oxygen flowing to the muscles.

Take Care of Your Back

In our profession, back problems are a major health concern. Back problems can cause farmers to lose months of work, and some back injuries can become a permanent disability. It is very important to take good care of your back.

Maintain proper posture As you work, walk, or sit, and especially while you lift things, maintain good posture. Stomach in, spine aligned and straight, shoulders back. It is a also good idea to learn some techniques of proper lifting.

Strengthen the muscles that support the spine, particularly the abdomen (stomach) and buttocks A few minutes a day of abdominal exercises (like sit-ups or crunches) will go a long way in keeping your back healthy.

Balance out your body Whether you are right-handed or left-handed, chances are you favor your dominant side when you use tools. Whenever possible, try to use your other hand (or foot) equally. In other words, if you normally hold your shovel in your right hand, try switching to your left for awhile during your work day. At first it will be more clumsy, but you will soon improve. Giving both sides of your body a similar level of activity will help prevent your muscles from becoming unbalanced or causing your back to torque too much to one side.

Stretch Daily

After you work hard, it is important to stretch to prevent stiffness, knots, and soreness in your muscles. Stretching daily will also improve your range of motion, preventing injuries. You may notice if you haven't been stretching and you finally do, that it feels really good! Your sore muscles have been waiting for this.

Stretch while your muscles are *warm* Take short breaks and stretch during or immediately after your work, rather than waiting until your muscles are cooled off.

Take special care to stretch any muscle that you flex while your work For example, if you spend large parts of your day hunched over, do some moves that stretch your back out in the opposite direction. (Dogs and cats do this regularly, and if you watch them you will get the idea immediately—they will sleep curled up, then stretch completely in the opposite direction to recover.)

Hold stretch positions for about 30 seconds *Do not bounce* or strain—just get in the stretch position and hold it without forcing, allowing the muscle to extend.

Other factors are important in maintaining good physical health, including a good diet and enough rest. We hope this chapter will help inspire you to continue to learn about and improve your health over your lifetime.

Exercise: go outside, to your field or project site, or just the stoop of your home. Inhale deeply, and then exhale, saying, "Ahhh!" Take a few moments to look around, and allow yourself to appreciate all the good things that you have achieved.

Disclaimer We are not medical or health professionals. The techniques, ideas, and suggestions in this document are not intended as a substitute for proper medical advice. Consult your health care professional before performing any new exercise or exercise technique, particularly if you are pregnant or nursing, or if you are elderly, or if you have any chronic or recurring conditions. Any application of the techniques, ideas and suggestions in this document is at the reader's sole discretion and risk, and the authors are not liable or responsible for any damage caused directly or indirectly by the information contained herein.

References

Robbins, A. 1993. Awaken the Giant Within: How to Take Immediate Control of Your Mental, Emotional, Physical & Financial Destiny! pp. 439–450. Fireside.

Edwards, S. 1996. Sally Edwards' Heart Zone Training: Exercise Smart, Stay Fit and Live Longer. Adams Media.

Maffetone, P.B. 1997. In Fitness and in Health: Everyone Is an Athlete. David Barmore Productions.

Bob Anderson, B. 1980. Stretching. Shelter Publications.

Original Source

This article was originally published as *The Overstory* #24.

Cultivating Connections with Other Farmers

Kim M. Wilkinson and Craig R. Elevitch

Practical experience is a key source of information on sustainable farming that can only be gained first-hand and can't be found in any book. The study of books is valuable too, but there is no substitute for seeing something in action. Many aspiring farmers feel awkward and don't know how to start to approach local old-timers, neighbors, or complete strangers whose work they have heard about or seen from a distance. Yet, it is an essential part of learning to meet other farmers in your region and get a first-hand look at their work, and hear about their experiences. These valuable relationships can be a wellspring of information, ideas, and inspiration for you, as well as result in long-term supportive friendships.

Meeting other farmers is a priceless learning experience. Pictured: Kamilo Faleofa. (photo: C. Elevitch).

So, how does one go about approaching that person for the first time to ask to see their farm practices? To make it more comfortable, effective and enjoy-able, there is a certain code of conduct that goes along with tapping into a farmer's wealth of information.

Do your homework in advance Before asking a hard-working farmer to take time out from their day to share information with you, be sure you have checked the local resources that provide free information first. Extension agents, some University educators who work with farmers, and farmer advisory organizations can be excellent sources of assistance, and are being paid to help you. The World Wide Web has also become an excellent means to research farmer practices. The public library can also give you some leads, as can friends who have farming experience. Through this up-front research, you will begin to learn which farmers in your region have been successful in practicing new, innovative and sustainable techniques. Then, when you do get to visit a farmer, you won't have to take their time for basic information that is readily available elsewhere.

Be very respectful of a farmer's time and space Find out if the farmer is willing to have you as visitor. While some farmers are happy to show off their activities, most farmers are also very busy, sometimes downright overwhelmed. Some are even wary of strangers invading their private gardens, or reluctant to share because they don't want to be criticized. Call the farmer, and ask if they have a couple minutes to talk about what you are interested in. Start a conversation by letting them know how familiar you are with them, such as "I've been admiring your products in the market...," or, "Word is you are the expert in..." or "You seem to have a special skill to..." Then, introduce yourself briefly. If the farmer does not have a phone, stop by briefly in person for this purpose. But don't expect them to drop what they are doing to show you around then; you should stop by first for a few minutes just to see if it would be O.K. to come back, and if so to make an appointment for a future visit.

Start with a small request, and be specific In other words, don't ask, "Hey, can I come over and have a tour of your farm?" which can be a large, time-consuming request to fulfill. Instead say, "I see you are trying an interesting technique to control weeds. I am working on some similar problems at my place. I was wondering if sometime I could stop by for a few minutes and have a quick look at what you are doing?"

If the farmer is willing, make a firm appointment
Treat the appointment just as you would an appointment with any professional. Be on time, and ready to go when you arrive. Don't expect the farmer to be on time, just be ready when the farmer is ready.

The Farm Visit

After you have successfully scheduled a meeting, you are ready to go for your visit! Here are a few guidelines to keep in mind during your visit:

Arrive on time, ready to go. Ten minutes early is courteous and relieves doubt whether or not you will show up. If they are not ready yet, wait patiently until they can be with you. While you are waiting, do not snoop around! Stay on the main road, path, or driveway, and wait patiently.

Some things to do

- Thank them up front for being willing to see you.
- Have just a few specific things you want to ask about or see, or have a short list of questions.
- Ask for permission if you want to take photos or videos of them or their farm.
- Be brief and leave on time or early. Even if you are all having a great time, it is much better to have them wishing you would stay longer than wishing you would leave! If they see that you do in fact respect their time, they'll be glad to have you back again.
- Thank and acknowledge them at the end of your visit. Let them know how much you value their time and knowledge, and admire their work. The work of farming is endless, and this person is surrounded by it. It is nice for them to sit back for a moment and see through your eyes all that they have accomplished.
- If possible, send a short note or gift to thank them again.

Some things to avoid

- Don't pry if they seem reluctant to discuss certain aspects of their operation. Remember, their farm is also their business and livelihood, and some things may be proprietary, "trade secrets" they may not be ready to share with you.
- Don't focus on or talk about yourself and your own farm while you are there. You'll get the most value if you focus on what they are doing in their situation, and try to apply it to your own later.
- Don't give unsolicited advice. You are there to learn, not to teach, and it can change the whole tone of the meeting if you start offering advice. Of course, if they ask for your opinion or help, by all means share what you do know.
- Don't ask for or expect them to be willing to give you cuttings, seeds, or other plant materials. This is very important. Their time and knowledge is their gift. If you very dearly want plant materials from them, contact them a separate time and offer to pay or trade for it.
- Don't ask to use their phone, home or bathroom. If you are not a house guest, your request to use private family space may be a burden.
- Always respect local and traditional customs in the way to dress, act and treat your hosts.

With these few guidelines in hand, hopefully you will be more comfortable approaching that neighbor or old-timer in your region to tap into some of their experience. If you still feel shy about it, remember the "start small" rule by approaching a nearby neighbor (start with one who seems most likely to be friendly!) to chat for a few minutes about their farm. Soon you'll be hooked on cultivating connections with your farming neighbors.

Also, do pass it on. If farmers have hosted you and taught you, keep the cycle going by being willing to show others the successes and failures on your farm.

Original Source

This article was originally published as *The Overstory* #15.

Related Chapters

Creating an Internship

Craig R. Elevitch and Kim M. Wilkinson

Practical, hands-on experience is a key part of learning to work with trees and forests. Many people of all ages and career paths are seeking ways to increase their practical skills through internships. Internships are short- or long-term practical experiences (usually between 1–12 months) supervised by a mentor. Frequently the mentor is not a school or university professor, but instead a farmer, agroforester, traditional plant gatherer, or other practitioner.

An internship represents a unique opportunity to work closely with an expert and gain untold knowledge that can't be had from any other source. There's just no substitute for hands-on, practical experience.

However, an internship position can be a big shift from being a high school or university student, surrounded by teachers and staff who are being paid to assist and educate students as their first priority. Even locating and making contact with the right mentor differs greatly from applying to a formal learning institution.

Keep in Mind the Mentor's Position

Farmers, on-farm researchers, tree planters, or agroforesters can be excellent choices to supervise the internship. Very few practitioners have formal internship programs. Usually internships involve creating a one-on-one arrangement with a particular person. There are many ways to locate prospective mentors, including:

- lists of expert practitioners
- farmer organizations
- recommendations from teachers
- journal articles by or about expert practitioners, and
- finding someone in your own community who's work you admire.

Although almost all of these potential mentors would like to share what they know with an intern, they are usually fully engaged with professional responsibilities and family obligations. Often there's no time to answer internship inquiries, let alone take on an intern. Agroforestry experiences are often located in rural or remote areas, making it an even larger burden to reply to or host prospective interns. Farmers who have taken on interns or visitors may find that novices can require far more time and energy to supervise than expected.

Applying for an Internship

While you can expect to be richly rewarded with new skills and knowledge, the path to a truly valuable internship is to focus not on your needs and wants, but on those of your mentor. Learning how to best serve their goals and projects will help you gain what you need to know later as you pursue your own projects. Furthermore, from the initial contact onward, find ways to make having you as an intern easy for the mentor. Here are some tips for finding an internship and making the most out of it.

Use these as guidelines to apply for an internship:

- Find out as much as you can about your prospective mentor's work, business, writings, and current projects. Do this as best you can without bothering them for information. The ideal way to get accepted is to cause your prospective mentor as little work as possible.
- Send a brief introductory letter and resume instead of calling. You can communicate better about yourself in a letter, you won't be interrupting your potential mentor's day, and you don't have to worry about bumbling it. They can look at your letter at their convenience, and answer when they get a chance. Make sure to enclose a self-addressed stamped envelope. Any requests just add to their workload. The kind of application that will get read is one that minimizes the work to respond. If you really want to impress, send a self-addressed postcard with a variety of responses for them to put a check mark next to.
- Type a concise (1 page) introduction that clearly shows you are familiar with your prospective mentor's work. Get a book on writing cover letters to help you. Describe what you offer as an intern, rather than how great your ideals are. Most importantly, submit your presentation to at least one

friend or teacher (not a parent) and ask them to give you corrections for clarity and conciseness, and correct spelling and grammar.

- Include a brief, professional resume. Study a book on writing resumes if you don't know how to write one that communicates your abilities. Highlight your relevant experience. If you don't have any directly related practical experience, highlight your ability to produce results, be in service, and do excellent work. Volunteer work with specific accomplishment can impress as much as or more than paid work. Some experience doing physical labor is also helpful. The foremost significance of your resume is that it demonstrates that you can do complete work.

- Follow-up on your letter by telephone or email about 7–10 days after your contact receives it. When you follow-up, check first to make sure your first communication arrived. If you are very interested in the position, ask for an opportunity to talk with them by telephone or in person. Express your interest in an internship, while keeping the conversation as brief as possible so as demonstrate you value the person's time.

- If you are rebuffed or get rejected, you might find a way to pose the question, "What would it take to be able to work with you?" Listen carefully to their considerations. If you are still convinced you are a great match for the position, start over. If you were informed about your shortcomings when you were turned down, improve areas where you were weak before you reapply. It is amazing how easily most people give up. Persistence, an ability to improve, learn from mistakes, and follow through on stated intentions are all necessary characteristics of an intern. If the considerations involved other, practical barriers, you can find ways around these. For example, if the mentor did not want an intern because there was no place for you to live on their farm, offer to handle your own accommodations without their help.

Avoid these application pitfalls

- Do not attempt to use your internship as a tourist opportunity. The convenience of surfing, sunbathing, and drinking the local brew will not impress your mentor, but instead usually indicate a lack of seriousness about an internship. Instead, use the internship to get a unique inside look into a situation which tourists will never see.

- Do not launch into a lecture about how important it is that we all get to work saving the earth, or some such. The person you are writing to is already walking their talk, and will not appreciate a lecture from you.

- Do not waste you mentor's time inquiring about things you can learn about from other sources once you arrive such as where to surf or see a cricket match. Your prospective mentor certainly does not have time to be a travel guide to intern applicants.

- Do not call collect, or ask for return phone calls, especially long distance. Do not leave messages with your name and number—instead, call back until you reach a live person. When you call, originate the call yourself and always ask "Do you have a few minutes?" If they say yes, keep your call brief (it helps to have the points you want to cover written down in front of you). If they say it is not a good time, ask when is a good time to call them back. Call them back when you say you will, and again ask if it's a good time.

- Do not send a mass-produced letter, it's almost certain it won't be answered. Unless you know there is a formal internship program, do not write, "send me information about your program."

- Do not lie or exaggerate on your resume or application letter. Ultimately there will be a consequence. People who lie to get an internship usually continue to do so. An internship relationship is usually close enough to expose lies very quickly.

Launching the Internship

Once you find a person willing to work with you as your mentor, you've gotten over a major hurdle and are on your way to a unique and exciting educational experience. To get the most out of this experience, clarify things about your internship up front.

- Set some clear, measurable, and realistic goals. Write them down, show them to your advisor, and get his or her support. Be specific. Examples of goals include: be able to plant trees with less than 10% attrition; make an entry in a journal each day about bird sightings; learn the names of five medicinal plants and their uses; etc.

- Ask your mentor if he or she likes to have sit down meetings each week or if you are supposed to catch him or her on the fly each day.

- Be honest with your prospective mentor about what you want out of the internship experience, and what you are willing to do. Are you willing to pay for the internship experience, or not? How many hours of field work are you willing to agree to per week? How many days do you need free for study and project work per month? Do you need a place to stay during the internship? Are you willing to live in a tent with rudimentary facilities, or are you dreaming of a fully furnished studio with ocean view? Do you need an income during your internship, or will you have saved enough money to carry you through? Are you willing to commit to a certain time period, or do you want the option of leaving on a few weeks" notice?

- Get a clear agreement with your mentor about the terms of the internship. Put it in writing, sign it, and get your mentor's signature. Although this sounds formal and uncomfortable, it will help avoid many miscommunications during the internship. Set starting and ending dates. Specify what expenses you are responsible for, what they are responsible for, how many days a month you have off, etc. Keep your agreements. If you blow it at some point, acknowledge it, and fix it. For example say, "I said I would bathe the cat this morning, and I forgot to do it."

- Ask about how to borrow books, care for tools (what happens if a tool breaks while you are using it?) etc. Remember, you want your mentor to feel as if you are an asset, not a liability. It's best to be willing to pay for any physical damage to tools or books that you cause to relieve your mentor from any worry about possible damage. Let your mentor know your consideration if you can't afford to repair or replace something.

- Stay away from alcohol and drugs (by no means ever conduct illegal activities such as drug use during the internship).

- Get clear up front about who is responsible for health care, injuries, etc. Offer to sign any liability waiver required.

- Devote yourself 100% to the subject for the duration of the internship. This is not a time to be on the lookout for a new romantic partner, surfing or training for a marathon. You are there to serve and learn from your mentor, and distractions have no place. Keep in mind much of what you learn will be absorbed through osmosis, merely being in the presence of an expert.

- Even if you were a star academic student or are a master in your current profession, bear in mind you will most likely be a novice in many of the activities during your internship. There is really no such thing as "unskilled labor"—most agricultural activities that look simple require experience and practice to do with speed and proficiency.

- You will probably be given (or want to take on) tasks around the farm or business to help out (feeding the animals, watering the nursery, etc.). Start small with this. If you will not be supervised, only take on tasks you are comfortable with. When you complete it, have your mentor check that you did it right. Then, you will be able to perform this task whenever needed. Expand your task areas as you become more proficient. But do not take on, or let your mentor put on you, a task that could damage your mentor's livelihood if you did it wrong.

- When you are being helpful around the farm, be willing to take on some chores that at first might not interest you. You might think, "I don't need to know how to pull weeds from the garden. I don't want to do this job—I'm not learning anything." If your mentor needs it done, just do it, and do it at the level of excellence. They are watching to see the level of responsibility you operate at. You may find one day that the experience you thought was worthless drudgery was an important step. Remember also that the more of an asset you are, the more time your mentor can devote to you.

- Find out if there is a communication process to handle upsets. It is a great relief to know there is a way to deal with problems, resentments, etc. rather than to try to avoid problems at all cost. One excellent way to begin such a conversation is, "I'm having an upset..." Upsets are an essential part of learning and growing.

- Keep a journal. Make daily entries. If you are not comfortable communicating your upsets to your mentor, write them in your journal. This helps clear your mind in preparation for your next day's activities. Write down your goals, your questions, your realizations each day. Experiential learning seems slow, and outside of formal academics there is rarely the chance to be tested and graded. By keeping a journal you will be amazed at how much you've learned in a short amount of time!

Original Source

This article was originally published as *The Overstory* #79.

Giving back: making research results relevant to local groups and conservation

Patricia Shanley and Sarah A Laird

A great deal of research is underway to assess and characterize biodiversity and associated resource management systems. This research yields information critical to the design of conservation programmes and national strategies for biodiversity conservation and furthers scientific understanding of threatened ecosystems. However, researchers and research institutions generally regard the scientific process as complete once an article is sent to press. The result is that most information and scientific understanding generated by researchers remains in the hands of scientists, academics and policy-makers geographically and conceptually distant from the region of study. Rarely are research programmes designed in a way that incorporates the resource management needs of local groups, nor are results put in a form that communities can employ when making resource management decisions. And yet, local groups are widely considered key stewards and stakeholders in biodiversity and forest conservation today.

In part, this situation results from the fact that the outlook and skills necessary to extend and disseminate results are not often found within the organizations that collect and analyse scientific data (Orr 1999). Education and extension groups in the industrialized North acquire scientific data and make valuable use of it in their outreach programmes, but these groups are traditionally small and underfunded in poorer and more biologically diverse regions of the world. For example, school children in the temperate North are taught that while tropical forests cover only 7% of the Earth's surface, they contain 50% of the world's species and are the lungs and medicine chest of the earth. This information is taught not only in schools, but is also displayed for Northern consumers on candy bar wrappers, shampoo bottles and in coffee table books. Villagers living within tropical forests, however, are not privy to such information. Most live unaware that leading world scientists predict the demise of the forests they call home—in only a few decades.

The result is that governments, conservation organizations, researchers and companies often promote or make land-use decisions without fully informing or involving the local populations most affected. At the same time, groups living in close proximity to forests or high biodiversity zones are often badly in need of scientific data that can assist them in negotiations with logging companies, the development of management plans for community forests, assessing the relative value of a given forest area for non-timber forest products versus agriculture, and so on. Increasingly drawn into national and global economies and politics, remote groups more than ever need information and tools to effectively participate, and negotiate their position, in this broadened context.

Traditionally considered distinct from science, education and extension can effectively be twinned with research through institutional or departmental collaborations. Many researchers will not have the skills or interest to translate and transmit their data to local groups; but if they are aware of the importance of this activity, they can forge alliances to ensure this results. Some researchers—as we will see in the case studies—integrate science and extension in their research design. The fields of education, development and rural agriculture extension have for decades worked to effectively transfer information to local groups—including through workshops, manuals, theatre and farmer-to-farmer exchanges—and there is much to be learned from these experiences (e.g., Chambers 1983; Kowal and Padilla 1998; http://www.oneworld.org/odi).   Unfortunately, communication between most biodiversity researchers and these professionals has been limited.

This article addresses an often overlooked element of equitable research relationships and an invaluable form of benefit-sharing: returning data in forms relevant to local groups and applied conservation.

A Growing Awareness of the Need for Giving Back

A new, more equitable approach to sharing—or "giving back"—scientific results can be built into the scientific process, and there are increasing calls for this approach. For example, the *International Society of Ethnobiology Code of Ethics* (1998) incorporates the concept of a "dynamic interactive cycle" for research in which projects should not be initiated unless all stages can be completed. This includes "training and education as an integral part of the project, including practical application of results." In an editorial for *Conservation Biology,* Colvin (1992) recommends a "code of ethics for research in the third world" that suggests, among other points, that researchers "help develop educational outreach programmes and interpretative centres that include...research results, reflect the knowledge and values of indigenous cultures, and can be used by both visitors and the local community."

In India, the Honey Bee Network has worked to transform the paradigm of benefit-sharing to include professional accountability towards those whose knowledge and resources are studied. Researchers realized that their work was published mainly in English, and in ways that remained unavailable and not immediately useful to local groups. As part of their work, the Honey Bee Network shares scientific knowledge in local languages and pools both formal scientific and so-called "informal" solutions to resource management problems developed by people around the world in order to share experiences across communities (Gupta 1995; 1999).

Why Give Back?

Most biodiversity researchers feel an affinity for the ecosystems and communities that they study or with whom they work. Indeed, most proposals for biodiversity research include in the project's objectives their service to these ecosystems and communities. But how do researchers generally propose to make this connection? This is accomplished, primarily, by building understanding and organization of the subjects and, secondly, by providing information that will influence policy-makers and the general public, and might also be adopted by applied conservation projects.

While these are important objectives, another significant way that research results can be magnified to serve communities and conservation is by taking the results and, effectively, returning them to the groups and communities in or around which they were generated. As described in the case studies, research designed and directed to serve local resource-management needs, and shared in ways that allow groups to make informed decisions about long-term resource use, often has surprisingly significant—albeit localized—effects. As we move through conservation fad after conservation trend, often with mixed results, concrete small steps in a positive direction seem an increasingly sufficient objective.

Not only is giving back research results to local stakeholders (rural and urban communities, governments, industries, conservation projects, etc.) an important ethical responsibility that should be taken up by researchers, there are also practical reasons to do this that serve immediate scientific and conservation objectives, as well. Some reasons why a researcher should work to give back results in locally relevant forms include:

- Local stakeholders represent a critical set of actors who will determine if and how natural resources are used and protected. Generally far from enforcement agencies, these groups determine how and if policies are manifested on the ground, and the ways in which resources are managed.

- The knowledge of local populations is an invaluable perspective in examining data. Their specific commentary and critiques of research can serve as a local test of methods and results (Richter and Redford 1999). As Anil Gupta (pers comm 1999) said, it is common that when research results are handed back to local groups, they say something like: "Oh, is that why you were asking that question... I didn't tell you the full story because I didn't know the full context for your inquiry—now that I know it, I will tell you something I did not tell you earlier."

- By returning the results of research locally, the information can be immediately applied. Data fed into the scientific publication circuit can take years to emerge, and must compete for policy-makers' attention in an avalanche of published documents.

- Local groups often have key research questions that they want addressed and their livelihoods, and conservation of local resources and habitats, may depend upon concrete answers.

Forms of Giving Back

There are many ways in which researchers can "translate" their data into forms that are immediately relevant to local groups and conservation. These include written sources (such as manuals, illustrated booklets, curricula, colouring books and technical books) as well as oral and in-person sources (such as interactive workshops, seminars, theatre, travelling shows, music and lectures). In part, the choice of medium will depend upon the objectives to be served, as well as the intended audience. Local audiences will vary, and will include rural and urban communities and organizations, companies (e.g., loggers, ranchers, commercial agriculture), governments and applied conservation and development projects. Materials should be dynamic and constantly revised in light of feedback and experiences (Pyke *et al* 1999).

For example, we see that communities are struggling with ways in which to determine the value of their forests in order to strike better deals with loggers and to assess whether a given area is more valuable to the community for its non-timber products (game, medicine, fruits) or for its timber rights. In one case, given the geographic distance across which communities are grappling with these issues, illustrated manuals (that make them accessible to the illiterate as well as literate), exchanges between groups and travelling theatres and workshops were found to most effectively capture the key scientific results, and allowed for broad dissemination (see full article).

In Belize, traditional healers asked researchers to help them produce a book for teaching children, and which might serve as a reference for, and validation of, threatened medicinal plant knowledge. The published book includes both local knowledge and clinical information gathered by researchers in the US through databases and literature. Other products include colouring books for children and a video used in local schools to teach the importance of traditional knowledge (Balick and Arvigo 1998).

The Jump with Whales programme in the eastern Caribbean tailors its materials in ways that create a sense of ownership and feeling of being "at home" in young and old alike. Colouring books for children, curricula material for schools, and a *BLOWS! Newsletter* distributed free to schools have all helped to translate scientific data into forms that build wider awareness of marine mammal conservation, and a

constituency "to bring about changes in attitudes and values while instilling a sense of heritage for stewardship of the marine environment" (see full article).

Lessons Learned in Giving Back Scientific Data

The case studies and other efforts to link dissemination of results with research have yielded some significant lessons and have flagged key issues that researchers might consider in the design of their research programmes. These include lessons associated with the ways in which data are translated and transmitted, as well as lessons connected to the broader research context in which giving back takes place.

Lessons learned include the following:

- Conduct locally relevant research, in response to locally articulated needs.
- Provide research results in a range of forms as you go through the data collection and analysis process.
- Present economic value and units of measurement appropriate for different audiences; to be most effective this may entail using non-monetary value systems and non-metric local measuring systems.
- Integrate traditional and scientific knowledge, usually highly complementary, when returning results.
- Understand how and why local groups use and manage resources in the ways that they do—this will help make your contribution accurate, relevant and useful.
- Provide information on the range of options available to groups, and not only those a researcher considers optimal—this will help to ensure that recommendations and information are adequately placed in the decision-making reality that local groups face.
- Catalyse the learning process with new, useful and challenging concepts -do not assume that local groups are aware of all possible outcomes and options.
- Be innovative and creative in coming up with ways to transmit your information and lessons to communities—for example, explore the use of posters and songs and interactive dialogue to relay what is customarily illustrated in scientific graphs and charts or technical language.

- Extend dissemination beyond the study area—neighbouring groups and communities often face many of the same challenges and information shortages; train local collaborators to extend results to neighbours.
- Encourage local stakeholders involved in generating information to give back the information, blending in their knowledge, experience and perspectives.
- Reflect local social, economic and cultural norms when giving back, and seek to make the audience feel at home with the information and the message.

Broader Issues Associated with Giving Back Scientific Data

Broader issues include the following:

- Researchers are often limited by the availability of funds. Education and extension are an additional cost that many feel they have neither the time nor money to afford. It is important, therefore, that funders not only respect this additional cost within a proposed budget, but, when possible, seek to promote giving back as a standard part of the research they fund, including in some cases assisting in linking research and extension institutions.
- Researchers tend to look upon information transfer as a "lower" endeavour, and one not of immediate relevance to their work. Academic promotion systems do not generally reward the multidisciplinary, applied work that giving back entails, nor the manuals and other products that do not enter the peer review system. Professional societies might help to promote the concept of the "dynamic interactive research cycle", as well as giving back results within research institutions and universities unaccustomed to considering this part of the research process.
- Researchers' and local groups' time frames are often markedly different. Local groups' livelihoods or resource-management decisions may require immediate access to information, while journal articles presenting scientific data may take months or years to emerge. Researchers should seek to share preliminary results within a reasonable time frame with local groups.

Forms of Giving Back Data

There are many ways of translating data into valuable forms for local groups, and the method selected will depend upon both the groups and the objectives you seek to serve. Below are some ideas that might be considered.

Interactive workshops and seminars for many industry groups, technicians, and government officials, this form of exchange will prove most useful; structured loosely, and involving field trips or site-based interaction, they can help to create dialogue and awareness.

Theatre and travelling shows rural and urban groups alike often respond better to stories, enacted by fellow community members or visitors, which relay lessons learned in a more engaging format than a lecture or seminar. In the realm of theatre, people find it possible to relay information that they might normally find embarrassing to share. In some cases, travelling theatres and shows have proven invaluable for neighbouring communities and groups to share lessons they have learned with each other.

Exchanges exchanges between groups with like needs and backgrounds but from differing geographical regions can be an extremely effective means of transferring information. When neighbouring stakeholders present information to each other in culturally appropriate forms, there are many benefits. Firstly, language, expressions and manner of communication are clearly understood. Secondly, trust is more readily built; information is better accepted from "insiders" because they have no motivation to "sell" ideas. Thirdly, individuals in one region may have personally experienced the positive or negative effects of particular land-use decisions, and are able to relate the consequences in a far more moving and convincing way than an outside extension agent.

Music and songs are a powerful method of cultural expression. New or familiar songs that integrate research findings into lyrics can convey not only relevant scientific facts but also embody the feelings of cultural loss surrounding ecosystem impoverishment. Music has the additional benefit of migrating from community to community on its own, thereby carrying messages across geographical distances.

Lectures in some cases, presentation of scientific results in a fairly standard academic format will be appropriate and useful, particularly for local research institutions, universities and sometimes government departments. Even in these forums, however, it is important to occasionally integrate aspects of the presentation styles listed above. Standard format lectures are far less memorable than those eliciting audience participation.

Manuals and illustrated booklets the content of manuals will vary greatly. Some may be illustrated guides to local uses and management of species, intended for largely illiterate audiences who are concerned about the loss of their cultural knowledge and seek in some way to record and validate this knowledge; others may take the form of field guides that local groups can sell to tourists or can use in managing resources; others may be hands-on technical manuals that help local groups better manage resources or negotiate with commercial and government representatives interested in local resources and lands. When seeking to reach semi-literate and illiterate populations, it is critical to test illustrated materials with local people; rural persons, in particular, exhibit acute perceptivity regarding the size and shape of fruits, leaves and wildlife, and have well-developed opinions on natural resource processing and management techniques.

Curricula teachers in high-biodiversity developing countries often have limited access to materials that assist in teaching about the local environment, traditional use of resources and wider environmental concerns; researchers can provide an invaluable service by translating their results into forms that are easily adopted by teachers in the classroom.

Colouring books children respond well to colouring books in their local language or vernacular; colouring books allow them to become engaged in the subject and are important education and learning tools.

Books publication of books can help to disseminate information more widely that otherwise might not reach a broad cross-section of society; however, many groups cannot afford books, and researchers should be clear on who this form of dissemination can reach—generally academic and governmental, rather than the rural and urban poor.

References

Balick, M. and R. Arvigo. 1998. "The new ethnobotany: sharing with those who shared". Herbalgram No. 42.

Chambers, R. 1983. Rural Development: Putting the Last First. Longman, Harlow.

Colvin, J. 1992. "Editorial: a code of ethics for research in the Third World." Conservation Biology, vol 6, no 3, September, pp. 309–11.

Hands-on workshops are a wonderful way to give back. (photo: C. Elevitch)

Gupta, A.K. 1995. Accessing Biological Diversity and Asso-
ciative Knowledge System: Can Ethics Influence Equity?
IIMA Working Paper No 1340, November, Presented at
the Global Biodiversity Forum, Jakarta, 4–5 November.

Gupta, A.K. *et al.* 1999. "Blending universal with local ethic:
accountability toward nature, perfect stranger and society". In: C. Potvin, M. Kreanzel, and G. Seutin (eds), Protecting Biodiversity: Roles and Responsibilities. McGill-
Queens University Press, Toronto.

International Society of Ethnobiology (ISE). 1998. Code of
Ethics and Guidelines for Research, Collections, Databases and Publications, ISE, Aotearoa/New Zealand, November.

Kowal, M. and E. Padilla. 1998. Collaborative Links between
Research and Extension Organizations: Lessons from the
CONSEFORH Project Experience in Farm Forestry with
Intermediary Agencies. Rural Development Forestry Net-
work Paper 24c, winter 1998–99, Overseas Development
Agency, London.

Orr, D. 1999. "Education, careers, and callings: the practice
of conservation biology." Conservation Biology, vol 13, no
6, December, pp. 1242–5.

Pyke, C.R. *et al.* 1999. "Letter to the Editor: a plan for outreach – defining the scope of conservation education".
Conservation Biology, vol 13, no 6, December, pp. 1238–9.

Richter, B.D. and K.H. Redford. 1999. "The art (and science) of brokering deals between conservation and use".
Conservation Biology, vol 13, no 6, December, pp. 1235–7.

Original Source

This excerpt was reprinted with the kind permission
of the authors and publisher from:

Shanley, P. and S.A. Laird. 2002. "'Giving Back:'
making research results relevant to local groups and
conservation." In: S.A. Laird (ed), Biodiversity and
Traditional Knowledge: equitable partnerships in
practice. Earthscan Publications Ltd., London.

To order this excellent title in the U.S.:

Stylus Publishing
PO Box 605
Herndon, VA 20172-0605
Tel: 800-232-0223; Fax: 703-661-1501
Web: http://www.styluspub.com

For all other orders:
Earthscan Publications Ltd
8-12 Camden High Street
London, NW1 0JH, UK
Tel: +44 (0)20 7387 8559; Fax: +44 (0)20 7387 8998
Web: http://www.Earthscan.co.uk

This chapter was originally published as *The Overstory* #133.

The Contribution of Forestry to Food Security

Marilyn Hoskins

"Food will last so long as forests do"...so runs an ancient Kashmiri adage (*Ann poshi tele yeli poshi van*—Sheik Nur-ud-Din Wali).

Forestry has a large and indispensable role to play in improving present and future food security. Although a great deal remains to be understood about the specifics of this role, it is clear that foresters must make food security a basic consideration in policy formulation, as well as in programme planning, design and implementation.

Trees have been an integral part of the food security strategies of rural people for so long that it is curious and disturbing to note how this relationship has often been neglected in the planning of forestry activities. Even more disturbing, agriculture and forestry have often been, and sometimes still are, viewed as being in opposition. Project reports include such statements as "farmers may be too concerned over providing the daily food to become interested in planting trees". This false dichotomy is perhaps based on the outdated view that forestry is concerned only with raising timber trees on government lands and that agriculture only involves growing crops in open fields.

Diverse agroforest. Chiang Mai, Thailand. (photo: C. Elevitch)

In fact, farmers have long recognized the importance of trees. They almost invariably incorporate trees in production systems in areas where they have lived for an extended period of time (Sène 1985; Hoskins 1985; Niamir 1989). Inquiry into current and past farming practices has clearly shown that rural people have a wealth of knowledge as to which trees make agricultural crops grow more successfully, which provide fodder during dry seasons, and which help to hold soils for more successful farming on sloping land, etc.

Physical Access to Food

The range and importance of foods that rural people obtain either directly from the flora and fauna that comprise the forest environment, or produce in an environment sustained and protected by trees vary significantly, depending on living conditions and availability of resources. However, it is safe to say that forest products provide a large range of locally important goods and services in most parts of the developing world.

In wooded areas of Northeast Thailand, for example, 60% of all food comes directly from the forests. At a regional workshop held in Khon Kaen, Thailand, local villagers prepared an exhibit comprising more than 40 plant and animal products gathered from the natural forests nearby, and then carefully explained the use of each. The foresters and nutritionists participating in the workshop were amazed at the variety and quantity of forest foods (FAO 1988a).

By contrast, in a densely inhabited area of Java, where there is very little forest, 60% of all food comes from home gardens where planted trees play an integral role (Widagda 1981).

Trees and Nutrition

Tree and forest products play an extremely important role in ensuring adequate nutrition. Although availability of calories is accepted as the most important issue for the world's hungry, certain micro-elements are essential for health. By providing many of these essential nutrients, forest products help to improve both the physical and mental well-being of rural people.

For example, many trees are rich in oil seeds, edible leaves or yellow fruits, all of which provide vitamin A. In parts of Africa, diets based on staple grains de-

Forests of Samoa provide numerous foods and medicines. Pictured: Loi Letoga. (photo: C. Elevitch)

pend largely on sauces made from tree products to provide this vitamin which is essential to prevent nutritional blindness. Yet as natural vegetation is depleted, the range of products available for these sauces is narrowed. In many areas, products rich in vitamin A are becoming unavailable; careful forestry planning, including appropriate species selection, could reverse this trend (UN 1987; FAO 1983; FAO 1984; FAO 1986a).

In many countries the distinction between food and medicine is not clear-cut; many plants or other products obtained in the forest are thought to have medicinal qualities and are added to daily meals. For example, honey eaten as a sweetener in many countries is valued as a medicine in Sri Lanka and in Zambia. In other cases, forest products are used as curative rather than preventive medicines in nutritional disorders. In Nigeria, for example, 80% of mothers questioned used a forest-based herbal cure for infant dysentery (Abosede and Akesode 1986). Forest medicines also help to keep the labour force healthy during the agricultural season, thus ensuring higher productivity. Finally, forest plants often provide medicines for livestock diseases (FAO 1986a; FAO 1989a).

Famine Foods

A number of forest perennials are not foods of choice in good times but are lifesaving reserves in times of food shortage. Different trees or shrubs or different parts of the same plant may be eaten during famines (FAO 1989a). For example, during periods of extended drought, fruits sometimes contain fewer nutrients since trees store their energy supply in their roots. Under these circumstances, the roots of many trees are rich in calories but often require a great deal of processing to make them edible. When the range of strategies for providing food security in specific areas is understood, foresters can select species and management strategies so as to ensure availability of food at all times and periodic crises, such as droughts, will have less drastic consequences (Falconer 1990a).

Fuelwood and Food Security

In almost all areas of the developing world, wood provides most of the energy for cooking. Although the exact effects of fuelwood scarcity on diet have not yet been adequately researched, the implicit relationship between fuelwood availability and nutrition should not be overlooked. Cooking releases the nutrients in grains and fibrous foods, making them edible and appealing. Some foods, for example certain varieties of cassava and beans, can even be poisonous if not cooked properly. In this respect, therefore, wood for energy is essential if adequate food supplies are to be converted into adequate diets.

Fuelwood is also essential in processing and preserving foods. In fishing communities, for example, a scarcity of fuel for drying and smoking fish, by far the two most widely used preservation methods in the developing countries, can effectively limit the utilizable daily catch.

However, fuelwood scarcity is not an isolated problem; where wood is in short supply, food and time are apt to be scarce as well. Forestry strategies that attempt to deal with fuelwood shortages alone seldom attract farmer interest. Farmers realize that trees, even those that produce fruit or other products, all provide some wood for cooking. Therefore, strategies that emphasize the use of multipurpose trees to address various locally identified needs are more likely to gain support (FAO 1988c).

Sustaining Agricultural Production

Beyond the direct contribution of food, trees and forests play a critical role in ensuring sustained agricultural production, including animal husbandry and, in some instances, fisheries.

Under the most basic forms of agriculture, where land availability allows a relatively low labour strategy to work effectively, shifting cultivators alternate cropping with fallow periods in which tree cover is allowed to regenerate and restore soil fertility. As land pressure increases, forcing a move toward continuous cultivation, various forms of intercropping develop. On hillsides in Haiti and the Philippines, living hedgerows of *Leucaena leucocephala* stabilize soil on terraces and increase fertility, allowing farmers to produce crops on a sustainable basis on what would otherwise be marginal farmland. In Nigeria, research centres have developed an extremely intensive intercropping system in which trees and crops are grown in alternating rows. This system uses the leaves of the trees as green manure to enrich the soils and enhance crop production (Ngambeki 1985). However, to be valid under field conditions, intensive approaches such as this require secure long-term use rights to land which is a luxury not available to most shifting cultivators.

Trees are also used to protect crops from wind damage. For example, in the Antilles, Argentina, China, India, the Niger, Papua New Guinea and Tunisia, the use of trees as shelter-belts has resulted in increases in grain production ranging from 30 to 200%. In Algeria, China, India, Mauritania, the Niger, Senegal and other countries, trees are being used to stabilize dunes and protect soils from being covered by sand.

Of course, the use of trees in cropping systems is not limited to the production of food crops. For example, Costa Ricans plant trees to give shade necessary in the production of coffee and several other crops; Cameroonians use natural forest for the same purpose. Trees are also an important source of fodder for the animals of the world's 30–40 million pastoralists. In the Sudano-Sahelian zone, *Faidherbia albida* (formerly termed *Acacia* albida) provides 30–40% of all livestock feed in the dry season (Wending, in New, 1984), while in Mexico *Prosopis* spp. is the main dry season fodder. Seventy-five percent of all indigenous tree species in tropical Africa are used for browse (Wickens *et al* 1985).

Under special circumstances, trees also have a role in supporting fisheries, thus ensuring a major food source for many coastal populations. In the Pichavaram mangrove in southern India, for example, 74% of the prawns caught in adjacent coastal waters use the mangrove as nursery grounds (Krishnamurthy 1984).

Thus, tree and forest resources contribute to food security of ensuring physical access to adequate food supplies since they:

- provide a direct source of regularly utilized foods, often in significantly greater quantity and variety than is generally recognized;
- provide essential nutrients and medicines that increase the nutritional impact of other foods, and help to maintain the health of rural people. Medicines from the forest are especially important for populations with no access to other types of medication;
- fill the gap in "hungry seasons" by supplying food during seasonal shortage periods and act as emergency foods in times of drought or other crises;
- yield fuelwood for cooking, preserving and processing foods;
- support sustainable food and agricultural production by helping manage soil and water systems and by controlling wind;
- support livestock systems by providing fodder, especially during seasonal shortages in arid and semi-arid zones;
- provide a storehouse of genetic resources for the improvement of domesticated food crops.

References

Abosede, A.O. & Akesode. 1986. Self-medication with Agbo-Jedi in Lagos, Nigeria. J. Research on Ethnomedicine, 1(1).

Falconer, J. 1990a. "Hungry season" food from the forests. Unasylva, 41: 14–19.

Falconer, J. 1990b. The major significance of "minor" forest products. Community Forestry Note 6. Food and Agriculture Organisation, Rome, 232 pp

FAO. 1983. Food and fruit-bearing forest species. FAO Forestry Paper No. 44/1. Rome.

FAO. 1984. Food and fruit-bearing forest species. FAO Forestry Paper No. 44/2. Rome.

FAO. 1986a. Food and fruit-bearing forest species. FAO Forestry Paper No. 44/3. Rome.

FAO. 1988a. Proc. FAO/Khon Kaen University Workshop on Nutrition in Forestry, Khon Kaen, Thailand, 18–21 October 1988. ESN/NIF/88/27. Rome. FAO.

FAO. 1988b. Forestland for the people. A forest village project in Northeast Thailand. Bangkok, Thailand, Bureau regional de la FAO for Asia and the Pacific.

FAO. 1988c. Planning self-help fuelwood projects in Asia. Based on the Workshop on Planning self-help Fuelwood Projects in Asia, Chiang Mai and Khon Kaen, Thailand, 2–13 February 1987. Bangkok, Thailand, FAO Regional Office for Asia and the Pacific.

FAO. 1988d. Report of the Expert Consultation on Forestry and Food Security. Trivandrum/Bangalore, India, 7–20 February 1988. Rome, FAO.

FAO. 1989a. Forestry and nutrition: a reference manual. Rome, FAO.

Hoskins, M. 1985. The promise in trees. Food and Nutrition, 11(2): 44–46.

Krishnamurthy, K. 1984. Humans' impact on the Pichavaram mangrove ecosystem: a case study from southern India. Proc. Asian Symposium on Mangrove Environment, Research and Management. Kuala Lumpur, 25–29 August 1980, p. 624–632.

New, T. 1984. A biology of Acacias: a new source book and bibliography for biologists and naturalists. Australia, Oxford University Press.

Ngambeki, D.S. 1985. Economic evaluation of alley cropping Leucaena with maize and maize-cowpea in southern Nigeria. Agric. Systems, 17: 243–258.

Niamir, M. 1989. Herder decision-making in natural resource management in arid and semi-arid Africa. Rome, FAO, Forestry Department.

Sène, E.H. 1985. Trees, food production and the struggle against desertification. Unasylva, 37(150): 19–26.

UN. 1987. First Report on World Nutrition. UN Administrative Committee on Coordination, Subcommittee on Nutrition. ACC/SCN. Rome.

Wickens, G.E. et al (eds). 1985. Plants for arid lands. Proc. Kew Int. Conf. on Economic Plants for Arid Lands. London, Allen and Unwin.

Widagda, L.C. 1981. An ecosystem analysis of West Javanese home gardens. Document de travail. East-West Centre, Environment and Policy Institute.

Original Source

This article is excerpted with the gracious permission of the publisher and author from:

Hoskins, M. 1990. The contribution of forestry to food security. Unasylva 160, Vol. 41–1990/1. FAO, Rome.

Web: http://www.fao.org/docrep/t7750e/t7750e02.htm

This excerpt was originally published as *The Overstory* #127.

Learning More (Resources)

"As long as you live, keep learning how to live."—Seneca

Section Contents

The Agroforester's Library (page 496)

The Agroforester's Library

Craig R. Elevitch and Kim M. Wilkinson

Books

This section presents book favorites of agroforestry specialists from around the world. For sources of books, see Book Sources (page 506). Arranged alphabetically by title:

Agroforesteria en el CATIE: bibliografia anotada (Serie Bibliotecologia y Documentación #27, 1999) and
Agroforesteria en el CATIE: suplemento bibliografico (Serie Bibliotecologia y Documentación #28, 2001)
Publisher: CATIE, Turrialba, Costa Rica
ISBN: 9977-57-346-8 and 9977-57-367-0, respectively
Two annotated bibliographies summarizing research and development in agroforestry at Centro Agronómico Tropical de Investigación y Enseñanza's (CATIE). Over 1000 references included (mostly in Spanish).

Agroforestry in Australia and New Zealand
Authors: R. Reid and G. Wilson, 1985
Publisher: Goodard and Dobson, Victoria, Australia
ISBN: 0-949200-00-X
Scientifically based practical information on how to productively integrate trees into farming systems.

Agroforestry in Dryland Africa
Authors: D. Rocheleau, F. Weber, and A. Field-Juma, 1988
Publisher: ICRAF, Nairobi, Kenya
ISBN: 92-9059-049-1
This book is especially useful for field workers, researchers, and extension agents, providing guidelines for evaluating and planning agroforestry projects in drier environments in Africa.

Agroforestry in Sustainable Agricultural Systems
Editors: L.E. Buck, J.P. Lassoie and E.C.M. Fernandes, 1999
Publisher: CRC Press LLC, New York, NY
ISBN: 1-56670-294-1
Examines the environmental and social conditions that affect the roles and performance of trees in field- and forest-based agricultural production systems. Various types of ecological settings for agroforestry are analyzed within temperate and tropical regions.

The Agroforester's Library consists of titles recommended by agroforestry experts

Agro-Forestry in the Pacific Islands: Systems for Sustainability
Editors: W.C. Clark and R.R. Thaman, 1993
Publisher: United Nations University Press, Tokyo
ISBN: 92-808-0824-9
Very thorough treatment of agroforestry practices in the Pacific. Includes tables and descriptions of many traditional agroforestry species.

Agroforestry for Soil Management
Author: A. Young, 1997 (Second Edition)
Publisher: CAB International, New York, New York and ICRAF, Nairobi, Kenya
ISBN: 0-85199-189-0
Now in a revised second edition, this book presents a synthesis of evidence from agriculture, forestry, and soil science, drawing on over 700 published sources dating largely from the 1990's. Very well written and accessible to practitioners and academics. Highly recommended.

Agroforestry Guides for Pacific Islands
1. Information Resources for Pacific Island Agroforestry
2. Multipurpose Trees for Agroforestry in the Pacific Islands
3. Nontimber Forest Products for Pacific Islands: An Introductory Guide for Producers

4. Integrating Understory Crops with Tree Crops
5. Introduction to Integrating Trees into Pacific Island Farm Systems
6. Choosing Timber Species for Pacific Island Agroforestry
7. Economics of Farm Forestry: Financial Evaluation for Landowners
8. Multipurpose Windbreaks: Design and Species for Pacific Islands

Editors: C.R. Elevitch and K.M. Wilkinson, 2000.
Publisher: Permanent Agriculture Resources, Holualoa, Hawai'i
Series of 22–50 page guides covering eight topics in Pacific Island agroforestry. Published with support from the US Department of Agriculture's Western Region Sustainable Agriculture Research and Education (WSARE) Program. The guides can be downloaded at http://www.agroforestry.net.

Agroforestry Technology Information Kit (ATIK)
Author: Various authors, 1990
Publisher: International Institute of Rural Reconstruction (IIRR), Cavite, Philippines
ISBN: 0-942717-31-7
This practical agroforestry guide details nursery techniques, seed collection, seed treatment, soil and water conservation strategies, animal systems, and more. Available from IIRR Bookstore and several other sources. Highly recommended.

Amaranth to Zai Holes: Ideas for Growing Food Under Difficult Conditions
Editors: L.S. Meitzner and M.L. Price, 1996
Publisher: ECHO, North Fort Myers, Florida
ISBN: 0-9653360-0-X
This useful book contains many practical and technical tips from extension workers and small farmers from around the world including information on vegetables, fruits, multipurpose trees, urban gardening, and more.

Cultural and Spiritual Values of Biodiversity
Editor: D.A. Posey, 1999
ISBN: 1-85339-397-5
Publisher: Intermediate Technology Publications, London on behalf of United Nations Environment Programme (UNEP)
This 730 page volume presents the vast array of threads that make up our cultural and spiritual diversity. Available from ITDG Publications (see Book Sources).

The Dictionary of Forestry
Editor: J.A. Helm, 1998
Publisher: Society of American Foresters, Bethesda, Maryland
ISBN: 0-939970-73-2
A comprehensive dictionary defining over 4,500 terms used in forestry and conservation.

The Farmer's Forest - Multipurpose Forestry for Australian Farmers
Authors: R. Reid and P. Stephen, 2001
Publisher: Australian Master TreeGrower Program
ISBN: 0-642-58352-8
Rich in photographs and data, this practical reference is an essential reference for anyone carrying out forestry on a farm. Available from publisher at: Australian Master TreeGrower Program, Department of Forestry, The Institute of Land & Food Resources, The University of Melbourne, Victoria 3010, Australia; Tel: +61 3 8344 5011; Fax: 61 3 9349 4172; Email: rfr@unimelb.edu.au; Web: http://www.mtg.unimelb.edu.au/farmers_forest.htm

Forest Gardening
Author: R. Hart, 1991
Publisher: Green Books, Devon, UK
ISBN: 1-870098-44-7
Describes the design of predominately temperate multistory garden plantings which incorporate fruit and nut trees.

Glossary for Agroforestry
Editors: P. Huxley and H. van Houten, 1997
Publisher: CTA and ICRAF, Nairobi, Kenya
ISBN: 92-9059-124-2
Includes 1,400 agroforestry terms arranged alphabetically, with extensive cross-referencing. Also available in electronic form at:
http://www.bugwood.caes.uga.edu/glossary/

Income Opportunities in Special Forest Products: Self-Help Suggestions for Rural Entrepreneurs (Agriculture Information Bulletin AIB-666)
Authors: M.G. Thomas and D.R. Schumann, 1993
Publisher: USDA Forest Service, Washington, DC
In depth discussion of temperate special forest products (nontimber forest products) that represent opportunities for rural entrepreneurs to supplement their incomes. Order from Southern Research Station, USDA Forest Service, Blacksburg, Virginia; or

download   at: http://www.sfp.for-
prod.vt.edu/pubs/pubs.htm

An Introduction to Agroforestry

Author: P.K.R. Nair, 1993
Publisher: Kluwer Academic Publishers, Dordrecht,
The Netherlands
ISBN: 0-7923-2134-0
A widely used comprehensive textbook on agrofor-
estry which is both practical and theoretical, cover-
ing many agroforestry practices and species. Highly
recommended.

Land Resources: Now and for the Future

Author: A.Young, 2000
Publisher: Cambridge University Press, Cambridge,
UK.
ISBN: 0-521-78559-6
An authoritative review of soils, water, climate, for-
ests, and pastures on which agriculture and rural
land use depend. Available from the publisher at:
http://www.cambridge.org

Nontimber Forest Products of the United States

Editors: E.T. Jones, R.J. McLain, and J. Weigand,
2002
Publisher: University Press of Kansas
ISBN: 0-7006-1166-5
Presents a wide variety of case studies. A valuble reference in the United States and globally. Available
from   publisher   at: http://www.kan-
saspress.ku.edu/jonnon.html

Non-Wood Forest Products: FAO Technical Papers

Author: Various Authors, 1995-1997
Publisher: FAO, Rome
ISBN: Various
An excellent ten volume series on non-wood forest
products and their role in integrated forestry, agroforestry, and conservation. Provides useful information on the various products, and also the basics of
non-wood forest products enterprises for those
products for practitioners, policy makers, and scientists. Order from FAO in Rome (see Book Sources).

North American Agroforestry: An Integrated Science and Practice

Edited by: H.E. Garrett, W.J. Rietveld, and R.F.
Fisher,2000
Publisher: American Society of Agronomy, Madi-
son, Wisconsin

ISBN: 0891181423
The first few chapters focus on the development,
ecological foundations, and the status of agroforestry. Separate chapters cover technical aspects of
the five major agroforestry practices, namely windbreaks, silvopastures, alley cropping, riparian forest
buffers, and forest farming.

Pacific Agroforestry: An Information Kit

Editors: S. Rogers and P. Thorpe, 1999
Publisher: PRAP/SPC, Suva, Fiji
Covers many specific practices, techniques, and spe-
cies of Pacific Island Agroforestry. Order from: Sec-
retariat of the Pacific Community, Private Mail Bag,
Suva, Fiji; Tel: +679 370-733; Fax: +679 370-021;
Email: tomo@spc.org.fj

Permaculture: A Practical Guide for a Sustainable Future

Author: B. Mollison, 1997
Publisher: Ten Speed Press, Berkeley, California
ISBN: 0-9082-2801-5
The premiere guide to designing resource systems in
harmony with natural processes. Highly recom-
mended.

The Overstory Book: Cultivating Connections with Trees, 2nd Edition

Editors: C.R. Elevitch, 2001
Publisher: Permanent Agriculture Resources, Holualoa, HI
ISBN: 0-9702544-3-1
130 concise, easy to read chapters covering key agroforestry concepts.

Plantation Forestry in the Tropics

Author: J. Evans, 1992 (2nd edition)
Publisher: Oxford University Press, New York, NY
ISBN: 0-19-854257-7
This comprehensive text covers plantation, commu-
nity, and social forestry, tree planting to control ero-
sion, and agroforestry.

Practical Guide to Dryland Farming

I   Introduction To Soil And Water Conservation
Practices
II   Contour Farming With Living Barriers Order
III   Integrated Farm Management
IV   Planting Tree Crops Order
V   Soil Fertility Management Order
Publisher: World Neighbors, Oklahoma City, OK

This series of five booklets (30 to 40 pages each) is useful for agroforestry and soil improvement in dryland areas. Each booklet contains simple drawings and is easy to read. Available from ECHO (see Book Sources).

Proceedings from the Five North American Agroforestry Conferences

1 Agroforestry in North America; P. Williams, Ed.; February 1989, Guelph, Ontario.
2 Second Conference on Agroforestry in North America; H.E. 'Gene' Garrett, Ed.; August 1991, Columbia, Missouri.
3 Opportunities for Agroforestry in the Temperate Zone Worldwide: Third North American Agroforestry Conference; R. Schultz and J. Colletti, Eds.; August 1993, Ames, Iowa.
4 Growing a Sustainable Future: Fourth North American Agroforestry Conference; J.H. Ehrenreich and D.L. Ehrenreich, Eds.; July 1995; Boise, Idaho.
5 Exploring the Opportunities for Agroforestry in Changing Rural Landscapes: Fifth North American Agroforestry Conference; L. Buck and J. Lassoie, Eds.; August 1997, Ithaca, New York.

Order the above proceedings at: http://web.missouri.edu/~afta/

A Review of Uses and Status of Trees and Forests in Land-Use Systems in Samoa, Tonga, Kiribati and Tuvalu with Recommendations for Future Action

Authors: R.R. Thaman and W.A. Whistler, 1996
Publisher: South Pacific Forestry Development Programme, Suva, Fiji.
Information on the status of existing agroforestry systems and related programs with extensive species tables. Order through Pacific Islands Forests & Trees Support Programme (see Organizations).

Temperate Agroforestry Systems

Editors: A.M. Gordon and S.M. Newman, 1997
Publisher: CAB International, Oxon, UK
ISBN: 0-8519-9147-5
A landmark reference for agroforestry for temperate regions, including agroforestry practices in North America, New Zealand, Australia, China, and Europe.

Tree Crops: A Permanent Agriculture

Author: R.J. Smith, 1950
Publisher: Island Press, Washington, DC
ISBN: 0-9332-8044-0
A classic reference on the use of trees in agricultural systems.

A Tree for All Reasons: the introduction and evaluation of multipurpose trees for agroforestry

Authors: P.J. Wood and J. Burley, 1991
Publisher: ICRAF, Nairobi, Kenya
ISBN: 92-9059-075-0
Available in English, French or Spanish, this book provides guidance on researching and evaluating agroforestry trees for their suitability to a specific need, site, and purpose.

Trees on the Treeless Plains: Revegetation Manual for the Volcanic Landscapes of Central Victoria.

Author: D. Holmgren, 1994
Publisher: Holmgren Design Services, Victoria, Australia
ISBN: 0-646-17-568-8
Covers design of revegetation systems in detail including windbreaks and farm forestry. The presentation is based on practical experience and is well illustrated. Order through Permaculture International LTD (see Book Sources).

Tropical Agroforestry

Author: P. Huxley, 1999
Publisher: Blackwell Science, Oxford, UK, http://www.blackwell-science.com
ISBN: 0-632-04047-5
Provides an in-depth, analytical account of the principles as well as the practical implications of agroforestry.

Tropical Environments

Author: M. Kellam and R. Tackaberry, 1997
Publisher: Routledge, New York, New York
ISBN: 0-4151-1609-0
Introduces the complex systems of a broad, cross-regional range of humid to semi-arid tropical climate zones and offers an integration of biophysical and human management issues.

Tropical Home Gardens

Editors: K. Landauer and M. Brazil, 1990
Publisher: United Nations University Press, Tokyo
ISBN: 92-808-0732-3

Extensive treatment of home gardens in a research context, covering the development and management of home garden programs.

Species References

References are arranged alphabetically by title.

Agroforestree database: a tree species reference and selection guide

Authors: A.S. Salim, A.J. Simons, A. Waruhiu, C. Orwa, and C. Anyango, 1998
Publisher: International Centre for Research in Agroforestry (ICRAF), Nairobi, Kenya
A selection guide for agroforestry trees covering more than 300 species. Valuable for field workers and researchers who are engaged in activities involving trees suitable for agroforestry systems and technologies. Available as CD-ROM from ICRAF and online at: http://198.93.235.8/cfdocs/examples/treessd/AFT/AFT.htm

Choosing the Right Trees--Setting Priorities for Multipurpose Tree Improvement, Research Report No. 8

Authors: S. Franzel, H. Jaenicke, and W. Janssen, 1996
Publisher: ISNAR, The Hague, The Netherlands
ISBN: 9-29118-025-4
Provides a procedure for selecting species based on maximizing potential benefits. Download from http://www.cgiar.org/isnar/publications/enviro.htm or order from ISNAR Publication Services, PO Box 93375, 2509 AJ The Hague, The Netherlands; Fax: +31-70-381-9677; Email: isnar@cgiar.org

Cornucopia II: A Source Book of Edible Plants

Author: S. Facciola, 1998
Publisher: Kampong Publications, Vista, California
ISBN: 0-96280-872-5
An encyclopedic reference on over 3,000 edible plants, their cultivars, and sources of plant materials. Direct inquiries to the author Stephen Facciola at Kzyl-ruk@worldnet.att.net (or see Book Sources, page 506).

The Cultivated Plants of the Tropics and Subtropics

Authors: S. Rehm and G. Espig, 1991
Publisher: Verlag Josef Margraf

ISBN: 3-8236-1169-0
A detailed overview of culturally and economically important plants, well illustrated and full of practical information.

Domestication of Agroforestry Trees in Southeast Asia

Editors: J.M. Roshetko and D.O. Evans, 1999
Publisher: Winrock International, Morrilton, Arkansas
ISBN: 1-57360-019-9
Presents detailed reports concerning tree domestication and specific tree species in smallholder agroforestry systems.

Edible Leaves of the Tropics (Third Edition)

Authors: F.W. Martin, R.M. Ruberté, L.S. Meitzner
Publisher: Educational Concerns for Hunger Organization, Inc (ECHO)
ISBN: 0-96533609-1-8
An indispensable guide to annual and perennial plants with edible leaves. Available from ECHO.

FACT Sheets (formerly NFT Highlights)

Authors: various, 1987–1999
Publisher: FACT Net, Winrock International, Morrilton, Arkansas
For a concise summary of information about a multipurpose tree or shrub species, see the appropriate FACT Sheet at http://www.winrock.org/forestry/factpub/factsh.htm or order hard copies from FACT Net (see Organizations). Many available in Spanish, French, Indonesian, Chinese, Vietnamese, and Khmer.

Farm, Community, and Tree Network (FACT Net) research journals, conference proceedings, field and training manuals

1. Agroforestry Species and Technologies. Roshetko, J.M. Ed. (2001). A compilation of the highlights and factsheets published by NFTA and FACT Net 1985-1999.

2. Albizia and Paraserianthes Production and Use: A Field Manual. Roshetko, J.M. (1998).

3. Calliandra calothyrsus production and use: A Field Manual. Powell, M. H. (1997).

4. Dalbergia: Proceedings of an International Workshop. Westley, S. B. and J. M. Roshetko, Eds. (1994).

5. Erythrina in the New and Old Worlds. Westley, S. B. and M. H. Powell, Eds. (1993).

6. Erythrina Production and Use: A Field Manual. Powell, M. H. and S. B. Westley (1993).

7. Financial and Economic Analyses of Agroforestry Systems. Sullivan, G. M., S. M. Huke, et al. (1991). Proceedings of a workshop.

8. International Workshop on Albizia and Paraserianthes Species. Zabala, N. Q. (1994).

9. International Workshop on the Genus Calliandra. Evans, D. O. (1996).

10. Marketing of Multipurpose Tree Products in Asia. Raintree, J. B. and H. A. Fransisco (1993). Proceedings of an international workshop.

11. Nitrogen Fixing Trees for Acid Soils. Evans, D. O. and L. T. Szott (1995). Proceedings of a workshop.

12. Nitrogen Fixing Trees for acid soils: a Field Manual. Powell, M. H. (1996).

13. Nitrogen Fixing Trees for Fodder Production. Daniel, J. N. and J. M. Roshetko (1995). Proceedings of an international workshop.

14. Nitrogen Fixing Trees for Fodder Production: A Field Manual. Roshetko, J.M. and R. C. Gutteridge (1996).

15. Tree Domestication in Southeast Asia: Results of a Regional Study on Institutional Capacity for Tree Domestication in National Programs. Gunasena, H.P.M. and J. M. Roshetko (2000).

Publisher: Winrock International, Morrilton, Arkansas

Particularly valuable for the practical agroforester, these are some of the best species resources available at a reasonable cost. For a list of the many publications available contact FACT Net (see Book Sources) or visit

http://www.winrock.org/forestry/factnet.htm

A Field Guide to the Families and Genera of Woody Plants of Northwest South America (Colombia, Peru, and Ecuador)

Author: A.H. Gentry, 1993
Publisher: Conservation International and The University of Chicago Press, Chicago, Illinois
ISBN: 0-226-28943-5
Covers the extraordinarily diverse flora of Colombia, Ecuador, and Peru. Order from: The University of Chicago Press, 11030 S. Langley Avenue, Chicago, IL 60628, USA; Tel: 800-621-2736; Fax: 800-621-8471; Web:
http://www.press.uchicago.edu

Forage Tree Legumes in Tropical Agriculture

Editors: R. Gutteridge and M. Shelton, 1994 (republished 1998).
Publisher: The Tropical Grassland Society of Australia, St Lucia, Queensland, Australia (previously published by CAB International, Wallingford, UK)
ISBN: 0-9585677-1-9
Covers a number of multipurpose tree legumes that can serve as ruminant forage in silvopastoral agroforestry systems. Download the text or order from:
http://193.43.36.7/waicent/faoinfo/agricult/agp/agpc/doc/publicat/Gutt-shel/x5556e00.htm

Forest Production for Tropical America

Agriculture Handbook 710
Author: F.H. Wadsworth, 1997
Publisher: USDA Forest Service, Washington, DC, USA.
A very useful text on tropical forestry. Includes extensive species data for about 150 forestry species, including wood uses. Order from: International Institute for Tropical Forestry, Publications, USDA Forest Service, P.O. Box 5000, Rio Piedras, Puerto Rico   00928-5000;
Web: http://www.fs.fed.us/global/iitf/welcome.html

Forestry Compendium (2003 Edition)

Authors: Various
Publisher: CAB International (CABI)
ISBN: 0-85199-697-3
Includes information (text, maps and pictures) on over 1,200 tree and shrub species of importance to forestry and agroforestry. Tropical, subtropical, temperate and boreal species are included. Orders:
http://www.cabicompendium.org

The Leguminosae: A Source Book of Characteristics, Uses, and Nodulation

Authors: O.N. Allen and E.K. Allen, 1981
Publisher: Wisconsin Press
ISBN: 0-29908-400-0
A global survey of leguminous root nodulation and essential reference for research in tree legumes.

Plant Resources of South-East Asia (PROSEA) Handbooks

PROSEA 1: 'Pulses'
PROSEA 2: 'Edible fruits and nuts'
PROSEA 3: 'Dye and tannin-producing plants'

PROSEA 4: 'Forages'
PROSEA 5: 'Timber trees'
PROSEA 6: 'Rattans'
PROSEA 7: 'Bamboos'
PROSEA 8: 'Vegetables'
PROSEA 9: 'Plants yielding non-seed carbohydrates'
PROSEA 10: 'Cereals'
PROSEA 11: 'Auxiliary plants'
PROSEA 12: 'Medicinal and poisonous plants'
PROSEA 13: 'Spices'
PROSEA 14: 'Vegetable oils and fats'
PROSEA 15: 'Cryptogams 1: Algae'
PROSEA 16: 'Stimulants'
PROSEA 17: 'Fibre plants'
PROSEA 18: 'Exudates'
PROSEA 19: 'Essential-oil plants'
Publisher: PROSEA Foundation, Bogor, Indonesia
An encyclopedic series on plant resources for Southeast Asia which is useful for researchers and practitioners in all tropical regions. Network Office: Dr Made Sri Prana, Director; c/o Herbarium Bogoriense, RDCB - LIPI, Jl. H. Juanda 22, P.O. Box. 332, Bogor 16122, Indonesia; Tel: +62-251 322859,377762 Fax: +62-251 370934; Email: info@proseanet.org, pran@proseanet.org; Web site: http://www.proseanet.org/

The Plant–Book: A Portable Dictionary of the Vascular Plants
Author: D.J. Mabberley, 1997
Publisher: Cambridge University Press, Cambridge, UK
ISBN: 0-52141-421-0
A comprehensive botanical reference combining taxonomic details with information on English names and uses.

Plants for Use in Permaculture in the Tropics
Author: F.W. Martin, 1994.
Publisher: Yankee Permaculture, Dahlonega, Georgia
Presents extensive tables of plants and their characteristics for use in agroforestry systems.

Selection and Management of Nitrogen-Fixing Trees
Author: K.G. MacDicken, 1994
Publisher: Winrock International, Morrilton, Arkansas
ISBN: 0-933595-86-7

A very useful reference for agroforestry uses of nitrogen fixing trees, including species selection, plant inoculation, growth characteristics, and potential uses.

Tropical Trees: Propagation and Planting Manuals
Vol 1. Rooting Cuttings of Tropical Trees, (in English, Spanish and a number of other languages) with five associated video tapes in English and Spanish. (ISBN 0-85092-394-8)
Vol 2. Raising seedlings of tropical trees (In press)
Vol 3. Preparing to Plant Tropical Trees (ISBN 0-85092-535-5)
Vol 4. Growing Good Tropical Trees for Planting (ISBN 0-85092-418-9)
Author: K.A. Longman, 1993–present
Publisher: Commonwealth Science Council, London, UK
These books promote the growing and planting of trees and cover all stages from genetic selection and nursery development to successful planting in the field. These titles use nontechnical language and are extensively illustrated with line drawings. Order from: Information and Publications Division, Commonwealth Secretariat, Marlborough House, Pall Mall, London, SW1y 5HX, UK; Fax: +44 20 7 839 9081; Email: r.jones-parry@commonwealth.int; Web:
http://www.thecommonwealth.org/htm/info/journals/order.htm

Organizations

Alternatives to Slash-and-Burn (ASB) is a global partnership of over 50 institutions around the world with a shared interest in conserving forests and reducing poverty in the humid tropics. ASB Programme, ICRAF, P.O. Box 30677, Nairobi, Kenya; Tel: +254 2 524139/524000 or +1 650 833 6645; Fax: +254 2 524001 or +1 650 833 6646; Email: asb@cgiar.org; Web: http://www.asb.cgiar.org

The Agroforestry Research Trust researches temperate agroforestry and all aspects of plant cropping and uses, with a focus on tree, shrub and perennial crops. Martin Crawford, Agroforestry Research Trust, 46 Hunters Moon, Dartington, Totnes, Devon TQ9 6JT, England, UK;
Email: mail@agroforestry.co.uk;
Web: http://www.agroforestry.co.uk/

Appropriate Technology Transfer for Rural Areas (ATTRA) provides technical assistance to farmers, Extension agents, market gardeners, agricultural researchers, and other ag professionals in the US. ATTRA, P.O. Box 3657, Fayetteville, AR 72702, USA, Tel: 1-800-346-9140, Web: http://www.attra.org/attra-pub/index.html

The Association for Temperate Agroforestry focuses on temperate agroforestry, with an emphasis on North America. School of Natural Resources, 1-30 Agriculture Bldg., University of Missouri, Columbia, MO 65211 USA; Web: http://web.missouri.edu/~afta/

Australian Centre for International Agricultural Research (ACIAR) works to improve the well-being of people in developing countries and Australia through international collaboration in research and related activities that develop sustainable agricultural systems and appropriate strategies for natural resource management. Address: The Director, ACIAR, GPO Box 1571, Canberra ACT 2601 Australia; Tel: +61 2 6217 0500; Fax: +61 2 6217 0501; Email: aciar@aciar.gov.au, Web: http://www.aciar.gov.au/

CAB International (CABI) has as its mission to help improve human welfare worldwide through the dissemination, application and generation of scientific knowledge in support of sustainable development, with emphasis on agriculture, forestry, human health and the management of natural resources. Address: CAB International, Wallingford, Oxfordshire, OX10 8DE, UK; Tel: +44 1491 832111; Fax: +44 1491 833508; Email: cabi@cabi.org; Web: http://www.cabi.org/

The Center for Subtropical Agroforestry (CSTAF) is a multidisciplinary, multi-institutional center established in 2001 at the School of Forest Resources and Conservation (SFRC), University of Florida, to undertake activities in research, extension, and education and training related to agroforestry, and sponsor of the June 2004 1st World Congress of Agroforestry http://conference.ifas.ufl.edu/WCA/. CSTAF, School of Forest Resources and Conservation, University of Florida, Building 191 Mowry Road, PO Box 110831, Gainesville, FL 32611-0831, USA; Tel: 352-846-0146; Fax: 352-846-2094; Email: mikebann@ufl.edu; Web: http://cstaf.ifas.ufl.edu/

The Centre for Ecology and Hydrology Edinburgh (formerly the Institute of Terrestrial Ecology and the Institute of Freshwater Ecology) conducts research on air pollution, climate change, and sustainable land use in the tropics. The Centre for Ecology and Hydrology, Bush Estate, Penicuik, Midlothian, Scotland EH26 0QB, UK; Tel: +44-0131-445-4343; Fax: +44-0131-445-3943; Email: bush@ceh.ac.uk; Web: http://www.ceh.ac.uk/aboutceh/edinburgh.htm

Centro Agronómico Tropical de Investigación y Enseñanza (CATIE) works to improve the well-being of humanity through scientific research and postgraduate education applied to the development, conservation and sustainable use of natural resources. Address: CATIE, 7170, Turrialba, Costa Rica; Web: http://www.catie.ac.cr/catie/

Educational Concerns for Hunger Organization (ECHO) has many online publications related to agroforestry. Address: ECHO, 17430 Durrance Rd., N. Ft. Myers, FL 33917, USA; Tel: 941-543-3246, Fax: 941-543-5317; Email: echo@echonet.org; Web: http://www.echonet.org/

The Forest Garden Initiative Program supported by Counterpart International is developing a flexible model silvicultural system that fosters the restoration of degraded land through the development of family-owned Forest Gardens by rural agriculturalists around the world. Address: Counterpart International, Inc., 1200 18th Street NW, Suite 1100, Washington, DC 20036, USA; Tel: 202-296-9676; FAX: 202-296-9679; Email: info@counterpart.org; Web sites: http://www.forestgarden.org/, http://www.counterpart.org/

Forest, Trees and People Programme supports rural populations in participating in developing their forest resources. FTPP Newsletter, Swedish University of Agricultural Sciences, PO Box 7005, 75007 Uppsala, Sweden, Fax: 46-18-673420; Email: daphne.thuvesson@lbutv.slu.se; Web: http://www-trees.slu.se/

Forestry Programme of the Food and Agriculture Organization of the United Nations (FAO) addresses how to use trees, forests and related resources to improve people's economic, environmental, social and cultural conditions while ensuring that the resource is conserved to meet the needs of future generations. Many useful publications are available on-line. Address: Publications and Information Coordinator, Forestry Department, Food and Agriculture Organization of the United Nations, Viale delle Terme di Caracalla 00100 Rome, Italy; Tel.: +39-06-57054778 F ax: +39-06-57052151; Email: Forestry-www@fao.org; Web: http://www.fao.org/fo/

The International Institute of Rural Reconstruction (IIRR) publishes many practical works emphasizing participatory approaches to development and agroforestry. Address: Yen Center and Headquarters, Silang, Cavite, Philippines 4118; Tel: (63-46) 4142417, Fax: (63-46) 4142420; Email: iirr@cav.pworld.net.ph; Web: http://www.iirr.org

New Forests Project (NFP) helps farmers initiate reforestation projects. Address: NFP, 731 Eighth Street, SE, Washington, DC 20003, USA; Tel: 202-547-3800, Fax: 202-546-4784; Email: ic-nfp@erols.com; Web: http://www.newforestsproject.com/

Pacific Islands Forests & Trees Support Programme works to strengthen national capabilities in Pacific Island countries to manage, conserve, use and develop their forest and tree resources sustainably. Address: SPC/UNDP/AusAID/FAO SPC Private Mail Bag Suva, Fiji; Web: http://www.spc.org.nc/En/forestry.htm

Permanent Agriculture Resources (PAR) carries out agroforestry education and research in the Pacific, provides workshops, and publishes *Agroforestry Guides for Pacific Islands* and *The Overstory*, a free email journal. Address: Permanent Agriculture Resources, P.O. Box 428, Holualoa, HI 96725, USA; Tel: 808-324-4427; Fax: 808-324-4129; Email: par@agroforestry.net; Web: http://www.agroforestry.net

The People and Plants Initiative carries out applied research projects, community workshops, exchanges and training courses with young ethnobotanists from developing countries and disseminates results and information through their People and Plants Online Program. Web: http://www.rbgkew.org.uk/peopleplants/index.html

The Rainforest Conservation Fund is dedicated to preserving the world's tropical forests, and features current applications of agroforestry species, their advantages and disadvantages (marketing, soil needs, growth, pests, etc.), and farmers' preferences for agroforestry species in northeastern Peru. Rainforest Conservation Fund, 2038 North Clark Street, Suite 233, Chicago, IL 60614; Tel: 773-975-7517;

Email: rcf@interaccess.com; Web: http://www.rainforestconservation.org.

The Silvoarable Agroforestry For Europe (SAFE) project will provide models and databases for assessing the profitability of silvoarable systems. Web: http://www.ensam.inra.fr/safe/

Sustainable Harvest International (SHI) provides farmers and communities in the tropics with long-term assistance implementing environmentally and economically sustainable technologies. SHI, P.O. Box 3114, Portsmouth, New Hampshire 03802-3114, USA, Tel: 603-427-0735, Fax: 603-422-8762; Email: info@sustainableharvest.org; Web: http://www.sustainableharvest.org/

Trees for the Future is a non-profit organization initiating and supporting agroforestry self-help projects in cooperation with groups and individuals in developing countries. Address: Trees for the Future, P.O. Box 7027, Silver Spring, MD 20907-7027, USA; Email: info@treesftf.org; Web: http://www.treesftf.org/

Unit of Agroforestry and Novel Crops, School of Tropical Biology, James Cook University, PO Box 6811, Cairns, QLD 4870, Australia; Tel: +61-07-4042-1573; Fax: +61-07-4042-1284; Email: roger.leakey@jcu.edu.au

The US Department of Agriculture's National Agroforestry Center (USDA NAC) supports practices which integrate trees and agriculture. Publishes Inside Agroforestry, a newsletter for natural resource professionals, and many other practical materials. Temperate focus. Address: USDA Forest Service/Natural Resources Conservation Service, East Campus - UNL Lincoln, Nebraska 68583-0822, USA; Tel: 402-437-5178, Fax: FAX: 402-437-5712; Web: http://www.unl.edu/nac/

The World Agroforestry Centre (formerly International Center for Research in Agroforestry, ICRAF) has extensive worldwide programs in agroforestry research and training. World Agroforestry Centre, PO Box 30677, Nairobi, Kenya; Tel: +254-2-521450 or +1-650-833-6645; Fax: +254-2-521001 or +1-650-833-6646, Email: ICRAF@cgiar.org; Web: http://www.worldagroforestrycentre.org

Periodicals

Agroforesteria en las Americas promotes the use of natural resources with greater consideration of ecological potentialities and the social needs of the countries in Latin America. Agroforesteria en las Americas,

CATIE 7170 Turrialba, Costa Rica; Tel: +506 556 1789; Fax: +506 556 7766; Email: agrofor@catie.ac.cr; Web: http://www.catie.ac.cr/information/RAFA/

Agroforestry News is a periodical published in Australia featuring practical, timely information for farm foresters growing timber. Address: Agroforestry News, NRE Port Phillip Region, Locked Bag 3000, Box Hill 3128 Victoria, Australia; Fax 03-9296-4722

Agroforestry Today is a quarterly magazine that carries practitioner oriented reports from around the world on trees and crops on farms, and on the people who plant them. Published by International Centre for Research in Agroforestry (ICRAF). Contact: Agroforestry Today, PO Box 30677, Nairobi, Kenya, Fax: +254 2 521001, Email: aftoday@cgiar.org

Agroforestry Systems journal published in cooperation with the International Centre for Research in Agroforestry (ICRAF) is very helpful with the hard science of agroforestry, and of practical use. Agroforestry Systems is expensive; available at many university libraries. Address: Kluwer Academic Publishers, Journals Department, PO Box 322, 3300 AH Dordrecht, The Netherlands; Tel: (+31) 78 639 23 92, Fax: (+31) 78 654 64 74; Email: services@wkap.nl; Web: http://www.wkap.nl/journals/afs

APANews published by the Asia-Pacific Agroforestry Network publishes a newsletter dedicated to the exchange of information on agroforestry research and development issues in the Asia-Pacific Region. Address: APAnews, FAO Regional Office for Asia and the Pacific, 39 Phra Atit Road, Bangkok, 10200, Thailand; Email: fao-rap@fao.org

Forest Ecology and Management is an international journal concerned with the application of biological, ecological and social knowledge to the management of man-made and natural forests. Address: Elsevier Science, Regional Sales Office, Customer Support Department, PO Box 211, 1000 AE Amsterdam, The Netherlands; Tel: (+31) 20 485 3757; Fax: (+31) 20 485 3432; Email: nlinfo-f@elsevier.nl; Web: http://www.elsevier.nl/locate/foreco

Forests, Trees and People Newsletter published by the Forest, Trees and People Programme supports rural populations in developing their forest re-

sources. Edited by Daphne Thuvesson and published by the Swedish University of Agricultural Sciences (SUAS). Address: FTPP Network. SLU Kontakt, Swedish University of Agricultural Sciences (SLU), Box 7034, 750 07 Uppsala, Sweden. Tel. +46-18-672001; Fax: +46-18-671980; Email: FTPP.Network@kontakt.slu.se; Web: http://www-trees.slu.se/

ILEIA Newsletter covers technical and social options for ecological and sustainable agriculture, and has frequent articles on tree-based systems. Address: LEISA, PO Box 64, 3830 AB Leusden, The Netherlands; Tel: +31 33 494 30 86, Fax: +31 33 495 17 79; Email: iliea@iliea.nl

The Indigenous Knowledge & Development Monitor focuses on the role that indigenous knowledge can play in participatory approaches to sustainable development, and is a good place for learning and networking. Web: http://www.nuffic.nl/ciran/ikdm/

Inside Agroforestry, a newsletter for natural resource professionals, and many other practical materials. Temperate focus. USDA Forest Service/Natural Resources Conservation Service, East Campus - UNL Lincoln, Nebraska 68583-0822, USA; Tel: 402-437-5178, Fax: 402-437-5712; Web: http://www.unl.edu/nac/

ISTF News published by the International Society of Tropical Foresters (ISTF) is dedicated to providing a communications network for tropical forestry disciplines. Address: International Society of Tropical Foresters, 5400 Grosvenor Lane Bethesda, Maryland 20814, USA; Tel: (301) 897-8720 Ext. 126; FAX at (301) 897-3690; Email: istf@igc.apc.org; Web: http://www.cof.orst.edu/org/istf/

The International Forestry Review is a peer-reviewed scientific journal that publishes papers, research notes and book reviews on all aspects of forestry and forest research. Commonwealth Forestry Association, PO Box 142, Bicester OX26 6ZJ, United Kingdom; Tel: +44 (0) 1865 820935; Fax: +44 (0) 1865 820935; Email: cfa@cfa-international.org; Web: http://www.cfa-international.org/

The International Tree Crops Journal focuses on the development and promotion of the diversity of tree-based systems within the field of rural development forestry, particularly in the tropics. Address: International Tree Crops Journal, Editors, Michelle A Pinard & Martin G Barker, Department of Forestry, University of Aberdeen, Aberdeen AB24 5UA, UK; Fax: 44-01224-272685;

Email: tree.crops@abdn.ac.uk;
Web: http://www.abdn.ac.uk/forestry/tropical/tre
ecrop/itcjde.htm

Non-wood News is an information-rich newsletter produced by FAO's Wood and Non-wood Products Utilization Branch, providing readers with current information on nontimber forest products and their contribution to the sustainable development of the world's forest resources. Address: Non-Wood News, Forest Products Division, Forestry Department, FAO, Viale delle Terme di Caracalla 00100 Rome, Italy; Tel: +39-06-570-52746, Fax: +39-06-570-55618; Web: http://www.fao.org/forestry/FOP/FOPW/NWFP/newsle-e.stm

The Overstory is the bimonthly email journal covering topics and concepts central to agroforestry practice on which this book is based. Geared towards agroforestry practitioners, extension agents, and researchers. Contact: *The Overstory*, P.O. Box 428, Holualoa, HI 96725 USA; Tel: 808-324-4427, Fax: 808-324-4129;
Email: overstory@agroforestry.net, Web: http://www.overstory.org

People and Planet focuses on themes such as sustainable energy, coral reefs, and forests. It does an admirable job of linking population and demographic change with natural resources. Address: People & the Planet, Suite 112, Spitfire Studios, 63-71 Collier Street, London N1 9BE, UK; Tel: + 44 -(0)-207-713-8108; Fax: + 44 - (0)-207-713-8109; Email: planet21@netcomuk.co.uk;
Web: http://www.peopleandplanet.net

World Association of Soil & Water Conservation (WASWC) Newsletter covers global news and announcements for association members. Soil and Water

Conservation Society, 7515 NE Ankeny Rd., Ankeny, Iowa 50021, USA; Tel: +1-515-2892331 ext. 18, Fax: +1-515-2891227; Email: memberservices@swcs.org

University Programs

There are hundreds of university and college programs worldwide that have agroforestry programs, and the number grows every year. A comprehensive listing is beyond the scope of this newsletter. Fortunately, ICRAF publishes a Directory of International Training and Educational Opportunities in Agroforestry, with information on 140 institutions

(mainly colleges and universities) that offer formal education and/or short courses in agroforestry.

Rudebjer, Per. 1996. Directory of International Training and Educational Opportunities in Agroforestry. ICRAF, PO Box 30677, Nairobi, Kenya. See also ICRAF's page on agroforestry resources for links to academic institutions at:
http://www.cgiar.org/icraf/inform/AFLinks/AFLinks.cfm

Other Sources of Information

Agroforesters can also find support and information from many local and national sources that were not listed here. Possibilities include forest service staff, county extension agents, local and regional economic development organizations, small business development centers, conservation organizations, and local universities and community colleges. Local interest groups and societies dedicated to agroforestry species or sustainable practices can also be invaluable, for example fruit, bamboo, or palm societies, sustainable agriculture organizations, etc.

Book Sources

Large retailers of books carry a wide selection of the agroforestry titles. We also encourage you to use the following bookstores, each of which supports the activities of an educational organization:

ECHO's Global Bookstore offers hundreds of titles in agriculture, agroforestry, and agricultural development, many of which are very hard to find elsewhere. Address: ECHO's Global Bookstore, 17391 Durrance Rd., N. Ft. Myers, FL 33917, USA; Tel: 941-543-3246; Fax: 941-543-5317; Email: books@echonet.org; Web:
http://echonet.org/shopsite_sc/store/html/index.html

International Institute of Rural Reconstruction (IIRR) publishes many top-notch practitioner resources. Address: IIRR Bookstore, Publications Unit, International Institute of Rural Reconstruction, Y.C. James Yen Center, Silang, Cavite 4118, Philippines; Tel: +63-46- 414-2417; Fax: +63-46-414-2420; Email: Information@iirr.org; Web: http://www.iirr.org

The International Palm Society Bookstore offers many palm references, and several covering traditional and agroforestry uses. International Palm Society, P.O.Box 1897, Lawrence, Kansas, 66044-

8897, USA; Fax: 1-785-843-1274;
Web: http://www.palms.org/

ITDG Publishing builds on the skills and capabilities of people in developing countries through book publishing and a development bookshop. ITDG Publishing, 103-105 Southampton Row London, WC1B 4HL, UK; Tel: +44(0)20 7436 9761; Fax +44(0)20 7436 2013; Email: orders@itpubs.org.uk; Web: http://www.itdgpublishing.org.uk.

Farm, Community, and Tree Network (FACT Net) publications are sold by Winrock International at a very reasonable cost. Address: FACT Net, Winrock International, 38 Winrock Drive, Morrilton, Arkansas 72110-9370, USA; Tel: 501-727-5435; Fax: 501-727-5417; Email: forestry@winrock.org; Web: http://www.winrock.org/forestry/factnet.htm

Granny Smith's Bookshop has a wide range of hard to find titles in tropical agroforestry. Address: P.O. Box 27, Subiaco, WA 6008, Australia; Tel: +61 8-9388-1965; Fax: +61-8-9388-1852;
Email: granny@AOI.com.au;
Web: http://www.AOI.com.au/granny/index.htm

Good Earth Book Store sells a wide range of practical texts for organic farming primarily in temperate environments. Address: P.O. Box 898, Shelburne, Vermont 05482, USA. Tel/Fax: 802-425-3201; Email: info@goodearthpub.com; Web: http://www.goodearthpub.com.

Food and Agriculture Organization of the United Nations (FAO) has a comprehensive list of its publications, and many are available to read from the web site as well. Address: Sales and Marketing Group, Information Division FAO, Viale delle Terme di Caracalla, 00100 Rome, Italy. Fax: +39-06-5705-3360; Email: publications-sales@fao.org; Web:
http://www.fao.org/catalog/giphome.htm

The Association for Temperate Agroforestry Book Shop has several important agroforestry books for sale. Address: Association for Temperate Agroforestry, 203 ABNR Bldg., University of Missouri, Columbia, MO 65211, USA; Tel: 573-882-9866; Fax: 573-882-1977; Email: afta@missouri.edu;
Web: http://www.missouri.edu/~afta/Shop/AFbookshop_books.htm

Holmgren Design Services offers many publications, including David Holgren's works: Holmgren Design Services, 16 Fourteenth St, Hepburn, Victoria 3461, Australia; Tel/Fax: +61 (0)353483636; Email: info@holmgren.com.au;
Web: http://www.holmgren.com.au

The Permaculture Activist sells a wide variety of permaculture related texts; excellent selection. Address: P.O. Box 1209W, Black Mountain, NC 28711, USA; Tel: 828-298-2812; Fax: 828-298-6441; Email: pcactiv@metalab.unc.edu; Web: http://metalab.unc.edu/pc-activist/

Tagari Publications Sells Bill Mollison's many excellent permaculture titles. Tagari Publications, 31 Rulla Road, Sisters Creek Tasmania 7325, Australia; Tel: +61 (0)3 6445 0945; Fax: +61 (0)3 6445 0944; Email:
tagariadmin@southcom.com.au; Web http://www.tagari.com/

The World Agroforestry Centre (formerly the International Centre for Research in Agroforestry (ICRAF)) sells many of its own excellent publications. Address: World Agroforestry Centre, PO Box 30677, Nairobi, Kenya; Tel: +254-2-521450 or +1-650-833-6645; Fax: +254-2-521001 or +1-650-833-6646; Web: http://www.worldagroforestrycentre.org

Original Source

This chapter combines material originally published as *The Overstory* #39, #52, #54, #57, #99, #100, #114 and #115.

Glossary for Agroforestry Practices

by Peter Huxley and Helen van Houten

A wide range of topics and many agroforestry terms have been used in this book. This chapter features a glossary (collection of specialized terms and their meanings) for agroforestry terms. Here you will find the meanings of 27 of the 1400 terms found in the full version of *Glossary for Agroforestry*.

"If people defined their terms, arguments would be less than three minutes."—Voltaire

Selected Agroforestry Terms (Agroforestry Practices)

afforestation

1　Conversion of bare land into forest land by planting of forest trees.

2　The planting of a forest crop on land that has not previously, or not recently, carried a forest crop. Related term: reforestation.

alley cropping

An agroforestry intercropping system in which species of shrubs or trees are planted at spacings relatively close within row and wide between row, to leave room for herbaceous cropping between, that is, in the "alleys" (syn: hedgerow intercropping).

buffer zone

An area around a forest, national park, or any other conserved place that provides the local community with products that they would otherwise take from the forest, or that provides an opportunity to produce alternative products.

bush fallow

The natural vegetation that arises when land is left uncultivated for some time. Composed of small trees, shrubs, grasses (and sedges) and herbaceous plants. Bush fallow may be grazed or browsed and firewood collected from it before it is returned to cultivation. Related terms: enriched fallow, shifting cultivation

community forestry

Forestry developed in areas marginal to agriculture, with many members of the community being landless or small-scale farmers, often characterized by ecological and cultural diversity and the employment of traditional technologies. Communal land development is basic to this type of forestry. Related term: social forestry

enriched fallow

A form of agroforestry in which useful, mainly woody species are sown or planted before cultivation ceases, or at the time it does, so that during the fallow period, or when the land is next cleared for cultivation, products are available for household use or market that would not otherwise have been there (for example, fruits, bamboos, rattans, medicinals). Related term: fallow

fallow

1　Allowing crop land to lie idle, either tilled or untilled, during the whole or greater portion of a growing season. Tillage is usually practised to control weeds and encourage the storage of moisture in the soil.

2　Land rested from deliberate cropping, not necessarily without cultivation or grazing but without sowing.

3　State of land left without a crop or weed growth for extended period, often to accumulate moisture. Related term bush fallow

farm forestry

Growing trees for timber, poles, fuelwood on farmland. This may be done in small woodlots or as boundary plantings. Related term: tree gardens

forest garden

A land-use form in which planted trees and sometimes additional perennial crops occur.

green manure

1 A crop that is grown for soil protection, biological nitrogen reduction, or organic matter and ploughed, disked or hoed into the soil.

2 Any crop grown for the purpose of being turned under while green, or soon after maturity, for soil improvement.

homegarden

A land-use form on private lands surrounding individual houses with a definite fence, in which several tree species are cultivated together with annual and perennial crops; often with the inclusion of small livestock. There are many forms of such gardens varying in how intensively they are cultivated and their location with regard to the home, for example, village forest gardens, "compound gardens", "kitchen gardens."

intercropping

1 The cultivation of two or more crops simultaneously on the same field, with or without a row arrangement (row intercropping or "mixed intercropping").

2 The growing of two or more crops on the same field with the planting of the second crop after the first one has already completed development. Also called relay cropping. Related terms: mixed cropping, multiple cropping

live fence

A way of establishing a boundary by planting a line of trees and/or shrubs (the latter usually from large stem cuttings or stumps), at relatively close spacing and by fixing wires to them. If animals are to be kept in or out, more uprights (dead sticks) can be tied to the wires. Also called a "living fence." Related terms: hedge, hedgerow

mulch

1 A natural or artificially applied layer of plant residues or other materials such as stones, sand, paper or brush on the surface of the soil.

2 A covering of plant material put on the soil to improve its fertility, moisture retention capacity and organic content.

3 A loose surface horizon that forms naturally or may be produced by cultivation and consists of either inorganic or organic materials.

permaculture

"Permanent agriculture." The design and maintenance of sustainable, ecologically favourable, energy efficient agricultural and horticultural systems. The concept includes not only agroforestry but the integration of organic farming principles and intermediate technology, the use of renewable resources and recycling, the exploitation of biodiversity, conservation and habitat protection, as well as social and institutional well-being. It can be applied to urban as well as rural environments.

sequential cropping

1 A pattern of multicropping in which one crop follows another on the same land without any break (continuous cropping = continuous land occupancy) or with a break (intermittent cropping = intermittent land occupancy).

2 Growing more than one crop on the same piece of land with each seasonal crop component being grown during a different time of the year. Related term: simultaneous cropping

shelterbelt

An extended windbreak of living trees and shrubs established and maintained for the protection of farmlands over an area larger than a single farm.

shifting cultivation

Found mainly in the tropics, especially in humid and subhumid regions. There are different kinds; for example, where a settlement is permanent, but certain fields are fallowed and cropped alternately ("rotational agriculture"). In others, whole settlements move and clear new land once the old is no longer productive. Also called "swidden" (Old English for a "burnt clearing"), used more to designate the social group, or "slash-and-burn", so-called because of the operations undergone. Related term: slash-and-burn system

silvopastoral system

Any agroforestry system that include trees or shrubs and pastures and animals. Related term: forest grazing

slash-and-burn system

1 A kind of shifting cultivation in high rainfall areas where the cropping period is followed by a fallow period during which grass, herb, bush or tree growth occurs.

2   A pattern of agriculture in which existing vegetation is cut, stacked and burned to provide space and nutrients for cropping; also called "swidden" cultivation and shifting cultivation.

strip cropping

1   Growing two or more crops simultaneously in different bands wide enough to permit independent cultivation but narrow enough for the crops to interact agronomically. Related term: zonal agroforestry system

2   Growing crops in a systematic arrangement of strips or bands to serve as vegetative barriers to wind and water erosion. Related terms: windstrip, barrier hedge

3   The practice of growing crops in narrow bands along the contour in an attempt to reduce runoff, thereby preventing erosion or conserving moisture.

sustainable development

The management and conservation of the natural base, and the orientation of technological and institutional change, in such a manner as to ensure the attainment and continued satisfaction of human needs for present and future generations. It conserves land, water, plant and animal genetic resources, is environmentally non-degrading, technically appropriate, economically feasible and socially acceptable.

taungya system

Method of raising forest trees in combination with (seasonal) agricultural crops. Used in the early stages of establishing a forest plantation. It not only provides some food but can lessen the establishment costs.

tree farming

Any agroforestry practice that incorporates trees into farmland. Related term: farm forestry

tree garden

A multistoreyed agroforestry system in which a mixture of several fruit and other useful trees is cultivated (that is, for a mixture of products), sometimes with the inclusion of annual crops. Related terms: homegarden, mixed garden, village forest garden

windbreak

A group of trees or shrubs in any arrangement that will afford protection from high winds to animals or crops or both. When the arrangement is in a long line the group is called a shelterbelt. If an associated reason is also to harvest timber at some future date it is sometimes called a "timberbelt." Related term: windstrip

zero tillage

Growing crops without any significant cultivation of the soil, and often by leaving the previous crop residues on the soil surface as a protective mulch. Related terms: minimum tillage, stubble mulching

Original Source

The terms above are excerpted from the *Glossary for agroforestry*, compiled and edited by Peter Huxley and Helen van Houten and published by the International Centre for Research in Agroforestry (ICRAF) in 1997. The entire text of the glossary can be viewed in its entirety at http://www.bugwood.caes.uga.edu/glossary/. This excerpt is reprinted with the kind permission of the editors and publisher.

This excerpt was originally published as *The Overstory* #75.

General Index

Botanical Names Index

Made in the USA
Middletown, DE
02 December 2019